PROFITABILITY AND
ECONOMIC CHOICE

•   •   •   •   •   •   •   •   •   •

The Iowa State University Press, Ames, Iowa   •

PROFITABILITY AND ECONOMIC CHOICE

PAUL H. JEYNES

WITH THE HELP OF **MARGARET O. JEYNES** AND OTHERS

PAUL H. JEYNES, now retired after forty-three years with Public Service Electric & Gas Company, Newark, New Jersey, has combined careers as engineering economist, author, teacher, and consultant. Holding Ph.B. and M.E. degrees from Yale University, he is the author of two books dealing with engineering economy which are widely used in the public utility industry, as well as more than fifty technical articles published in such journals as Accounting Review, Electrical World, Electric Light and Power, Engineering Economist, Financial Analysts Journal, Public Utilities Fortnightly, Transactions of the American Institute of Electrical Engineers, Westinghouse Engineer, and others. He is a fellow and member-for-life of the Institute of Electrical and Electronics Engineers, member emeritus of the Joint Depreciation Committee of Edison Electric Institute and American Gas Association, and member of American Accounting Association, American Society for Engineering Education, and Sigma Xi.

© 1968 The Iowa State University Press
Ames, Iowa, U.S.A. All rights reserved

Printed in the U.S.A.

First edition, 1968
Second printing, 1969

Standard Book Number: 8138-1312-3
Library of Congress Card Number: 67-28033

• TO ALL ADMIRERS OF THE SPIRIT OF FREE ENTERPRISE

• • • • • Preface • • •

THIS BOOK deals with the principles and practices of business generally classified as engineering economy, managerial accounting, or capital management. It is concerned with the making of investment decisions, with a view to achieving the most productive and rewarding use of capital.

The scope of the book approximates that of previously available texts, so far as the nature of subjects treated is concerned. Presentation of the material is also designed for that same application — primarily as a textbook for undergraduate/graduate courses in engineering, accounting, or industrial management, and for use as a reference work by businessmen.

However, the nature of the material presented will be found to differ appreciably from other textbooks in this field. It constitutes a comprehensive introduction to the Minimum Revenue Requirements Discipline, which is a distinctly superior technique of economic analysis. MRRD possesses manifold virtues and advantages which will appeal to teachers, students, and industrialists alike. Rather than to enumerate them here, it seems preferable to let the reader discover and verify them himself.

In general, MRRD facilitates arriving at more trustworthy decisions by simpler, more direct, more convincing, and more efficient means. One reviewer of the manuscript has remarked that it also contains a good deal of epistemology, but no claim will be made for that. However, one special feature is worth mentioning that is believed to be unique in a book on this subject: it contains no self-contradictions, and it will lead the reader away from self-contradictions.

It might also be said that MRRD makes certain demands of its users. It insists upon respect for basic principles of finance which are not in dispute; it insists upon exact definitions of terms and of intent; and it insists upon recognition of the exact arithmetic necessary to carry out that intent. Simplifications, safe shortcuts, and adequate approximations are encouraged and facilitated, but only <u>after</u> exact principles, exact definitions, and exact arithmetic are recognized; not before. It is impossible to simplify, cut short, or approximate safely before understanding what is to be simplified, cut short, or approximated. Contrary to popular opinion, the principles involved in this

vii

activity are as clear-cut and rigorous as those of any other science or technology.

The usual "first course" covers the subjects treated in Chapters 1 through 9, plus Appendix A. Most instructors find it necessary to do judicious skipping, whatever textbook is used, in view of time exigencies, special individual needs, and so on. The material has been arranged to facilitate judicious skipping, only if it is unavoidable, partly by relegating certain discussions to appendices and partly by the considered order of presentation within each chapter.

The nature of the problems at the end of each chapter has been given careful thought. It is a mistake to overemphasize "practical" problem-solving before the student has acquired a fairly comprehensive outlook, and this has been kept in mind in devising problems, particularly for the first eight chapters. Details such as these are the result of several years of classroom experience and experimentation.

It is hoped that this exposition of the Minimum Revenue Requirements Discipline may help to make legislators, public utility commissioners, and members of the legal profession better acquainted with some particular details and underrated merits of the free enterprise system which have been obscured by lack of a disciplined method of analysis of the basic objectives of competitive industry. Indeed, it is expected that this book may also prove to be of great interest to the general reader and to all corporate stockholders and creditors, as a clearer approach to better understanding and appreciation of the American free enterprise system.

The author gratefully acknowledges his tremendous indebtedness to a host of contributors and to reviewers of this work, particularly to his associates throughout the public utility industry, most particularly to those in Public Service Electric & Gas Company, Newark, New Jersey, and the Depreciation Committees of American Gas Association and Edison Electric Institute. Also to many members and committees of American Society for Engineering Education, Institute of Electrical and Electronics Engineers (formerly AIEE), Association of Edison Illuminating Companies, Pennsylvania Electric Association, and others. The influence of pioneering research at Iowa Engineering Experiment Station Iowa State University (Ames), on the treatment of life estimates, depreciation, income taxes, renewals, and the whole manner of dealing with probability will be apparent throughout the book. We are most grateful to Robert H. Sarikas, Illinois Power Company, Decatur, Illinois, and to Professor Harold A. Cowles, and his associates, Iowa State University, for many valuable suggestions incorporated into the final draft.

A most important contribution was that of Martha B. Roberts, who did the final editing. Finally, the invaluable collaboration of Bert J. Blewitt and Leonard Van Nimwegen, upon whom the author has leaned heavily for help and advice, deserves special mention and profoundest thanks.

Paul H. Jeynes

Contents

Tables

xi

. . . . . Figures . . . . .

Figures

PROFITABILITY AND ECONOMIC CHOICE

1

. . . . . Introduction . .

N o businessman needs to be told that two major sources of his
problems are change and uncertainty. Conditions just will not
stay put. Fashions change; new products appeal to customers
and old ones lose their popularity. New materials and new inventions
become available as do new processes and more efficient machines and
automation. Price levels vary, and so do wage scales, repair costs,
and tax rates. At times new money may be easy to obtain; at other
times credit may be tight. New ways of financing, new distribution
channels, new community habits are continually developing. Expansion
may be highly desirable — even necessary.

For a business to be successful its management must be able to
cope with this change and uncertainty and take advantage of it. Effective means to that end are the planning and budgeting functions. In a
small company planning and budgeting activities may constitute only a
part of one person's duties. In a larger company the foreman of each
department may be expected to originate, for his own group, proposals
to be transmitted to a higher executive or committee of higher executives for a decision as to the action taken. In still larger corporations
a whole department — usually of engineers — may devote full time to
planning, while another department does only budgeting, the two departments all the while working in close coordination. Activities of
these departments may be so extensive as to require electronic computers and a staff of programmers.

Other functions of large enterprises are closely related to planning and budgeting. For example, a separate group may be assigned
to research and development, with significant effect on plans for the
future. Pricing of the company's product, marketing, and sales promotion affect, and are affected by, planning and budgeting.

The branch of industrial management that deals with activities of
this kind is conveniently identified as capital management, managerial
accounting, or engineering economy. The reason for such descriptive
terms is obvious: a major consideration in the decision process is the
question of effects on the company's profit margin.

Often the planners are able to suggest several possible alternative

3

proposals, all practical and attractive. Someone must then decide
which, if any, is most desirable. Will it pay? Which is apt to pay
more? Sometimes other important things must be considered (aside
from financial results) in making a decision. In fact, almost always
there are other considerations besides profit; usually, however, the
profit aspect is controlling. In any event, someone must decide
whether, how, and when to proceed. And someone must provide the
information on which to base these decisions.

At some point in the process of reaching a decision one of two
questions is almost sure to arise:

1. Profitability. How much would this proposal earn if it were adopted?
2. Economic Choice. Which of these alternative proposals would earn
   the most if both (or all) produced the same product, the same sales,
   and the same revenues?

Importance of Exact Intent

For very good reason it is essential to recognize and respect exact
intent when making economic studies. This situation is not peculiar to
economics. For instance, consider some examples from sports. A
football team that leads in number of first downs may be a winner, but
it could end the season at the bottom of the league. It is desirable for
a baseball team to maximize its number of base hits, but the World
Series is sometimes won by "hitless wonders." The exact objective in
football is to score the larger number of points per game; in baseball,
the greater number of runs per game.

Similarly, in making economic studies the exact objective is not to
maximize percentage return on new capital investment, or to minimize
"annual costs," or to recover (that is, "pay back") the capital investment in the shortest time. All those objectives may be desirable, in
general. But they correspond to maximizing first downs or base hits;
they are not the exact intent of economic studies. Accepting such inexact objectives can be disastrous, just as trying for a first down when
good management calls for a punt can be disastrous and unforgivable.

For two special reasons, this book gives a great deal of attention
to the dangers that lie in inexact concepts. First, while the ability to
recognize and avoid inexact procedures, and thus avoid possible disaster, is a skill worth acquiring, it is one not generally taught.

Second, this emphasis on exact intent relates to a curious attitude
that is peculiar to the business world, where it is commonly encountered and widely accepted. In order to decide upon the profitability of
a proposal it is necessary to estimate future sales, future taxes, future
wage scales, future service life, future price levels, and so forth. No
one can be 100% certain of future behavior of these variables. Therefore, many people argue, why waste time on small differences, on precise calculations, and on exact definitions of intent when we must deal
with figures that are not exact?

This "let's be practical" attitude may be appealing, but it has worked great mischief. It has resulted in widespread acceptance of analytical methods that do not carry out the analyst's intent at all. These methods concentrate on maximizing first downs and number of base hits, so to speak, instead of winning games. This situation is frequently encountered, even in some of the largest and most successful corporations. Successful though such companies may be, their performance could have been much better still if sound methods of making economic decisions had been used.

Accordingly, our first task will be to agree upon an exact statement of our purpose in making studies of profitability and economic choice. This will be found to be quite easy to do, even for those having minimal knowledge of business, because it amounts simply to devising a more careful statement of a principle that is generally familiar.

The next step will be to describe the unique method of analysis which carries out that exact intent, the procedure known as the Minimum Revenue Requirements Discipline (MRRD).

It will be discovered that MRRD makes use of simple financial facts and principles which are not in dispute. It recognizes that there can be honest differences of opinion with respect to estimated quantities, but no room for difference of opinion as to exact intent, which is one of the things that is not in dispute. MRRD is unique in its insistence on exact definitions of terms and of intent. That insistence actually encourages and facilitates use of good-enough approximations and safe shortcuts. It is not difficult to see why that is so: nobody can be sure that an approximation is good enough, or a shortcut safe, until the exact intent is perceived and the nature of the thing to be simplified is thoroughly understood.

Because techniques other than MRRD do not insist upon this precaution, they are best regarded basically as rules of thumb. They may work sometimes, just as maximizing the number of base hits or first downs often wins games. However, they do not always work; and reliance on inexact methods often courts disaster.

Students of divinity, of law, and of medicine find that they must give early and extensive consideration to ideas and procedures that are wrong. The same thing applies to our present studies of human activity. Just as courses in motor vehicle operation must give specific attention to recognition and avoidance of bad driving practices which the student will inevitably encounter, so this book gives brief but specific attention (in Chapter 11) to questionable economic practices which the student will find himself exposed to on all sides.

For example, at least eight "methods," aside from MRRD, are used for making economic comparisons.[1] Applied to a single problem,

---

[1] Among the methods other than MRRD which are in common use are:

1. Percentage Return or "Investors'" Method
2. Payout (or Payback, or Payoff) Period Method
3. Annual Cost Method
4. Discounted Cash Flow (Profitability Index) Method
5. Capitalized Cost Method
6. MAPI Formula
7. Avoided Cost Method
8. The Test Year

they are apt to arrive at eight different conclusions. Some may pick Alternative A as best; others may pick Alternative B, or some other proposal. Even if all eight agree as to the best choice, they will differ as to the degree of its superiority. The trouble is that these several "methods" do not agree as to the exact intent of the study. Furthermore, these methods have other shortcomings, too, which can be very serious indeed under certain circumstances, as will be explained in Chapters 11 and 14.

Appendix A, The Case for Exactness, presents several examples from commonplace experience to illustrate the gravity of this situation, how readily it can be corrected, and how this book goes about its central purpose of accomplishing that objective.

How a Rule of Thumb Can Mislead

At best, a rule of thumb only works sometimes. An illustration is this generally accepted basis for decisions, well described as "Unsound Notion 1":

A new project is profitable if its adoption increases the company's percentage return. It is not profitable, and should not be adopted, if it reduces the company's percentage return.

This rule certainly sounds reasonable on first thought. It is generally regarded as one good way to make decisions; it is the basis for the Percentage Return or "Investors'" Method. Who could possibly quarrel with such statements, whose truth would seem apparent even to the relatively inexperienced?

If you already have a capital investment of $1,000 earning 6%, and you invest another $1,000 which earns 6.5%, have you not increased your overall return to 6.25%? Isn't this profitable and desirable? Nevertheless, it is not a safe rule. It will be discovered that it overlooks a factor of first importance in business. This additional invest-

	Capital Investment	Annual Earnings	
		In Dollars	In Percent
Initial	$1,000	$ 60	$\frac{60}{1,000} = 6.00\%$
Additional	1,000	65	$\frac{65}{1,000} = 6.50$
Total	$2,000	$125	$\frac{125}{2,000} = 6.25\%$

ment could be an unprofitable and unwise deal indeed — when considered in the exact way you really mean to consider it. Decisions reached in this manner may often hurt the company's profit margin and lead to promoting the wrong line of products. The fundamental fault should be obvious; it disregards a principle that is recognized by every young- ster who ever set up a lemonade stand on a hot summer day, financed by borrowing from his dad. It ignores a basic motivation of the free enterprise economy, as will be discussed in Chapter 2.

It is hoped that this demonstration may convince the reader that it is unwise to accept rules of thumb just because "everybody does it that way." A safer rule is the healthy skepticism expressed in the ancient First Rule of Business: "Don't trust nobody."

Some Exact Definitions

Already we encounter the need for some exact definitions. For example, exactly what is the meaning of "revenue requirements," and of "dilution of the equity"? What is the difference, if any, between sales, revenues, gross receipts, and income? How about earnings, return, income, interest, and profit? Income, and gross income, and net income?

A few terms are defined here to help ensure greater understand- ing. Definitions of exact intent are more involved; we will take that up later.

This book contains no glossary of terms, for a good reason. A comprehensive glossary, adequate for our purpose, would be intoler- ably voluminous. Anything less might do more harm than good. For example, at least forty different definitions of "depreciation" could be listed. Where any danger of misunderstanding our use of the word exists, it is simpler and safer to spell out the exact intent on the spot.

Everyone, even though totally unfamiliar with accounting principles and terminology, can appreciate that a business must have certain cash inputs and certain cash outlays. Inputs are expected to be greater than outlays, so that a cash gain will be realized from carrying on the busi- ness. For purposes of making studies of profitability and economic choice, it is not necessary to know a great deal more than that about accounting. It is essential, though, that this little be understood ex- actly. It is necessary to understand both its exact intent and the exact terms to describe that intent. Many wrong decisions are the direct result of failing to recognize this situation.

The two distinctly different kinds of cash inputs are:

1. Capital funds, obtained: (a) from outside the company, by issu- ing the company's securities (stocks, bonds) to investors or by borrowing from the bank, or (b) from inside the company, by

retaining some part of earnings or by accumulating depreciation charges;

2. Revenues, obtained from sales of the company's products of goods or services.[2]

The two distinctly different kinds of cash outlays are:

1. Capital outlays, representing expenditures of capital funds to buy such assets as land, buildings, and equipment to carry on the business;
2. Expenses, representing expenditures of funds obtained from revenues, to pay for such things as upkeep of assets (raw materials, operation, maintenance, taxes, and so forth), for administrative costs (managerial, legal, and supervisory salaries; accounting; and so forth), and costs of selling the company's products (advertising, billing and collecting, warehousing, shipping, and so forth).

Let's consider how careful we must be to use correct terms to convey exact intent with respect to these inputs and outlays. For example, the word investment has three quite different meanings:

1. the act of putting capital to productive use;
2. the amount of money so spent; and
3. the assets purchased with that money.

Owners of the company (its stockholders) look at their dividends as a percentage of their investment in the stock they own. They may not have purchased that stock from the company but from another stockholder, in a transaction on the Stock Exchange. The Stock Exchange is a secondhand market. Thus, the stockholder's "investment" in a stock (meaning 2) may have no relation to the cost of assets purchased by the company (meaning 3) with capital funds obtained from initial issuance of the stock. The stockholder may think of his dividends as a percentage of current market price of the stock. He can sell at any time at current market price.

The company has its "investment" (meaning 3) in such fixed assets as land, buildings, and equipment. It thinks of earnings as a percentage of that original cost of those assets, not as a percentage of market price of stock.

Failing to observe this differentiation between "investments" has caused some economists to commit errors in reasoning.

To identify the cash input of capital funds with the corresponding cash outlay to purchase fixed assets, the expression investors' committed capital may be used in place of the ambiguous word "investment." This will be found important in Chapter 3.

Similarly, we must be careful in our use of the word sales, to make it clear whether we mean: (a) units of product sold, such as

---

[2] Other minor cash inputs will be noted later, such as salvage value, which comes from sales, but not from sales of the company's products.

number of automobiles, tons of steel, and kilowatt-hours; or (b) the dollars received from such sales. This difficulty is readily avoided by always referring to the dollars as revenues or gross receipts.

Expenses are exactly identified by the way the accountants dispose of them, not by the nature of the goods or services purchased. For example, the tires on a new car are treated by the accountant as an investment (= capital outlay for an asset). But a blowout may be replaced by an identical tire charged to expense (= upkeep of the asset). Because it makes a difference in the determination of profitability or economic choice, we must know exactly how the accounting is done.

Expenses are sometimes called revenue deductions. The reason is that income is always found by difference:

Income = Revenues less expenses

If the company has raised some of its capital funds by borrowing (that is, by going into debt, as it does when issuing bonds, or by making bank loans), then it must pay interest on such borrowings. In such case:

Revenues less expenses = Gross income

and

Gross income less income deductions = Net income

While income deductions consist mainly of interest on debt, they sometimes include also other outlays connected with borrowing money.[3] The exact status of interest is neither a profit nor an expense; it is one component of gross income or of earnings.

The terms gross income, earnings, and return are almost synonymous, but situations arise where only one will best convey the user's exact intent. For example, gross income ordinarily refers to the company's periodic earnings (quarterly, annual, and so forth) as reported in the firm's financial statements. The amount of gross income depends upon the company's method of depreciation accounting, because that accounting fixes the amount of depreciation expense used in preparing the statement for that period. This is one of the expenses deducted from revenues to find gross income. Earnings is the more general term, as illustrated by its use in this paragraph. The word return is used in two different ways; only one refers to earnings. That is in the sense of return on an investment. (Return of an investment refers to repayment or recovery of the principal amount, not earnings.) Return on an investment (meaning earnings) is most often used to express earnings as a percentage, rather than in dollars. It is also favored when referring to long-term earnings, as distinguished from the short-term (quarterly or annual) gross income.

---

[3] Other outlays connected with borrowing money might include such things as: amortization of debt discount and expense; special kinds of interest charges, such as short-term notes payable; miscellaneous amortization charges or nonrecurring deductions; and interest charged to construction (a credit), for many public utilities.

At this point, the reader can perceive how important it is to avoid referring to revenues from sales as income. Many people do it. However, it is just about as sensible as referring to the "port" side of a boat as its "stern." At times that can be disastrous!

An investor may speak of the dividend yield of a stock he owns. This is another version of earnings. He ordinarily means:

$$\frac{\text{Annual dividend payment}}{\text{Purchase price of the stock}}$$

Obviously, one must make certain that he does not mean a different figure:

$$\frac{\text{Annual dividend payment}}{\text{Current market price of the stock}}$$

Everyone understands the meaning of profit, in a general way. The difficulty arises in assigning to it an exact meaning, to permit stating profit in dollars. As mentioned before, all the popular methods for evaluating proposals differ on this score. In the Minimum Revenue Requirements Discipline, in order to designate the exact essential concept, we will refer to the Profit Incentive (not "profit margin") as an arithmetically determinate figure, representing the earnings above an exactly defined "critical" level which is MAR (=Minimum Acceptable Return). This usage permits envisioning a company that is not doing well, one which has some earnings but zero or negative Profit Incentive. Profit Incentive is the direct evidence of profitability and economic choice; yet MRRD is the only method of analysis that looks to Profit Incentive as the basis for decisions.

The word value is another troublemaker that is well understood in a general sense, but is almost impossible to express in dollars. The difficulty is that one must ask, "Value to whom, and when, and for what purpose?" This problem is one of the most ancient in the whole field of economics. In Adam Smith's The Wealth of Nations, dated 1776, the author found it necessary to distinguish between value in use and value in exchange (that is, the price the owner could obtain for it if he wished to sell). The two parties to a sale may agree, at that moment, on value to themselves as to the amount of cash exchanged, but nobody else may agree. Without an adjective to modify the term, "value" is quantitatively meaningless. It is necessary to specify market value, or book value, or going value, or depreciated value, or salvage value, and so forth. In brief, no such thing as absolute, actual, or real value exists. For this reason, we will avoid use of the word "value" so far as possible, and make certain of complete understanding when we are forced to use it.

Cost is something else again. Cost represents a price actually paid and recorded; there can be no question as to the amount of a cost. Since we express cost in dollars, and the purchasing price of the dollar may change, it is often proposed to adjust the initial cost of an asset by applying factors representing the subsequent change in the purchasing price of the dollar. We must be extremely careful to avoid the attitude of the cartoon-strip character Pigeon who always loses in the stock market: "I overpaid for it, but it was worth it."

Usually, companies do not pay out as common stock dividends 100% of the funds available for that purpose (loosely, net income less preferred stock dividend obligations). Here, the concept of payout ratio is useful:

$$\text{Payout ratio} = \frac{\text{Common stock dividends paid out}}{\text{Amount of earnings available for the purpose}}$$

The residual not paid out is utilized in the business and recorded as retained earnings or earned surplus.

Book value of a company's capital stock outstanding represents the amounts received by the company from the original sale of that stock to the public. Usually it is reported as a net figure, all costs of selling it (advertising, taxes, and so forth) deducted. This is not always done, so it is necessary to specify.

Equity refers to ownership, hence, by general consent, to common stock ownership. Thus, common equity refers to book value of common stock outstanding, plus retained earnings.[4] If that figure has to be spread over a larger number of shares, the amount per share is reduced; common equity is then said to be diluted.

It is impossible to describe or comprehend the exact intent of profitability studies or economic comparisons without a complete understanding of all these matters. Additions to this vocabulary will be made as necessary. Two additions that require most careful consideration are MAR (minimum acceptable return) and revenue requirements. The next three chapters will be devoted to the exact definition of these terms and the exact intent of their application.

---

[4] Book value is sometimes referred to as the paid-in cost. Thus, book value of common stock is the amount actually paid in to the company at the time of its purchase from the company. Similarly, book value of common equity is (a) paid-in value of common stock, plus (b) paid-in amounts accumulated as retained earnings (= earned surplus).

Problems

Foreword:

Note: Although this book avoids higher mathematics, it is necessary that the reader have a knowledge of simple arithmetic and elementary algebra. It is also assumed that he has some rudimentary understanding of the conduct of business in a free enterprise economy. For this reason, this book may not include all the answers to problems at the end of each chapter. An inability to solve some problems may suggest certain gaps in the reader's background of information that might be corrected by supplementary reading or class discussion.

1. To judge from television shows and popular novels, many people think that the opposite of "assets" is "debits." What is the correct word? Exactly what are debits?

(Hint: A handy way to remember is to think of the term DIACIL, which sounds like a wonder-drug. It stands for "Debits i _ _ _ _ _ _ assets; credits i _ _ _ _ _ _ liabilities." Fill in the appropriate verb.)

2. If you buy securities on the Stock Exchange, you do not increase the assets of the company that issued that stock. In fact, you cause it to incur a small expense. Explain.

3. Just how does the ordinary mortgage bond differ from the government's Series E savings bonds?

4. What is the difference between a debenture and an indenture?

5. A major difference between the free enterprise system and communism is that in a free enterprise economy no one can tell you how you must invest your own money. Corporations offer their securities to the public; but no one is obliged to buy them. To what extent does government ownership of productive facilities depart from this principle? Where would you draw the line if it were your decision? If the Post Office is desirably government-owned, why not public utilities; why not the steel industry; bakeries; doctors; your own company?

6. If you work for a cigarette manufacturer, are you promoting economic objectives if you try to increase its domestic sales? Explain.

7. In many businesses, financial success is gauged by their earnings expressed as a percentage of sales. Is percentage return, in that sense, an acceptable criterion of profitability? Why?

8. A company sells a 10-year-old truck for $500 and buys its replacement for $3,500. What is the company's capital investment in the new truck?

9. Measures taken to insure the safety of factory workers are sometimes quite expensive. Where should the money come from:
    a. lower wage scales for the employees?
    b. increased prices charged for the company's products?
    c. reduced earnings to the owners of the business?
Do you see any other possibilities? Does it make a difference if the employees are also customers and investor-owners of the firm? Explain all your answers.

10. It is sometimes said that public utilities, particularly electric, gas, and telephone companies, are in noncompetitive industry. To what extent is this not true?

11. It is generally believed that adequate shortcuts and adequate approximations are sufficient in studies of profitability and economic choice. Yet many of the illustrative examples in this text are carried out to several decimal places. Can you suggest any possible good reasons?

12. Some companies report their interest payments on bonds as "interest expense." Comment on that usage.

13. What is meant by "elasticity of demand"?

14. Most states in the United States have departments known as "public utilities commissions," or some similar title. What are the usual functions of such bodies?

15. What are the exact differences between (a) a parameter, (b) a paragon, (c) a paradigm, and (d) a paramour?

16. a. Quote the infield-fly rule of baseball and explain why <u>exact</u> definition is essential.

(<u>Note</u>: If you are not familiar with the history of the infield-fly rule, you may find <u>it</u> worth looking up. It is interesting, even to those who are not baseball fans.)

b. Suggest illustrations from other sports to indicate the importance of exact definitions of terms and intent.

(<u>Hint</u>: Foul, in basketball; touchdown and safety, in football.)

17. Define (a) fixed assets, (b) liquid assets, (c) price/earnings ratio, (d) unamortized debt discount and expenses, and (e) debt premium.

18. What is the exact meaning of "profit margin"? How does it differ from "net profit"? Where would you go to discover the annual "profit margin" or "net profit" of a company whose stock you own? Demonstrate by quoting actual figures for an actual company. Comment on this question.

19. It is sometimes asserted that the purpose of a corporation is to supply human needs at the lowest possible cost. What is the important oversight, in that statement, which ignores the very feature of a free enterprise economy which makes it so far superior to any other system?

20. Some strange and unsound notions are entertained by some who fail to comprehend the exact nature of studies of profitability and of economic choice. One such is the notion that an allowance should be made in such studies for the probability that the project under study might be rejected when it should be adopted, or that it might be adopted when it should be rejected. But if you consider the specific question that is answered by a profitability study, or the related question answered by a study of economic choice, it is clear that no such allowance should be made.

Discuss this situation, and the unclear reasoning that is responsible for the proposition as stated.

2

•   •   •   •   • **Exact Intent**   •   •
of Studies

Needed: A Discipline

The exact intent of studies of profitability and economic choice is to optimize benefits to owners of the business.

"Optimizing" benefits means more than just maximizing profits, though profit is always the basic motivation of investor-financed enterprises in a free enterprise economy.[1] Optimizing benefits means placing the company in the best position to do two things of advantage to the firm's owners and creditors:

1. Maximize earnings for present owners of the business, out of given sales and revenues; and/or
2. Minimize price of the company's products while earning a satisfactory return for present owners of the business.

This dual objective must be a distinguishing feature of any disciplined approach; however, it is overlooked by all methods other than the Minimum Revenue Requirements Discipline (MRRD).

(Note: The exact objective of MRRD is not quite the same as maximizing earnings per common share. Neither is it quite the same as maximizing the present value of the company's common stock nor quite the same as maximizing return [in dollars or in percent] on the new capital investment. None of these criteria is the exact intent of economic studies. In Chapter 11, we will see how dangerous decisions can be when based on criteria that are not quite exact — criteria that are essentially rules of thumb rather than a disciplined procedure.)

A second departure of MRRD from all other methods is recognition that benefits to present owners ("pre-project" shares) supply the criterion. It is not percentage return on investment in the new project alone, the payoff rate of the new project, or the cash flow from the new project.

The third distinguishing feature of MRRD is that the pricing problem (that is, whether to retain price of output at present levels and

---

[1] It is necessary to say investor-financed, because government-owned enterprises are tax-financed, and their basic motivation is not profit. It should be, and is ordinarily believed to be, economic use of resources. But we will discover some surprising things about that in Chapter 14.

thus maximize earnings, or whether to improve competitive position by reducing price of output as made possible by adopting the superior proposal) is recognized as a matter separate and distinct from identifying the economic choice.

All three of these characteristics of MRRD will be discussed further.

Nature of Profitability

Exactly what is meant by profitability of a proposal? How is profitability defined and measured? Is there more than one definition; more than one way to measure it? Obviously, we must stipulate "profitability to whom?" Exactly how does profitability differ from economic choice?

All procedures other than MRRD are surprisingly vague with respect to such matters. This is the important reason why the eight different methods, listed in Chapter 1, commonly give eight different answers to a single problem. Not one of those eight solutions answers the exact question asked.

A disciplined analysis, leading to the one exactly intended answer, is sometimes disparaged as "dogmatic." That kind of argument often passes for thoughtful reasoning in this decision making. But all physical laws are dogmatic. How useful would Ohm's law or Boyle's law be, if they were not dogmatic? Necessarily, in order to be functional, MRRD admits of only one definition and one measure of profitability and of economic choice. Otherwise, it could not qualify as a discipline.

1. Profitability. Profitability studies start with an estimate of revenues. The question to be answered is: In view of these revenues, how much Profit Incentive does this project offer?

Whether the proposal should be adopted or rejected, on the basis of that finding, is a separate budgeting problem. If the Profit Incentive is great enough, considering the risks involved, adoption may be wise. If Profit Incentive is discouragingly small compared to the risk, presumably it will be rejected.

Profit Incentive, then, must be exactly defined. It is the earnings, in dollars, in excess of the cost of capital required to finance the project. We need, in turn, a term to express our exact meaning when we say "cost of capital." The expression is minimum acceptable return (MAR), not minimum attractive return. The exact definition of "cost of capital" is discussed in detail in Chapter 3.

2. Economic Choice. Studies of economic choice refer to a special situation which must be described exactly. It is specifically stipulated that all alternatives to be compared are to produce: (a) the same product or services; (b) the same amount of product or services; and (c) the same annual revenues, in dollars, as for all other alternatives. Only if all these requirements are met does the procedure yield the intended solution.

If not all of these requirements are satisfied, special allowances must be made. Sometimes those "special allowances" require making a profitability study, which starts by estimating revenues. It is not necessary to estimate revenues in making economic comparisons. This is because, regardless of their amount, revenues are the same figure for all the alternatives to be compared.

The economic choice (that is, the superior alternative) is the one that has smallest minimum revenue requirements.[2] Out of the given identical revenues, this plan will yield the largest Profit Incentive, found by difference.

It will be apparent that determining the amount of Profit Incentive (not "profit margin" nor "profit") does not commit the analyst to any particular disposition of benefits. Whether the potential benefits are used to increase earnings and dividends or to reduce the selling price of the product (reduce revenues for the same output) is another matter — the pricing problem. Whether the decision is to accept or reject the proposal is also another matter — the budgeting function.

Good reasons for this separation of the three activities will be evident, even at this early stage of our discussion. It will become more forcefully apparent particularly in Chapters 3, 9, and 11.

Absentee Ownership

A homely example that is helpful in explaining the profit incentive of a free enterprise system is the lemonade stand analogy.[3]

An industrious youngster borrows a dollar from his dad, invests it in lemons and sugar, and devotes a hot summer Saturday afternoon to selling lemonade. He takes in revenues of $1.50, realizing a profit incentive of 50 cents after paying back his loan. Is that enough to induce a repeat performance next Saturday? What if it rains? What if he'd like to see the ball game? What if he encounters competition, other youngsters selling better lemonade cheaper? How much must the profit incentive be to decide in favor of selling lemonade? All such problems have their parallels in management of the largest corporations. They are obvious and will not be investigated further. But one problem may arise that does merit discussion.

Suppose a young sister tries to talk him into expanding the business. She has a dollar in her piggy bank. Together with dad's dollar, twice as much lemonade could be made. The larger revenues ($3), less the larger expenses ($2), would give the original entrepreneur his 50 cents; sister expects to get back her dollar, plus 50 cents for supplying the extra capital.

---

[2] In order to avoid the repetitious expression "smallest minimum revenue requirements," or "minimum minimum revenue requirements," we ordinarily omit the adjective "minimum," and refer to it simply as the "smallest revenue requirements."

[3] Being an analogy only, and not an identity, similarities must not be pursued too far. Our purpose is to use the lemonade stand analogy in a manner similar to use of the hydraulic analogy in explaining the theory of electrical circuits.

The answer is, "Nothing doing." It might be a deal if sister would accept only 25 cents of the additional "profit incentive," so that the original owner of the business increases his take to 75 cents. But why turn over all the additional earnings to a "newcomer"? The original owner would gain nothing if all the lemonade is sold — and he has a chance of increased losses if it is not.

This illustrates the important principle we have stated: <u>the reason for making an additional capital investment is to benefit preproject owners of the business.</u>

Another principle of corporate finance can be illustrated in amusing terms. As an individual you hold ultimate title to your possessions. Should it strike your fancy, you could sell all your assets, turn the proceeds into dollar bills, pile them up, and set fire to them. You might be considered rather eccentric, but you would have committed no criminal offense.

On the other hand, the president or management of a corporation could do no such thing with their company's assets without going to jail. Speaking loosely, a corporation <u>owes</u> someone for everything it owns. All its facilities were purchased by using funds provided by somebody else: bondholders, stockholders, or creditors of the company. Some facilities may be bought with funds provided by depreciation reserves; special attention will be given to that situation.

By reason of their absentee-ownership, stockholders do not make the company's business decisions at first hand. Decisions are made on their behalf by management. Of course, this hardly justifies the conclusion that management's objective is to make decisions of greatest benefit to management. There is no question as to where earnings or profits go; they go to bondholders (as interest) and to stockholders (as dividends), or they are reinvested in the business.[4]

The scale of measurement obviously is in dollars. But a mental reservation makes us ask: What is the significance of the amount of capital required to produce given earnings in dollars? Isn't the appropriate measurement of earnings a <u>percentage</u> of capital investment rather than <u>dollars</u> per year? The answer is quite simple and an important matter of exact intent. It is curious that it is so rarely perceived because it is quite clear-cut. The appropriate measurement is <u>dollars per year above the cost of money (MAR), also in dollars per year.</u>

Importance of Financing

One might expect, on first thought, that whether it is correctly described as "economic" or not, the stockholders' selfish interests would favor <u>maximized</u> earnings in percent of their capital investment

---

[4] Disposition of other small amounts, such as interest on customers' deposits, are in the nature of earnings, but they are ignored here for simplicity.

in the business. This is the criterion employed in the Percentage Return or "Investors'" Method. It is quite easy to demonstrate its incompetency; it does not respect our exact intent.

That is, surely it is common knowledge that when corporations seek to raise capital by offering to sell new issues of their securities to the investing public, they make every effort to obtain the highest possible price for the new issue. Quite often the sale is made to the highest bidder, a dealer who in turn sells to the public, hopefully at a small profit. This means that the company makes every effort to minimize percentage return to investors who supply the ~apital for a new venture, since:

$$\text{"Minimized cost of new money"} = \frac{\text{Earnings per share}}{\text{Maximized price per share}}$$

The expression "minimized cost of new money" is placed in quotation marks because it introduces the concept of MAR (= Minimum Acceptable Return), a factor of first importance which we will discuss at length.

A serious shortcoming of the eight popular methods listed in Chapter 1 is their failure to recognize this basic objective, the minimized cost of financing. Let's consider "Notion 1," Chapter 1, in the light of this cost of financing. Is a project necessarily profitable if it earns a percentage return greater than the company's average percentage return? Or if its adoption would increase the company's overall percentage return?

Suppose a company is presently earning 10% on its capital investment of $400,000, or $40,000 per year. With 10,000 shares of stock outstanding, this would mean earnings of $4 per share.

A new venture, also earning 10%, will require $100,000 of new capital. Would it be profitable; would it reduce profit; or would it do neither? If you believe "Notion 1" you will conclude that percentage earnings would not change, as follows:

Capital Investment		Annual Earnings	
		In Dollars	In Percent
Initial	$400,000	$40,000	10.00%
Additional	100,000	10,000	10.00
Total	$500,000	$50,000	10.00%

Accordingly, the deal would appear to be neither more nor less profitable than the initial situation.

Now turn to Table 2.1, and see how mistaken that conclusion can be. Project 1 of Table 2.1 demonstrates that your actually intended conclusion depends upon the price you could obtain for the securities sold to finance the deal. Project 2 goes one step further. Even if the new venture were to earn only 9% on the additional capital, it still could improve earnings per share. And Project 3 shows that even if the new venture were to earn more than 10%, adopting it could reduce profitability, in terms of earnings per share.

Table 2.1. Importance of new financing.

Initial Situation
    Investors' committed capital = $400,000.
    Outstanding stock = 10,000 shares at $40 per share book value.
    Earnings = $40,000 per year = 10% = $4.00 per share.

New Project 1
    Additional capital investment = $100,000. Additional earnings = $10,000 pe year = 10%, as initially.

    The situation after making the new investment: capital investment = $500,000; annual earnings = $50,000 per year; return = 10%.

New Project 2
    Additional capital investment = $100,000. Additional earnings = $9,000 per year = 9%, or less than initially.

    The situation after making the new investment: capital investment = $500,000; annual earnings = $49,000 per year; return = 9.8%.

New Project 3
    Additional capital investment = $100,000. Additional earnings = $11,000 per year = 11%, or more than initially.

    The situation after making the new investment: capital investment = $500,000; annual earnings = $51,000 per year; return = 10.2%.

(Note: The price per share in A in each project is above book value; in B, at book value; in C, below book value.)

	Number of Shares New Financing	Price Per Share	Total Shares	Earnings Per Share
Project 1				
A.	2,000	$50	12,000	$\frac{50,000}{12,000} = \$4.17$
B.	2,500	$40	12,500	$\frac{50,000}{12,500} = \$4.00$
C.	3,000	$33.33	13,000	$\frac{50,000}{13,000} = \$3.85$
Project 2				
A.	2,000	$50	12,000	$\frac{49,000}{12,000} = \$4.08$
B.	2,500	$40	12,500	$\frac{49,000}{12,500} = \$3.92$
C.	3,000	$33.33	13,000	$\frac{49,000}{13,000} = \$3.77$
Project 3				
A.	2,000	$50	12,000	$\frac{51,000}{12,000} = \$4.25$
B.	2,500	$40	12,500	$\frac{51,000}{12,500} = \$4.08$
C.	3,000	$33.33	13,000	$\frac{51,000}{13,000} = \$3.92$

Table 2.2. Yield on pre-project and incremental shares.
(Calculated from the data of Table 2.1.)

The Problem:
   The company's pool of investors' committed capital (i.e., its capitalization) amounts to $400,000. 10,000 shares of common stock are outstanding, issued at $40 per share. Current earnings are $4 per share = $40,000 per year = 10%. A new project is proposed; its capital investment = $100,000.

Part A.
   This new project is expected to earn 9%, or $9,000 per year. The new capital is raised by issuing 2,000 new shares at $50 per share (i.e., above book value of $40).

Part B.
   This new project is expected to earn 11%, or $11,000 per year. The new capital is raised by issuing 3,000 new shares at $33.33 per share (i.e., below book value of $40).

	Company Earnings		Newcomers' Earnings		Pre-Projects Owners' Earnings	
	Percentage	Dollars Per Share	Percentage	Dollars Per Share	Percentage	Dollars Per Share
Part A Before	$\frac{40,000}{400,000} = 10.0\%$	$\frac{40,000}{10,000} = \$4.00$			$\frac{4.00}{40} = 10.00\%$	$4.00
After	$\frac{49,000}{500,000} = 9.8\%$ (Down)	$\frac{49,000}{12,000} = \$4.08$ (Up)	$\frac{4.08}{50} = 8.16\%$	$4.08	$\frac{4.08}{40} = 10.20\%$ (Up)	$4.08 (Up)
Part B Before	$\frac{40,000}{400,000} = 10.0\%$	$\frac{40,000}{10,000} = \$4.00$			$\frac{4.00}{40} = 10.00\%$	$4.00
After	$\frac{51,000}{500,000} = 10.2\%$ (Up)	$\frac{51,000}{13,000} = \$3.92$ (Down)	$\frac{3.92}{33.33} = 11.76\%$	$3.92	$\frac{3.92}{40} = 9.80\%$ (Down)	$3.92 (Down)

Clearly, any sound precepts and any methods of solution designed
to carry out exact intent must make specific allowance for this "cost of
new capital" and its effect on the profit situation. Unfortunately, this
situation is commonly overlooked.

Our Exact Intent

The main contribution of Table 2.1 is the help it gives toward
identifying whose profits we hope to improve.

When new shares are issued at a price per share that differs from
book value per share of equity, two distinct classes of shares are
thereby created, even though the stock certificates are identical; even
though they entitle their holders to identical dividends per share; and
even though they command the same market price per share. The two
classes are:

1. The old shares, outstanding before the new issue was made.
   To identify them clearly by their special relation to new proposals, we will refer to them as pre-project shares; and
2. The new issue of incremental shares, sold to newcomers.

To illustrate the importance of distinguishing between these two
classes of shares, see Table 2.2. Here we have calculated percentage
yield on the two classes of shares, based on the data of Table 2.1. It
shows that when new shares are issued at a price above book value of
pre-project shares, the latter (held by existing owners of the firm) enjoy an increased percentage yield, as the result of their improved
earnings per share. This can remain the case even though the company's percentage return is reduced by adopting the new project, as in
Part A.

In Part A, a new project earning 9% — less than average company
earnings before the expansion — boosts pre-project yield to 10.20%,
although it reduces company earnings from 10% to 9.8%. The reason:
new shares sold at a price above book value per share.

In Part B, the new project now earning 11% increases the company's percentage earnings from 10% to 10.2%. But the yield on pre-
project shares goes down from 10% to 9.8%. The reason: new shares
sold at a price below book value per share.

This explains why skillful financing of company growth is just as
important as finding profitable new ventures. It is one of the most re-
markable and little appreciated features of the free enterprise economy.

(Note: Retained earnings were zero in Tables 2.1 and 2.2. The
situation is altered slightly if there are retained earnings; it is then
desirable to sell new shares at a price above book value per share of
common equity. We will return to this in Chapter 3 and Appendix B.)

Why should new investors be willing to buy incremental shares at a
price greater than the book value of equity, thus obtaining a yield less
than that enjoyed by pre-project shares? The answer to this question

casts light on the "cult of equity" that has influenced the stock markets
so much in the past decade. It explains why, in favored industries, investors are willing to pay a relatively high multiple of earnings (=
price/earnings ratio) for common stock: having purchased stock in the
company, the new investor attains the status of a pre-project shareholder the moment the company further increases its assets. As each
new venture is undertaken, all stockholders, old and new, are offered
the inducement of future increase in yield on their now pre-project
shares. It is this phenomenon that permits estimating the "cost of
capital" in the manner described in Chapter 3.

Pre-project shareholders can enjoy this benefit without contributing one cent to the new capital needed; usually, though, they automatically contribute to some extent by way of retained earnings, which
further increases their yield. Newcomers are induced by that prospect
to join the club; they pay a little higher admission charge (= current
higher price per share), in the expectation of shortly becoming a pre-
project shareholder and participating in his benefits.

This is the simple arithmetic which makes it possible for a growing company to pay a continually increasing percentage yield to its
owners, even though the company's earnings remain a fixed percentage
of investors' committed capital in the enterprise. A simple example,
in Table 2.3 illustrates the principle involved.

(Note the need for an exact definition of investors' committed capital mentioned before and to be discussed shortly.)

Our exact intent with respect to earnings, then, must be stated in
two parts:

1. Minimize percentage return to suppliers of increased capital;
   and
2. Maximize return to already committed owners of the business,
   represented by the pre-project shares.

It can be demonstrated that exactly this same principle applies
when no incremental stock issues are contemplated, and when new
projects are financed entirely by so-called internally generated funds,
meaning retained earnings and depreciation reserves. We will return
to this refinement in Appendix B.

Implementation of Our Exact Intent

How can we devise a method for evaluating proposals that will
carry out this exact intent and select the alternative which will maximize percentage return on pre-project shares, while minimizing return
on incremental capital?

It can be done by selecting the plan which minimizes total outlay,
including the minimized return on incremental capital (one outlay being
the income taxes on that minimized return). Out of identical revenues
(remember that special stipulation?), the alternative having the smallest

Table 2.3. How incremental ("newcomer") shares become pre-project shares.

(The moment a "newcomer's" current instantaneous rate of return — dividends plus capital gains, in percent of purchase price — departs from his starting rate of MAR, he has become the most recent "pre-project owner.")

Initial Situation (Before Adopting First New Project)
    Investors' committed capital = $400,000.
    Outstanding stock = 10,000 shares at $40 per share book value.
    Earnings = $40,000 per year = 10% = $4.00 per share; 100% payout.
    Price/earnings ratio = 10.

First New Project (Project 1-A of Table 2.1)
    Additional capital investment = $100,000.
    Additional earnings = $10,000 per year = 10% as initially.

    New financing = 2,000 new shares at $50 per share (over book value).
    Total capital investment = $500,000.
    Total annual earnings = $50,000.
    Total number of shares = 12,000.
    Earnings per share = $4.17 = Dividend.
    Price/earnings ratio = 12.

    Dividend on pre-project shares = 4.17/40 = 10.42% (from Table 2.2).
    Dividend on incremental shares = 4.17/50 = 8.34% (from Table 2.2).

Second New Project (Note: This is not included in Table 2.1)
    Additional capital investment = $100,000.
    Additional earnings = $9,000 per year = 9%, or less than initially.
    Book value of shares before expansion = $41.67.

    New financing = 2,000 new shares at $50 per share (over book value).
    Total capital investment = $600,000.
    Total annual earnings = $59,000.
    Total number of shares = 14,000.
    Earnings per share = $4.21 = Dividend.
    Price/earnings ratio = 11.88.

    Dividend on initial pre-project shares = 4.21/40 = 10.52%.
    Dividend on first incremental shares = 4.21/50 = 8.42% (now pre-project).
    Dividend on second incremental shares = 4.21/50 = 8.42% ("newcomers").

Comment: The first new project increased original investors' yield from 10.00% to 10.42%. "Newcomers" accepted 8.33% initially, expecting that new projects would benefit them similarly.
    The second new project did just that, even though the second generation of "newcomers" paid the same price per share of $50.
    It is more likely that the price/earnings ratio would have increased or remained the same (= 12). If the second generation of newcomers paid $50.67 per share, the second new project would perform as follows:

    New financing = 1,974 new shares at $50.67 per share (over book value).
    Total capital investment = $600,000.
    Total annual earnings = $59,000.
    Total number of shares = 13,974.
    Earnings per share = $4.22 = Dividend.
    Price/earnings ratio = 12.

    Dividend on initial pre-project shares = 4.22/40 = 10.55%.
    Dividend on first incremental shares = 4.22/50 = 8.44% (now pre-project).
    Dividend on second incremental shares = 4.22/50.67 = 8.33% ("newcomers").

This illustrates the mechanism by which newcomers become pre-project owners and enjoy increasing percentage earnings on their initial investment.

minimized total outlay will provide the largest profit, found by difference.

That "minimized total outlay" represents minimum revenue requirements. This term will be discussed in detail and defined exactly in other words, to clarify its significance and practical evaluation.

It is important to note, as part of our exact intent, that our criterion in evaluating proposals is the dollars of earnings, above that minimized outlay, not the margin in percent. That is, suppose that minimized return on the new capital is 6%, on a capital investment of P. Then we select the alternative that would yield the greater dollars per year in excess of .06P. The reason?

$$\text{Yield in dollars per share} = \frac{\text{Dollars of earnings}}{\text{Number of shares}}$$

Thus, a large percentage return on a small incremental investment improves dollar earnings very little. A small percentage return on a large incremental investment may improve earnings in dollars much more. It is the dollar earnings, in excess of MAR (that is, in excess of .06P in this example), that are essential to improve the yield on preproject shares. That is the measure of Profit Incentive.

This fact will be utilized in:

1. Developing a graphic Diagram of Intent;
2. Testing solutions, to assure ourselves that they really do accomplish our exact intent; and
3. Demonstrating a fault of all other procedures which is often overlooked by those who use them.

Should there be any possible doubt as to our desire to maximize the yield on pre-project shares, consider what would happen if new common stock were to be sold at a price less than book value per share of common equity. By approving such an action, newcomers (buyers of incremental shares) would enjoy a higher percentage yield on their holdings than the existing members of the firm (pre-project shares) are themselves permitted.

To recapitulate, our exact intent in making studies of profitability and economic choice is a great deal more sensible and ingenious than is commonly appreciated. Too many do not realize how good the American economic system is, because they have not bothered to study its exact nature. Instead, they have been inclined to take a foolish pride in being inexact and amateurish, which is described in a self-satisfied manner as the "practical" way of doing business. It is also a practical way to reduce profit margins.

This does seem unfortunate, when you consider that everything discussed thus far in this book is "practical." Probably everything we have talked about the reader already knew in a general way. All we have done is to try to persuade the reader to organize his own ideas in an orderly way by not jumping to conclusions. Instead, he should start with his own exact definitions of objectives and do his own reasoning to reach his own conclusions, which he then can trust.

The remainder of this book will proceed in this same manner, adding more detail and further complications in a methodical progression.

Résumé

I. The major objective of studies of profitability and economic choice is to increase the company's Profit Incentive, while reducing the price of its products at the same time if possible.

II. One important and practical means toward accomplishing this objective is to obtain new capital funds at the lowest possible cost.

III. The free enterprise system of stock-ownership of companies provides a unique and automatic incentive which attracts low-cost new funds, that rewards pre-project owners and employees for superior performance of their business, and that benefits consumers by lower prices of products. No other economic system has yet been invented which accomplishes these results by offering these inducements.

IV. In order to select proposals most likely to produce all these benefits, it is essential that the method of selection recognize two distinct classes of common shareholders:

1. Pre-project or already committed shares, whose yield is to be improved by adopting new projects; and
2. Incremental or new suppliers of additional capital funds, who accept a smaller initial yield on their investment, anticipating that they themselves will become pre-project shareholders as the company grows. Thus, they participate in that increased yield and improved market price of their holdings (= capital gains) in the future.

V. The Minimum Revenue Requirements Discipline is the only method of selecting proposals which makes the choice by investigating that improved yield to existing owners — to the pre-project shares — which is the one essential point of such studies.

VI. As Tables 2.1, 2.2, and 2.3 suggest, selecting proposals on any other basis, such as maximized profit, without distinguishing between new investors and existing owners, can result in making wrong decisions. In order to avoid such mistakes, we will devote some space to reviewing wrong methods, as well as exploring the one and only right way that we really intend.

VII. It is commonly asserted, particularly by advocates of the Annual Cost Method, that the correct percentage return for use in economic studies is the "opportunity cost," meaning the rate of earnings foregone by not investing the same capital elsewhere than in the project under study. Such a conclusion is an error of classical proportions. "Opportunity cost" has no place in the determination of profitability or economic choice. If it enters into investment decisions at all, it is only in connection with the budgeting function, which is a separate matter discussed in Chapter 9.

VIII. Since our exact intent demands consideration for <u>minimized</u> <u>cost of new money</u>, we will proceed to define this concept exactly, dis- cuss how it behaves, and describe ways to estimate it for any company, in Chapter 3. In later chapters, we will explain in detail how to use this concept to make decisions most likely to accomplish our major desire — increased Profit Incentive together with reduced prices for our product.

Problems

(Note: Make your best attempt to answer these questions and, if you cannot, try again after completing Chapter 3 and Appendix B.)

1. Some writers have said that profits are offensive to the Puritan ethic. What is the "Puritan ethic"?

2. Ohm's law is sometimes used to illustrate the essential nature of a discipline. It may be expressed by the formula $E = IR$. What does it signify? Is it universally applicable? Why is it a good example of a disciplined technology?

3. What is the difference between studies of (a) profitability, and (b) economic choice?

4. What is meant by "break-even point"?

5. Are bondholders owners of the business that issued the bonds? Explain in detail.

6. What is an analogy?

7. What is meant by the term "funded"? What is a "funded reserve"? Are depreciation reserves funded?

8. Exactly what is meant by the word "criterion"?

9. If you do not increase a company's assets when you buy its stock on the Stock Exchange, how does the company go about increasing its assets by sale of its stock?

10. Does a company charge you a commission for selling you its own stock? Explain.

11. What is meant by a "growth stock"? When you speak of a company's growth, exactly what do you mean? Increase in sales, in earnings, in number of employees, or what?

12. What does the expression "price/earnings ratio" mean? Since a stockholder's cash receipts from the company whose stock he holds are dividends, and dividends per share are usually less than earnings per share, why not "price/dividends ratio"?

13. What is the difference between (a) gross income, (b) net income, and (c) "earnings per share"?

14. What is the difference between (a) payout ratio, (b) payout period, (c) payoff period?

15. Define "pre-project owner."

16. Define "dividend yield."

17. Give an example of a rule of thumb and point out its shortcomings. (Hint: In contract bridge, "Second hand low." Or, "Many a man's in the gutter who didn't lead trumps.")

18. What is the "Dow theory"?

19. What is meant by "trading on the equity"?

20. Why are reserves listed as liabilities? What is the difference between (a) surplus, and (b) a reserve? Why is surplus listed as a liability?

21. What is a "contra asset"? Why do some companies report depreciation reserves as a liability, while others list it as a contra asset?

22. In exactly what respect is the objective of MRRD:
   a. Not quite the same as maximizing earnings per common share?
   b. Not quite the same as maximizing present value of common stock?
   c. Not quite the same as maximizing return (in dollars or in percent) on the new capital investment?

23. The reason for making economic studies is to decide upon courses of action most likely to put the firm in the best position to do two things, as discussed on page 14.

In making a study of the profitability of a proposal, suppose it is discovered that it could be expected to earn a very small profit incentive. That would improve potential company earnings per share and therefore might put the firm in a better position than if the project were not adopted. But these earnings are deemed insufficient to make the proposal attractive in view of its cutoff rate. That is, its earnings would be less than the minimum required to make it attractive because the associated risk is substantial; so the project would be rejected on that basis.

Explain how you would reconcile (a) the cutoff rate criterion with (b) the stated purpose of "putting the firm in the best position," if you reject the proposal.

24. It is not correct to describe the two objectives of economic studies as: (a) to maximize earnings of present owners, and (b) to minimize price of the firm's products. In fact, it might be argued that these two objectives, so stated, are mutually contradictory.

Discuss the essential qualification, in each case, which removes all possibility of contradiction and makes the proposition meaningful.

3

Minimum · · · ·
Acceptable Return

General Level of MAR

Because the Minimum Revenue Requirements Discipline (MRRD) depends upon an exact concept of minimum acceptable return (MAR), or "cost of capital," it is essential that we give most careful attention to the definition of MAR, to its peculiar behavior, and to practical means for estimating percentage MAR for any enterprise.

This is doubly important for another reason. That is, the idea of a minimized cost of money, which is not to include profit, is not new. But the literature of the subject exhibits strikingly the evil effects of failing to define terms and intent exactly. Avoiding such difficulties by insisting upon observance of small details which conform to exact intent reaps surprising rewards. It will be discovered that the principles underlying economic studies are not only simpler but much more rigorous than is generally realized. A number of questions, some regarded as posing problems of classical proportions, can be easily and convincingly resolved.

First of all, corporations make use of "hired" capital provided by investors.[1] Interest and dividend payments made to investors constitute the compensation to investors for the use of their money. The company then reinvests this capital in its fixed assets.

Nobody "hires" capital at a cost of $i\%$ in order to reinvest it at that same $i\%$. Even for projects having zero risk, some margin of earnings must be gained from the investment, in excess of $i\%$, to make the transaction attractive (that is, worthwhile). The attractive rate of return, for any project, is necessarily greater than the cost of "hiring" capital which is MAR. MAR is not an attractive rate. It is the lowest rate at which capital can be obtained for reinvestment at some higher attractive rate.

Businessmen have a descriptive term they apply to the lowest attractive rate of return for a project; it is called the cutoff rate. If a proposal promises any smaller earnings than the cutoff rate, it will not be undertaken. The cutoff rate depends upon the risks involved. A project having little risk has a low cutoff rate; it will be undertaken

---

[1] The expression "hired money" has been attributed to President Calvin Coolidge.

even though it earns a relatively small margin above MAR. The greater the risk, the greater the margin required.

Naturally, it is expected that all projects will earn more than their cutoff rate, which is the rock-bottom level of attractiveness. For all a company's projects, in the aggregate, there is some company average cutoff rate which is greater than the company's MAR but less than overall company earnings. In other words, MAR is less than the cutoff rate, which in turn is less than average percentage return of the company. This describes the upper limit for MAR.

Since MAR is the cost of "hiring" capital (some perhaps at the low interest rate on debt, but mostly at the higher rate on equity funds), it is difficult to imagine a company's MAR percentage dipping below the dividend rate on a new issue of its preferred stock, if a new issue were to be offered. Old issues of preferred, floated when dividend rates were abnormally high, might conceivably approach the MAR percentage, or even exceed it a little.

Thus, although a firm's MAR is subject to small changes from time to time, its range of variability is narrow for a financially successful company.[2] MAR lies between two limits: (a) less than the company's average actual earnings, as a percentage of investors' committed capital; and (b) more than the percentage dividend rate on a new issue of the firm's preferred stock, if offered, which is in turn more than interest rate on its debt.

Much more precise estimates are readily made, as will be explained. This introductory discussion of the general level of MAR will permit the reader to acquire a "feel" for the subject before embarking on the detailed course of reasoning that develops an exact concept. The discussion will also produce simple but dependable evaluations of the exactly intended figure.

Importance of having some idea of the exactly intended rate can be appreciated by knowing what MAR is not.

What the Revenue Requirement for Return (MAR) Is Not

1. The rate of earnings foregone by not investing the capital elsewhere, outside the enterprise as well as within it (sometimes called the internal or external "lending rate").
2. The "market rate," sometimes described as the going rate of return on conservative investments.
3. Expected, hoped-for, or "target" rate of return for the company as a whole.
4. Anticipated actual return for the specific project, department, product, or class of service.
5. The cutoff rate, representing management's opinion as to the least return a project must promise to earn before its adoption can be justified, in view of the risks involved.

---

[2] If the company is not financially successful, its actual earnings could be less than interest rate on debt, even zero or a minus quantity. But we are interested mostly in profitable investments.

6. Marginal return, occasionally defined as the maximum return imaginable from new projects in the near future; sometimes defined as the "marginal external lending rate."
7. Average interest rate on the company's outstanding debt; sometimes called "cost of money."
8. For regulated public utilities, the so-called "fair return" on rate base; or, alternatively, the maximum rate permitted by regulatory authorities.
9. Two or three times the rate obtainable from conservative investments, such as high-grade bonds.
10. Average rate of actual earnings of the company in recent years; sometimes called the "internal rate."

These ten different rates of return have been proposed by various writers as the appropriate percentage for use in economic studies, but not one of them is defensible. Because of such a wide range of proposals (ranging from possibly 4.5% to 15%; a greater percentage was suggested by the author of 6) the analyst cannot accomplish his exact intent in making the study. Some introduce not only monstrous quantitative errors but also errors in reasoning.

Some Fancied Uncertainty

First we will explain how the company's actual earnings, in percent, can be determined by reference to its regular annual financial statements.

It may surprise the uninitiated to learn that accountants have some difficulty in deciding exactly what is meant by "actual" earnings. This may seem strange, because income is clearly defined as the quantity calculable by the simple formula:

$$\text{Income} = \text{Revenues less expenses}$$

Both revenues and expenses are reported in the company's income statements. However, one item of expense is depreciation expense, and accountants and management are permitted some leeway in its definition and evaluation. Although depreciation expense is often said to represent "loss in value," actually no attempt is made, with any degree of accuracy, to charge amounts which approximate loss in value, because simply no way exists to determine loss of value within any period shorter than total service life.

Fortunately, this situation tends to simplify the problem at hand, rather than otherwise. Charges to depreciation expense are in fact amortization charges — regular periodic charges which are expected to recover initial capital investment adjusted for salvage, over service life. These regular periodic payments are determined by:

1. Making reasonable estimates of probable service life, in a manner discussed in Chapter 7.

2. Estimating probable ultimate net salvage, based on experience; and

3. Adopting some simple arithmetical formula, such as the "straight-line" formula, which converts estimated life and salvage into "depreciation expense."

Resultant annual charges to "depreciation expense" bear no relation to loss in value within the year. However, they do provide a consistent and reasonable basis by which to establish annual income, by subtracting reported expenses from reported revenues.[3]

In making economic studies we must recognize one of the three levels of return: actual rate of return, cutoff rate, and MAR. It is only MAR that need be evaluated for purposes of making economic comparisons, but the relation of MAR to the other two quantities is of greatest importance, and will be discussed.

Measurement of Actual Return

Earnings, income, or return may be expressed in various terms, as convenient: in dollars per year, in dollars per share of stock, or as a percentage. Whenever any quantity is expressed as a percentage, it is well to inquire, "Percentage of exactly what?" A few examples will illustrate the point.

In most studies of profitability or economic choice the element of first importance is the amount of capital investment involved. Several components of revenue requirements such as return, depreciation, and income taxes are desirably expressed as a percentage of capital investment. Occasionally earnings in percent of sales provide a meaningful statistic, but not for the present purpose.

It is regrettably common to find return derived as a percentage of market price of stock, or as a percentage of replacement cost, which percentage is then applied to a new capital investment in order to estimate return thereon. Errors of this sort are obvious once pointed out, but they often escape detection.

Recalling the three definitions of the word "investment" in Chapter 1, we may correctly apply one and the same percentage to either: (a) the capital funds put to productive use, or to (b) the property so procured. The reason: (a) = (b), in dollars. Therefore, it is the same capital investment.

We will make use of this feature of double entry bookkeeping by investigating return on the company's capitalization (liabilities) in order to evaluate its return on the purchase price of facilities (assets) which represents the proposed capital investment. We will also indicate a common error that results from deriving percentage return on

---

[3] For a frank and penetrating, yet simple, appraisal of this situation, see:

C. N. Ostergren, "Depreciation— A Few Unsolved Problems," 1962 Proceedings of the Iowa State Conference on Public Utility Valuation and the Rate Making Process (Ames, Iowa, 1962), pp. 284-311.

market price of stock and applying that figure to the company's capitalization.

Our exact intent, of course, is to derive percentages in the same manner as that in which they are to be applied. We wish to calculate return in percent of average annual capital investment in service; therefore the figure must be derived as a percentage of that same quantity. The average of twelve monthly figures, if available, or the mean of consecutive year-end data would serve our purpose. Midyear data might be adequate in some cases. But first-of-year or end-of-year will not, so long as the numerator represents outlays throughout that period, as is our intent. Whatever application is to be made of the percentage, its derivation must be on that same basis.

Because the investor looks at return on his capital commitment in the business (which funds are used to purchase the proposed facilities), our exactly intended denominator is average investors' committed capital in those facilities during the period. Use of this exact term, investors' committed capital, helps to clarify several points that are sometimes obscure.

First, it clearly represents the funds invested in the business by investors. These are not the amounts paid by investors to purchase the company's securities from other owners of the company's securities on the stock or bond exchanges. It was noted before that such transactions are secondhand deals which do not affect the amount of investors' committed capital in the company at all. Investors' committed capital represents strictly amounts obtained by the company from initial issuance of the securities — "paid-in" capital used to buy equipment.

Second, because certain funds, such as depreciation reserves, accrued income tax savings (under any accounting designation), contributions in aid of construction (in public utility experience), and a few other similar items were not paid in by investors, they clearly are not to be included in investors' committed capital.

Third, since retained earnings (= earned surplus) do belong to investors, but are not currently paid out to them, these earnings must be included in investors' committed capital. Customers' deposits, if interest is paid on them, are a special form of investors' committed capital, also to be included.

Table 3.1 presents a summary of items which make up the investors' committed capital in a typical case, and it may be helpful. The annual financial statements of the company, whatever their "uncertainty" are conveniently referred to as presenting the company's "actual" earnings and asset position. We will adopt that usage.

Tables 3.2-3.6, inclusive, illustrate our exact intent in calculating "actual percentage return" for a particular year. Economists call this the "internal" rate of return.

Because public utilities report their finances in greater and more explicit detail than many nonregulated industries, because they respect exact nomenclature more assiduously, because they show an item called

Table 3.1. Components of investors' committed capital.

The sources of capital on which a return is to be paid comprise Items 1 to 9, in-clusive; their total is <u>investors' committed capital</u>.

The terms at the left, in quotation marks, are common but bad usage; they refer to the sum of respective items indicated by arrows. Note the opportunities for mis-understanding:

1. "Bonds," in common parlance, ordinarily does not refer to the company's total debt; sometimes otherwise.
2. "Capitalization," in common parlance, does not refer to total investors' capital; see <u>Good Usage</u>, below.
3. "Equity" is sometimes used incorrectly to include accumulated deferred income taxes as part of Item 9, earned surplus.

In this book, such poor usage will be avoided, so far as possible.

<u>Good Usage:</u>

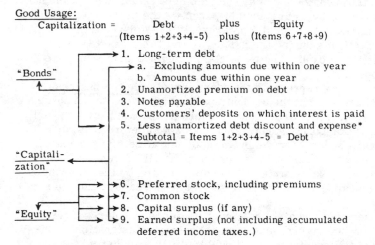

Capitalization =   Debt   plus   Equity
                 (Items 1+2+3+4-5)   plus   (Items 6+7+8+9)

"Bonds"

1. Long-term debt
   a. Excluding amounts due within one year
   b. Amounts due within one year
2. Unamortized premium on debt
3. Notes payable
4. Customers' deposits on which interest is paid
5. Less unamortized debt discount and expense*
   Subtotal = Items 1+2+3+4-5 = Debt

"Capitali-
zation"

6. Preferred stock, including premiums
7. Common stock
8. Capital surplus (if any)
9. Earned surplus (not including accumulated deferred income taxes.)

"Equity"

*It might be said that Item 5 adjusts the overstatement of Items 1 and 2 to correctly represent the true amount of investors' committed capital in debt.

"interest charged to construction" which is special to that industry and whose treatment might be unclear, and because they are more apt to have special charges or credits to earned surplus that call for expla-nation, these tables purport to represent the reports of a public utility, as a superior source of helpful information.

Table 3.2. Earnings, Year 1965; by source of funds.

Income before interest charges	$18,100,000
Interest charged to construction	400,000
Charges to earned surplus:	
Utility plant acquisition adjustments	(50,000)
Loss on sale of property, less related income taxes	(1,150,000)
Total earnings	$17,300,000

Table 3.3. Earnings, Year 1965; by disposition of funds.

Interest charges (excluding interest charged to construction)	$ 4,800,000
Dividends declared	10,900,000
Increase in earned surplus, by difference:	
12/31/65 $26,600,000	
12/31/64 $25,000,000	1,600,000
Total earnings	$17,300,000

Table 3.4. Investors' committed capital, Year 1965; by source of funds.

	12/31/65	12/31/64
Common stock	$ 66,700,000	$ 66,700,000
Earned surplus	26,600,000	25,000,000
Preferred stock	45,000,000	45,000,000
Long-term debt	143,000,000	130,660,000
Miscellaneous debt	100,000	---
Unamortized premium on debt	160,000	170,000
Unamortized debt discount and expense	(560,000)	(530,000)
Total investors' committed capital	$281,000,000	$267,000,000

Table 3.5. Investors' committed capital, Year 1965; by disposition of funds.

	12/31/65	12/31/64
A. Total Capital in Productive Use		
Utility plant	$367,400,000	$347,400,000
Other property and investments	1,800,000	1,800,000
Total current assets	25,700,000	23,400,000
Deferred debits (except for unamortized debt discount and expense)	1,000,000	900,000
Total in productive use	$395,900,000	$373,500,000
B. Less Funds From Sources Other Than Investors' Committed Capital		
Reserves for depreciation and amortization	$ 80,300,000	$ 73,900,000
Current liabilities	27,400,000	26,100,000
Deferred credits (except for unamortized premium on debt)	1,200,000	400,000
Contributions in aid of construction	1,900,000	1,800,000
Accumulated deferred income taxes	4,100,000	4,300,000
Total from other sources	$114,900,000	$106,500,000
C. Investors' Committed Capital, by Difference (= A-B)		
Year end	$281,000,000	$267,000,000
Average (mean)	$274,000,000	

Table 3.6. "Actual" return on investors' committed capital, Year 1965.

Earnings, from Tables 3.2 and 3.3	$ 17,300,000
Investors' committed capital (average) from Tables 3.4 and 3.5	$274,000,000

$$\text{Percentage actual return} = \frac{17,300,000}{274,000,000} = 6.31\%$$

The first step in preparing estimates of a company's MAR is to calculate the firm's "actual" percentage return, in the manner shown in Table 3.6, for a period of several successive years — enough years so that the results may be regarded as reasonably informative of the financial performance investors have come to expect of the enterprise. This means informative as to future expectations of the company, looked at through the eyes of the investing public, or "the market place."

Introduction to MAR

So much for actual return, its determination in past experience before adoption of a proposed new project, and its anticipated amount in the future. Let us now turn our attention to the cost of financing the new project, the importance of which was demonstrated in Chapter 2. If the new project is to be worth undertaking, its actual earnings must be greater than this cost of financing which is to be minimized (= MAR).

An important fact, to be explained, is that it is the long-term minimum acceptable return (MAR) on the company's pool of investors' committed capital that is in question, not merely the minimized cost of the immediate financing of the new project.

The incremental capital needed for the new project may come from within the enterprise (that is, "internally generated" funds, such as depreciation reserves or retained earnings); it may be obtained from outside the firm by sale of new issues of company securities (stocks, bonds, debentures); or it may be acquired by negotiating bank loans, which are just one more form of debt.

The cost of this new capital is measured by the amounts that buyers demand by way of returns on their investment in these securities. Two components of the return expected by buyers of the company's securities are:

1. Dividend or interest payments; and
2. Capital gains, meaning the difference between the initial purchase price and the higher price obtainable at subsequent sale, if and when the investor chooses to sell.

This poses a problem, because what is sought is the company's MAR, which is expressed as a percentage of the firm's investors' committed capital. We have taken great pains to define investors' committed capital exactly. It represents the company's investment in assets, mostly in fixed assets (land, buildings, equipment), purchased by use of capital funds "hired" from investors.

Company MAR on common equity is a percentage of the common equity component of its investors' committed capital, represented by book value of its common stock plus retained earnings. It is not expressed as a percentage of the market price of the stock.

On the other hand, investors look at their MAR as a percentage of the market price they paid for their holdings. Consequently, one must think twice before jumping to the conclusion that common stockholders' MAR is the same percentage as company MAR on its common equity.

We may base our estimate of company MAR on observations of investor's MAR, but our fundamental objective is to do two things:

1. Estimate the company's current and near-future actual earnings, as a percentage of its investors' committed capital; and
2. Estimate the company's current and near-future MAR, which is somewhat less than actual earnings, also as a percentage of investors' committed capital.

It is this essential margin of Profit Incentive, the difference between actual earnings and MAR (all in percent of investors' committed capital), that is our ultimate concern.

The Practical Approach

It is true that buyers of stock purchase anticipated returns. They cannot look far into the future, and they do not usually attempt to do so. Their conclusions, however, establish their MAR at the moment. Successive estimates of MAR at the moment (that is, "one-shot" estimates) can be made over a period of years. They will be found to vary surprisingly little. These independent successive estimates can be trended, projected, and averaged. This is the practical approach that really works.

Investors establish their current MAR by looking at current and near-future rates of return on their purchase price of a security. That is, they look at the current and near-future dividend rate and the capital gains rate. The practical means of estimating company MAR duplicates that process.

Investor's MAR may be defined as:

$$\frac{d + x\% \text{ of } p}{p}$$

where

d = current dividend rate.
p = maximum price he is willing to pay per share
= current market price.
$x\%$ = current rate of annual increase in market price.

The same expression also defines the company's MAR on that same security. But that takes a little explaining, because company earnings, in percent, are ordinarily expressed differently:

$$\frac{\text{Earnings per share available for dividends}}{\text{Investors' committed capital per share}}$$

We have no reason to expect that the numerator (earnings available for dividends) will equal dividend payout plus capital gains per year per share. Furthermore, investors' committed capital per share (the denominator) can differ widely from market price per share; it equals proceeds from prior stock issues per share plus retained earnings per share.

It is not our present purpose to find the company's percentage ac-tual earnings. That was disposed of in Tables 3.2-3.6. We now seek the smaller "cost of money" — the company's MAR.

In dollars, company MAR is whatever investors demand. As a percentage, both the company and the investor relate those same dollars per share to the same capital investment per share; the company's sale price (reinvested in fixed assets) is also the investor's purchase price per share. Investors' MAR, for this particular security, is also the company's MAR rate.[4]

This situation seems to be commonly misunderstood and misrepresented. The investor buys an annuity — an annual rate of return made up of cash dividends plus capital gains. He hopes for a regularly in-creasing annual return, in dollars and in percent of his initial purchase price (increases in dividend rate and corresponding increases in capital gains rate). His first-year rate is smallest, in dollars and in percent of purchase price; hence, newcomer's minimum acceptable return, or his MAR.

The company, on its part, invests the funds obtained from sale of stock in its new fixed assets. It expects to earn more than MAR% on that capital investment; no one raises money at a cost of $i\%$ in order to reinvest it at that same $i\%$. The company hopes for actual earnings enough greater than MAR so that it can produce the future dividend increases that investors look for, and so that future additions to capital can be obtained at a continuing low rate of MAR.

It is absolutely essential that this profit incentive mechanism be understood. Implications of this situation are far-reaching, and they are not clearly understood by a surprising number of businessmen. Some of the phenomena that flow from it will be discussed at length in Chapter 5 and in Appendix B.[5]

The direct approach just described differs subtly but importantly from another approach which has been given a great deal of attention by economists: the "stream of earnings" concept. This latter course of

---

[4] For simplicity, this explanation contemplates external financing and ignores use of re-tained earnings. However, the same reasoning applies to internal financing. See Appendix B.

[5] For an exceptionally penetrating analysis of relations between earnings, book value, and market price, see:

Frank E. Block, "A Study of the Price to Book Value Relationships," *Financial Analysts Journal* (September-October, 1964), p. 108.

The hopelessness of long-term estimates (the "stream of earnings" approach) is emphasized by another paper in that same issue: S. Eliot Guild, "The Case for Stock Value Tables," p. 80.

In consulting any references, it is important to remember the exact concept of MAR as described herein. That is, an instantaneous rate, of which a series of independent observations are made at intervals, to be trended, projected, and averaged.

reasoning is unsound as a basis for estimating MAR. It does, however, deserve attention for other reasons that will appear in Tables 3.8 and 3.9.

The "Stream of Earnings" Fallacy

When an investor buys a share of stock, what he purchases is future cash receipts, of (a) cash dividends, and (b) capital gains (= increase in market price).

The amount he pays for the stock today is the "present worth" to him of those future cash receipts, discounted by applying a factor (the discount rate) which allows properly for the delay between date of outlay (immediate) and date of receipts (future). An exact explanation of present worth calculations appears in Chapter 5. One fact is of particular importance to the present discussion. It will simply be stated here; its proof appears in Chapter 5.

Economists point out, correctly, that the investor buys anticipated cash receipts. Accordingly, it appears that we must attempt to peer into the future to gauge what percentage investors have in mind as an acceptable return on their today's purchase price. But the investor's return depends upon how long he holds the stock. Usually a successful company's earnings and dividends per share increase as time passes. The market price follows suit. The investor is said to buy this future "stream of earnings" when he purchases the stock.

The "stream of earnings" for how many years? Economists reply, "Forever." That is, whenever the investor may sell the stock, the market price then obtained represents other investors' evaluation of the worth to them of the "stream of earnings" from then on. Thus it is reasoned that at any date the market price must be the investors' evaluation of the present worth to them, at that date, of the "stream of earnings" from then on — forever. Then why not estimate investors' MAR in that way, by discovering the discount rate that will reduce the anticipated "stream of earnings forever" to a present worth equal to today's market price of the security?

This is an appealing suggestion except for two things:

1. No investor is capable of peering very far into the future. He does not attempt to. There is no good way to guess what cash dividends and market price will be more than a very short period ahead, with any accuracy.
2. Even if the "stream of earnings" could be accurately predicted forever, the proposed arithmetic would not reveal MAR.

It is the second fact that is frequently overlooked. Briefly, discounting actual future earnings at a discount rate to yield a present worth equal to market price would reveal the levelized actual rate of return. What we seek, though, is MAR, which is less than actual return by the margin of Profit Incentive.

Discounting future <u>minimum acceptable earnings</u> at a discount rate that will yield a present worth equal to market price would identify MAR. Investors, however, attempt to foresee actual, not minimum acceptable, earnings. That is explained in Chapter 5. This is why the "stream of earnings" approach does not work.

The Nature of MAR

It was pointed out before that when a company offers a new issue of its stock for sale, it makes every effort to obtain the maximum possible price per share. At the same time, the buyer will not pay one cent more per share than he must. If that maximized price is divided into the buyer's anticipated annual returns, the resultant percentage is at once: (a) the <u>minimum</u> rate the buyer will accept; and (b) the <u>minimum</u> rate on the new financing that the seller càn obtain.

As noted before, it is not essential that an actual transaction take place. The resultant percentage can be established by inference, by observing the price that would be obtainable and acceptable, if there were to be such an offer of a new issue.

Also as noted before, prospective returns foreseen by the purchaser of a share of stock consist of: (a) anticipated dividend payments; and (b) anticipated increase in market price above purchase price (= capital gain).

The estimate of these returns is necessarily a strictly <u>prospective</u> process. It may be helpful to review the company's past record of actual earnings, dividends per share, and price/earnings ratio, to assist in predicting the near future. But who can say whether past performance represented earlier expectations or not?

Table 3.7 assembles the data necessary for making an estimate of MAR on the company's common equity. Let's see how the figure behaves.

Behavior of MAR on Common Equity

For purposes of this initial discussion of the principles involved, "ideal" data have been used in Table 3.7. That is, market price, earnings per share, and annual dividends per share all increase at a constant rate each year (5.8%). This circumstance has no bearing on the basic principles.

In discussing Table 3.7, it is necessary, of course, to distinguish sharply between:

1. Already committed stockholders, represented by <u>pre-project</u> <u>shares at the moment,</u> whose percentage earnings it is our intent to <u>maximize;</u> and
2. The outsiders ("newcomers" who supply the new capital <u>at the</u>

Table 3.7. Behavior of MAR on common equity.

The concensus among investors interested in purchase of the company's stock is as follows. (Optimistic and pessimistic limiting views may also be investigated and given limited weight.)

Year	Market Price (First of Year)	Earnings per Share	Dividend per Share (End of Year)
1	$75.00	$4.00	$2.40
2	79.35	4.23	2.54
3	83.95	4.48	2.69
4	88.82	4.74	2.84

Part I-A. Annual Returns to the Year 1 "Newcomer"

	His First Year	His Second Year	His Third Year
Dividend	$2.40	$2.54	$2.69
Capital gain	4.35	4.60	4.87
Total	$6.75	$7.14	$7.56
In % of $75	9.00%	9.52%	10.08%

Part I-B. Annual Returns to the Year 2 "Newcomer"

	His First Year	His Second Year
Dividend	$2.54	$2.69
Capital gain	4.60	4.87
Total	$7.14	$7.56
In % of $79.35	9.00%	9.53%

Part I-C. Annual Returns to the Year 3 "Newcomer"

	His First Year
Dividend	$2.69
Capital gain	4.87
Total	$7.56
In % of $83.95	9.00%

Part II. Average "First-Year" Return to Three Generations of "Newcomers"

1. From Part I-A	9.00%
2. From Part I-B	9.00
3. From Part I-C	9.00
Sum	27.00%

Averaged MAR on common equity = $\frac{27.00}{3}$ = 9.00%

moment) whose return at this moment it is our intent to mini-mize.

It is essential to recognize that rate of return is an instantaneous phenomenon. Our problem would be solved if only we had a tachometer or speedometer to read the rate at any moment. MAR at any moment is not a function of earnings far into the misty future beyond the sight of today's investors.

The moment a new stockholder's rate of return changes from that instantaneous percentage at the moment of purchase, he is no longer a newcomer, in the exact sense defined here. He may be the most recent new stockholder, but he has become the most recent new pre-project stockholder. By definition, "newcomers" exist only momentarily, and are distinguished by having a momentary rate of return on their new stock purchase of exactly MAR — no more and no less.

Thus, the Year 1 newcomer is a pre-project owner in Year 2; he is succeeded by another generation of newcomers in Year 2, who in turn become pre-project owners in Year 3; and so on. The company obtains new capital from this succession of annual newcomers. At the risk of tiresome repetition, it must be reiterated that the cost of new capital depends upon the rate paid to newcomers, which is the figure the company seeks to minimize. This principle is a distinguishing feature of the Minimum Revenue Requirements Discipline.

In Part I-A of Table 3.7, the Year 1 newcomer's percentage returns are calculated in each year and reduced to a percentage of his purchase price of $75 per share. Note how his annual percentage return increases in each successive year. That is because he has by Year 2 joined the ranks of pre-project owners, and participates in earnings of subsequent new projects in excess of their cost of financing — even though he may not contribute one cent to their capital cost.

This is the Profit Incentive principle of the free enterprise system at work. It is this anticipation of future benefits, as pre-project owners, that induces newcomers to join the party at a relatively low first-year percentage return, which is the company's cost of new financing.

In Part I-B of Table 3.7, the Year 2 newcomer's percentage returns are calculated each year and reduced to a percentage of his purchase price of $79.35 per share. As for all newcomers, this percentage increases each successive year. Note particularly that his first-year (Year 2) acceptable return is 9% — the same as the Year 1 newcomer's first-year return. This is necessarily so for the "ideal" data used here.

Part I-C repeats the calculations for the Year 3 newcomer. Again, the first-year minimum attractive return is found to be that same 9%, which is the cost of new financing and which is to be minimized.

Because we assumed "ideal" data in Table 3.7, the same 9% MAR is discovered for three successive generations of "newcomers." We could have made the final estimate by looking at Year 1 alone, but in actuality each of the three might have been different. The analyst would then feel that some sort of three-year average or trended or "smoothed" value would be a more reliable estimate.

In Part II a simple arithmetical average is calculated. Of course, it results in the same 9% for each of the three years.

The "Smoothing" Operation

In Chapter 5 we will discover that the foregoing simple arithmetical average, although possibly adequate, is not quite the analyst's

Table 3.8. An estimate of MAR.

Based on a reasonable projection of past experience and the opinion of management and financial analysts, together with owners of large blocks of company stock, plus whatever other information may be available, current market opinion is believed to be as follows (beginning of Year 1):

Year	Earnings (End of Year)	Dividend (End of Year)	Price/Earnings Ratio	Market Price (First of Year)
1	$1.75 (est.)	$1.30 (est.)	20 (calculated)	$35.00 (actual)
2	1.85 (est.)	1.35 (est.)	20 (est.)	37.00 (est.)
3	1.95 (est.)	1.40 (est.)	20 (est.)	39.00 (est.)
4	...	...	...	41.00 (est.)

"Newcomer's" return, Year 1:
Dividend	$1.30
Capital gain	2.00
Total	$3.30 ÷ 35 = 9.43%

Year 1 Newcomer's Return, "Smoothed" Over Next Three Years
   Try 9% and 9.5% to bracket the Year 1 observation:

Dividend	Trial MAR% = 9.0%		= 9.5%	
1.30	÷ (1.09) =	$ 1.19	÷ (1.095) =	$ 1.19
1.35	÷ $(1.09)^2$ =	1.14	÷ $(1.095)^2$ =	1.13
1.40	÷ $(1.09)^3$ =	1.08	÷ $(1.095)^3$ =	1.07
41.00	÷ $(1.09)^3$ =	31.33	÷ $(1.095)^3$ =	31.23
Total present worth		$35.07		$34.62

Present worth, discounted at 9%, almost exactly duplicates purchase price. Accordingly, MAR on common equity is currently 9%.

Allowance for Pressure* and Selling Cost
   A total allowance of $2 per share is made. Thus, the company would realize $33 net per share.
   Assuming that this is acceptable to the proprietors, the company's MAR on common equity would be calculated as follows:
   9% of $35 = $3.15 per share
   3.15/33   = 9.55%

MAR on Company Pool of Investors' Committed Capital
   Anticipated capital structure, and components of MAR during the next three years are:

Debt	40% at 4.5% interest	= 1.80%
Preferred stock	10% at 6.0% dividend	= 0.60%
Common equity	50% at 9.55% (as above)	= 4.78%
	The company's MAR	= 7.18%

   (The "one-shot" estimate.)

*Pressure refers to the drop (if any) in market price experienced when the company announces its intention to float a sizeable new issue of stock.

exact intent. It is impossible to judge whether the approximation is sufficient until we investigate the exact intent. This is done in the example of Table 3.8, which introduces two other practical considerations mentioned before but omitted from Table 3.7 for simplicity.

1. It makes allowance for "pressure" and for selling costs of the new issue.
2. It allows for MAR on senior securities (debt and preferred stock) in proper proportion in order to ascertain the company's MAR, not just on common equity but on its pool of investors' committed capital.

In order to promote acquisition of a "feel" for this method of estimating MAR, Table 3.9 is included. It represents a company which

Table 3.9. Another estimate of MAR.

An estimate for another company having slower growth, greater payout ratio, smaller price/earnings ratio, and no preferred stock is:

Year	Earnings (End of Year)	Dividend (End of Year)	Price/Earnings Ratio	Market Price (First of Year)
1	$1.75 (est.)	$1.40	10.3 (calculated)	$18.00 (actual)
2	1.80 (est.)	1.40	10.0 (est.)	18.00 (est.)
3	1.85 (est.)	1.45	10.0 (est.)	18.50 (est.)
4	...	...	...	19.00 (est.)

Newcomer's return, Year 1:
Dividend	$1.40
Capital gain	None
Total	$1.40 ÷ 18 = 7.78%

Year 1 Newcomer's Return "Smoothed" Over Next Three Years

Try 8% first, based on Year 1 observation; the final conclusion is that the appropriate "smoothed" figure is 9.5%:

	Trial MAR% = 8.0	9.0%	9.5%
1.40	÷ (1.08) = $ 1.30	÷ (1.09) = $ 1.28	÷ (1.095) = $ 1.28
1.40	÷ $(1.08)^2$ = 1.20	÷ $(1.09)^2$ = 1.18	÷ $(1.095)^2$ = 1.17
1.45	÷ $(1.08)^3$ = 1.15	÷ $(1.09)^3$ = 1.12	÷ $(1.095)^3$ = 1.10
19.00	÷ $(1.08)^3$ = 15.08	÷ $(1.09)^3$ = 14.67	÷ $(1.095)^3$ = 14.47
Total present worth	$18.73	$18.25	$18.02

Allowance for Pressure and Selling Cost

A total allowance of $2 per share is made. Thus, the company would realize $16.00 per share.

The company's MAR on common equity, assuming $16 to be acceptable, is:

$$9.5\% \text{ of } 18.00 = \$1.71 \text{ per share}$$
$$1.71/16 = 10.7\%$$

MAR on Company Pool of Investors' Committed Capital

Anticipated capital structure and components of MAR during the next three years are:

Debt	20% at 5.0% interest	= 1.00%
Common equity	80% at 10.7%	= 8.56
The company's MAR		9.56%

(The "one-shot" estimate.)

does not impress investors as highly as the firm of Table 3.8. It also calls attention to one other phenomenon: the Year 1 return to investors is not typical of conditions expected in the near future.

To illustrate, compare the return of Year 1, Year 2, and Year 3 newcomers, in their respective first years:

	Year 1 Newcomer	Year 2 Newcomer	Year 3 Newcomer
Dividend	$1.40	$1.40	$1.45
Capital gain	None	.50	.50
Total	$1.40	$1.90	$1.95
In percent	1.40/18.00	1.90/18.00	1.95/18.50
	= 7.78%	= 10.56%	= 10.54%

This emphasizes the importance of the three-year "smoothing" device. The arithmetical average is 9.66% compared to the "smoothed" estimate of 9.5% per Table 3.9.

MAR on the Pool of Capital

The contribution of senior securities to MAR on the pool of investors' committed capital consists of interest and preferred stock dividend obligations during the period of analysis in Table 3.8 only. This is because earnings per common share are specifically defined as amounts available for common dividends after payment of the company's obligations for interest and preferred stock dividend payments, out of current total earnings (that is, out of gross income). Current market price of common stock is a function of those same earnings per common share. Were those interest and preferred dividend obligations different, earnings per common share out of the same gross income would be different, as would be market price.[6]

It is possible that future makeup of total capitalization and its incremental cost may differ from that of the moment. This possibility has not been overlooked in recommending the procedure of Tables 3.8 and 3.9. We are concerned strictly with a "one-shot" observation of MAR at the moment. Should tomorrow's incremental debt change the interest rate on the then-outstanding debt, then tomorrow calls for another independent estimate of MAR on that basis, to be averaged and trended along with the series of other "one-shot" estimates. It is

---

[6] An essential difference between (a) MAR on common equity, and (b) interest and preferred dividend components of pool MAR must be recognized. Each separate issue of debt, or of preferred stock, contributes its own particular and established rate to pool MAR on debt and preferred equity. This is not so for common equity — all issues of which have identical book value per share, identical market price per share, and identical earnings per share, regardless of price per share obtained when first issued (= assets purchased with receipts from sale). Thus, MAR on all common equity, already committed or incremental, is one and the same percentage at any moment. Profit Incentive per share is also the same for all shares, but not Profit Incentive in percent of price per share when issued.

essential that this concept of averaged "one-shot" estimates of instantaneous conditions be recognized.

A Helpful Recapitulation

The following brief review of exact objectives and some suggestions for their practical implementation will be found helpful at this point.

It is the objective of every company's management to:

1. <u>Maximize</u> potential return to existing owners; and
2. <u>Minimize</u> cost of new capital.

If projects are financed internally, by using retained earnings, this dual objective may seem to present a paradox: it aims to maximize return to the same people whose return is to be minimized. And if financing is external, by issuing new shares, it aims to minimize return to new shareholders (by making issue price per share as high as possible) who by their purchase become owners whose return is to be maximized.

Only MRRD recognizes this apparent contradiction and indicates how to reconcile the two objectives. It is this explanation which reveals how a company can earn a level return of 7%, for example, while continually increasing its earnings per share and paying a continually increasing dividend rate. It has nothing to do with "leverage" obtained by borrowing part of the company's funds at an interest rate less than 7%.

The explanation lies in the inducement mechanism described before. The phenomenon originates in earnings in excess of MAR (= Profit Incentive) and the accompanying increase in market price per share, or capital gains; hence the all-important difference between book value of common equity per share and market price per share.

All shares, new or old, enjoy the same earnings per share. Percentage return <u>to newcomers</u> is <u>minimized</u> by demanding the <u>highest</u> price obtainable per new share. That highest price obtainable <u>at the</u> <u>moment</u> divided into return per share <u>at the moment</u> (= dividend rate plus capital gain rate) represents MAR on common equity <u>at the moment</u>. The objective of every new project thereafter is to increase earnings per share, the same increased earnings per every share, new or old. The latest newcomer becomes the newest pre-project owner, as discussed in Chapter 2.

Thus, current MAR on common equity may be defined as:

$$\frac{d + x\% \text{ of } p}{p}$$

where

d = current dividend rate.
p = current market price per share.
$x\%$ = current rate of annual increase in p.

Because we have no way to measure d and $x\%$ momentarily, it is necessary to regard our most nearly instantaneous rates as current figures. Because market price fluctuates daily, we must regard some sort of "present average price" as the current amount obtainable for a new issue per share, if it were to be offered.

This normal daily variation in market price has troubled some students newly introduced to MRRD. For example, if there are "short" sales of record, do not some investors expect a negative rate for $x\%$? Also, daily swings may result from affairs outside the company, such as war news, the President's sudden illness, or Federal Reserve action with respect to interest rates.

Estimating MAR must not be degraded to mechanical application of a formula. However, it is possible to suggest ways to handle such situations, per the following example.

A Suggestive Example

The following figures represent observed data for an actual company. Price Obtainable per New Share (in absence of a better informed source) is placed at the average of high and low prices for each year, except in 1962. It is helpful to remember that new issues would not be offered if market price were unfavorable.

	Per Share		Price	Price Obtain-		
Year	Earn-ings	Divi-dends	Price Range	able per New Share	Payout Ratio	Price/Earnings Ratio
1965 (est.)	$2.40	$1.44	$36-32	$34	60.0%	14.2
1964	2.17	1.36	34-30	32	62.7	14.8
1963	2.29	1.30	37-29	33	56.8	14.4
1962	2.15	1.225	31-23	27(31)	57.0	12.6(14.6)
1961	1.84	1.20	33-24	28	65.2	15.2

In 1962, the average of high and low prices would be $(31 + 23)/2 = 27$. The resultant p/e ratio would be $27/2.15 = 12.6$, which would be out of line with typical experience in other years. Average p/e ratio for the other four years is 14.6, and the figure is quite stable. Accordingly, price obtainable per new share in 1962, if offered, is placed at $31, as indicated parenthetically. ($14.6 \times 2.15 = 31$.)

MAR on common equity in 1965 may then be estimated as:

$$\frac{1.44 + 5.15\% \text{ of } 34}{34} = 9.3\%$$

Here the <u>average</u> rate of increase in price obtainable per share has been inserted in the formula, calculated at 5.1%, as follows:

$$
\begin{array}{llll}
1965 & (34 - 32)/\ 32 = & 6.2\% \\
1964 & (32 - 33)/\ 33 = & (3.0) \\
1963 & (33 - 31)/\ 31 = & 6.5 \\
1962 & (31 - 28)/\ 28 = & \underline{10.7}
\end{array}
$$

$$20.4/4 = 5.1\%$$

Reviewing these results, it will be seen that they assign a negative value to $x\%$ in 1964.

It might be pointed out that a growing company such as this would be most reluctant to sell a new issue for less than was obtainable the previous year, as discussed in Chapter 2. The firm would probably resort to a short-term loan instead. How then should we proceed with the estimate?

It is possible to modify the estimates of price obtainable slightly, but not much without offending reasonably expected behavior of the p/e ratio in view of earnings from year to year. That is, the p/e ratio might decrease temporarily while earnings per share are increasing, owing to nonsimultaneity of cause and effect — the cause being partly current and partly anticipated return. But a continuously decreasing p/e ratio accompanying continuously increasing earnings per share is illogical and unlikely.

An alternative approach would be to evaluate $x\%$ for the whole four-year period. From 1951 to 1965, price obtainable has increased $34/28 = 1.214$ times. Referring to compound interest tables (see Chapter 5) reveals that this means an equivalent sustained rate of almost exactly 5% growth, or substantially the same figure as estimated above (5.1%).

The simplified formula for MAR on common equity (and the means of its evaluation just described) is perhaps not the preferred procedure because it tends to obscure the important principle that estimates of current instantaneous rates of MAR are essentially prospective in nature. However, this version is readily understood and applied, and results are often just as dependable as those obtained by the more meticulous approach.

In this example, a new issue of one common share in 1965, representing new assets of $34, could be sold at a cost of:

Current dividend rate	$1.44
Current capital gains rate (5.1%)	1.73

$3.17 per year

Each $34 of capital reinvested in fixed assets of the firm in 1965, whether externally or internally obtained, has the same cost of $3.17/34 = 9.3\%$, which is the newcomer's initial rate in 1965. This MAR on common equity applies to the company's total common equity investment, incremental and already committed.

Every common share of the company, new or old, newcomer or pre-project, has the same earnings per share, the same capital gains per year per share, the same market price per share, at any moment.

The rate of return on newcomer shares differs from rate of return on pre-project shares only because their respective initial issue prices differ.

Accordingly, a "unit of investment" (per share) committed to fixed assets in 1961 is in 1965 earning a pre-project rate of return of $3.17/28 = 11.3\%$, compared to the 1965 newcomer rate of return of only $3.17/34 = 9.3\%$. This reflects the force of the all-important inducement mechanism, so often overlooked. Note that the rate of increase in earnings per share (about 7%, from 1961 through 1965) is not the same as the capital gains rate of 5.1% for the same period.

An Unsound Estimate of MAR

Attention must be called to the unsound procedure described by Table 3.10. This is a superficially appealing but thoroughly incompetent estimate that has occasionally been proposed. It is wrong in principle, in that it completely overlooks the major objectives of minimizing return to newcomers while maximizing return to pre-project owners, out of given sales and revenues.

Table 3.10. An unsound estimate of MAR.

Net earnings per share = $1.75.
Market price per share = $25.00.
Earnings/price ratio = 1.75/25 = 7.00%.

Common equity = $110,000,000.
Debt, at 3.8% interest = $50,000,000.
Preferred stock, at 5% dividend = $10,000,000.

Capitalization and acceptable (?) earnings:

Debt	$ 50,000,000 at 3.8% =	$1,900,000 per year
Preferred stock	10,000,000 at 5.0% =	500,000
Common equity	110,000,000 at 7.0% =	7,700,000
	$170,000,000	$10,100,000 per year

Incorrect estimate of acceptable return = $\dfrac{10,100,000}{170,000,000} = 5.94\%$

Note: The above approach assumes that the same percentage return on common equity is acceptable to pre-project owners and to investors who supply incremental capital. Actually, both classes of stockholders accept the same earnings, in dollars per share, which may amount to a substantially different acceptable percentage of the price paid by each per share.

Long-Term Aspects of MAR

A few additional facts remain for thoughtful consideration before the percentage MAR derived in Tables 3.8 and 3.9, or the MAR calculated by the simplified formula, can be safely used.

All these procedures estimate company MAR on its pool of

investors' committed capital at the moment. But, as noted before, the concept of averaged and projected "one-shot" estimates of MAR must be recognized. In passing upon the profitability or relative economy of projects, it is their lifetime earnings in excess of the company's MAR over that same lifetime that is of concern. The appropriate MAR, for purposes of these studies, is a long-term average obtained by projecting a series of "one-shot" estimates made at intervals, perhaps intervals of one year over a period of years.

In this connection, it must be appreciated that investors who finance a project do not obtain their return from that particular project. They obtain their dividends, or interest, from the company's pool earnings on its pool of investors' committed capital, whether the new project they finance be a bonanza or a catastrophe. If the new project is a bonanza but the company's overall earnings are poor, the investor who financed the bonanza may obtain only miserably poor returns on his investment.

There is nothing new in this, but it points up a fact that is often overlooked or denied: It is not the project's earnings in excess of its immediate cost of financing that measures its profitability, but its earnings in excess of MAR on the company pool of investors' committed capital over the service life of the project. This is why profitability and economic choice of projects cannot be determined without inquiring into MAR on the company pool of investors' committed capital. Only MRRD respects this principle.

Feedback Effects

Exhibits A and B of Figure 3.1 show the relations between the three levels of return:

1. Actual company earnings;
2. Company average cutoff rate (that is, the aggregate of all individual project cutoff rates); and
3. Company MAR on its pool of investors' committed capital.

Nothing succeeds like success. The more prosperous an enterprise is, the more prosperous investors anticipate it will be. The larger the percentage return to the proprietors, the cheaper new money is apt to be; the higher the percentage actual earnings, the lower is MAR. This inverse relation works in the opposite direction, too. The poorer a company is doing, the more it probably will have to pay for new financing; the higher is its MAR.

One has no absolute assurance that this will be so, because investor reaction to a change in earnings is never 100% predictable. It certainly would be irrational, however, to assume that an improvement in earnings per share, present and anticipated, would cause a drop in market price of stock, absolute or relative.[7] Consequently, we cannot

---

[7] It is assumed, of course, that the change in earnings per share is not the result of a change in debt ratio for given total earnings.

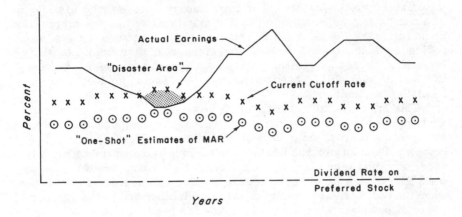

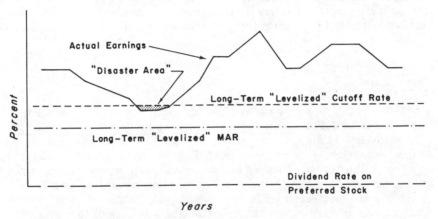

Fig. 3.1. Exhibit A: Actual earnings, current cutoff rate, and "one-shot" estimates of MAR. Exhibit B: Actual earnings, long-term "levelized" cutoff rate, and long-term "levelized" MAR.

make exact quantitative plots of the data; it is for this reason that no scales are indicated in Exhibits A and B in Figure 3.1.

A company has a continuing source of outside capital at a lower cost than its actual percentage earnings so long as new issues of its common stock can be sold at a price above book value per share of its common equity. But it is quite possible for a company that is doing poorly to find that the reverse is true: that market price (reflecting price obtainable per share for a new issue) lies below book value per share of common equity.

Unless new projects are so profitable that they can reverse this relation, the pre-project owners then worsen their percentage return with every additional dollar invested. Newcomers then enjoy a better percentage return than the proprietors themselves. Such a situation is intolerable; further investment in the company is not worthwhile. Loss of a market for the company's product may bring about such a situation. Some railroads are today facing this problem. Airplanes, trucks, superhighways, and the automobile have taken away their business; their large investment in rights-of-way and equipment can perform no function but the supply of transportation, and the demand for that service has fallen off sadly.

This situation calls attention to a proposition that has long been advanced as though it were almost axiomatic; yet it is demonstrably unsound. This proposition is usually stated more or less as follows: A company should undertake further capital investment, raising capital as necessary, up to the point where the cost of additional capital rises to meet the falling rate of actual earnings. The optimum level is reached when the two rates are exactly equal to each other and to the earning power of incremental investment outside of the firm.

Quite often the falling rate of actual earnings is dignified by the term "marginal internal lending rate"; the rate obtainable outside the firm is known as the "external lending rate." Let's examine this assertion, in the light of our present understanding of MAR, to see why it is unsound.

Cutoff Rate

In Table 3.8, the company's MAR, or minimized cost of new capital, was found to be 7.18%. Nobody raises new money at 7.18% in order to reinvest it at 7.18%. Pre-project owners would then obtain zero benefit and the expansion would be pointless. This is the very reason why MAR constitutes the "break-even" floor, or bench mark, above which we tend to measure the profitability or relative economy of new proposals.

For a new project to be deemed worth undertaking, it must promise some margin of earnings in excess of MAR. The size of that margin depends upon the degree of risk involved in adopting the project. Note that this statement is compounded of:

1. Ordinary common sense;
2. A matter of principle, recognized in our statement of exact intent in Chapter 2; and
3. Recognition of investor reaction. If a margin of profit acceptable to investors in view of their evaluation of risk is not maintained, that will be evidenced by a drop in market price (our index to minimum acceptable earnings by way of an inference) and consequent increase in MAR — a purely arithmetical result.

Even projects having zero risk (if that can be imagined) demand some motivating margin, as just noted. The greater the assessed risk, the greater the margin, on up to the riskiest ventures that the management is willing to consider at all. In the aggregate of all projects, which comprise the company's total capital investment, some fairly constant margin in excess of MAR is thus established as the company average cutoff rate, whether it is ever formally recognized or evaluated, or not.

Clearly, then, cutoff rate — which is greater than MAR by some margin — is the company's minimum attractive level of return. This exact concept of the situation is of greatest importance. Exhibit A, Figure 3.1, shows why, graphically. If actual earnings of the company fall below its cutoff rate, the business is in trouble. Unless new projects can be developed which are sufficiently profitable to reverse this condition, expansion of the business will only aggravate the difficulty; hence identification of "disaster areas" at points where earnings fall below cutoff rate — which cutoff rate lies above MAR.

Now refer back to the assertion quoted, that additional investment should be continued beyond this disaster point, until actual earnings fall still further — to the MAR level! What sort of "optimum" can that be which deliberately aggravates a disaster?

Common sense would say incremental investment must cease if it threatens to reduce the internal rate (actual earnings) below cutoff rate, not to the lower MAR level.

Consider this "dynamite analogy." If a high explosive were known to detonate at exactly 100 degrees centigrade, nobody would describe 100 degrees as the "maximum safe temperature." Similarly, company MAR cannot possibly be described as its minimum "attractive" rate. This careless habit of confusing minimum acceptable rate (MAR) with the company's cutoff rate accounts for a great deal of the inexcusable vagueness so prevalent in this field of technology.

Actual earnings are determinate, in retrospect. MAR and cutoff rate are strictly prospective concepts. The situation envisioned by the businessman-analyst in making estimates of profitability or economic choice is shown by Exhibit B. The problem is one of relating observable actual current return to estimated long-term cutoff rate and MAR.

Note that the range of MAR is quite limited. Its upper limit, for a project to be worthwhile, is some figure less than cutoff rate, which in turn is less than actual earnings by some finite margin if investment in the company is worthwhile. The lower limit of MAR on common equity is greater than the divided rate on a new issue of preferred stock, if such were to be offered and found acceptable. See Appendix B for further discussion of this point.

It is for such reasons that MAR, which is by essential nature a relatively stable statistic for any successful business, can be estimated with greater assurance than can most other variables involved in economic studies, such as future sales, taxes, raw material costs, and labor rates.

Résumé

This chapter is probably the most important part of this book, because the first step in any analysis of profitability or economic choice is to gain an understanding of minimum acceptable return (MAR), how it behaves, how it enters into managerial decisions, and what it is proposed to do about it. However difficult it may be to grasp the concept, or to evaluate it as a percentage, the fact remains that <u>exactly intended conclusions as to the financial effect of adopting proposed projects cannot be reached in any other manner.</u>

The principles discussed in this chapter are recognized, perhaps intuitively, by every businessman. The major contribution here is an organization of these familiar principles in such a way (MRRD) that the quantitative evaluation of MAR (= "cost of capital") becomes possible, with a high degree of assurance.

This organization of the facts may be reviewed briefly: The purchaser of a share of stock buys a contemplated "annuity" of receipts, not a <u>level</u> annuity but one that is expected to increase each successive year. These annual receipts consist of: (1) cash dividend payments; and/or (2) capital gains, representing increase in market price. Thus, the annual rate of such receipts is minimal <u>at the date of purchase.</u> This minimal initial rate is identified as MAR; the margin of later increase is Profit Incentive; both are expressed as a percentage of initial purchase price.

That same minimal initial rate of MAR on that same purchase price (adjusted for expenses of sale) represents the company's "cost of capital," obtainable from successive generations of "newcomers." Company Profit Incentive, meaning the earnings in excess of MAR on that purchase price per share, rewards <u>previous</u> generations of "newcomers," which have now become pre-project shares. Thus, the investor's "MAR plus minimal Profit Incentive" rate, which constitutes his minimal <u>attractive</u> rate of return, coincides with the company's "MAR plus minimal Profit Incentive" rate (adjusted for expense of selling the initial stock).

The matter of the appropriate percentage to use in <u>discounting</u> calculations will be taken up in Chapter 5. In general, exact intent is carried out by using MAR (minimum <u>acceptable</u>, not minimum <u>attractive</u> rate), as the "interest" rate.

Steps in the presentation of MAR in this chapter may be reviewed as follows:

     I. Imaginary difficulties, which have led many to conclude that studies of profitability and economic choice are "uncertain," "inexact," "elusive," or "loose," are not really difficulties at all. They are misunderstandings, which are easily exposed and avoided by:

    1. Respecting exact definitions of terms and of intent;

    2. Avoiding dependence on vague concepts such as "value," "loss of value," and "depreciation," which cannot be exactly defined in terms capable of measurement; and

    3. Recognizing the exact nature of actual accounting practice, in order to avoid being misled by deceptive terminology such as "depreciation expense."

    II. The first step toward the estimate of a company's MAR is a review of its "actual" earnings in recent years, in percent of the company's pool of investors' committed capital, exactly defined.

III. The second step is developing a "feel" for the exact nature and behavior of MAR. This demands use of exact phraseology and respect for the exact intent of analyses of profitability or economic choice, as described herein.

IV. It is the margin of a project's future earnings above the company's long-term MAR that determines profitability or economic choice of proposals. This is just an extension of the reasoning introduced in Tables 2.1, 2.2, and 2.3, of Chapter 2. Any method of solving problems that overlooks effects of financing is certain to give wrong answers.

V. Some margin of company earnings in excess of its MAR is essential to a company's financial health. A firm's well-being is evidenced by the existence and magnitude of this margin of actual earnings above MAR. When actual earnings threaten to fall below the company's cutoff rate, which is greater than MAR by some amount dependent on the degree of risk, the company enters a "disaster area." Incremental capital investment cannot then be justified unless it reverses that situation.

VI. As a company's percentage earnings increase, its percentage MAR can be expected to decrease (both figures in percent of the same investors' committed capital), and vice versa.

VII. It is possible to estimate MAR for any enterprise without great difficulty and with a high degree of assurance. However, the reasons why this is the case call for careful consecutive reasoning, commonly overlooked.

VIII. The essential feature of the estimate is the observation that so long as new issues of a firm's common stock could be marketed at a price above book value per share of common equity, the company has a continuing source of outside capital at a cost less than its rate of actual earnings on its pool of investors' committed capital.

IX. The cost of hiring equity capital is the momentary percentage return $[= (d + x\% \text{ of } p)/p]$ to a "newcomer" at the instant of his purchase of a new issue of stock, if offered. This is the component of company return to be minimized, in the manner of any cost or minimum revenue requirement. The other component of company return, Profit Incentive, may be desirably maximized. "Newcomers" exist only momentarily; the instant after purchase, as owners of the firm, they participate in Profit Incentive, which is not a component of minimum revenue requirements.

X. "Newcomers" contribute to the company pool of investors' committed capital, from which all new projects are financed. Their return comes from earnings on that pool, not from earnings of the project they may appear to finance.

XI. It is not the project's earnings in excess of its immediate cost of financing that measures its profitability or economic choice, but its lifetime earnings in excess of the company's long-term MAR on its pool of investors' committed capital.

XII. MAR is by essential nature a uniquely stable statistic, restricted to a narrow range, and almost a constant. It tends to vary in opposite direction to total return. Its upper limit is less than company cutoff rate, which in turn is less than company earnings. Its lower limit is normally above dividend rate on the firm's preferred stock, which in turn lies above interest rate on the firm's outstanding debt.

MAR on equity has two components: (a) dividend yield, and (b) capital gains rate. With any change in market price, as one component increases, the other decreases; the effect tends to be offsetting. It is relatively immune to effects of price inflation; the numerator and the denominator of the fraction are both in terms of the same current dollars.

XIII. The important reasons why the percentage estimated as proposed is MAR are: (1) the seller of a new issue of capital stock insists upon the maximum price per share obtainable; (2) the buyer will not pay one cent more than he must. Thus, when the price so established is divided into anticipated returns (dividends plus capital gains), the result is, at once: (a) the minimum percentage acceptable to the investor; and (b) the minimum cost of the capital obtainable by the seller.

XIV. For companies unable to make actual earnings in excess of MAR (that is, unable to market new issues of common stock at a price above book value per share of common equity), incremental investment is not profitable or economic unless and until that situation can be reversed. In such case, there may be little point in making studies of profitability, but management may still desire to determine the alternative proposals that would minimize losses.

XV. Since the whole objective of productive investment is to maximize percentage return on pre-project shares, while minimizing return to "newcomers," great care must be taken to ascertain that proposed analytical techniques recognize and promote that purpose. One should avoid them if they do not.

XVI. It may be helpful to review the list of things that MAR is not, on page 30. All of them have been proposed at some time or other for use in making studies of economic choice; not one of them is defensible.

XVII. If the economic analysis does not make use of MAR, as exactly defined herein, then the procedure is not MRRD and the conclusions reached are not to be trusted.

The general subject of the exact financial objectives of a business enterprise, which involves the course of reasoning pursued in Chapters 3 and 4, is known as the "theory of the firm." Much more is involved than the elementary outline presented herein. Appendix B is devoted to some of the commoner misunderstandings which have arisen from failure to respect exact definitions of terms and of intent in applying the "theory of the firm."

Problems

1. What does "ceteris paribus" mean? Is there a good reason for this usage, or do authors like it just because it displays their erudition? What does erudition mean?

2. What does MAR stand for? Why do some people prefer to call it "critical return"?

3. What is meant by the expression "scrupulously observed"?

4. Explain some of the circumstances which make it impossible to measure "value" of physical objects.

(Hint: The classical example is the "value" of diamonds to a man dying of thirst in the desert.)

5. Define "amortization." Exactly how does it differ from "depreciation"?

6. Define (a) service life, (b) economic life, (c) useful life, (d) probable life, (e) life expectancy. Explain the importance of each word in the phrase "probable future service life."

7. It is the usual practice not to depreciate land. Why?

8. At some places in the text, quotation marks are used in the expression "actual" return. What is their significance?

9. What is meant by "internally generated funds"?

10. What are the two components of return expected by purchasers of capital stock? What is the significance of the adjective "capital" in the preceding sentence?

11. If you were a director of a corporation, what factors would you take into account in deciding upon the desirable dividend rate?

12. What is meant by the expression "present worth"? How can it represent any specific figure, in dollars, if it is impossible to measure value of physical objects (see Problem 4)?

13. How do you go about identifying (a) the investor's cash return, with (b) company earnings per share on the same share of stock?

14. If the financial objective of management is to maximize percentage return, why do they try to sell new security issues at the highest possible price per share? Doesn't that do the direct opposite? Explain.

15. Why does MAR go down as earnings go up? Can you quibble over this statement of the case? Explain your arguments.

16. What is the direct opposite of a "prospective process"?

17. Define "common equity."

18. Starting with the same figures for Year 1 as in Table 3.7, derive the figures in subsequent years that would result in MAR on common equity at 11%, using "ideal" data.

19. Draw up a table similar to Table 2.1, on page 19 assuming:
   a. The company is earning 15% before adopting the new project;
   b. Project A is expected to earn 16%; and
   c. Project B is expected to earn only 14%.
   Use your table to illustrate the points emphasized in Chapter 2.

20. Using your table of Problem 19, illustrate the important conclusions drawn in Table 2.2, on page 20.

21. Using the data of Table 3.10, plus other information that could be reasonably expected to be encountered at the same time, demonstrate that the true value of MAR for the company in question could be far removed from 5.94%.

22. a. Extend the "ideal" data of Table 3.7 another three years.
   b. Calculate percentage returns in Years 4, 5, and 6 to the investor who purchases a share of stock at the beginning of Year 4.
   c. Discover the discount rate that will convert the return of (b) to a present worth, at the date of purchase, exactly equal to the purchase price.

    d. Repeat the calculations of (c), using a discount rate 1% greater, and
       1% less, than the percentage established in (c).
    e. Explain the significance of your calculations.
  23. Many companies nowadays include in their annual report to stockholders
a summary of the firm's financial statistics over the past ten years. Some
(Glidden Company, for example) even include the high and low market prices of
the company's stock during each of the ten years. The commonest omission of
helpful information is the amount of debt in the firm's capitalization each year.
    Secure such an annual report. With the help of current stock market reports
(and possibly your broker if he is good-natured) project the necessary data three
years into the future, and estimate the company's MAR on its pool of investors'
committed capital, in the manner of Tables 3.8 and 3.9.
    Try doing it retroactively. How do you decide what past earnings were an-
ticipated in still earlier years?
  24. A company's capitalization consists of:
    a. A moderate amount of debt, in the form of mortgage bonds paying 5%
       interest (coupon rate);
    b. A small amount of preferred stock, 5.5% dividend rate;
    c. Mostly common stock, paying a current dividend of $2 per year per
       share and having a market price of $50; and
    d. Retained earnings (earned surplus).
  The company's planners estimate MAR at 7% for purposes of their studies of
profitability and economic choice. Yet the highest rate of return on any of their
securities, as above, is the 5.5% dividend on preferred stock. Dividend yield on
the common stock is only 2/50 = 4%! Are the planners making a serious mistake?
Explain.
  25. A notorious error in economic thinking is illustrated by the proposal to
base estimates of minimum acceptable return (carelessly called minimum "attractive" return by those who make this proposal) on so-called "opportunity cost."
Opportunity cost is the rate of return that is foregone by adopting the immediate
project, instead of investing the same capital elsewhere. See the first proposal
under Item XVI of the Résumé.
    Explain the circular reasoning involved that brands the proposal as incom-
petent.
  26. In 1966, an analyst tabulated behavior of his company's common stock as
shown in Table 3.11. Based on this information, he predicted its future as indicated below the broken line.
    But later that same year, something drastic happened in the stock market;
price per share dropped about one-third. As a result, the analyst revised his
forecast. He now predicted that price per share in 1967 would be 38% under his
previously estimated figure; that earnings per share would show a growth rate of
only 5% instead of the formerly forecast 7%, and that price/earnings ratio would
fall to about 14 in place of the previous 20. He anticipated that the usually expected dividend increase would not be realized in 1967, and that thereafter dividend
payout would be at the reduced rate of 60% of the smaller earnings per share.
    a. Calculate the company's estimated MAR on common equity suggested
       by the early 1966 prediction.
    b. Recalculate MAR on common equity based on the revised forecast.
    c. Assuming that the company's capitalization included 50% debt at 4.5%
       interest (no preferred stock), calculate the company's MAR on its pool
       of investors' committed capital, a "one-shot" estimate, before and
       after the drastic change.
    d. Comment on the effect of the drastic change in market behavior on
       long-term MAR to be used in making economic studies for this
       company.

Table 3.11. An analyst's prediction of the future of a stock.

Initial Estimate

Year	Earnings per Share	Price per Share	Dividends per Share
1961	$1.50	$30.00	$0.90
1962	1.60	32.10	0.96
1963	1.71	34.40	1.03
1964	1.83	36.60	1.09
1965	1.96	39.20	1.17
1966	2.10	42.00	1.23
1967	2.25	45.00	1.35
1968	2.40	48.00	1.44
1969	2.57	51.40	1.54
1970	2.74	54.80	1.64

Revised Forecast

(Something drastic happened in 1966)

Year	Earnings per Share	Price per Share	Dividends per Share
1967	2.10	28.00	1.23
1968	2.20	30.00	1.32
1969	2.31	32.00	1.39
1970	2.43	34.00	1.45

27. Repeat the calculations of Problem 26, and comment on results, using actual data for the common stock of any company with which you are familiar.

4

. . . . . **Minimum Revenue .**
Requirements

Outlays and Revenues

In Chapter 3, reference was made to proposals which call for the minimized outlay during their lifetime. This is the very essence of studies of profitability and economic choice. Our primary objective is to discover the alternative plans which will result in minimized outlays throughout their service life.

Lifetime outlays are of two distinctly different kinds:

1. The initial capital investment; and
2. Periodic expenses thereafter, such as taxes, operation and maintenance expense, administrative and general expense, and sales and collection expenses.

In addition, a small credit is sometimes received at the end of service life in the form of net salvage when physical assets are scrapped.[1] Notice particularly that neither of these two kinds of outlays, whose minimization concerns us, includes return on the investment nor depreciation expense.

These outlays might reasonably be called "costs." But with customary human perversity, the word "costs" is not reserved for this purpose. Instead, we discover that a commonly used phrase unfortunately has succeeded in introducing all manner of misconceptions concerning minimized outlays. Instead of sensibly reserving the word "cost" to mean an outlay, the expression "annual cost" has been unwisely adopted to mean the revenues received by the company to compensate it for outlays. We will avoid this bad usage wherever possible.

The word revenues means receipts from the company's sales of its output. Other expressions substantially synonymous with "revenues" are gross receipts or gross sales billed. Both are good usage. Revenues is preferred, partly because it is shorter ("minimum gross sales billed requirements" is a little awkward), partly because it is familiar in governmental usage (the Internal Revenue Service) and public utility practice. It is most unlikely that the term "revenues" can be misunderstood.

---

[1]Sometimes this ultimate net salvage is an additional outlay, as when expenses of removal are greater than payments received from the junkman.

Surely, it must be obvious that revenues are not outlays. Revenues are not costs. Revenues are the receipts from sales which do two things:

1. Compensate the company for its outlays (= "costs"); and
2. Hopefully, return a profit over and above those outlays.

It is for this reason that we are forced to propose a special and unique phrase to express our exact intent: minimum revenue requirements, which is the subject of this chapter. These are the minimized lifetime outlays for the project under investigation.

Table 4.1 illustrates the point of all this. Expression I summarizes the outlays (properly described as "costs," but we wish to avoid that expression here) whose minimization is our concern. Expression II describes the revenues that must be obtained to compensate the company for these lifetime outlays, exclusive of any profit — mere compensation for actual expenditures, not including profits.

Table 4.1. Outlays over the service lifetime of a project
(which are to be minimized).

Expression I. Outlays (= Disposition of Funds)

1. The initial capital investment (= purchase price installed)
   a. Less ultimate net salvage, when received
2. Taxes
3. Operation and maintenance expense
4. Other expenses, such as administrative and general expense and sales and collection expense

Expression II. Revenue Requirements (= Source of Funds)

A. Minimum acceptable return on the capital investment (not including any profit)
B. Retirement cost (or amortization, commonly known as "depreciation expense," adjusted for ultimate net salvage)
C. Taxes
D. Operation and maintenance expense
E. Other expenses, such as administrative and general expense and sales and collection expense

Both of these expressions describe the same minimum revenue requirements of a project.

It will be observed that the recognition of duplicate sources of information, in Table 4.1, resembles our treatment of annual earnings and related investors' committed capital, in Tables 3.2 through 3.5 on pages 34 and 35, where identical figures could be established by looking at either (a) the source or (b) the disposition of funds.

In Table 4.1, the source of funds is a portion of revenues; their disposition represents the outlays. Note once more that the outlays do not include return or depreciation. Return (the minimum acceptable return, or MAR) and depreciation are components of revenues (Expression II), not of outlays (Expression I).

It appears to be a widespread misunderstanding of this simple fact which accounts largely for the popularity of the incompetent "standard" methods of analysis listed in Chapter 1. Instead of inquiring into minimized outlays — which is our clear intent — analysts look at behavior of some other quantity believed to be a magic indicator of minimized outlays. The Minimum Revenue Requirements Discipline consists of looking directly at minimized outlays, by way of the minimum revenue requirements which are their exact equivalent, per Table 4.1.

Revenue Requirements Defined

Throughout the remainder of this book we propose to employ the foreshortened expression revenue requirements to mean "minimum revenue requirements."

The reason is simply one of convenience. That is, the financially superior alternative is the one having the smallest minimum revenue requirements of the alternatives under consideration; in other words, the minimum minimum revenue requirements for the group. We propose to drop that second repetitive "minimum," and say revenue requirements wherever the clear intent is minimum revenue requirements. This has, in fact, been accepted usage for many years in the public utility industry.

With this understanding we can provide in a simple sentence the exact definition of revenue requirements, as visualized in the Minimum Revenue Requirements Discipline: Revenue Requirements are strictly defined as the revenues which must be obtained in order to cover all expenses incurred, associated with and including the company's minimum acceptable return (MAR) on investors' committed capital, no more and no less.

As in the case of our earlier discussion of MAR, it is necessary to emphasize that when we say exact we mean it. For example:

1. The concept is strictly a special portion of revenues. These revenues must equal certain exactly defined outlays; it is the recovery of these outlays in the form of revenues that enables the company to break even, before making a profit.
2. "Expenses incurred" refers to actual outlays, not to some notion of "normal" amounts, as has occasionally been incorrectly stated.
3. Only minimum acceptable return (MAR) is included in revenue requirements, not actual return, which is normally expected to be greater than MAR.
4. The annual revenue requirement for depreciation (discussed in Chapter 6) is the annuity calculated for an "interest" rate of MAR only, not actual percentage earnings.
5. Certain taxes, such as income taxes and taxes levied on sales or on gross receipts, depend on the amount of earnings. But revenue requirements for these expenses are the amounts associated with earnings in the amount of MAR only (Chapters 8 and 9).

6. This is not an attempt to estimate actual revenues. Actual revenues are expected to be greater, but may (hopefully not) be less than minimum revenue requirements. They must be greater if the capital investment is to be justified; if any Profit Incentive is to be realized.
7. Minimum revenue requirements may be specified as annual, as service lifetime, or as a single amount financially equivalent to their amounts over any specified period (see Chapter 5). In general, we are concerned with minimum revenue requirements from now on. In any case, they include all expenses incurred in the specified period, associated with and including MAR for that period; that is, total outlays (Table 4.1) for that period. This calls for a little further explanation.

At the beginning of Chapter 3, attention was given to the problem of ascertaining earnings for any period less than a lifetime of the project. If we are going to discuss annual revenue requirements, or revenue requirements for any period less than lifetime of a project, we must have an exact understanding as to our treatment of interim retirement expense (Item B of Expression II, in Table 4.1). A good deal of space will be devoted to that problem later on.

The Diagram of Intent; Figure 4.1

Armed with this exact definition of revenue requirements, it is now possible to produce a simple graphic representation of the exact intent of studies of profitability and economic choice. Figure 4.1 is the Diagram of Intent which explains the objective of a study of profitability.
The size of the rectangle in solid lines represents estimated revenues. This estimate of revenues is the first step in any study of profitability. The smaller shaded area represents revenue requirements of the project. The items which make up total revenue requirements are indicated. Note particularly that these are the total revenue requirements of the project, the amounts that must be recovered in order to compensate the company for all expenditures made as the result of adopting this project (which expenditures would not be made if it were not adopted).
Such estimates are not easy to make. If any expenditure chargeable to this project directly or indirectly is overlooked, then profits will be overestimated. The answer will be wrong. Economic comparisons are much simpler than studies of profitability on this score. In making economic comparisons we are concerned with the difference in revenue requirements; thus it is permissible to omit items that would be incurred in the same amount in any event, whichever alternative is adopted. This is not so in studies of profitability.
The difference between (1) revenues and (2) minimum revenue requirements consists of two components:

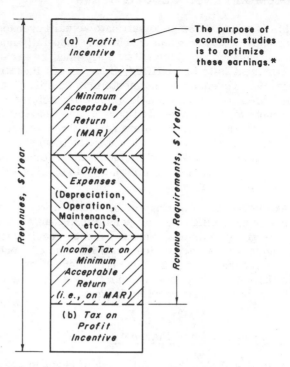

Fig. 4.1. The diagram of intent in profitability studies (for all industry, regulated or not).

*The "Profit Incentive" may be defined as the excess of actual earnings over the minimum acceptable return, both in dollars per year. Maximizing these earnings in dollars (not in percent) maximizes earnings for pre-project investors, both in dollars and in percent.

Out of any obtainable revenues from sales, the Profit Incentive is maximized by minimizing Revenue Requirements.

(1) Revenues - (2) Revenue Requirements
equals
(a) Profit Incentive + (b) Tax on Profit Incentive

Profit Incentive is shown by the unshaded area at top of the Diagram of Intent. Tax on Profit Incentive is shown by the unshaded area at the bottom of the diagram. In some cases more than one tax may be imposed on Profit Incentive. The important tax is that on income, and there may be state income taxes as well as federal income tax. In addition, taxes may be levied on sales or on gross receipts; if so, they also apply to Profit Incentive, which is a component of gross receipts.

Note that the expression Profit Incentive is used here, rather than profit margin. The reason is that too often an inexact meaning is assigned to "profit margin." Everybody knows in a general way what is meant by "profit margin," but a "general idea" is not satisfactory for the present purpose. Profit Incentive, as used here, conveys the exact intent, which is the amount of earnings in dollars, after taxes, over and above MAR.[2] This is the exact measure of profitability, in dollars.

If you want to maximize profitability, then you want to maximize this Profit Incentive, in dollars. Nothing is inexact, elusive, nor loose about that.

Note that nothing was said about annual, lifetime, or other periodic data. If revenues are annual dollars, so must all the other quantities be annual dollars; the Profit Incentive will then be in dollars per year. If these annual figures are typical of lifetime results, they may serve the purpose of the study. We will go into that matter thoroughly, too. But the index to profitability of a project has to reflect the whole lifetime behavior of the project to be meaningful. To do otherwise would be like deciding the World Series by the results of the first game. It would be pure happenstance if conclusions so reached turned out to be correct.

Figure 4.2 shows the situation when a project is found to be unprofitable. (Heavens forbid!) Here revenue requirements (the shaded areas, as in Figure 4.1) are greater than revenues (the area heavily outlined). As a result, Profit Incentive is negative. These small earnings are not sufficient to make this a profitable venture; they are

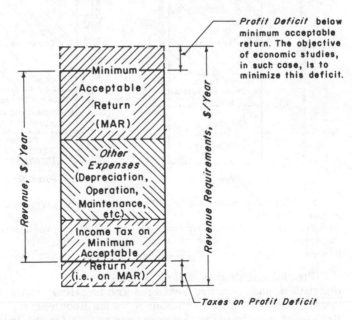

Fig. 4.2. The unprofitable situation (for all industry, regulated or not).
Out of any inadequate revenues obtainable from sales, the Profit Deficit is minimized by minimizing Revenue Requirements.

---

[2]Surely it is obvious that we intend all earnings to be "earnings after taxes," since taxes are just one more expense. But to make doubly sure, let it be formally stated that Profit Incentive means earnings after taxes in excess of MAR.

less than MAR. Income taxes actually payable are less than the revenue requirement for income taxes, in such case. Note that, as a result,
any taxes on gross receipts would be less than the revenue requirement for taxes on gross receipts.

An Amplified Intent; Figure 4.3

     In order to represent our exact intent in making economic com-
parisons, as distinguished from studies of profitability, it is necessary
to prepare a separate diagram for each of the proposals which are to
be compared. Figure 4.3 illustrates this situation.

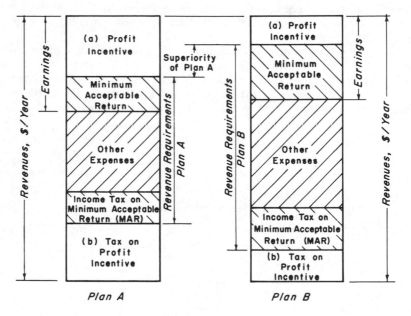

Fig. 4.3. The diagram of intent in economic comparisons (for all industry,
regulated or not).
     The purpose of economic comparisons is to select the alternative providing
the greater Profit Incentive out of the same revenues. Here, Plan A is superior
(that is, the "economic choice").

     Special attention is called to one feature of this diagram — the
tentative assumption that revenues are identical, whatever proposal
may be chosen. In the Minimum Revenue Requirements Discipline no
firm prediction is made that revenues will in fact be identical. It is
essential that this be understood. All we do is investigate earnings of
the several proposals if revenues were to be the same for all.
     It would defeat our purpose to predict firmly that revenues will be
the same in all cases. Our purpose is to select the plan that will accomplish two objectives simultaneously:

Objective 1. Earn the greatest <u>Profit Incentive,</u> in dollars, out of <u>the same revenues;</u> and

Objective 2. <u>Permit the greatest reduction in price of product,</u> with <u>the same Profit Incentive.</u>

Obviously, Objective 2 becomes impossible of realization if we firmly predict identical revenues for the same output. Other methods overlook the self-contradiction that is committed by basing the analysis on a firm prediction of identical revenues.

A similar self-contradiction arises if it is firmly predicted that <u>percentage return</u> will be the same, whatever alternative is chosen. In such case, the company (pre-project shareholders) would have no incentive to prefer the economic choice, since all hope is abandoned of any improvement of their percentage yield. Objective 1 then becomes impossible of realization.

This firm assumption of identical percentage return, in any case, is one more serious fault of the <u>Annual Cost Method,</u> to be explored in Chapter 11 and Appendix B.

No such self-contradiction is involved in the Minimum Revenue Requirements Discipline. Benefits obtained by determining and adopting the superior plan may flow to:

Case 1. Owners of the business alone, by way of increased yield on their pre-project shares; or

Case 2. Customers of the company (= the public alone) by way of reduced prices of the company's product; or

Case 3. Both investors and customers in any proportion, thus increasing the Profit Incentive (to somewhat smaller extent than in Case 1) while at the same time reducing the price of the company's product (to somewhat smaller degree than in Case 2).

Consequently, it is possible to select the alternative proposal capable of accomplishing both objectives, under any of the three cases, by applying a single criterion. Simply select the proposal promising minimum revenue requirements.

The proposal that accomplishes either Objective 1 <u>or</u> Objective 2 will accomplish the other as well. It will do so regardless of the disposition of benefits, be it Case 1, 2, or 3.[3]

This simple and complete fulfillment of our exact intent can be achieved only in the manner described, by respecting the two attributes which are special to the Minimum Revenue Requirements Discipline: (a) minimum acceptable return (MAR); and (b) Profit Incentive (= earnings above MAR).

It is impossible to achieve this result if we look only at <u>total</u> earnings, either in dollars or in percent, as some other methods of

---

[3]Although benefits to employees are not involved in this decision, selection of the superior plan on this basis places the company in the best possible competitive position, thus making it more capable of maintaining wage scales equal to or better than those of its competitors.

analysis undertake to do. Simple examples will be produced later on to provide a quantitative demonstration of this observation. Such, then, is the unique nature of the Minimum Revenue Requirements Discipline.

This technique is not committed to any particular disposition of benefits flowing from adoption of the superior plan. For that reason we are free to start with an "iffy hypothesis" as to revenues. We are free to say, "Let's consider the situation if revenues happened to be the same for all plans." We can then draw correct and intended conclusions by comparing the Profit Incentives that result for the several plans. Or, alternatively, we can say, "Let's consider the situation if Profit Incentive were the same dollars for all plans." We can then arrive at the same correct and intended conclusions by comparing the selling prices of products that would result for the several plans.

One other unique feature of the revenue requirements approach will be apparent, once it is pointed out. That is, by selecting the superior plan in this special manner, the company is placed in the best possible competitive situation. Accordingly, if MAR is affected at all, it will be reduced. The better a company's finances, the lower is its MAR.

Consider how this affects our choice of plans. We started by tentatively assuming the same percentage MAR for all alternatives, and made our selection on that basis. Actually, then, our selection must be on the conservative side; MAR is apt to be a trifle less than assumed for the superior plan, and the Profit Incentive advantage over other plans slightly greater, by reason of this feedback effect.

Note the reservation: "if MAR is affected at all, it will be reduced." This is the normal and logical expectation; the better company finances are, the cheaper is new money, and the lower is MAR. Our only reservation is that investors are never 100% predictable. This reduced MAR may be the rational and logical result of improved finances; it is substantially always realized in the long run. It would be absurd to base an analysis of profitability or economic choice on any other assumption or hypothesis. Nevertheless, the short-term reaction of investors is not quantitatively predictable with assurance.

Many cases have occurred where announcement of improved earnings and an increase in the dividend rate have been reflected in a temporarily lower market price of the company's securities. In such cases, financial analysts commonly rationalize the abnormality by saying that the investing public had anticipated even larger improvement in earnings and a greater increase in the dividend rate. These overly optimistic expectations were reflected in an abnormally high market price before the announcement. The downward revision of market price after the announcement is referred to as a "correction," in the jargon of Wall Street.

It is for such reason, simple in nature but requiring many words for exact understanding, that it is wise to hedge a little by saying "if MAR is affected at all, it will be reduced." In the long run, MAR almost certainly would be reduced, other things remaining the same.

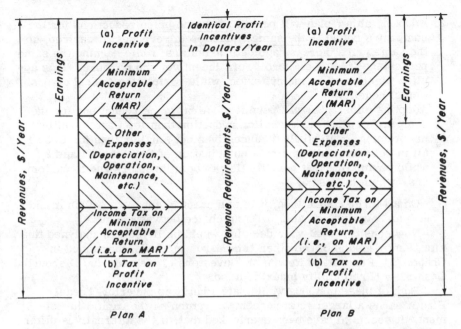

Fig. 4.4. The standoff situation in economic comparisons (for all industry, regulated or not).

Here, Profit Incentive in dollars is identical for both alternatives, out of the same revenues. This means that they are equally profitable or "economic." It makes no difference which is adopted.

Plan A has the smaller capital investment. Thus, the same Profit Incentive in dollars for both plans means a large percentage Profit Incentive for Plan A. Since MAR is the same percentage for both, MAR is smaller dollars for Plan A. Total Earnings in dollars are greater for Plan B.

A Special Case; Figure 4.4

Figure 4.4 illustrates a special case which deserves particular attention. This diagram represents the situation where two proposals are discovered to be equally profitable. No choice between them is offered, and it does not matter which one is adopted.

In the case displayed here, Plan A involves a smaller initial outlay for the capital investment than does Plan B, but subsequent periodic outlays — for operation and maintenance expense and taxes other than income taxes — are greater than for Plan B. The two effects are exactly offsetting, so that the result is a standoff.

Here we encounter a situation with respect to profitability or economic choice which can be described, alternatively, in any one of three ways:

1. Adopting either plan will produce the same Profit Incentive out of the same revenues, both in dollars. This applies Objective 1 as the criterion, while postulating Case 1 disposition of benefits.

2. Adopting either plan will permit the same price reductions for the
   company's output (= the same reduction in revenues, if desired, or
   the same price increase avoided) in dollars, while earning the same
   percentage MAR (i.e., zero Profit Incentive) and no more. This applies Objective 2 as the criterion, while postulating Case 2 disposition of benefits.
3. Adopting either plan will permit identical price reductions for the
   company's output but a smaller reduction than for Case 2, while
   maintaining identical Profit Incentives but smaller than for Case 1,
   all in dollars. This applies a combination of Objectives 1 and 2,
   while postulating that benefits flow to both investors and to customers, which is Case 3.

On all three counts then, it is our exact intent to rate Plan A and
Plan B as equally profitable, with no choice between them.

Now consider what your decision would be if you had analyzed this
situation by means of two other "standard" methods, mentioned in
Chapter 1: Percentage Return or "Investors'" Method; and Discounted
Cash Flow (Profitability Index) Method.

Both of these methods would rate Plan A as superior, because
Plan A earns a larger total percentage return on the capital investment. It seems to have been overlooked that, if the alternatives differ
as to the amount of capital investment, simply maximizing percentage
return does not accomplish our exact intent. It does not necessarily
maximize the yield to existing owners of the business — the yield on
pre-project shares. In addition, by ignoring the important effects of
new financing (Tables 2.1, 2.2, and 2.3, on pages 19, 20, and 23), these
other methods fail to select the proposal that will make the largest
earnings per share or permit the greatest reduction in the price of the
product while making the same earnings per share.

It was remarked in Chapter 1 that some analytical "methods" lose
sight of the exact intent of economic comparisons. Looking to percentage return (as the foregoing methods do) for the decision, rather than
to Profit Incentive, is like concentrating on first downs while overlooking the importance of touchdowns; like accumulating base hits without
attempting to score runs.

Merits of a Unique Solution

The basic principle displayed graphically by the Diagram of (Exact) Intent provides the foundation for a number of helpful and interesting developments.

For example, it has been mentioned (Chapter 1) that at least eight
different methods of analysis other than MRRD are in common use;
applied to a single problem they are apt to yield eight different conclusions. This situation has prompted a rebuke unhappily familiar to
those responsible for economic studies: "You engineers (or you teachers, or you accountants, or you economists) can make the figures prove
anything you like!"

No such criticism can be aimed at those who recognize the single intent of such studies. This is the single decision that is expected to optimize benefits to owners of the business, and thereby maximize benefits to the community.[4] It is this single decision that minimizes outlay of resources (not the same thing as minimizing "annual costs"). It is this single decision that offers investors the maximum inducement to prefer that solution, the solution which places the firm in the best position to maximize earnings per share while minimizing the price of output. If some other course of action should be adopted, for other reasons, then MRRD permits evaluating the penalty that goes along with that other decision.

All this is reassuring to students being newly introduced to this subject; or to those concerned primarily with the simplest dependable solutions to immediate problems, without great interest in economic philosophy. That is, little or no need is seen to study eight different methods of calculation, because none of them is particularly useful. For purposes of this book, all eight can be dismissed with brief attention (Chapter 11) sufficient to indicate concisely the nature of their shortcomings and how to recognize and avoid them.

For more advanced students, the unique solution described by the Diagram of (Exact) Intent opens new avenues to better understanding of numerous troublesome questions long regarded as controversial. The widely misunderstood significance of "reinvestment rate"; the businessman's practical problem of external versus internal financing; the often debated matter of ideal capital structure; most advantageous disposition of income tax deferrals; claimed merits of leasing versus owning the same facilities; the heated question of tax-financed versus investor-financed power or desalinating plants; "fair return" in public utility regulation — all yield to rational analysis only in the light of the principle illustrated by the Diagram of (Exact) Intent.

Discussions of these advanced problems are conveniently segregated in later chapters and in appendices.

Practical Applications

The next step to be taken in this presentation could be anticipated: how to make estimates of each separate component of minimum revenue requirements.

---

[4] It is interesting to observe that the same end objective — maximized benefits to the community and most efficient outlay of resources — is professed by both free enterprise capitalism and by communism. The major distinction between the two ideologies is that free enterprise offers profit inducement to all individuals, as individuals, to promote their selfish interests which automatically benefit the community, as well as the common interests which individuals share with others as members of the community. Free enterprise might even be regarded as a sophisticated and enlightened development beyond communism in the gradual evolution of social ideals. The basic principle of offering individual rewards to members of sports teams, as individuals, to promote team results is well recognized in communistic states, whose accomplishments in sports outshine their economic record.

Practical application of MRRD is the simplest of all "methods." Adequate approximations and shortcuts are favored, because the estimator understands the exact nature and behavior of the variables he proposes to approximate. One such convenient shortcut deserves special mention.

Our ultimate objective is to establish the amount of Profit Incentive, shown at the top of the Diagram of Intent. It represents the margin of earnings after taxes; taxes on Profit Incentive appear at the bottom of the diagram. However, as a practical shortcut, it is sufficient in most routine problems in economic choice simply to establish the difference in revenue requirements of competing proposals.

As noted before, this difference in revenue requirements includes both: (a) the difference in Profit Incentive; and (b) the difference in related taxes. In other words, it might be described as "profit before tax."

Since income tax on Profit Incentive is the same percentage (by law) for any and all proposals, the comparison "before tax" always makes the correct and intended selection. Usually it is sufficient to let it go at that. However, if one desires to estimate the amount of advantage of the superior plan in dollars of Profit Incentive after tax, it is necessary only to calculate and subtract the tax. Thus, if the statutory tax rate is 52% of taxable income, profit margin after tax is 48% of profit margin before tax (that is, 48% of the difference in revenue requirements of the competing proposals). This calculation will be more throroughly explained in Chapter 8.

It must be obvious that it is misleading and poor usage to refer to a difference in revenue requirements as the "savings" to be realized by adopting the superior alternative. Recognizing that there are several possible ways to assign these benefits of adopting the best proposal (Cases 1, 2, and 3, described in this chapter), one must ask, "Savings to whom?" We do not predict, and usually cannot foresee with certainty, whether a change will be made in revenues, or in return, or in both, as a result of our decision; it could be any or all. It would be necessary to specify the exact disposition of benefits in order to permit a calculation of "savings." Correct usage is to refer to a difference in revenue requirements as an advantage of the alternative having the minimum revenue requirements.

Résumé

I. One obstacle to be hurdled in this chapter is widespread loose usage of financial and accounting terms, which has invited misunderstanding and is responsible for many unsound business decisions and untold financial loss. This chapter is concerned particularly with exact usage in connection with outlays and the revenues needed to recover those outlays; minimum acceptable return (MAR) and Profit Incentive, which is the margin of earnings in excess of MAR; and revenue requirements and minimum revenue requirements.

II. Lifetime outlays resulting from adoption of a project are of two distinctly different kinds: (a) the initial capital investment; and (b) periodic expenses thereafter.

III. These outlays, whose minimization concerns us, do not include return on investment or depreciation.

IV. Return on investment and depreciation enter the picture only when we refer to the revenues that are needed in order to compensate the company for such outlays.

V. Revenues are not costs. Revenues are the receipts from sales which accomplish two things: (a) compensate for outlays; and (b) hopefully, return a profit over and above such outlays.

VI. Revenue requirements, explained in tabular form by Table 4.1, are strictly defined as the revenues which must be obtained in order to cover all expenses incurred, associated with and including the company's minimum acceptable return (MAR) on investors' committed capital, no more and no less.

VII. The Diagram of Intent presents a graphic illustration of the manner in which our exact intent may be accomplished by investigating revenue requirements of proposals.

VIII. The difference between (a) revenues, and (b) revenue requirements, consists of two components: (1) Profit Incentive; and (2) tax on Profit Incentive.

IX. Our exact intent, in economic comparisons, is to select the alternative that will accomplish two objectives:

Objective 1. Earn the greatest Profit Incentive, in dollars, out of the same revenues; and

Objective 2. Permit the greatest reduction in the price of the product, with the same Profit Incentive.

X. The Minimum Revenue Requirements Discipline carefully refrains from stipulating how benefits are to be distributed. Selection of the superior plan may:

Case 1. Benefit investors only;

Case 2. Benefit customers only; or

Case 3. Benefit both investors and customers.

XI. Selecting the superior plan in this manner tends to reduce the company's MAR, which adds to the advantage of that selection.

XII. As a practical shortcut accomplishing the same intent, it is customary in most routine problems to base the economic choice on a direct comparison of revenue requirements of competing proposals. The difference in revenue requirements represents a difference in "Profit Incentive plus income tax thereon." It is not properly referred to as a "saving."

Problems

1. Some foreign phrases are helpful because they have been assigned exact meanings, which can thus be expressed in fewer or less offensive words than in English. For example, grand barré (ask a guitar player), derrière (ask a dressmaker), entrepreneur, raison d'être. What do the last two mean? Why are they useful?

2. Interpret:
   a. IRS
   b. SEC
   c. NYSE
   d. ICC
   e. TVA
   f. Kva
   g. MAR
   h. Par

3. What is the meaning of:
   a. explicit
   b. implicit
   c. objective
   d. subjective
   e. power series
   f. discrete series
   g. dichotomy
   h. financial equivalency

4. What is the meaning usually ascribed to "net worth"?

5. Exactly what is the difference between:
   a. revenues and revenue requirements
   b. depreciation expense and depreciation reserves
   c. depreciation and depletion
   d. interest and return
   e. gross receipts and sales
   f. expenses and outlays
   g. scrap value and ultimate net salvage
   h. amortization and depreciation

6. Referring to Figure 4.1, can you suggest reasons for designating the area at the top of the diagram as Profit Incentive, rather than: (a) profit margin, (b) excess earnings, (c) "Gravy"?

7. The revenue requirements analysis is applied by way of two "iffy hypotheses": (a) if sales and revenues were identical for the competing proposals; and (b) if MAR were identical for both. Explain.
   (Hint: Why would it be absurd to predict identical sales and revenues, or identical MAR, for both? There is more than one reason.)

8. Why is it necessary to make the reservation "if MAR is affected at all," when observing that selection of the superior alternative reduces MAR?

9. Some writers have felt that an analytical technique based on estimated MAR is impractical, for the following reason: MAR is essentially a percentage return just too low to attract further capital investment. But any return, however small, is sufficient to attract some minute capital investment. Consequently, it is said, MAR must be indeterminate. Pinpoint the fallacy.

10. How can you determine, beyond any question, whether a proposed analytical technique carries out your own intent, when you undertake a study of profitability or economic choice?
    (Hint: Refer to Chapters 1 and 2.)

11. What is the difference between: (a) minimum revenue requirements; and (b) annual revenue requirements?

12. Why is it misleading to refer to the "savings" accomplished by adopting the superior alternative?

13. What is the meaning of:
    a. debt service
    b. unamortized debt discount and expense and premium (net)
    c. fully registered bonds
    d. debt financing

    e. refunding
    f. sinking fund
    g. full disclosure

14. a. Where would you go to discover payout ratio or book value of common equity for corporations other than your own company?

    b. How do income deductions differ from revenue deductions?

15. With the help of the Diagram of Intent, explain how you can hope to improve a company's competitive position by <u>increasing</u> percentage return to the owners of the business.

16. Redraw Figure 4.4 for the situation where annual revenues are <u>not</u> the same for both plans. What is the significance and practical application of such a diagram?

17. Suggest simple and helpful definitions for the following terms.
    a. internal lending rate
    b. external lending rate
    c. marginal internal lending rate
    d. marginal external lending rate
    e. borrowing rate

18. If you have a mortgage on your home who owns the real estate? Who owns the United States Steel Company? Who owns The Peoples Gas Light & Coke Company (Chicago)?

19. List twelve things that MAR is not.

20. The following actually appeared in a highly regarded financial magazine in 1963, and not one reader objected. A few words (not their meaning) have been changed to avoid embarrassment. Comment on its validity and the situation revealed by the incident.

"Several ways have been suggested to measure earning power of an enterprise. Probably the ratio

$$\frac{\text{Net income before deducting interest}}{\text{Total assets}}$$

is as good as any."

21. With the help of the Diagram of Intent, demonstrate:
    a. That it is necessary to estimate revenues in problems of profitability.
    b. That it is not necessary to estimate revenues in problems of economic choice.
    c. That expenses common to alternative proposals may be omitted from revenue requirements in economic comparisons, and that this question does not arise in profitability studies.

22. It is commonly assumed that, since public utilities are limited to a return dictated by the regulatory commission, the return component of minimum revenue requirements will be the same for all alternatives in an economic comparison. Then could this common return be omitted from the Diagram of Intent when applied to economic comparisons for public utilities? Explain.

23. Minimum revenue requirements are frequently expressed in percent, rather than in dollars per year. Could the Diagram of Intent be drawn up in percent, rather than in dollars per year? If so, how would you handle expenses such as fuel for power generation, which is a function of output rather than of capital investment?

24. Making use of the Diagram of Intent, demonstrate convincingly that minimum <u>attractive</u> return cannot possibly be correct for use in making studies of profitability or economic choice. Do the same for the nine other inappropriate percentages commonly used, listed on pages 30-31. One fundamental misunderstanding accounts for the incompetency of most of these ten proposed percentages. It is difficult to understand how it could be overlooked by their advocates,

because the principle is undisputed and recognized by every businessman. State the principle in seventeen words.

25. It has been pointed out that if a company is in financial trouble, its MAR could exceed its actual earnings, both in percent. Under such circumstances, it is concluded, further capital investment in the firm is not justified. What special reservations to that general rule can you suggest?

26. Most economists appear to agree that the objective of economic studies is to maximize market price of the firm's common stock.

Using the Diagram of Intent to illustrate, demonstrate the error of omission in that assertion, and explain how it suggests an imperfect understanding of an important essential of the free enterprise system.

(Hint: How are consumers and the general public benefitted by putting the firm "in best position"?)

27. Studies of profitability and economic choice are a form of input/output analysis. We have two basic equations that express this situation:

      A. Input less outlays = Earnings
      B. Revenues less expenses = Income

Since earnings = income, we can equate A and B, as follows: input less outlays = revenues less expenses. And since input = revenues, it must be concluded that: outlays = expenses. But we know that this conclusion is not correct, because outlays consist of (a) capital outlays, plus (b) expense outlays.

Where does the error in reasoning arise? How can such errors be avoided?

5

• • • • • Financial • • •
Mathematics

Function of Financial Mathematics

Alternative proposals under consideration frequently differ as to the timing of outlays. Or they may involve balancing a difference in capital investment (a single outlay) against a difference in expenses (annually throughout service lifetime). Or facilities to be compared may be expected to have different service lives. Financial mathematics provides the tools whereby the awkward cross-comparisons in such cases may be readily made in the exactly intended manner. The same device greatly facilitates comparisons between alternative series of outlays, by converting each series to its equivalent "levelized" form — the level annuity which cannot be evaluated by simply averaging arithmetically.

An elementary example will be presented first to illustrate a typical practical application. Reasons why proposed calculations accomplish the intended purpose will be explained in detail. You will discover that there is no room here for differences of personal opinion either with respect to exact intent or with respect to the arithmetic that carries out that intent.

As so often happens, a host of popular misconceptions, unhelpful notions, and unsound theories are easily dispelled by the simple device of insisting upon observance of those small details which respect exact intent, together with use of the arithmetic which carries out that intent.

An Illustrative Example

The following example illustrates a typical practical application of financial mathematics described as a calculation of the "present worth" of alternative investment opportunities.

Here, the investor has a choice between Plans A and B, which contemplate different capital outlays to produce the same sales and revenues per year but for different periods of time (service lives). No other outlays are involved:

77

	Plan A	Plan B
Capital investment	$100,000	$125,000
Service life	20 years	25 years

This means that for a given percentage MAR the proposal having the smaller outlay would produce the greater Profit Incentive out of the identical revenues, if the service lives were identical. But they are not. The 25% increase in capital investment of Plan B buys 25% increase in service life. The question is: Is the extra investment worthwhile? That question cannot be answered unless the investor's MAR is known. Suppose we assume that his MAR is 6%.

Table 5.1 shows that the extra investment is not justified, because an immediate premium of $25,000 would be paid for the extra life which has no value until after Year 20. Thus, by adopting Plan A one would have $25,000 available for profitable use elsewhere for 20 years. The immediate value of the reduced outlay is greater than the discounted value of the future benefit. Another way to say it is that by adopting Plan B one would have the extra $25,000 tied up for 20 years for no useful purpose.

The amount of Plan A's advantage could be calculated over a period of 100 years (four replacements, Plan A; three replacements, Plan B) by use of present worth factors, obtained from Table 5.1, as follows:

The differential of $17,614 is the hard-cash-in-hand-today advantage of Plan A over Plan B. Some might be inclined to call the $17,614 a "saving," realized by not adopting Plan B. However, for reasons discussed before, it is not accurately described as a "saving"; it is an advantage of Plan A over Plan B. The smaller present worth of Plan A over Plan B outlays represents a larger Profit Incentive for Plan A, out of identical revenues.

However, instead of expressing this advantage in terms of dollars

Table 5.1. Present worth of future outlays.
MAR = 6%; period of study = 100 Years.

	Present Worth Factors		Capital Outlays		Present Worths
Plan A (20-year life)					
1st outlay	1.000000	x	$100,000	=	$100,000
1st replacement (end of 20th year)	0.311805	x	100,000	=	31,180
2nd replacement (end of 40th year)	0.097222	x	100,000	=	9,722
3rd replacement (end of 60th year)	0.030314	x	100,000	=	3,031
4th replacement (end of 80th year)	0.009452	x	100,000	=	945
Present worth of total outlays					$144,878
Plan B (25-year life)					
1st outlay	1.000000	x	$125,000	=	$125,000
1st replacement (end of 25th year)	0.232999	x	125,000	=	29,125
2nd replacement (end of 50th year)	0.054288	x	125,000	=	6,786
3rd replacement (end of 75th year)	0.012649	x	125,000	=	1,581
Present worth of total outlays					$162,492

per year for some specified number of years, it is expressed in the
more convenient form of a single hard cash immediate receipt. That
is, the investor would just as soon receive the single lump-sum payment as to receive the alternative annual payments. The whole approach rests upon an exact concept of this "just as soon" deal.

Note that two effects contribute to the total of $17,614:

Part 1: postponement of the initial outlay of $25,000 for 20 years;
and

Part 2: a change in the dates and amounts of capital outlays for
replacements thereafter.

This simple example will call attention to a number of details
which must be scrutinized carefully before the exact intent of such
calculations can be understood and their results correctly interpreted.

Financial Equivalency

Table 5.1 illustrates the highly important concept of financial
equivalency, whose exact nature is commonly misrepresented.

Despite the difficulty of defining "value," discussed before, one
interpretation is completely rigorous and universally acceptable: the
value to the parties involved of a freewill immediate payment that is
agreeable to both. This is the exact definition of present worth. Similarly, suppliers of capital to a corporation signify, by their own acceptance of preferred payments, the immediate value (present worth) to
themselves of financial transactions.

An absolute essential in such calculations is selection of the correct discounting "interest" rate; 6% was used in Table 5.1. Table 5.1
demonstrates that the only possible "interest" rate to establish the exactly intended result is MAR — MAR of the individual companies or individuals involved in the deal. This follows exact definition of terms
and intent which allows no room for difference of opinion. Use of any
percentage other than MAR (minimum acceptable return) indicates that
the analyst must intend to calculate something other than present worth
as exactly defined herein.

Some extremely ingenious arguments have been devised to becloud
this simple principle, reminiscent of the classical "proof" that 2 = 1.
Described briefly in Appendix C, these arguments rest upon misconceptions of the effect of income tax on revenue requirements.

Table 5.1 also introduces a phenomenon of great consequence in
economic studies which is quite easily handled once it is recognized
and understood. This is the fact that an initial capital outlay often
commits the company to future replacements.

It is too often overlooked that the continuing plant concept is the
usual basis for decisions. It is implicit in most solutions, even though
the analyst often appears to overlook that his calculations are made
on that basis. For this reason, the initial-placement model is best

regarded as a special case, justified only when a set of special assumptions apply to the situation. Otherwise, serious errors of omissions may be made. For example, in Table 5.1 we would improperly conclude that Plan A is superior by $25,000.

An old story tells about the fond parent who asked his youngster in first grade, "How many oranges are two oranges plus two oranges?" The child replied, "Try me on apples. We haven't come to oranges yet."

Teaching addition as the mechanical summation of objects is apt to produce such an impression. It is overlooked that the statement $2 + 2 = 4$ is an abstract equivalency. It remains a statement of fact in the absence of any physical objects to be added up. It does not imply any act of addition. It simply states that the left-hand side of the expression $(2 + 2)$ is equivalent to the right-hand member (4). This is so obvious that any contrary conception becomes a childish joke, as above.

Nevertheless, a parallel misconception of compound interest equivalencies appears to enjoy great popular appeal, as witnessed by the following assertion that is frequently made: "Present worth calculations assume that reinvestment opportunities are always available at the same rate of return."

This notion might be dismissed as an amusing but harmless misconception except that it has been advanced with all seriousness to justify unsound conclusions reached in this manner. Appendix C discusses a related misconception sometimes advanced to support some ingenious fallacies.

Apparently such misunderstandings are invited and encouraged by the usual way of introducing the subject of financial mathematics. This usual approach is to describe financial equivalencies as though they represented transactions with a bank, which credits interest on deposits at a stipulated rate and at specified intervals on the principal amounts on deposit. This seems, to beginners, to imply that an actual act of deposit and actual interest credits are necessary, just as the first-grade student is led to believe that apples and oranges are necessarily at hand before the process of addition can be performed, and that the act of addition must be performed before $2 + 2 = 4$.

The six headings of abstract financial equivalencies in Tables 5.2a-5.2d, on pages 82-89 are of interest:

5.1   The Future Payment that is Equivalent to $1 Spot Cash $= s^n$.
5.1a The Spot Cash Equivalent of a Future Payment $= v^n$.
5.2   The Future Spot Cash Equivalent of an Annuity $= s_{\overline{n}|}$.
5.2a The Annuity Finally Equivalent to $1 Spot Cash $=_i d$.
5.3   The Immediate Spot Cash Equivalent of a Future Annuity $= a_{\overline{n}|}$.
5.3a The Future Annuity that is Equivalent to $1 Spot Cash $= 1/a_{\overline{n}|}$.

Note two things:

1. The six customary titles in Tables 5.2a-5.2d have been slightly reworded here to introduce the phrase "equivalent to" in each case.

2. It is emphasized that there are really only three basic expressions (5.1, 5.2, 5.3); the others are their reciprocals.

The point of Number 1 is that these expressions and the related tables represent financial equivalencies. They do not imply any physical act of investment or any actual earnings on a physical investment. A bank, or its equivalent, is not needed any more than apples are needed for addition. Just as a table of decimal equivalents permits fractions to be expressed alternatively as decimals, so do these equivalencies permit any schedule of payments to be expressed alternatively, to suit one's convenience.

One hundred dollars in hand today is the financial equivalent of $106 in hand one year from today if the recipient's MAR is 6%. This remains the case even if the owner of the $100 continues to hold it in his hand for one year and fails to invest it at all. If his break-even rate of return (= MAR) is 6%, he has then failed by $6 to break even at the end of the year.

On the other hand, if he invests that $100 and is repaid $110 at the year end, he has done better than break even by $4 (110 - 106 = 4). In this case, the fact that his investment earned 10% has no bearing whatever on this break-even calculation. The fact that income tax must be paid on earnings has no bearings whatever on this break-even calculation, beyond the fact that both MAR and actual earnings must be stated in consistent terms. Here, by exact definition of intent, they are both "after taxes."

Any slightest departure from this procedure, such as use of any discounting interest rate other than MAR, asserts a different intent. Such departures are necessarily "wrong" so long as the foregoing financial equivalency is their intent. Consequently, in deciding whether use of MAR is "correct" for purposes of present worth or levelizing calculations, one need only consider the computer's exact intent, stated or implicit.

A Classical Error

An error of classical proportions is the proposal to discount at the so-called "internal" rate of return, meaning at the same percentage as actual earnings. This was illustrated in the preceeding paragraphs by assuming an investment of $100 which returns $110 at the end of one year, meaning annual earnings of 10%. Discounting the total recovery ($110) at the discount rate of 10% (= actual earnings, or the "internal" rate):

$$\text{Present worth} = \frac{110}{1.10} = \$100 \tag{A}$$

Discounting at the investor's MAR of 6%,

$$\text{Present worth} = \frac{110}{1.06} = \$103.7736 \tag{B}$$

Table 5.2a. Financial equivalencies for MAR at 5%, compounded annually.

	5.1	5.1a	5.2	5.2a	5.3	5.3a
Period in Years	Future Equivalency Having Present Worth of 1	Present Worth of a Future Payment of 1	Future Equivalency of an Annuity of 1	Annuity Finally Equivalent to 1	Present Worth of an Annuity of 1	Annuity Having a Present Worth of 1
n	s^n	v^n	$s_{\overline{n}|}$	$_i d$	$a_{\overline{n}|}$	$1/a_{\overline{n}|}$
1	1.050 000 000	.952 380 952	1.000 000 000	1.000 000 000	.952 380 952	1.050 000 000
2	1.102 500 000	.907 029 478	2.050 000 000	.487 804 878	1.859 410 430	.537 804 878
3	1.157 625 000	.863 837 598	3.152 500 000	.317 208 564	2.723 248 029	.367 208 564
4	1.215 506 250	.822 702 474	4.310 125 000	.232 011 832	3.545 950 504	.282 011 832
5	1.276 281 562	.783 526 166	5.525 631 250	.180 974 798	4.329 476 670	.230 974 798
6	1.340 095 640	.746 215 396	6.801 912 812	.147 017 468	5.075 692 067	.197 017 468
7	1.407 100 422	.710 681 330	8.142 008 453	.122 819 818	5.786 373 397	.172 819 818
8	1.477 455 443	.676 839 362	9.549 108 875	.104 721 813	6.463 212 759	.154 721 813
9	1.551 328 216	.644 608 916	11.026 564 319	.090 690 080	7.107 821 675	.140 690 080
10	1.628 894 626	.613 913 253	12.577 892 535	.079 504 575	7.721 734 929	.129 504 575
11	1.710 339 358	.584 679 289	14.206 787 162	.070 388 891	8.306 414 218	.120 388 891
12	1.795 856 326	.556 837 418	15.917 126 520	.062 825 410	8.863 251 636	.112 825 410
13	1.885 649 142	.530 321 350	17.712 982 846	.056 455 765	9.393 572 987	.106 455 765
14	1.979 931 599	.505 067 953	19.598 631 988	.051 023 969	9.898 640 940	.101 023 969
15	2.078 928 179	.481 017 098	21.578 563 588	.046 342 287	10.379 658 038	.096 342 287
16	2.182 874 588	.458 111 522	23.657 491 767	.042 269 908	10.837 769 560	.092 269 908
17	2.292 018 317	.436 296 687	25.840 366 356	.038 699 141	11.274 066 247	.088 699 141
18	2.406 619 233	.415 520 654	28.132 384 673	.035 546 222	11.689 586 902	.085 546 222
19	2.526 950 195	.395 733 957	30.539 003 907	.032 745 010	12.085 320 859	.082 745 010
20	2.653 297 705	.376 889 482	33.065 954 102	.030 242 587	12.462 210 342	.080 242 587
21	2.785 962 590	.358 942 364	35.719 251 808	.027 996 107	12.821 152 707	.077 996 107
22	2.925 260 719	.341 849 871	38.505 214 398	.025 970 508	13.163 002 578	.075 970 508
23	3.071 523 755	.325 571 305	41.430 475 118	.024 136 821	13.488 573 884	.074 136 821
24	3.225 099 943	.310 067 910	44.501 998 874	.022 470 900	13.798 641 794	.072 470 900
25	3.386 354 940	.295 302 771	47.727 098 818	.020 952 457	14.093 944 566	.070 952 457
26	3.555 672 687	.281 240 735	51.113 453 758	.019 564 320	14.375 185 301	.069 564 320
27	3.733 456 322	.267 848 319	54.669 126 446	.018 291 859	14.643 033 620	.068 291 859
28	3.920 129 138	.255 093 637	58.402 582 769	.017 122 530	14.898 127 257	.067 122 530
29	4.116 135 595	.242 946 321	62.322 711 907	.016 045 514	15.141 073 578	.066 045 514
30	4.321 942 375	.231 377 448	66.438 847 503	.015 051 435	15.372 451 026	.065 051 435
31	4.538 039 493	.220 359 474	70.760 789 878	.014 132 120	15.592 810 501	.064 132 120
32	4.764 941 468	.209 866 166	75.298 829 372	.013 280 418	15.802 676 668	.063 280 418
33	5.003 188 542	.199 872 539	80.063 770 840	.012 490 043	16.002 549 208	.062 490 043
34	5.253 347 969	.190 354 799	85.066 959 382	.011 755 445	16.192 904 007	.061 755 445
35	5.516 015 367	.181 290 285	90.320 307 351	.011 071 707	16.374 194 292	.061 071 707
36	5.791 816 136	.172 657 414	95.836 322 719	.010 434 457	16.546 851 707	.060 434 457
37	6.081 406 942	.164 435 633	101.628 138 855	.009 839 794	16.711 287 340	.059 839 794
38	6.385 477 289	.156 605 364	107.709 545 798	.009 284 228	16.867 892 705	.059 284 228
39	6.704 751 154	.149 147 966	114.095 023 088	.008 764 624	17.017 040 671	.058 764 624
40	7.039 988 712	.142 045 682	120.799 774 242	.008 278 161	17.159 086 354	.058 278 161
41	7.391 988 147	.135 281 602	127.839 762 954	.007 822 292	17.294 367 956	.057 822 292
42	7.761 587 555	.128 839 621	135.231 751 102	.007 394 713	17.423 207 577	.057 394 713
43	8.149 666 932	.122 704 401	142.993 338 657	.006 993 332	17.545 911 978	.056 993 332
44	8.557 150 279	.116 861 334	151.143 005 590	.006 616 250	17.662 773 312	.056 616 250
45	8.985 007 793	.111 296 508	159.700 155 869	.006 261 734	17.774 069 821	.056 261 734
46	9.434 258 183	.105 996 675	168.685 163 663	.005 928 203	17.880 066 496	.055 928 203
47	9.905 971 092	.100 949 214	178.119 421 846	.005 614 210	17.981 015 711	.055 614 210
48	10.401 269 646	.096 142 109	188.025 392 938	.005 318 430	18.077 157 820	.055 318 430
49	10.921 333 129	.091 563 913	198.426 662 585	.005 039 645	18.168 721 733	.055 039 645
50	11.467 399 785	.087 203 727	209.347 995 715	.004 776 735	18.255 925 460	.054 776 735

Table 5.2a continued.

	5.1	5.1a	5.2	5.2a	5.3	5.3a
Period in Years	Future Equivalency Having Present Worth of 1	Present Worth of a Future Payment of 1	Future Equivalency of an Annuity of 1	Annuity Finally Equivalent to 1	Present Worth of an Annuity of 1	Annuity Having a Present Worth of 1
n	s^n	v^n	$s_{\overline{n}|}$	$i\,d$	$a_{\overline{n}|}$	$1/a_{\overline{n}|}$
51	12.040 769 775	.083 051 168	220.815 395 500	.004 528 669	18.338 976 629	.054 528 669
52	12.642 808 263	.079 096 351	232.856 165 275	.004 294 496	18.418 072 980	.054 294 496
53	13.274 948 677	.075 329 858	245.498 973 539	.004 073 336	18.493 402 838	.054 073 336
54	13.938 696 110	.071 742 722	258.773 922 216	.003 864 377	18.565 145 560	.053 864 377
55	14.635 630 916	.068 326 401	272.712 618 327	.003 666 863	18.633 471 962	.053 666 863
56	15.367 412 462	.065 072 763	287.348 249 243	.003 480 079	18.698 544 725	.053 480 097
57	16.135 783 085	.061 974 060	302.715 661 706	.003 303 430	18.760 518 786	.053 303 430
58	16.942 572 239	.059 022 914	318.851 444 791	.003 136 256	18.819 541 701	.053 136 256
59	17.789 700 851	.056 212 299	335.794 017 030	.002 978 016	18.875 754 001	.052 978 016
60	18.679 185 894	.053 535 523	353.583 717 882	.002 828 184	18.929 289 525	.052 828 184
61	19.613 145 188	.050 986 213	372.262 903 776	.002 686 273	18.980 275 738	.052 686 273
62	20.593 802 448	.048 558 298	391.876 048 965	.002 551 827	19.028 834 036	.052 551 827
63	21.623 492 570	.046 245 998	412.469 851 413	.002 424 419	19.075 080 034	.052 424 419
64	22.704 667 199	.044 043 807	434.093 343 984	.002 303 652	19.119 123 842	.052 303 652
65	23.839 900 559	.041 946 483	456.798 011 183	.002 189 151	19.161 070 326	.052 189 151
66	25.031 895 587	.039 949 032	480.637 911 742	.002 080 568	19.201 019 358	.052 080 568
67	26.283 490 366	.038 046 697	505.669 807 329	.001 977 575	19.239 066 055	.051 977 575
68	27.597 664 884	.036 234 949	531.953 297 696	.001 879 864	19.275 301 005	.051 879 864
69	28.977 548 129	.034 509 475	559.550 962 581	.001 787 147	19.309 810 481	.051 787 147
70	30.426 425 535	.032 866 167	588.528 510 710	.001 699 153	19.342 676 648	.051 699 153
71	31.947 746 812	.031 301 112	618.954 936 245	.001 615 626	19.373 977 760	.051 615 626
72	33.545 134 152	.029 810 582	650.902 683 058	.001 536 328	19.403 788 343	.051 536 328
73	35.222 390 860	.028 391 031	684.447 817 211	.001 461 031	19.432 179 374	.051 461 031
74	36.983 510 403	.027 039 077	719.670 208 071	.001 389 525	19.459 218 452	.051 389 525
75	38.832 685 923	.025 751 502	756.653 718 475	.001 321 608	19.484 969 954	.051 321 608
76	40.774 320 219	.024 525 240	795.486 404 398	.001 257 092	19.509 495 194	.051 257 092
77	42.813 036 230	.023 357 371	836.260 724 618	.001 195 799	19.532 852 566	.051 195 799
78	44.953 688 042	.022 245 115	879.073 760 849	.001 137 561	19.555 097 682	.051 137 561
79	47.201 372 444	.021 185 824	924.027 448 892	.001 082 218	19.576 283 506	.051 082 218
80	49.561 441 066	.020 176 975	971.228 821 336	.001 029 623	19.596 460 482	.051 029 623
81	52.039 513 120	.019 216 167	1020.790 262 403	.000 979 633	19.615 676 650	.050 979 633
82	54.641 488 776	.018 301 111	1072.829 775 523	.000 932 114	19.633 977 762	.050 932 114
83	57.373 563 215	.017 429 630	1127.471 264 300	.000 886 940	19.651 407 392	.050 886 940
84	60.242 241 375	.016 599 648	1184.844 827 515	.000 843 992	19.668 007 040	.050 843 992
85	63.254 353 444	.015 809 188	1245.087 068 890	.000 803 156	19.683 816 229	.050 803 156
86	66.417 071 116	.015 056 370	1308.341 422 335	.000 764 326	19.698 872 599	.050 764 326
87	69.737 924 672	.014 339 400	1374.758 493 452	.000 727 400	19.713 211 999	.050 727 400
88	73.224 820 906	.013 656 571	1444.496 418 124	.000 692 282	19.726 868 570	.050 692 282
89	76.886 061 951	.013 006 258	1517.721 239 031	.000 658 882	19.739 874 829	.050 658 882
90	80.730 365 049	.012 386 912	1594.607 300 982	.000 627 113	19.752 261 742	.050 627 113
91	84.766 883 301	.011 797 059	1675.337 666 031	.000 596 894	19.764 058 802	.050 596 894
92	89.005 227 466	.011 235 295	1760.104 549 333	.000 568 148	19.775 294 097	.050 568 148
93	93.455 488 840	.010 700 281	1849.109 776 799	.000 540 800	19.785 994 378	.050 540 800
94	98.128 263 282	.010 190 743	1942.565 265 639	.000 514 783	19.796 185 122	.050 514 783
95	103.034 676 446	.009 705 470	2040.693 528 921	.000 490 029	19.805 890 592	.050 490 029
96	108.186 410 268	.009 243 305	2143.728 205 368	.000 466 477	19.815 133 897	.050 466 477
97	113.595 730 781	.008 803 147	2251.914 615 636	.000 444 066	19.823 937 045	.050 444 066
98	119.275 517 320	.008 383 950	2365.510 346 418	.000 422 741	19.832 320 995	.050 422 741
99	125.239 293 187	.007 984 714	2484.785 863 739	.000 402 449	19.840 305 710	.050 402 449
100	131.501 257 846	.007 604 490	2610.025 156 926	.000 383 138	19.847 910 200	.050 383 138

Table 5.2b. Financial equivalencies for MAR at 6%, compounded annually.

Period in Years n	5.1 Future Equivalency Having Present Worth of 1 s^n	5.1a Present Worth of a Future Payment of 1 v^n	5.2 Future Equivalency of an Annuity of 1 $s_{\overline{n}|}$	5.2a Annuity Finally Equivalent to 1 $_i d$	5.3 Present Worth of an Annuity of 1 $a_{\overline{n}|}$	5.3a Annuity Having a Present Worth of 1 $1/a_{\overline{n}|}$
1	1.060 000 000	.943 396 226	1.000 000 000	1.000 000 000	.943 396 226	1.060 000 000
2	1.123 600 000	.889 996 440	2.060 000 000	.485 436 893	1.833 392 666	.545 436 893
3	1.191 016 000	.839 619 283	3.183 600 000	.314 109 812	2.673 011 949	.374 109 812
4	1.262 476 960	.792 093 663	4.374 616 000	.228 591 492	3.465 105 612	.288 591 492
5	1.338 225 577	.747 258 172	5.637 092 960	.177 396 400	4.212 363 785	.237 396 400
6	1.418 519 112	.704 960 540	6.975 318 537	.143 362 628	4.917 324 326	.203 362 628
7	1.503 630 259	.665 057 113	8.393 837 649	.119 135 018	5.582 381 439	.179 135 018
8	1.593 848 074	.627 412 371	9.897 467 908	.101 035 942	6.209 793 811	.161 035 942
9	1.689 478 959	.591 898 463	11.491 315 983	.087 022 235	6.801 692 274	.147 022 235
10	1.790 847 696	.558 394 776	13.180 794 942	.075 867 958	7.360 087 051	.135 867 958
11	1.898 298 558	.526 787 525	14.971 642 638	.066 792 938	7.886 874 576	.126 792 938
12	2.012 196 471	.496 969 363	16.869 941 197	.059 277 029	8.383 843 940	.119 277 029
13	2.132 928 260	.468 839 022	18.882 137 669	.052 960 105	8.852 682 962	.112 960 105
14	2.260 903 955	.442 300 964	21.015 065 929	.047 584 909	9.294 983 927	.107 584 909
15	2.396 558 193	.417 265 060	23.275 969 885	.042 962 764	9.712 248 987	.102 962 764
16	2.540 351 684	.393 646 283	25.672 528 078	.038 952 143	10.105 895 271	.098 952 143
17	2.692 772 785	.371 364 418	28.212 879 762	.035 444 804	10.477 259 690	.095 444 804
18	2.854 339 152	.350 343 791	30.905 652 548	.032 356 540	10.827 603 481	.092 356 540
19	3.025 599 502	.330 513 010	33.759 991 701	.029 620 860	11.158 116 491	.089 620 860
20	3.207 135 472	.311 804 726	36.785 591 203	.027 184 557	11.469 921 218	.087 184 557
21	3.399 563 600	.294 155 402	39.992 726 675	.025 004 546	11.764 076 621	.085 004 546
22	3.603 537 416	.277 505 096	43.392 290 276	.023 045 568	12.041 581 718	.083 045 568
23	3.819 749 661	.261 797 261	46.995 827 692	.021 278 484	12.303 378 979	.081 278 484
24	4.048 934 641	.246 978 548	50.815 577 354	.019 679 005	12.550 357 527	.079 679 005
25	4.291 870 719	.232 998 630	54.864 511 995	.018 226 718	12.783 356 158	.078 226 718
26	4.549 382 962	.219 810 028	59.156 382 715	.016 904 346	13.003 166 187	.076 904 346
27	4.822 345 940	.207 367 951	63.705 765 678	.015 697 166	13.210 534 138	.075 697 166
28	5.111 686 697	.195 630 143	68.528 111 619	.014 592 551	13.406 164 281	.074 592 551
29	5.418 387 899	.184 556 738	73.639 798 316	.013 579 613	13.590 721 020	.073 579 613
30	5.743 491 172	.174 110 130	79.058 186 215	.012 648 911	13.764 831 151	.072 648 911
31	6.088 100 643	.164 254 840	84.801 677 388	.011 792 219	13.929 085 992	.071 792 219
32	6.453 386 681	.154 957 396	90.889 778 031	.011 002 337	14.084 043 388	.071 002 337
33	6.840 589 882	.146 186 223	97.343 164 713	.010 272 935	14.230 229 611	.070 272 935
34	7.251 025 275	.137 911 531	104.183 754 596	.009 598 425	14.368 141 143	.069 598 425
35	7.686 086 792	.130 105 218	111.434 779 871	.008 973 859	14.498 246 361	.068 973 859
36	8.147 251 999	.122 740 772	119.120 866 664	.008 394 834	14.620 987 133	.068 394 834
37	8.636 087 119	.115 793 181	127.268 118 664	.007 857 427	14.736 780 314	.067 857 427
38	9.154 252 347	.109 238 850	135.904 205 783	.007 358 124	14.846 019 164	.067 358 124
39	9.703 507 487	.103 055 519	145.058 458 130	.006 893 772	14.949 074 683	.066 893 772
40	10.285 717 937	.097 222 187	154.761 965 618	.006 461 535	15.046 296 871	.066 461 535
41	10.902 861 013	.091 719 045	165.047 683 555	.006 058 855	15.138 015 916	.066 058 855
42	11.557 032 674	.086 527 401	175.950 544 569	.005 683 415	15.224 543 317	.065 683 415
43	12.250 454 634	.081 629 623	187.507 577 243	.005 333 117	15.306 172 941	.065 333 117
44	12.985 481 912	.077 009 078	199.758 031 878	.005 006 056	15.383 182 019	.065 006 056
45	13.764 610 827	.072 650 074	212.743 513 790	.004 700 495	15.455 832 094	.064 700 495
46	14.590 487 477	.068 537 806	226.508 124 618	.004 414 852	15.524 369 900	.064 414 852
47	15.465 916 725	.064 658 307	241.098 612 095	.004 147 680	15.589 028 207	.064 147 680
48	16.393 871 729	.060 998 403	256.564 528 820	.003 897 654	15.650 026 611	.063 897 654
49	17.377 504 033	.057 545 663	272.958 400 550	.003 663 561	15.707 572 274	.063 663 561
50	18.420 154 275	.054 288 361	290.335 904 583	.003 444 286	15.761 860 636	.063 444 286

Table 5.2b continued.

	5.1	5.1a	5.2	5.2a	5.3	5.3a
Period in Years	Future Equivalency Having Present Worth of 1	Present Worth of a Future Payment of 1	Future Equivalency of an Annuity of 1	Annuity Finally Equivalent to 1	Present Worth of an Annuity of 1	Annuity Having a Present Worth of 1
n	s^n	v^n	$s_{\overline{n}}$	$_i d$	$a_{\overline{n}}$	$1/a_{\overline{n}}$
51	19.525 363 531	.051 215 435	308.756 058 858	.003 238 802	15.813 076 072	.063 238 802
52	20.696 885 343	.048 316 448	328.281 422 389	.003 046 166	15.861 392 520	.063 046 166
53	21.938 698 464	.045 581 555	348.978 307 733	.002 865 507	15.906 974 076	.062 865 507
54	23.255 020 371	.043 001 467	370.917 006 197	.002 696 020	15.949 975 543	.062 696 020
55	24.650 321 594	.040 567 422	394.172 026 568	.002 536 963	15.990 542 965	.062 536 963
56	26.129 340 889	.038 271 152	418.822 348 163	.002 387 647	16.028 814 118	.062 387 647
57	27.697 101 343	.036 104 861	444.951 689 052	.002 247 435	16.064 918 979	.062 247 435
58	29.358 927 423	.034 061 189	472.648 790 395	.002 115 735	16.098 980 169	.062 115 735
59	31.120 463 069	.032 133 197	502.007 717.819	.001 992 001	16.131 113 367	.061 992 001
60	32.987 690 853	.030 314 337	533.128 180 888	.001 875 721	16.161 427 705	.061 875 721
61	34.966 952 304	.028 598 431	566.115 871 742	.001 766 422	16.190 026 137	.061 766 422
62	37.064 969 442	.026 979 652	601.082 824 046	.001 663 664	16.217 005 789	.061 663 664
63	39.288 867 609	.025 452 502	638.147 793 489	.001 567 035	16.242 458 292	.061 567 035
64	41.646 199 665	.024 011 794	677.436 661 098	.001 476 152	16.266 470 086	.061 476 152
65	44.144 971 645	.022 652 636	719.082 860 764	.001 390 660	16.289 122 723	.061 390 660
66	46.793 669 944	.021 370 411	763.227 832 410	.001 310 224	16.310 493 135	.061 310 224
67	49.601 290 141	.020 160 765	810.021 502 355	.001 234 535	16.330 653 901	.061 234 535
68	52.577 367 549	.019 019 590	859.622 792 496	.001 163 300	16.349 673 491	.061 163 300
69	55.732 009 602	.017 943 009	912.200 160 046	.001 096 250	16.367 616 501	.061 096 250
70	59.075 930 179	.016 927 367	967.932 169 649	.001 033 130	16.384 543 869	.061 033 130
71	62.620 485 989	.015 969 214	1027.008 099 828	.000 973 702	16.400 513 084	.060 973 702
72	66.377 715 149	.015 065 297	1089.628 585 818	.000 917 743	16.415 578 381	.060 917 743
73	70.360 378 058	.014 212 544	1156.006 300 967	.000 865 047	16.429 790 926	.060 865 047
74	74.582 000 741	.013 408 060	1226.366 679 025	.000 815 416	16.443 198 986	.060 815 416
75	79.056 920 786	.012 649 114	1300.948 679 766	.000 768 669	16.455 848 100	.060 768 669
76	83.800 336 033	.011 933 126	1380.005 600 552	.000 724 634	16.467 781 227	.060 724 634
77	88.828 356 195	.011 257 666	1463.805 936 585	.000 683 150	16.479 038 893	.060 683 150
78	94.158 057 566	.010 620 440	1552.634 292 780	.000 644 066	16.489 659 333	.060 644 066
79	99.807 541 020	.010 019 283	1646.792 350 347	.000 607 241	16.499 678 616	.060 607 241
80	105.795 993 482	.009 452 153	1746.599 891 368	.000 572 541	16.509 130 770	.060 572 541
81	112.143 753 091	.008 917 126	1852.395 884 850	.000 539 841	16.518 047 896	.060 539 841
82	118.872 378 276	.008 412 383	1964.539 637 941	.000 509 025	16.526 460 279	.060 509 025
83	126.004 720 973	.007 936 210	2083.412 016 218	.000 479 981	16.534 396 490	.060 479 981
84	133.565 004 231	.007 486 991	2209.416 737 191	.000 452 608	16.541 883 481	.060 452 608
85	141.578 904 485	.007 063 199	2342.981 741 422	.000 426 806	16.548 946 680	.060 426 806
86	150.073 638 754	.006 663 395	2484.560 645 908	.000 402 485	16.555 610 076	.060 402 485
87	159.078 057 079	.006 286 222	2634.634 284 662	.000 379 559	16.561 896 298	.060 379 559
88	158.622 740 504	.005 930 398	2793.712 341 742	.000 357 946	16.567 826 696	.060 357 946
89	178.740 104 934	.005 594 715	2962.335 082 246	.000 337 571	16.573 421 411	.060 337 571
90	189.464 511 230	.005 278 033	3141.075 187 181	.000 318 362	16.578 699 445	.060 318 362
91	200.832 381 904	.004 979 276	3330.539 698 412	.000 300 251	16.583 678 721	.060 300 251
92	212.882 324 819	.004 697 430	3531.372 080 317	.000 283 176	16.588 376 152	.060 283 176
93	225.655 264 308	.004 431 538	3744.254 405 136	.000 267 075	16.592 807 691	.060 267 075
94	239.194 580 166	.004 180 696	3969.909 669 444	.000 251 894	16.596 988 387	.060 251 894
95	253.546 254 976	.003 944 053	4209.104 249 611	.000 237 580	16.600 932 441	.060 237 580
96	268.759 030 275	.003 720 805	4462.650 504 588	.000 224 082	16.604 653 246	.060 224 082
97	284.884 572 091	.003 510 193	4731.409 534 863	.000 211 353	16.608 163 440	.060 211 353
98	301.977 646 417	.003 311 503	5016.294 106 955	.000 199 350	16.611 474 943	.060 199 350
99	320.096 305 202	.003 124 059	5318.271 753 372	.000 188 031	16.614 599 003	.060 188 031
100	339.302 083 514	.002 947 226	5638.368 058 574	.000 177 356	16.617 546 229	.060 177 356

Table 5.2c. Financial equivalencies for MAR at 7%, compounded annually.

	5.1	5.1a	5.2	5.2a	5.3	5.3a
Period in Years	Future Equivalency Having Present Worth of 1	Present Worth of a Future Payment of 1	Future Equivalency of an Annuity of 1	Annuity Finally Equivalent to 1	Present Worth of an Annuity of 1	Annuity Having a Present Worth of 1
n	s^n	v^n	$s_{\overline{n}}$	$_i d$	$a_{\overline{n}}$	$1/a_{\overline{n}}$
1	1.070 000 000	.934 579 439	1.000 000 000	1.000 000 000	.934 579 439	1.070 000 000
2	1.144 900 000	.873 438 728	2.070 000 000	.483 091 787	1.808 018 167	.553 091 787
3	1.225 043 000	.816 297 876	3.214 900 000	.311 051 665	2.624 316 044	.381 051 665
4	1.310 796 010	.762 895 212	4.439 943 000	.225 228 116	3.387 211 256	.295 228 116
5	1.402 551 730	.712 986 179	5.750 739 010	.173 890 694	4.100 197 435	.243 890 694
6	1.500 730 351	.666 342 223	7.153 290 740	.139 795 799	4.766 539 659	.209 795 799
7	1.605 781 476	.622 749 741	8.654 021 092	.115 553 219	5.389 289 401	.185 553 219
8	1.718 186 179	.582 009 104	10.259 802 569	.097 467 762	5.971 298 506	.167 467 762
9	1.838 459 212	.543 933 742	11.977 988 748	.083 486 470	6.515 232 248	.153 486 470
10	1.967 151 357	.508 349 292	13.816 447 961	.072 377 502	7.023 581 540	.142 377 502
11	2.104 851 952	.475 092 796	15.783 599 318	.063 356 904	7.498 674 337	.133 356 904
12	2.252 191 589	.444 011 959	17.888 451 270	.055 901 988	7.942 686 296	.125 901 988
13	2.409 845 000	.414 964 447	20.140 642 859	.049 650 848	8.357 650 744	.119 650 848
14	2.578 534 150	.387 817 241	22.550 487 860	.044 344 938	8.745 467 985	.114 344 938
15	2.759 031 540	.362 446 019	25.129 022 010	.039 794 624	9.107 914 005	.109 794 624
16	2.952 163 748	.338 734 597	27.888 053 550	.035 857 647	9.446 648 602	.105 857 647
17	3.158 815 211	.316 574 390	30.840 217 299	.032 425 193	9.763 222 993	.102 425 193
18	3.379 932 275	.295 863 916	33.999 032 510	.029 412 601	10.059 086 909	.099 412 601
19	3.010 527 535	.276 508 333	37.378 964 786	.026 753 014	10.335 595 242	.096 753 014
20	3.869 684 462	.258 419 002	40.995 492 321	.024 392 925	10.594 014 245	.094 392 925
21	4.140 562 374	.241 513 086	44.865 176 783	.022 289 001	10.835 527 332	.092 289 001
22	4.430 401 741	.225 713 165	49.005 739 158	.020 405 773	11.061 240 497	.090 405 773
23	4.740 529 863	.210 946 883	53.436 140 899	.018 713 926	11.272 187 380	.088 713 926
24	5.072 366 953	.197 146 619	58.176 670 762	.017 189 020	11.469 334 000	.087 189 020
25	5.427 432 640	.184 249 177	63.249 037 716	.015 810 517	11.653 583 178	.085 810 517
26	5.807 352 924	.172 195 493	68.676 470 356	.014 561 027	11.825 778 671	.084 561 027
27	6.213 867 629	.160 930 367	74.483 823 281	.013 425 734	11.986 709 038	.083 425 734
28	6.648 838 363	.150 402 212	80.697 690 910	.012 391 928	12.137 111 251	.082 391 928
29	7.114 257 049	.140 562 815	87.346 529 274	.011 448 651	12.277 674 066	.081 448 651
30	7.612 255 042	.131 367 117	94.460 786 323	.010 586 403	12.409 041 183	.080 586 403
31	8.145 112 895	.122 773 006	102.073 041 366	.009 796 906	12.531 814 190	.079 796 906
32	8.715 270 798	.114 741 127	110.218 154 262	.009 072 915	12.646 555 317	.079 072 915
33	9.325 339 754	.107 234 698	118.933 425 060	.008 408 065	12.753 790 016	.078 408 065
34	9.978 113 537	.100 219 344	128.258 764 814	.007 796 738	12.854 009 361	.077 796 738
35	10.676 581 484	.093 662 939	138.236 878 351	.007 233 959	12.947 672 300	.077 233 959
36	11.423 942 188	.087 535 457	148.913 459 836	.006 715 309	13.035 207 757	.076 715 309
37	12.223 618 141	.081 808 838	160.337 402 024	.006 236 848	13.117 016 595	.076 236 848
38	13.079 271 411	.076 456 858	172.561 020 166	.005 795 051	13.193 473 453	.075 795 051
39	13.994 820 410	.071 455 007	185.640 291 578	.005 386 761	13.264 928 461	.075 386 761
40	14.974 457 839	.066 780 381	199.635 111 988	.005 009 138	13.331 708 842	.075 009 138
41	16.022 669 888	.062 411 571	214.609 569 827	.004 659 624	13.394 120 413	.074 659 624
42	17.144 256 780	.058 328 571	230.632 239 715	.004 335 907	13.452 448 984	.074 335 907
43	18.344 354 754	.054 512 683	247.776 496 495	.004 035 895	13.506 961 668	.074 035 895
44	19.628 459 587	.050 946 432	266.120 851 250	.003 757 691	13.557 908 100	.073 757 691
45	21.002 451 758	.047 613 488	285.749 310 838	.003 499 571	13.605 521 589	.073 499 571
46	22.472 623 381	.044 498 587	306.751 762 596	.003 259 965	13.650 020 177	.073 259 965
47	24.045 707 018	.041 587 465	329.224 385 978	.003 037 442	13.691 607 642	.073 037 442
48	25.728 906 509	.038 866 789	353.270 092 997	.002 830 695	13.730 474 432	.072 830 695
49	27.529 929 965	.036 324 102	378.998 999 507	.002 638 529	13.766 798 534	.072 638 529
50	29.457 025 063	.033 947 759	406.528 929 472	.002 459 849	13.800 746 294	.072 459 849

Table 5.2c continued.

	5.1	5.1a	5.2	5.2a	5.3	5.3a
Period in Years	Future Equivalency Having Present Worth of 1	Present Worth of a Future Payment of 1	Future Equivalency of an Annuity of 1	Annuity Finally Equivalent to 1	Present Worth of an Annuity of 1	Annuity Having a Present Worth of 1
n	s^n	v^n	$s_{\overline{n}}$	$_id$	$a_{\overline{n}}$	$1/a_{\overline{n}}$
51	31.519 016 817	.031 726 878	435.985 954 535	.002 293 651	13.832 473 172	.072 293 651
52	33.725 347 994	.029 651 287	467.504 971 353	.002 139 014	13.862 124 459	.072 139 014
53	36.086 122 354	.027 711 483	501.230 319 347	.001 995 090	13.889 835 943	.071 995 090
54	38.612 150 919	.025 898 583	537.316 441 702	.001 861 100	13.915 734 526	.071 861 100
55	41.315 001 483	.024 204 283	575.928 592 621	.001 736 326	13.939 938 810	.071 736 326
56	44.207 051 587	.022 620 825	617.243 594 104	.001 620 105	13.962 559 635	.071 620 105
57	47.301 545 198	.021 140 958	661.450 645 692	.001 511 828	13.983 700 594	.071 511 828
58	50.612 653 362	.019 757 905	708.752 190 890	.001 410 930	14.003 458 499	.071 410 930
59	54.155 539 097	.018 465 331	759.364 844 252	.001 316 890	14.021 923 831	.071 316 890
60	57.946 426 834	.017 257 319	813.520 383 350	.001 229 225	14.039 181 150	.071 229 225
61	62.002 676 713	.016 128 336	871.466 810 185	.001 147 490	14.055 309 486	.071 147 490
62	66.342 864 082	.015 073 211	933.469 486 898	.001 071 272	14.070 382 697	.071 071 272
63	70.986 864 568	.014 087 113	999.812 350 980	.001 000 187	14.084 469 810	.071 000 187
64	75.955 945 088	.013 165 526	1070.799 215 549	.000 933 881	14.097 635 337	.070 933 881
65	81.272 861 244	.012 304 230	1146.755 160 637	.000 872 025	14.109 939 567	.070 872 025
66	86.961 961 531	.011 499 280	1228.028 021 882	.000 814 313	14.121 438 848	.070 814 313
67	93.049 298 839	.010 746 991	1314.989 983 414	.000 760 462	14.132 185 839	.070 760 462
68	99.562 749 757	.010 043 917	1408.039 282 253	.000 710 207	14.142 229 756	.070 710 207
69	106.532 142 240	.009 386 838	1507.602 032 011	.000 663 305	14.151 616 594	.070 663 305
70	113.989 392 197	.008 772 746	1614.134 174 251	.000 619 527	14.160 389 340	.070 619 527
71	121.968 649 651	.008 198 828	1728.123 566 449	.000 578 662	14.168 588 169	.070 578 662
72	130.506 455 127	.007 662 456	1850.092 216 101	.000 540 513	14.176 250 625	.070 540 513
73	139.641 906 986	.007 161 174	1980.598 671 228	.000 504 897	14.183 411 799	.070 504 897
74	149.416 840 475	.006 692 686	2120.240 578 214	.000 471 644	14.190 104 485	.070 471 644
75	159.876 019 308	.006 254 846	2269.657 418 689	.000 440 595	14.196 359 332	.070 440 595
76	171.067 340 659	.005 845 651	2429.533 437 997	.000 411 601	14.202 204 983	.070 411 601
77	183.042 054 506	.005 463 225	2600.600 778 657	.000 384 526	14.207 668 208	.070 384 526
78	195.854 998 321	.005 105 818	2783.642 833 163	.000 359 241	14.212 774 026	.070 359 241
79	209.564 848 203	.004 771 792	2979.497 831 484	.000 335 627	14.217 545 819	.070 335 627
80	224.234 387 578	.004 459 619	3189.062 679 688	.000 313 571	14.222 005 438	.070 313 571
81	239.930 794 708	.004 167 868	3413.297 067 266	.000 292 971	14.226 173 307	.070 292 971
82	256.725 950 338	.003 895 204	3653.227 861 975	.000 273 730	14.230 068 511	.070 273 730
83	274.696 766 861	.003 640 377	3909.953 812 313	.000 255 757	14.233 708 889	.070 255 757
84	293.925 540 542	.003 402 222	4184.650 579 175	.000 238 968	14.237 111 111	.070 238 968
85	314.500 328 380	.003 179 646	4478.576 119 717	.000 223 285	14.240 290 758	.070 223 285
86	336.515 351 366	.002 971 632	4793.076 448 098	.000 208 634	14.243 262 390	.070 208 634
87	360.071 425 962	.002 777 226	5129.591 799 464	.000 194 947	14.246 039 617	.070 194 947
88	385.276 425 779	.002 595 539	5489.663 225 427	.000 182 160	14.248 635 156	.070 182 160
89	412.245 775 584	.002 425 737	5874.939 651 207	.000 170 214	14.251 060 894	.070 170 214
90	441.102 979 875	.002 267 044	6287.185 426 791	.000 159 053	14.253 327 938	.070 159 053
91	471.980 188 466	.002 118 733	6728.288 406 667	.000 148 626	14.255 446 671	.070 148 626
92	505.018 801 659	.001 980 124	7200.268 595 133	.000 138 883	14.257 426 795	.070 138 883
93	540.370 117 775	.001 850 583	7705.287 396 793	.000 129 781	14.259 277 379	.070 129 781
94	578.196 026 019	.001 729 517	8245.657 514 568	.000 121 276	14.261 006 896	.070 121 276
95	618.669 747 841	.001 616 371	8823.853 540 588	.000 113 329	14.262 623 267	.070 113 329
96	661.976 630 190	.001 510 627	9442.523 288 429	.000 105 903	14.264 133 895	.070 105 903
97	708.314 994 303	.001 411 801	10104.499 918 619	.000 098 965	14.265 545 696	.070 098 965
98	757.897 043 904	.001 319 440	10812.814 912 923	.000 092 482	14.266 865 136	.070 092 482
99	810.949 836 978	.001 233 121	11570.711 956 827	.000 086 425	14.268 098 258	.070 086 425
100	867.716 325 566	.001 152 450	12381.661 793 805	.000 080 764	14.269 250 709	.070 080 764

Table 5.2d. Financial equivalencies for MAR at 8%, compounded annually.

	5.1	5.1a	5.2	5.2a	5.3	5.3a
Period in Years	Future Equivalency Having Present Worth of 1	Present Worth of a Future Payment of 1	Future Equivalency of an Annuity of 1	Annuity Finally Equivalent to 1	Present Worth of an Annuity of 1	Annuity Having a Present Worth of 1
n	s^n	v^n	$s_{\overline{n}}$	$_i d$	$a_{\overline{n}}$	$1/a_{\overline{n}}$
1	1.080 000 000	.925 925 925	1.000 000 000	1.000 000 000	.925 925 925	1.080 000 000
2	1.166 400 000	.857 338 820	2.080 000 000	.480 769 230	1.783 264 746	.560 769 230
3	1.259 712 000	.793 832 241	3.246 400 000	.308 033 514	2.577 096 987	.388 033 514
4	1.360 488 960	.735 029 852	4.506 112 000	.221 920 804	3.312 126 840	.301 920 804
5	1.469 328 076	.680 583 197	5.866 600 960	.170 456 454	3.992 710 037	.250 456 454
6	1.586 874 322	.630 169 626	7.335 929 036	.136 315 386	4.622 879 664	.216 315 386
7	1.713 824 268	.583 490 395	8.922 803 359	.112 072 401	5.206 370 059	.192 072 401
8	1.850 930 210	.540 268 884	10.636 627 628	.094 014 760	5.746 638 943	.174 014 760
9	1.999 004 627	.500 248 967	12.487 557 838	.080 079 709	6.246 887 910	.160 079 709
10	2.158 924 997	.463 193 488	14.486 562 465	.069 029 488	6.710 081 398	.149 029 488
11	2.331 638 997	.428 882 859	16.645 487 463	.060 076 342	7.138 964 258	.140 076 342
12	2.518 170 116	.397 113 758	18.977 126 460	.052 695 016	7.536 078 016	.132 695 016
13	2.719 623 726	.367 697 924	21.495 296 577	.046 521 805	7.903 775 941	.126 521 805
14	2.937 193 624	.340 461 041	24.214 920 303	.041 296 852	8.244 236 983	.121 296 852
15	3.172 169 114	.315 241 705	27.152 113 927	.036 829 544	8.559 478 687	.116 829 544
16	3.425 942 643	.291 890 467	30.324 283 041	.032 976 872	8.851 369 155	.112 976 872
17	3.700 018 054	.270 268 951	33.750 225 685	.029 629 431	9.121 638 106	.109 629 431
18	3.996 019 499	.250 249 029	37.450 243 730	.026 702 005	9.371 887 136	.106 702 005
19	4.315 701 059	.231 712 064	41.446 263 239	.024 127 627	9.603 599 200	.104 127 627
20	4.660 957 143	.214 548 207	45.761 964 298	.021 852 208	9.818 147 407	.101 852 208
21	5.033 833 715	.198 655 747	50.422 921 442	.019 832 250	10.016 803 155	.099 832 250
22	5.436 540 412	.183 940 507	55.456 755 157	.018 032 068	10.200 743 662	.098 032 068
23	5.871 463 645	.170 315 284	60.893 295 569	.016 422 169	10.371 058 946	.096 422 169
24	6.341 180 737	.157 699 337	66.764 759 215	.014 977 961	10.528 758 283	.094 977 961
25	6.848 475 196	.146 017 904	73.105 939 952	.013 678 779	10.674 776 188	.093 678 779
26	7.396 353 211	.135 201 763	79.954 415 149	.012 507 126	10.809 977 952	.092 507 126
27	7.988 061 468	.125 186 818	87.350 768 360	.011 448 096	10.935 164 770	.091 448 096
28	8.627 106 386	.115 913 720	95.338 829 829	.010 488 905	11.051 078 491	.090 488 905
29	9.317 274 897	.107 327 519	103.965 936 216	.009 618 535	11.158 406 010	.089 618 535
30	10.062 656 889	.099 377 332	113.283 211 113	.008 827 433	11.257 783 343	.088 827 433
31	10.867 669 440	.092 016 048	123.345 868 002	.008 107 284	11.349 799 391	.088 107 284
32	11.737 082 995	.085 200 045	134.213 537 442	.007 450 813	11.434 999 436	.087 450 813
33	12.676 049 635	.078 888 930	145.950 620 438	.006 851 632	11.513 888 367	.086 851 632
34	13.690 133 605	.073 045 306	158.626 670 073	.006 304 110	11.586 933 673	.086 304 110
35	14.785 344 294	.067 634 542	172.316 803 679	.005 803 264	11.654 568 216	.085 803 264
36	15.968 171 837	.062 624 576	187.102 147 973	.005 344 674	11.717 192 792	.085 344 674
37	17.245 625 584	.057 985 719	203.070 319 811	.004 924 402	11.775 178 511	.084 924 402
38	18.625 275 631	.053 690 480	220.315 945 396	.004 538 936	11.828 868 992	.084 538 936
39	20.115 297 682	.049 713 408	238.941 221 027	.004 185 129	11.878 582 400	.084 185 129
40	21.724 521 496	.046 030 933	259.056 518 710	.003 860 161	11.924 613 333	.083 860 161
41	23.462 483 216	.042 621 234	280.781 040 206	.003 561 494	11.967 234 568	.083 561 494
42	25.339 481 873	.039 464 106	304.243 523 423	.003 286 840	12.006 698 674	.083 286 840
43	27.366 640 423	.036 540 838	329.583 005 297	.003 034 137	12.043 239 513	.083 034 137
44	29.555 971 657	.033 834 110	356.949 645 721	.002 801 515	12.077 073 623	.082 801 515
45	31.920 449 390	.031 327 879	386.505 617 378	.002 587 284	12.108 401 503	.082 587 284
46	34.474 085 341	.029 007 296	418.426 066 769	.002 389 908	12.137 408 799	.082 389 908
47	37.232 012 168	.026 858 607	452.900 152 110	.002 207 992	12.164 267 406	.082 207 992
48	40.210 573 142	.024 869 081	490.132 164 279	.002 040 266	12.189 136 487	.082 040 266
49	43.427 418 993	.023 026 926	530.342 737 421	.001 885 573	12.212 163 414	.081 885 573
50	46.901 612 513	.021 321 228	573.770 156 415	.001 742 858	12.233 484 643	.081 742 858

Table 5.2d continued.

	5.1	5.1a	5.2	5.2a	5.3	5.3a
Period in Years	Future Equivalency Having Present Worth of 1	Present Worth of a Future Payment of 1	Future Equivalency of an Annuity of 1	Annuity Finally Equivalent to 1	Present Worth of an Annuity of 1	Annuity Having a Present Worth of 1
n	s^n	v^n	$s_{\overline{n}}$	i^d	$a_{\overline{n}}$	$1/a_{\overline{n}}$
51	50.653 741 514	.019 741 878	620.671 768 928	.001 611 157	12.253 226 521	.081 611 157
52	54.706 040 835	.018 279 516	671.325 510 442	.001 489 590	12.271 506 038	.081 489 590
53	59.082 524 102	.016 925 478	726.031 551 278	.001 377 350	12.288 431 516	.081 377 350
54	63.809 126 030	.015 671 739	785.114 075 380	.001 273 700	12.304 103 256	.081 273 700
55	68.913 856 112	.014 510 869	848.923 201 411	.001 177 962	12.318 614 126	.081 177 962
56	74.426 964 601	.013 435 990	917.837 057 523	.001 089 518	12.332 050 117	.081 089 518
57	80.381 121 770	.012 440 732	992.264 022 125	.001 007 796	12.344 490 849	.081 007 796
58	86.811 611 511	.011 519 196	1072.645 143 895	.000 932 274	12.356 010 045	.080 932 274
59	93.756 540 432	.010 665 922	1159.456 755 407	.000 862 472	12.366 675 968	.080 862 472
60	101.257 063 667	.009 875 854	1253.213 295 840	.000 797 948	12.376 551 822	.080 797 948
61	109.357 628 760	.009 144 309	1354.470 359 507	.000 738 296	12.385 696 131	.080 738 296
62	118.106 239 061	.008 466 953	1463.827 988 268	.000 683 140	12.394 163 084	.080 683 140
63	127.554 738 186	.007 839 771	1581.934 227 329	.000 632 137	12.402 002 856	.080 632 137
64	137.759 117 241	.007 259 047	1709.488 965 515	.000 584 970	12.409 261 904	.080 584 970
65	148.779 846 620	.006 721 340	1847.248 082 757	.000 541 345	12.415 983 244	.080 541 345
66	160.682 234 350	.006 223 463	1996.027 929 377	.000 500 995	12.422 206 707	.080 500 995
67	173.536 813 098	.005 762 466	2156.710 163 727	.000 463 669	12.427 969 173	.080 463 669
68	187.419 758 146	.005 335 616	2330.246 976 826	.000 429 139	12.433 304 790	.080 429 139
69	202.413 338 797	.004 940 385	2517.666 734 972	.000 397 193	12.438 245 176	.080 397 193
70	218.606 405 901	.004 574 431	2720.080 073 770	.000 367 636	12.442 819 607	.080 367 636
71	236.094 918 373	.004 235 584	2938.686 479 671	.000 340 288	12.447 055 192	.080 340 288
72	254.982 511 843	.003 921 837	3174.781 398 045	.000 314 982	12.450 977 030	.080 314 982
73	275.381 112 791	.003 631 331	3429.763 909 888	.000 291 565	12.454 608 361	.080 291 565
74	297.411 601 814	.003 362 343	3705.145 022 680	.000 269 895	12.457 970 704	.080 269 895
75	321.204 529 959	.003 113 281	4002.556 624 494	.000 249 840	12.461 083 986	.080 249 840
76	346.900 892 356	.002 882 667	4323.761 154 454	.000 231 280	12.463 966 653	.080 231 280
77	374.652 963 744	.002 669 136	4670.662 046 810	.000 214 102	12.466 635 790	.080 214 102
78	404.625 200 844	.002 471 422	5045.315 010 555	.000 198 203	12.469 107 213	.080 198 203
79	436.995 216 912	.002 288 354	5449.940 211 399	.000 183 488	12.471 395 567	.080 183 488
80	471.954 834 264	.002 118 846	5886.935 428 311	.000 169 867	12.473 514 414	.080 169 867
81	509.711 221 006	.001 961 895	6358.890 262 576	.000 157 260	12.475 476 309	.080 157 260
82	550.488 118 686	.001 816 569	6868.601 483 582	.000 145 590	12.477 292 879	.080 145 590
83	594.527 168 181	.001 682 008	7419.089 602 269	.000 134 787	12.478 974 888	.080 134 787
84	642.089 341 636	.001 557 415	8013.616 770 450	.000 124 787	12.480 532 304	.080 124 787
85	693.456 488 966	.001 442 051	8655.706 112 086	.000 115 530	12.481 974 355	.080 115 530
86	748.933 008 084	.001 335 232	9349.162 601 053	.000 106 961	12.483 309 588	.080 106 961
87	808.847 648 731	.001 236 326	10098.095 609 137	.000 099 028	12.484 545 915	.080 099 028
88	873.555 460 629	.001 144 747	10906.943 257 869	.000 091 684	12.485 690 662	.080 091 684
89	943.439 897 479	.001 059 950	11780.498 718 498	.000 084 886	12.486 750 613	.080 084 886
90	1018.915 089 278	.000 981 436	12723.938 615 978	.000 078 592	12.487 732 049	.080 078 592
91	1100.428 296 420	.000 908 737	13742.853 705 256	.000 072 765	12.488 640 786	.080 072 765
92	1188.462 560 134	.000 841 423	14843.282 001 677	.000 067 370	12.489 482 209	.080 067 370
93	1283.539 564 944	.000 779 095	16031.744 561 811	.000 062 376	12.490 261 305	.080 062 376
94	1386.222 730 140	.000 721 384	17315.284 126 756	.000 057 752	12.490 982 690	.080 057 752
95	1497.120 548 551	.000 667 948	18701.506 856 896	.000 053 471	12.491 650 638	.080 053 471
96	1616.890 192 435	.000 618 471	20198.627 405 448	.000 049 508	12.492 269 110	.080 049 508
97	1746.241 407 830	.000 572 658	21815.517 597 884	.000 045 838	12.492 841 768	.080 045 838
98	1885.940 720 457	.000 530 239	23561.759 005 715	.000 042 441	12.493 372 008	.080 042 441
99	2036.815 978 093	.000 490 962	25447.699 726 172	.000 039 296	12.493 862 970	.080 039 296
100	2199.761 256 341	.000 454 594	27484.515 704 266	.000 036 384	12.494 317 565	.080 036 384

Which is the analyst's exact intent? What was the value (= present
worth) of the transaction to the investor at the date of the initial outlay?
Only the analyst himself can state exactly what his own intent may be.
If it is his intent to regard 6% as his definition of a "break-even" experience, then this deal assuredly enabled the investor to do better than
break even. Breaking even, in his own words, would mean earning $6
that first year, or a total recovery at year end of $106. This experi-
ence proved to be $4 better than that; it was in the ratio of 110/106
better than breaking even, or 1.037736 times better than breaking even.
By the analyst's own intent, then, (B) (discounting at MAR and not at
"actual" percentage return) is his clear intent.

Apparently, confusion enters here by way of the concept of present
worth of the value of the transaction at the date of the initial outlay.
Was it not said before that the $100 outlay represents the value (at the
time the outlay is made) of future earnings, in the opinion of the recip-
ient, whether anybody else agrees or not? Discounting at the actual
rate of return is the one and only way to find a present worth of $100
— exactly equal to the actual outlay — whatever the realized rate of return may be. For example, if earnings in that first year were 15%,
then the year-end recovery would be $115. Present worth is then
115/1.15 = $100, per (A).

It is not the analyst's intent, though, to calculate the amount of his
capital investment, which is $100 as already known. It is his intent to
calculate the value, to him, of the "deal." That must be more than its
cost of $100, or the effort was not worth making.

The question at issue is: What is the maximum capital investment
he would be willing to make in order to obtain the anticipated benefits
of the deal? Or, stated another way: What is the minimum present
worth of the deal that would justify making the capital investment required? This all-important question, so sensible and so simple, has
been unbelievably confused by practically all writers on the subject.
Let's take a look at an example that illustrates this curious misunderstanding.

Minimum Attractive Return

The smallest percentage return sufficient to justify making the
capital investment in a project is commonly known as the project's
cutoff rate. Cutoff rate is also called minimum "attractive" rate,
sometimes minimum required profit. In one special case it is regarded as "fair return."

Minimum attractive rate, by whatever title, is necessarily greater
than "cost of money" (= MAR). Nobody raises capital at a cost of $i\%$ in
order to reinvest it in a project capable of earning only that same $i\%$.
What good is borrowing funds from one bank at 5% interest just to deposit them in another to draw 5% interest?

Minimum attractive (cutoff) rate lies somewhere between:

(a) MAR, or "cost of capital"; and (b) expected actual earnings of the project. Minimum attractive rate (or cutoff rate, or minimum required profit, or "fair return") must not be used as the interest rate for discounting purposes.

This is important! This example will illustrate the nature of the error, repeated in most textbooks. Suppose a cigarette manufacturer is considering placing two new brands on the market. Both have special new features expected to make them popular: one a distinctive new filter, the other a new size and blend of tobacco. Each one will require a capital investment of $1,000,000; the company can raise the capital at a cost of 7% MAR.

The risk involved is substantial. It is extremely difficult to predict public acceptance; there is sure to be vigorous competition from other firms. The market may be hurt by recent widely publicized health hazards of smoking. Accordingly, it is decided that neither proposal is attractive unless first-year proceeds recover: (a) the capital investment of $1,000,000 plus (b) earnings of at least 15% (= minimum attractive return). The firm's sales department expects that first-year sales will recover $1,000,000 plus 20% for each brand. So the projects are undertaken.

It turns out that Brand A does better than expected; first-year sales recover the capital investment plus 25% earnings. Brand B, however, is a disappointment. A rival firm comes up with a competing product that captures popular fancy; sales of Brand B recover the capital investment plus only 8% earnings. To recapitulate:

	Brand A	Brand B
Capital investment	$1,000,000	$1,000,000
Expected return	20%	20%
Minimum attractive return (cutoff rate)	15%	15%
Actual return (internal rate)	25%	8%
Minimum acceptable return (MAR)	7%	7%

What was the present worth of each deal? We have seen that it is not correct to discount at the actual percentage earnings (25% and 8%, respectively). Why not discount at the common rate of minimum attractive return, 15%? The answer is that the firm would break even if it earned only cost of capital (MAR = 7%), which would mean zero Profit Incentive, by exact definition of terms.

Brand B, despite its poor showing, did earn some small Profit Margin; it did add a small amount to the company's net worth. It did not result in a loss.

$$\text{Present worth, Project B} = \frac{1,000,000 + 80,000}{1.07} = \$1,009,346$$

In other words, present worth of Project B was slightly greater than its cost, although the risk was not worth taking, as decided in advance.

What would have been concluded if we had discounted at 15%, (minimum attractive return), as prescribed by other textbooks:

$$\frac{1,000,000 + 80,000}{1.15} = \$939,131$$

It would have been improperly concluded that Brand B resulted in a loss; its present worth appears to be less than its capital cost. Whereas, in fact, it added a small and perfectly acceptable (but unattractive) amount to the firm's net worth. "Better is halfe a lofe than no bread."[1]

Differences of opinion on this vital subject have prompted innumerable learned treatises for more than a generation. It almost seems that economists have been blinded to the obvious by their diligent search for the abstruse.

The Continuing Plant

One consideration introduced by the foregoing present worth calculations was the important distinction between (a) investment in specific assets having finite service life; and (b) capital investment in a continuing plant, as visualized by anyone who regards his "investment" as made in the company, or in its securities, rather than in specific physical assets.

Both aspects of an investment are completely rational and defensible. We must be prepared to pass upon the profitability, or economic superiority, of the investment in either sense. Fortunately, it can be said that the exactly intended answer can always be obtained by examining the continuing plant situation. The situation represented by investment in specific physical assets having finite service life is a special case of that general solution, where events transpiring after expiration of that finite life remain the same in any event and therefore have no bearing on the decision.

In brief, the problem posed is simply where to end the study. The answer is of utmost simplicity: End it at any point beyond which events have no bearing on the answer. Under certain special conditions (for example, when mortality characteristics of alternatives are identical) this means ending the study at the end of service life of the facilities involved. We have even mentioned one special case where the study can end with the scrutiny of initial capital investments, but that is most unusual.

Because service life is not predictable with 100% certainty, and because different kinds of assets having different service lives may be involved in a single project, it is commonly impossible to specify any exact terminal date. This difficulty was hinted at in the present worth example which opened this chapter. Why restrict the period of study to 100 years? What if the need for these facilities is not some common multiple of 20 and 25 years? For instance, what if the facilities were needed for exactly 110 years, known in advance?

---

[1] From *Proverbes*, by John Heywood (about 1565); Part i, Chapter XI.

After the event, when it is too late, firm answers can be given to such questions with benefit of hindsight. The only possible way to give reasonable answers in advance, which is the practical necessity, is to rely on probabilities. The vast majority of economic studies are made in actual practice by ignoring this need to allow for the probability of service life's departing from any single estimate, in years. This amounts to firmly denying that life can be anything but that one estimated figure, which is statistically unsound. It means that the depreciation annuity, income tax, taxes on sales or gross receipts, and so forth, when so estimated, do not represent the estimator's actual intent. They do not represent the most probable annual expenditures. Also, depreciation reserves and net plant are deliberately placed at some unintended figure far removed from probable fact.

The depreciation annuity for a life of 20 years certain is not the same as for a probable average life of 20 years; the error can amount to more than 50% of the actually intended figure. This will be discussed in Chapter 6.

The exact intent is to pass upon the probable course of events "from now on." That is, we are concerned with the present worth of all future revenue requirements (PWAFRR) of projects. PWAFRR has a number of fortunate and desirable aspects. The calculation of PWAFRR is simple; and even that simple calculation can be cut short by adopting an acceptable approximation.

In Table 5.1, the comparison was not extended beyond 100 years, because any such extension would not have affected the solution significantly. For example, the differential of $17,614 may be regarded as an approximation of the difference in PWAFRR between Plan A and Plan B. Suppose we assume that after Year 110 there would be no further use for the facilities. The number 110 is not a common multiple of 20 and 25. It would be necessary to make a replacement at the end of Year 100, under either plan. Under either plan, facilities would have to be abandoned at Age 10, in Year 110. The solution of Table 5.1 would be affected as follows:

Plan A

Present worth, first 100 years	= $144,878
5th replacement (end of 100th year) 0.002947 x 100,000 =	295
Present worth of total outlays	$145,173

Plan B

Present worth, first 100 years	= $162,492
4th replacement (end of 100th year) 0.002947 x 125,000 =	368
Present worth of total outlays	$162,860

Advantage of Plan A, as above = 162,860 - 145,173	= $ 17,687
Advantage of Plan A, as per Table 5.1.	= 17,614
Difference	$ 93

Difference, in percent of $17,687 $= \dfrac{73}{17,687} = 0.413\%$

The same solution, per Table 5.1, would have been reached had the need for the facilities ended at any date from Year 81 to Year 100. The solution above would be reached if the need for the facilities ended at any date from Year 101 to Year 120. Thus, extending the period of study 50%, from Year 80 to any year up to 120, would affect the answer (that is, the approximation of PWAFRR) less than 1/2 of 1%.

Exact Definitions

Before presenting a sample of the six standard compound interest formulas and tables, a few exact definitions of terms and of intent are called for.

It would be desirable to restrict use of the word "interest" to return on debt, such as the coupon rate on bonds. In that sense, "interest" is only one component of total return on the pool of investors' committed capital. It would then be the portion that under present law is deductible from total income to establish taxable income subject to federal income tax. This is the portion occasionally referred to in nonregulated industry as "interest expense," presumably because it is not subject to income tax and is not paid to owners of the firm (that is, to stockholders).

Unfortunately, that desirable concept and usage is in conflict with common parlance. It is in conflict with the usual dictionary meaning assigned to "interest," which is simply "the payment for use of money." Also, many analysts speak of "interest on the investment" when they really mean return on the company pool of investors' committed capital. This term is frequently encountered in the public utility industry.

Recognizing this awkward situation, we will not attempt a reformation but will be satisfied with making our own intent perfectly clear and unmistakable. For this reason, when dealing with financial mathematics in this chapter, we will use the term "interest" in its generally accepted loose sense, not restricted to return on debt alone.

This means that in the calculation of financial equivalencies, which is the major use of these tables herein, our exactly intended and appropriate "interest" rate is MAR on the company pool of investors' committed capital. And by that decision we indicate our exact intent with respect to whom the calculated quantities are equivalent. They are equivalencies to investors who supply the pool of capital, as a group. This decision is up to the analyst himself. He could just as well decide to make the economic decisions from the standpoint of owners of the enterprise, meaning stockholders alone, not including creditors.

Some interesting reasons in favor of that procedure — using MAR on equity as the interest rate in discounting and annuitizing calculations — are discussed in Appendix B, which also explains why MAR on the company pool of investors' committed capital is preferred for purposes of this book. Use of either interest rate, when properly done, results

in selection of the same alternative as the economic choice in all cases.
The margin of preference is also found to be the same in dollars each
year, unless expressed in terms of lifetime-levelized equivalency.
Present worths and lifetime-levelized equivalencies necessarily differ
somewhat, because they express quantities in terms of their equivalency to different groups, to stockholders alone instead of to investors
(including creditors) as a group.

One might think that every schoolboy would be able to supply an
exact definition of "6% interest." The reader might like to pause at
this point to write down his own exact definition of "6% interest," for
later reconsideration.

The definition usually proposed is "$6 per year per $100 of principal." But that will not do. Two significant omissions are:

1. It does not specify when the interest payments are to be made.
   In a single payment at each year end? Or payments of $3 each,
   twice a year? Or $1.50 quarterly? Or 50 cents at the end of
   each month?
2. It does not specify the period of the deal. If an individual invests $100 on January 1, and on December 31 of that year re-
   ceives a payment of $6 and no more ever after, has he enjoyed
   a 6% return?

   If so, how about the individual who invests $100 on January
   1, and on December 31 receives $106 and no more ever after.
   Has he enjoyed a return of 106%?

   Or how about the individual who invests that same $100 on
   January 1, and receives $6 on every December 31 thereafter
   forever, without ever having his $100 of principal returned to
   him?

Obviously, it makes a difference, and that difference was not mentioned in the definition proposed above. Believe it or not, some college
graduates have suggested defining "6% interest" on an investment of
$100 as $6 per year for 16 2/3 years! It is for such reason that it
seems necessary to stipulate the universal understanding of "6% interest," in economic studies, as 6% compounded annually unless otherwise
stated. This means:

1. Interest payments will be made once annually, at the end of
   each year, this payment constituting return on the investment.
2. The year-end payment will amount to 6% of the average amount
   placed at interest during the year. In this case, 6% of $100 = $6.
3. The year-end payments will continue until the deal is ended by
   a terminal repayment of the principal amount, this payment
   constituting return of the investment. In this case, the terminal payment would be $100.

This definition describes annual compounding, which means one
compounding period per year. If $100 earns 3% payable at the end of
six months, it means semiannual compounding. It does not earn 6% per

year, because in the second six-month period the $103 then on deposit grows to 1.03 x 1.03 = $106.09 by year end.

Similarly, 1.5% compounded quarterly amounts to more than $6 per year, as follows:

100 x 1.015 x 1.015 x 1.015 x 1.015 = $106.136355

106.136355 - 100.000000 = $ 6.136355 per annum

$$\frac{6.136355}{100} = 6.136355\%$$ of the initial placement

Since interest on debt is commonly paid twice a year, stock dividends quarterly, salaries monthly, and wages weekly or bimonthly, it is sometimes important to define exact intent as to the number of compounding periods per year. Obviously it is important to explain when you say "6% annually" whether you mean (referring to the above example):

1. A nominal rate of 6%, and an effective rate of 6.136355%; or
2. An effective rate of 6% (which would result from compounding 1.467385% quarterly) and a nominal rate of only 5.869538% (= 4 x 1.467385%) per annum. This is the usual assumption.

In some later examples it will be necessary to make such fine distinctions; hence the reservation above, "unless otherwise stated."

It is possible to postulate any desired number of compounding periods per year, to suit one's purpose. The limiting value corresponding to effective rate i% is encountered when the number of compounding periods is infinite. The resultant nominal rate is called the force of interest. It is actually used in problems where surviving investment, throughout the year, is a continuously variable function.

The force of interest is a convenient as well as rigorously demanded variable when a process of integration rather than summation is used in the depreciation calculation. To those familiar with integral calculus, this would simplify much of the presentation of mathematics of depreciation, in Chapter 6. However, for the benefit of those not familiar with the calculus, our treatment will be one of summation. This is a compromise which accepts an adequate practical approximation for the sake of easier comprehension of the majority of readers. As a matter of fact, this adequate practical approximation has already been utilized in the calculations of actual return and estimates of MAR in Chapter 3.

The arithmetic of summation is just as rigorous as the arithmetic of integration. The difference arises from the greater rigor (on occasion) of the integration process as representative of the actual outlays during the course of each year.

Compound interest calculations quickly run to many decimal places, even in such simple problems as just discussed. Reciprocals often are irrational numbers with no end to the number of decimal places. How many decimal places are enough? A comment on this subject appears in Appendix A. When using calculating machines or computers, it is often a laborsaving device to retain as many decimal places as the machine will accommodate, postponing all rounding operations until the final result has been calculated. The objective is not so much improved accuracy as it is facilitation of operations, particularly where reconciliation of subtotals is required.

Notation and symbols adopted herein conform to recommendations of the report Letter Symbols for Mathematics of Depreciation, dated September 1, 1948.[2] In general, this notation is the same as that used in the field of financial and actuarial theory for many generations. It has been published in many places, particularly in the well-known Mathematical Tables from Handbook of Chemistry and Physics, Chemical Rubber Publishing Co., Cleveland, Ohio.

Standard compound interest tables are also widely available, and are reproduced in many textbooks dealing with industrial management and engineering economy. A particularly convenient collection is the book Financial Compound Interest and Annuity Tables, 2nd ed. (Financial Publishing Co., Boston, 1960).

Notations you will frequently encounter in the discussion are:

i = interest rate, in percent
= minimum acceptable return (MAR) in all calculations of financial equivalency.
n = number of compounding periods
= period in years, for annual compounding.

Others will be explained with their respective formulas and equations. For simplicity, 6% return will be used in this discussion, together with annual compounding.

5.1. The Future Payment That Is Equivalent to $1 Spot Cash ($s^n$)

This is commonly described as "the amount of $1 at compound interest." It may also be regarded as the amount in a bank account if $1 were deposited, accumulating $i\%$ interest compounded annually.

$1.00 today = $1.00 today
= 1.00   + .06 (1.00)   = $1.0600 after 1 year
= 1.06   + .06 (1.06)   = $1.1236 after 2 years
= 1.1236 + .06 (1.1236) = $1.1910 after 3 years

The formula is:

$$s^n = (1 + i)^n \qquad \text{(Formula 5.1)}$$

Interpreted in words, if minimum acceptable return is 6%, a payment of $1.06 one year from today, or $1.1236 two years from today,

---

[2]Prepared by a joint committee consisting of representatives of National Association of Railroad and Utilities Commissioners, American Gas Association, American Telephone and Telegraph Company, and Edison Electric Institute.

or $1.1910 three years from today, all have the same present worth, that is, $1 spot cash. Either alternative, the immediate cash settlement or the future payment, is equally acceptable to the investor whose minimum acceptable return is 6%.

5.1a. The Spot Cash Equivalent of a Future Payment (v^n)

This is commonly described as "the present worth of $1 due at a future date." It may also be regarded as the amount to be placed in the bank today, at $i\%$ interest compounded annually, in order to have a balance of $1 at a specified future date.

Spot cash equivalent of $1 paid today   = $1.0000
Spot cash equivalent of $1 paid one year from today

$$= \frac{1}{1.06}$$ = 0.9434

Spot cash equivalent of $1 paid two years from today

$$= \frac{1}{1.06 \times 1.06}$$ = 0.8900

Spot cash equivalent of $1 paid three years from today

$$= \frac{1}{1.06 \times 1.06 \times 1.06}$$ = 0.8396

The formula is the reciprocal of Formula 5.1:

$$v^n = \frac{1}{s^n} = \frac{1}{(1+i)^n} \qquad \text{(Formula 5.1a)}$$

Interpreted in words, if minimum acceptable return is 6%, a payment of $1 due in one year is equivalent to 94.34 cents spot cash; a payment of $1 due in two years is equivalent to 89 cents spot cash; and so on. Either alternative, the future payment or the immediate cash settlement, is equally acceptable to an investor whose minimum acceptable return is 6%.

5.2. The Future Spot Cash Equivalent of An Annuity $(s_{\overline{n}|})$

This is commonly described as "the amount of an annuity of $1." It may also be regarded as the amount in a bank account which earns $i\%$ interest compounded annually, if $1 were deposited at each year end.

Spot cash equivalent after 1 year   = $1.000
Spot cash equivalent after 2 years = 1.00 + 1.06   = $2.060
Spot cash equivalent after 3 years = 1.00 + 1.06 + 1.124 = $3.184

The formula is:

$$s_{\overline{n}|} = \frac{(1+i)^n - 1}{i} \qquad \text{(Formula 5.2)}$$

Note the relation to Formula 5.1:

$$s_{\overline{n}|} = \frac{s^n - 1}{i}$$

Interpreted in words, if deposits earn 6% compounded annually, regular year-end deposits of $1 will amount to $1 at the end of Year 1, $2.060 at the end of Year 2, and $3.184 at the end of Year 3. The investor whose <u>minimum acceptable</u> return is 6% would just as soon accept: (a) the regular annual year-end payments of $1 each; or (b) the single spot cash payment, as calculated, at the end of the period.

The formula may be derived from the above tabulation of Formula 5.2, as follows:

The sum at the end of Year n is:

$$s_{\overline{n}|} = 1 + (1 + i) + (1 + i)^2 + \ldots + (1 + i)^{n-2} + (1 + i)^{n-1} \tag{1}$$

Multiplying by $(1 + i)$ gives:

$$s_{\overline{n}|}(1 + i) = (1 + i) + (1 + i)^2 + (1 + i)^3 + \ldots + (1 + i)^{n-1} + (1 + i)^n \tag{2}$$

Subtracting (1) from (2):

$$s_{\overline{n}|}(1 + i) - s_{\overline{n}|} = -1 + (1 + i)^n$$

Simplifying:

$$s_{\overline{n}|} + i \cdot s_{\overline{n}|} - s_{\overline{n}|} = -1 + (1 + i)^n$$

Therefore,

$$s_{\overline{n}|} = \frac{(1 + i)^n - 1}{i}$$

5.2a. The Annuity Finally Equivalent to $1 Spot Cash ($_id$)

This is commonly described as "the annuity which will amount to $1 in a given time." It may also be regarded as the regular year-end payment which, if deposited in a bank paying $i\%$ interest, would amount to a balance of $1 by a specified date.

The 1-year annuity $\dfrac{1.000}{1.000}$ = $1.000

The 2-year annuity $\dfrac{1.000}{1.000 + 1.060}$ = $0.485

The 3-year annuity $\dfrac{1.000}{1.000 + 1.060 + 1.124}$ = $0.314

The formula is the reiprocal of Formula 5.2. Note the standard symbol for the annuity; it will be recognized as the depreciation annuity for nondispersed retirements (Type SQ), discussed in Chapter 6. The symbol is d, with presubscript i.

$$_i d = \frac{1}{s_{\overline{n}|}}$$

$$= \frac{i}{(1 + i)^n - 1} \qquad \text{(Formula 5.2a)}$$

Note the relation to Formula 5.1, by substituting s^n for $(1 + i)^n$ in the denominator:

$$_i d = \frac{i}{s^n - 1}$$

Interpreted in words, if deposits earn 6% compounded annually, then a bank account of $1 can be accumulated by making year-end deposits of $1 for one year, $0.485 for two years, or $0.314 for three years. The investor whose minimum acceptable return is 6% would just as soon accept: (a) the regular annual year-end payments; or (b) the single spot cash payment of $1 at the end of the period.

5.3. The Immediate Spot Cash Equivalent of a Future Annuity $(a_{\overline{n}|})$

This is commonly described as "the present worth of an annuity of $1 per year." It may also be regarded as the single cash deposit placed in a bank account earning i% compounded annually, which would be sufficient to provide a withdrawal of $1 each year end for n years.

Each withdrawal has a spot cash value, per Formula 5.1a. $a_{\overline{n}|}$ is the sum of those several spot cash values from Year $x = 1$ through $x = n$:

For a 1-year annuity $\qquad \dfrac{1}{1.06} \qquad = \$0.9434$

For a 2-year annuity $\qquad \dfrac{1}{1.06} + \dfrac{1}{1.124} \qquad = \$1.8334$

For a 3-year annuity $\dfrac{1}{1.06} + \dfrac{1}{1.124} + \dfrac{1}{1.1910} = \$2.6730$

The formula is:

$$a_{\overline{n}|} = \sum_{x = 1}^{x = n} \frac{1}{(1 + i)^x} \qquad \text{(Formula 5.3)}$$

More convenient forms of this expression may be derived as follows: Formula 5.2 gave the amount on hand at the end of n years. Formula 5.3 represents the present worth of those amounts, obtainable by multiplying Formula 5.2 amounts by v^n, per Formula 5.1a. In equation form, making use of Formulas 5.2 and 5.1a:

$$a_{\overline{n}|} = (s_{\overline{n}|}) \times \frac{1}{s^n}$$

$$= \frac{(1 + i)^n - 1}{i} \times \frac{1}{(1 + i)^n}$$

$$= \frac{(1 + i)^n - 1}{i(1 + i)^n}$$

(A variation of
Formula 5.3) (3)

Most handbooks show $a_{\overline{n}|}$ in this form, or as $\frac{s^n - 1}{is^n}$.

Substituting $\frac{1}{v^n}$ for $(1 + i)^n$, per Formula 5.1a, in both the numerator and denominator of (3):

$$a_{\overline{n}|} = \frac{\frac{1}{v^n} - 1}{i\, v^n}$$

(A second variation of
Formula 5.3) (4)

$$= \frac{1 - v^n}{i}$$

We may also take (3) and add and subtract i in the denominator:

$$a_{\overline{n}|} = \frac{(1 + i)^n - 1}{i(1 + i)^n - i + i}$$

Dividing numerator and denominator by $(1 + i)^n - 1$:

$$= \frac{1}{i + \frac{i}{(1 + i)^n - 1}}$$

Substituting $_id$ for the second term in the denominator (per Formula 5.2a):

$$a_{\overline{n}|} = \frac{1}{i + {_id}}$$

(A third variation of
Formula 5.3) (5)

Formula (5) is probably the one most frequently used.

Interpreted in words, if a deposit earns 6% compounded annually, a single deposit of 94.34 cents would provide for a withdrawal of $1 one year later; a single deposit of $1.8334 would provide for two successive year-end withdrawals of $1 each; or a single deposit of $2.673 would provide for three successive year-end withdrawals of $1 each; and so on.

The investor whose minimum acceptable return is 6% would just as soon accept: (a) the regular year-end payments of $1; or (b) the single spot cash payment calculated, at the beginning of the period.

5.3a. The Future Annuity That is Equivalent to $1, Immediate Spot Cash $(1/a_{\overline{n}|})$

This is commonly described as "the annuity that $1 will buy." It

may also be regarded as the amount of a withdrawal, made each year
end, that could be made for n years, if a single deposit is made today
in a bank account that earns $i\%$ compounded annually.

Being the reciprocal of Formula 5.3, Formula 5.3a may be written
several ways as follows:

From (3) $$\frac{1}{a_{\overline{n}|}} = \frac{i\,(1+i)^n}{(1+i)^n - 1}$$ (Formula 5.3a)

From (4) $$\frac{1}{a_{\overline{n}|}} = \frac{i}{1 - v^n}$$ (A variation of Formula 5.3a) (6)

From (5) $$\frac{1}{a_{\overline{n}|}} = i + {_id}$$ (The most used version of Formula 5.3a) (7)

In tabular form:

Formula 5.3a	Form (6)	Form (7)
For a 1-year annuity:		
$\dfrac{0.06(1.06)}{1.06 - 1}$ =	$\dfrac{0.06}{1 - 0.9434}$ =	$0.060 + 1.000 = \$1.060$
For a 2-year annuity:		
$\dfrac{0.06(1.1236)}{1.1236 - 1}$ =	$\dfrac{0.06}{1 - 0.8900}$ =	$0.060 + 0.485 = \$0.546$
For a 3-year annuity:		
$\dfrac{0.06(1.1910)}{1.1910 - 1}$ =	$\dfrac{0.06}{1 - 0.8396}$ =	$0.060 + 0.314 = \$0.374$

Interpreted in words, a single deposit of $1 immediate spot cash,
in a bank paying 6% interest compounded annually, would be sufficient
to provide for a single withdrawal of $1.06 after one year; or $0.546
each year end for two years; or $0.374 each year end for three years;
and so on.

The investor whose minimum acceptable return is 6% would just
as soon accept: (a) the single spot cash payment of $1 at the beginning
of the period; or (b) the regular equivalent year-end payments.

Summary

For easy memorizing, only three formulas need to be remembered:

5.1. $s^n = (1+i)^n$ 5.2. $s_{\overline{n}|} = \dfrac{s^n - 1}{i}$ 5.3. $a_{\overline{n}|} = \dfrac{s^n - 1}{is^n}$

Note that the numerators of Formulas 5.2 and 5.3 are identical ($= s^n - 1$); i appears in both denominators, multiplied by s^n in Formula 5.3.

5.1a. $v^n = \dfrac{1}{s^n}$ 5.2a. $\dfrac{1}{s_{\overline{n}|}} = \dfrac{i}{s^n - 1}$ 5.3a. $\dfrac{1}{a_{\overline{n}|}} = \dfrac{is^n}{s^n - 1}$

Practical Applications

If the reader wrote down his own definition of "6% interest" before reading the foregoing discussion, he may wish to review it at this point.

We will see that each of the six tables suggests a different arithmetical explanation of "6% interest, compounded annually," all amounting to variations on the same theme. It is necessary only to substitute 6% for i, in any of the formulas, stipulate the period n (say, one year), and describe the resultant equation in words. For example:

Formula 5.1. 6% is the annually compounded interest rate if \$1 in hand today is financially equivalent to \$1.06 in hand one year from today.

Formula 5.1a. 6% is the annually compounded interest rate if \$1 in hand one year from today is financially equivalent to 94.34 cents in hand today.

Formula 5.3. 6% is the annually compounded interest rate if \$2.06 in hand two years from today is the financial equivalent of a two-year annuity of \$1, paid at year ends.

The equations in words for the reciprocal formulas are stated in this same manner.

When a company makes or receives payments of any kind, it acts as the owners' agent. As an alternative to the outlay or receipt of these payments, numerous other schedules of payment would be financially equivalent so far as the owners of the business are concerned. For purposes of economic studies, it is often much more convenient to deal in terms of the financial equivalents than in terms of the actual payments. Ultimate conclusions and ultimate decisions will be identical in any event; the whole purpose of the substitution is one of convenience.

To illustrate, suppose the following schedule of payments is anticipated by the company:

One years from now	\$100,000
Two years from now	150,000
Three years from now	125,000
Total	\$375,000

These payments may be receipts from sales (= revenues), tax payments, or payroll obligations. Their nature does not affect the issue at all.

If the company's MAR is 6%, what immediate lump-sum payment

would be financially equivalent to this schedule of actual payments?
The answer is $332,790, obtained as follows:

Present Worth Factors for MAR = 6% (Formula 5.1a)		Actually Scheduled Payments		Present Worth of Actually Scheduled Payments
0.9434	x	100,000	=	$ 94,340
0.8900	x	150,000	=	133,500
0.8396	x	125,000	=	104,950
Equivalent present worth			=	$332,790

There is no need to consider whether opportunities for reinvestment are available, or what rate of return they would enjoy if they were
available. No physical act of investment is involved. The question is
simply, "What present worth would be equivalent to this schedule of
payments, if 6% interest represents the break-even situation?"

It is not germane to point out that a stockholder would find his
personal income tax obligations affected if he accepted a single lump-
sum payment of $332,790 instead of the three actual payments over a
three-year period. If that consideration did make a difference in the
problem posed, it would affect MAR, and we have stipulated that MAR
is 6% after all such considerations have been taken into account.

It makes no difference whether these actually scheduled payments
represent 6% return, or 3%, or 10%, or any other rate of return on
some capital investment. That "internal rate" is not involved in the
question asked. This is purely a matter of definition of terms and intent; it is not a matter of economic theory.

Another question might be asked about the foregoing schedule of
annual payments: "What level annual payment, over the three-year
period, would be financially equivalent to the three actual payments?"

The answer is not $125,000 per year (= 375,000/3). It is $124,497,
found by applying Formula 5.3a:

$$0.3741 \text{ x present worth} = 0.3741 \text{ x } 332,790$$
$$= \$124,497 \text{ per year}$$

The financially equivalent annuity is not restricted to the three-
year period of actual payments. One might legitimately ask: "What
level annual payment, over a two-year period beginning now would be
financially equivalent to the three actual payments?" The answer:

$$0.5454 \text{ x present worth} = 0.5454 \text{ x } 332,790$$
$$= \$181,504 \text{ per year}$$

Or, it might be asked: "What level annual payment, over a two-
year period beginning one year from now would be equivalent to the
three actual payments?" The answer:

$$1.06 \text{ x } 181,504 = \$192,394 \text{ per year}$$

The "just-as-soon" aspect of these financial equivalencies is known by economists as The Concept of Indifference. The reason for that appellation must be apparent.

One question of academic importance has been raised on occasion, as though it posed a profound question difficult to answer. It will illustrate how readily such puzzlers are solved by the simple device of relying on exact definition of intent.

It is admitted that although MAR is a notably stable statistic, nevertheless it can be expected to vary somewhat from year to year. Suppose, then, that MAR is expected to vary as follows (grossly exaggerated, to make the effect significant): first year, 6%; second year, 5%; third year, 4%. What then is the present worth of a payment of $1,000, payable at the end of Year 3?

By definition of terms, the $1,000 has a present worth at beginning of Year 3 (= end of Year 2), of 1,000/1.04. This present worth is financially equivalent, by definition of terms, to 1,000/1.04/1.05 at the beginning of Year 2 (= end of Year 1). Present worth at the beginning of Year 1 is therefore 1,000/(1.04 x 1.05 x 1.06). If any other solution is intended, it must be explained by producing a different statement of intent, which will involve some different concept of MAR not readily imagined.

Résumé

I. Referring to Expression I, Table 4.1, on page 61 the commonest type of economic problem consists in weighing a capital outlay differential (Item 1) against the related change in all other outlays.

II. This weighing process must allow for the fact that the capital outlay (Item 1) is a single immediate payment, while the related change in other outlays is a periodic annual outlay over service life of the facilities.

III. A simple example illustrates the importance of two separate phenomena affecting quantitative evaluation of problems such as this, where the due-date of alternative outlays differs:

a. The effect of postponing an initial capital outlay; and
b. The effect of resultant changes in dates and amounts of subsequent capital outlays for replacements.

IV. Financial equivalency is an expression of value. Accordingly, it is essential that the concepts of present worth equivalency, levelized annual equivalency, and all other financial equivalencies be rigorously defined in terms of value, in dollars, paid to whom, and at what date.

V. The appropriate interest rate, in calculations of financial equivalency, is MAR, no more and no less. This is purely a matter of exact definition of terms and of intent, not a matter of economic theory.

VI. The concept of a continuing plant is the basis for all economic studies, except for a special case where the outlays for specific initial assets throughout their lifetime, without replacement, are an adequate reference.

VII. The elements of financial mathematics are covered by six standard compound interest tables. Actually, only three table titles are necessary (5.1, 5.2, 5.3); the other three (5.1a, 5.2a, 5.3a) are their reciprocals:

5.1. $s^n = (1 + i)^n$ 5.2. $s_{\overline{n}|} = \dfrac{s^n - 1}{i}$ 5.3. $a_{\overline{n}|} = \dfrac{s^n - 1}{is^n}$

5.1a. $v^n = \dfrac{1}{s^n}$ 5.2a. $\dfrac{1}{s_{\overline{n}|}} = \dfrac{i}{s^n - 1}$ 5.3a. $\dfrac{1}{a_{\overline{n}|}} = \dfrac{is^n}{s^n - 1}$

In many technical papers dealing with financial mathematics, the whole concept of financial equivalency has been dismissed with the explanation that "a dollar now is worth more than a dollar one year from now." The incompetency of that explanation, in view of the discussion in this chapter, and further in view of changes in the purchasing price of the dollar, may now be assessed.

A thorough grasp of the principle of financial equivalency will serve to dispel all the mystery that has surrounded the subject of depreciation, which is the next topic for discussion.

Problems

1. Throughout this book you will find quotation marks around "straight-line" depreciation. Why?

2. a. Illustrate by a simple example the important difference between (1) averaging, and (2) levelizing or annuitizing.

   b. Is compound interest ever properly used if the term of the transaction is less than one year? Is simple interest ever properly used if the term is more than one year? Explain.

   c. The remark has been made that simple interest is so called because it is for simpletons. Explain the import of that witticism (or should we say "cynicism"?).

3. When you calculate present worths of revenue requirements, you do it in order to measure the value of something to someone. The value of what to whom?

   If, as claimed before, the word "value" does not denote any measurable quantity in the absence of some adjective, just how does adding the descriptive term "present" convert it into a measurable quantity?

4. Explain in your own words the importance of recognizing financial mathematics as a device for determining abstract equivalencies.

   (Here is another case where it is difficult to convey essentially simple ideas without using language that looks unnecessarily elegant. It is quite possible that you can improve upon the presentation in this chapter.)

5. Repeat the problem of Table 5.1 on page 78, using lives of 30 and 40 years, respectively. Carry out to 120 years.

6. What if the company had no use for the facilities of Problem 5 after Year 75? Produce appropriate calculations and explain.

7. In the problem on page 93, note how the difference in present worths decreases rapidly at advanced dates. How much would the difference be at eternity?

   (Hint: Compounding periods are not necessarily one year. Interest rates can be found from $s = (1+i)^n$. If $a_{\overline{n}|} = \dfrac{1-v^n}{i}$, what is $a_{\overline{\infty}|}$? Some people, like the author, consider this a tough question; others see it immediately. If you see it immediately, you're an expert.)

8. You will accept 6% return on a loan of $100. Your debtor agrees to pay you back after ten years, but cannot pay interest in the meantime. How much will you settle for at the end of Year 10? (Use a table; it's easier.)

9. The above debtor offers to settle for $155.13 at the end of Year 9. What rate of return would you then make? (Easy if you use a table.)

10. The same debtor offers to repay half of the original loan (= $50) at the end of Year 5. How much would you then settle for at the end of Year 10? (No annual return on the investment at any time.)

11. Suppose you were offered repayment of your $100 at the end of Year 10; with no interest up to that time, but annual interest thereafter forever. How much per year thereafter would you settle for, still assuming that your acceptable rate is 6%?

12. A 15-year bond, face value $1,000, can be bought for $850. The coupon rate is 4 1/2% semiannually. Calculate the percentage return to maturity.

13. A and B each deposit $1,000 in their respective savings accounts on the first of each year. At the end of each year, A withdraws an amount equal to his dividends. B leaves his accumulated amount on deposit. At the end of Year 10, A has $10,450 in his account. B has $13,206.79. Which bank pays the higher interest rate?

14. The relationship between (a) actual earnings per share, and (b) market price per share is normally expected to be as follows:

1	2	3
Actual Earnings	Price	MAR on Common Equity
Constant	Increasing	_____
Constant	Decreasing	_____
Constant	Constant	_____
Increasing	Increasing	_____
Increasing	Decreasing	_____
Increasing	Constant	_____
Decreasing	Increasing	_____
Decreasing	Decreasing	_____
Decreasing	Constant	_____

Complete Column 3.

15. Suppose you have a contract to be paid the following amounts:
   a. $1,000 on January 1, 1968
   b. $2,000 on January 1, 1969
   c. $3,000 on January 1, 1970
   d. $4,000 on January 1, 1971
   e. $5,000 on January 1, 1980

If your MAR on this deal is 6%:
   a. What lump sum would you settle for on January 1, 1968; on December 31 1980; on January 1, 1990?
   b. What level annuity would you settle for (payable annually; first payment January 1, 1969) if you were to receive it for 12 years; forever?

16. You buy a $100, 20-year bond which pays 5% interest at each year end, but your acceptable rate of return is 4%. How much are you willing to pay for it?

17. How many years does it take for money to double itself at 6% compounded annually? At 3%? Suggest a simple general rule worth keeping in mind.

18. A college plans to build a laboratory in 1970. The Ford Foundation granted them $840,000 in 1965. At what interest rate must the gift have been invested to have $1,000,000 for the purpose?

19. a. Without consulting interest tables, what is the lump-sum present worth of payments of $1 each, made at the end of Years 1 and 2, respectively, if MAR = 6%?

   b. Solve (a) using the following formula in the solution: $\dfrac{1}{s_{\overline{n}|}} = 0.4854$.

20. A series of year-end payments are as follows:

Year	Amount	Year	Amount
1	$1,000	6	$1,400
2	1,100	7	1,300
3	1,200	8	1,200
4	1,300	9	1,100
5	1,400	10	1,000

   a. If MAR = 6%, what is the equivalent single payment at (1) first of Year 1, (2) end of Year 5, (3) first of Year 11, (4) end of Year 15, (5) eternity?
   b. What is the equivalent level annuity (payable at year end) for (1) 1 year, (2) 5 years, (3) 10 years, (4) 15 years, (5) forever?

21. An investor can buy a 10-year bond, face value $1,000, that pays 5% interest (= $50) at the end of each year, for $990.
   a. If his MAR for such an investment is 6%, would he be interested?
   b. What is the maximum amount he would be willing to pay?
   c. Suppose he could borrow money at 4% interest to finance the deal. If he

purchases the bond for $990 and his MAR is 6%, what is the present worth of the Profit Incentive? Discuss this problem and your answer in a way that would be helpful to readers of this book. (Note: This is tricky.)

22. Some writers have applied the term "critical return," or "criterion return" to the concept of cutoff rate. Such usage is ill-advised and suggests that its advocates do not clearly understand the exact nature of profitability studies and studies of economic choice. Explain.

23. It might be said that, whatever percentage is assigned to MAR, present worth of annual revenue requirements for return plus depreciation (= capital recovery costs) will always equal the initial capital investment. But there are two important exceptions to that generality. One relates to salvage. If the assets have a net salvage value at retirement, the present worth so calculated will differ from the initial capital investment by an amount equal to present worth of ultimate net salvage realized. Discuss the other important exception.

24. In system planning, it is not an uncommon practice to estimate annual revenue requirements (or sometimes annual costs) for all alternative proposals and to make the economic comparison by investigating present worths of these annual data obtained by discounting over some relatively short period less than probable service life. The explanation given for that procedure is that service lives are so long, commonly more than forty years, that it is felt impossible to forecast events thus far into the future with any satisfactory degree of accuracy.

Comment on the self-contradiction in that explanation, and on the incompetency of conclusions so reached.

25. The following conclusions share a common fault; all are from recent books or articles. Identify the basic principle that is misunderstood or misrepresented in each, and discuss each of the fallacious conclusions helpfully:

a. Present-worth analysis has a serious inherent fault in that it fails to consider whether a project's cash flows can be reinvested at the same percentage return as is earned by the initial investment.

b. A project should not be adopted unless its percentage return on common equity equals or exceeds the minimum rate required on the specific type of common equity committed to this particular project, such as retained earnings versus a new issue of stock.

c. Since capital invested in wasting assets does not stay invested, calculation of a project's "absolute" return necessitates consideration for future reinvestment opportunities. But the latter is impracticable, and nothing can be done about it except to recognize this defect in recommended ranking procedures.

d. Because exceptionally profitable projects have their return "diluted" by reinvestment of their annual cash flows at the firm's lower average rate of return, analyses of such projects are extremely sensitive to assumed "horizon time" (a faddish term for "productive life").

6

• • • • • **Revenue** • • •
Requirement
for Depreciation

Definitions of Intent

T HIS CHAPTER deals with the second of the three components of
total revenue requirements which are directly proportional to the
initial capital investment (that is, to investors' committed capital):

1. Return on the capital investment (= MAR);
2. Return of the capital investment (= the depreciation annuity); and
3. Taxes on income.

Other components of revenue requirements are not ordinarily direct
functions of capital investment. For example, operation and maintenance expenses, raw materials, and sales expense are usually more
closely related to output than to capital investment.

In practice, the revenue requirement for depreciation, in percent,
is simply picked from a table, such as Tables 6.8-6.19 on pages 133-144.
No calculation is necessary beyond the adjustment for salvage, if any,
by multiplying by $(1 - c)$ where c = percentage net salvage (decimally
expressed). The following discussion is necessary only to explain just
why the analyst's exact intent is carried out so simply, and why any
other evaluation of depreciation is not correct.

As the tables indicate, four major variables are involved:

1. Percentage MAR;
2. Probable service life, in years;
3. The retirement-dispersion pattern (the Type Curve); and
4. Ultimate net salvage, in percent of the capital investment.

Chapter 3 explained how MAR is estimated; Chapter 7 will describe means for estimating average service life and the retirement-
dispersion pattern (that is, the way probable retirements will be scattered about average life, earlier and later). In the unusual case where
one has no experience whatever on which to base estimates of dispersion type, an arbitrary assumption near Type R_1 is recommended.
To illustrate:

Estimated average life = 20 years.
Probable dispersion type = R_1.
MAR = 6%; ultimate net salvage = 10%.

110

Referring to Table 6.17:
Revenue requirement for depreciation = 3.41 (1.00 - 0.10)
= 3.07%.
This is a percentage of the initial capital investment in the depreciable plant currently in service during the year.

The "Value" Notion

The important reason why such a simple evaluation is appropriate is that it satisfies the definition of exact intent, which is not concerned with depreciated "value" at any date short of total life, as discussed before. All we are interested in, for purposes of economic studies, is the lifetime-levelized revenue requirement — a simple and convenient financial equivalency of the type described in Chapter 5.[1]

Table 4.1 on page 61 describes this exact intent by listing: (a) the outlays in connection with a project; and (b) the revenue requirements which will recover those outlays.

Outlays are:

1. Initial capital investment (less net salvage, when received);
2. Taxes;
3. Operation and maintenance expense; and
4. All other expenses.

Corresponding revenue requirements are:

A. Revenue requirement for return (= MAR);
B. Depreciation;
C. Taxes;
D. Operation and maintenance expense; and
E. All other expenses.

Since outlays (2 + 3 + 4) are identical with revenue requirements (C + D + E), it is obvious that: Revenue requirements (A + B) recover Outlay 1 (= initial capital investment adjusted for salvage).

Thus, the exact intent is that lifetime-levelized revenue requirements for return plus depreciation be sufficient to recover the initial capital investment (adjusted for salvage). Depreciated "value" at any moment is of no concern at all.[2]

If we could predict the date of retirement exactly, and if net salvage were zero, then the lifetime-levelized revenue requirement for return plus depreciation would be represented by Formula 5.3a, on page 102:

---

[1] A technical reservation is possible in connection with replacement economics and related problems. In such cases, we are still concerned only with loss in "value" over total service life (= initial capital cost less ultimate net salvage); but service life for the particular property under study departs from the normally expected life in such cases.

[2] Except that at the end of service life, when the property is retired, the "value" is ultimate net salvage. Salvage credits come from the junkman, not from revenues.

$$1/a_{\overline{n}|} = i + {}_i d$$

where

i = MAR.

${}_i d$ = the annuity that will accumulate \$1 in n years (per Formula 5.2a on page 100).

n = service life, in years.

This illustrates the nature of the deal made by an investor when he commits his capital funds to a project:

1. He expects a return <u>on</u> his capital investment, at $i\%$ each year, until
2. He is repaid that principal amount (return <u>of</u> the investment), which could be accomplished by a level annual recovery at ${}_i d\%$ each year.

<u>Service life</u> is exactly defined as the period of years from (a) the date of initial purchase, to (b) the date of retirement from service, at which date the final recovery of the initial investment is required.[3]

Two practical considerations arise that have injected much unnecessary confusion and misrepresentation:

1. Accountants do not make book charges for depreciation expense at the rate of ${}_i d\%$. They customarily use some figure such as the "straight-line" rate (= 1/life), or sum-of-years'-digits percentage or double-rate declining-balance percentage.
2. It is impossible to predict the date of retirement, for any individual unit of property, with any worthwhile assurance of accuracy. We must settle for estimates of <u>probable</u> average life.

Together with the "value" notion, these two factors have accounted for practically all misconceptions of the depreciation problem.[4] All that ever was needed to resolve all the difficulty is disciplined insistence on <u>exact</u> definitions of terms and intent, which has been sadly lacking and which MRRD provides.

It cannot be said too forcefully that, even if by some magic the book charges for depreciation expense did happen to represent loss in value, that would be just an interesting coincidence so far as studies of profitability and economic choice are concerned. We would still be interested only in the initial capital cost, the amount of net salvage at

---

[3]Service life may not turn out as expected; it may be greater or less than anticipated. But, however good or bad the estimate, we are concerned with the revenues <u>required</u> to complete the capital recovery at the <u>actual</u> date of final retirement finally realized.

[4]For a brief discussion of "the malady which causes its victims to become enthralled with the objective proof of subjective values," see:

Raymond P. Marple, "Value-itis," <u>The Accounting Review</u>, (July, 1963), p. 478.

For a thoughtful and more comprehensive discussion, see:

<u>Report of Committee on Depreciation, National Association of Railroad and Utility Commissioners</u> (1943).

This was recently revised, but the essential nature of the problem has not changed since 1943.

retirement, and the probable dates of partial and/or total retirements. These data, together with MAR, fix the desired financial equivalency, $\beta_i d(1 - c)$, regardless of interim rates of "loss in value."

Book Charges for Depreciation Expense

Let's consider first exactly why the method used by the accountant to report "depreciation expense" has no effect on the lifetime-levelized revenue requirement for return plus depreciation. Here is an example of the need for little knowledge of accounting, but an exact understanding of that little.

The following simple example will serve to illustrate the bookkeeping entries actually made by the accountant when he practices "straight-line" depreciation. The reason for quotation marks around "straight-line" will develop; the expression is quite misleading.

The accountant's charges, at 1/life multiplied by capital investment of plant in service each year, are amounts much larger than the amount of property retired in the same year. The excess is recorded as an addition to the depreciation reserve, and the cash is used to buy new equipment — both replacements and additions to existing assets. In corporate finance, the reserves so accumulated are the source of a large fraction of the funds used to acquire plant. Look at any balance sheet, and see by how much the purchase price of the company's assets exceeds the firm's capitalization (that is, the book value of its securities, plus retained earnings). Usually, the major source of that difference is the depreciation reserve.

Whether the actual book charges for depreciation expense represent current loss in value or not, they assuredly do affect reported earnings. In fact, assuming any current charge other than the actual expense shown on the books would arrive at an incorrect statement of current gross income, as exactly defined.

Then, instead of expressing the revenue requirement for return plus depreciation (= $1/a_{\overline{n}|}$, above) as $i + _id$, why not express it more simply, and more nearly like the accountant's "actual" charges, as:

1. Return on the investment (= Item A) at MAR% of the capital investment, plus
2. Return of the investment at the actual charge for depreciation expense, which is 1/life times that same capital investment?

Many have done it this way, and some still do, though it is now generally recognized that such a calculation is unsound. However, a great many appear willing to accept the assertion that it is unsound without understanding the reason, as though that were beyond the comprehension of ordinary mortals.

The explanation lies in the nature of the transactions just described; the "simple" proposal above ignores the fact that the firm puts reserves to profitable use for many years between the date of the book charge (which must be recovered in current revenues from customers) and the final retirement (not currently charged to revenues).

The amount of the depreciation reserve at any moment is a net figure, the result to date of:

1. Credits to the reserve, from the regular charges made to depreciation expense for plant in service, plus credits for net salvage realized when property units are retired; and
2. Charges to the reserve made each time a property unit is retired.

To illustrate how the accounting is done, and its effect on revenue requirements, we will review the history of an installation having an initial cost of $1,000 installed. For simplicity, assume that net salvage will be zero. The equipment has a 10-year average life. Half of it serves for 8 years; the other half for 12 years. This will illustrate effects of retirement dispersion.

We will apply the accounting procedure ordinarily used for book purposes, known as the "straight-line" group-basis method. The bookkeeper charges for depreciation expense each year at one-tenth (= reciprocal of average life) of the original cost of plant in service. Attention is called to this exact definition of intent.[5]

For simplicity, we will assume that investors' committed capital is represented by common stock only, thus eliminating consideration for debt, retained earnings, and so forth, which only complicate things without affecting principles involved. Depreciation reserves provide funds for additional plant, as the reserves accumulate.

At installation (Year 1), the balance sheet will record the transaction as follows:[6]

Assets		Liabilities	
Plant	$1,000	Stock	$1,000

At the beginning of Year 2, a credit of $1,000/10 = 100 will have been made to the depreciation reserve, supplying funds for additional plant:

Assets		Liabilities	
Original plant	$1,000	Stock	$1,000
Additional plant	100	Depreciation reserve:	
Total	$1,100	On original plant	100
		Total	$1,100

At the end of the seventh year the balance sheet will appear as follows. There have been no retirements as yet. Additional plant may

---

[5]Other "straight-line" methods, some of which will be mentioned later, include the unit-basis procedure, which is sometimes used in nonregulated industry but rarely in public utilities.

[6]For clarity, depreciation reserve will be shown as a liability rather than a negative asset. Most companies actually report it as a "contra asset."

have any average life, or reserves may have been used to purchase nondepreciable land, so the reserves generated by this plant will be represented simply by R, which may have any value including zero:

Assets		Liabilities	
Original plant	$1,000	Stock	$1,000
Additional plant	700 + R	Depreciation reserves:	
Total	$1,700 + R	On original plant	700
		On additional plant	R
		Total	$1,700 + R

What will the balance sheet show at the end of the eighth year? Half of the initial installation will have been retired; $500 will have been removed from the plant account and from the depreciation reserve:

Assets		Liabilities	
Original plant		Stock	$1,000
(1,000 - 500)	$ 500	Depreciation reserves:	
Additional plant	800 + R'	On original plant	
Total	$1,300 + R'	(800 - 500)	300
		On additional plant	R'
		Total	$1,300 + R'

In Years 9, 10, 11, and 12, survivors of the original plant represent a capital investment of $500. Annual depreciation expense ("straight-line" group-basis) drops to 10% of $500, or $50 per year. At the end of the twelfth year the remainder of the initial installation is retired. The balance sheet:

Assets		Liabilities	
Original plant		Stock	$1,000
(500 - 500)	$ 0	Depreciation reserves:	
Additional plant	1,000 + R''	On original plant	
Total	$1,000 + R''	(300 + 200 - 500)	0
		On additional plant	R''
		Total	$1,000 + R''

To review the status of this project at the end of four critical years:

End of Year	Total Plant	Less	Depreciation Reserves	=	Net Assets
1	1,100	-	100	=	$1,000
7	(1,700 + R)	-	(700 + R)	=	1,000
8	(1,300 + R')	-	(300 + R')	=	1,000
12	(1,000 + R'')	-	R''	=	1,000

Two Pertinent Conclusions

The foregoing simple example illustrates two important phenomena that are often overlooked and which, being overlooked, lead to fallacious conclusions:

1. "Integrity of the investment" was maintained at $1,000. That is, investors' committed capital of $1,000 in the enterprise was kept intact, productively employed, throughout the period. The process of depreciation and reinvestment of investors' committed capital displaced by depreciation reserves will continue to accomplish that result indefinitely thereafter.

Earnings of the initial project only, at 6%, would be as follows:

Year	Residual Investors' Committed Capital in the Project	Return at 6% of Residual Investors' Capital in the Project	Return in Percent of the First Cost of Plant in Service
1	$1,000	$ 60	6.00%
2	900	54	5.40
3	800	48	4.80
4	700	42	4.20
5	600	36	3.60
6	500	30	3.00
7	400	24	2.40
8	300	18	1.80
9	200	12	2.40
10	150	9	1.80
11	100	6	1.20
12	50	3	.60
Totals		$342	37.20%

Average = 3.10%

Average annual percentage return, in the last column, referred to by some writers as "average interest," must not be mistaken for the levelized figure. It will be encountered again.

2. Although "straight-line" depreciation was employed in the accepted manner, the depreciation reserve does not grow at a straight-line rate. It is for this reason that the phrase "straight-line," when referring to the depreciation method, is always placed in quotation marks in this text. In brief, the expression "straight-line" depreciation is an egregious misnomer which has misled many people, and it is responsible for countless incorrect conclusions. Here is the way reserves generated by the original installation behaved in this example:

Year	Plant in Service	Reserve	% Reserve
1	$1,000	0	0%
2	1,000	100	10
3	1,000	200	20
4	1,000	300	30
5	1,000	400	40
6	1,000	500	50
7	1,000	600	60
8	1,000	700	70
9	500	300	60
10	500	350	70
11	500	400	80
12	500	450	90

This situation results from the fact that, although average life was ten years, the investment was not retired all at once at the end of Year 10. Some retirements occurred before Age 10; some later on. This phenomenon is known as retirement dispersion; actual retirements are dispersed about average life.

The importance of retirement dispersion in calculating return, depreciation, and taxes, will be explained later. Almost no textbooks mention it; none explain how to allow for it. The omission leads to grievous errors.

Before going further, review the following situations:

1. The charge at the time of retirement equals the initial purchase price less net salvage regardless of the amounts that have accumulated in the reserve.[7] Thus, the actual outlay is independent of the method of depreciation ("straight-line," SYD, DB, sinking fund, or some other method); it is independent of the amount of depreciation expenses charged on the books to date.
2. The charge is the same whether service life was correctly estimated or not. The charge is determined by the date of retirement and the amount of initial investment, not by estimated life.
3. The charge is the same whether the equipment retired is replaced or not, and regardless of the cost of the replacement if there is one.

With that background, let's take a closer look at the proposal to estimate return of the investment at the "straight-line" rate, which is 1/life.

The "Straight-Line" Fixation

Annual revenue requirements, for return plus depreciation, commonly called "capital-recovery costs," are not a level annual percentage

---

[7]"Charge" means the simultaneous deduction from plant accounts (from assets) and from depreciation reserve. There is no outlay.

of capital investment if "straight-line" depreciation is used. We have shown that they are a higher percentage in early years of service life, decreasing with age. They, too, must be levelized if a uniform annual percentage is desired.

Nevertheless, for reasons of their own, some analysts prefer to estimate the annual revenue requirement for depreciation at the "straight-line" rate, 1/service life, the standard symbol for which is $_0d$. They point out that it is perfectly admissible to do so, providing that they estimate associated return on the investment correctly. That is, the important thing is to estimate $(1/a_{\overline{n}|}) \cdot P$ correctly. $1/a_{\overline{n}|}$ can be broken down into its two components, per Formula 5.3a on page 102, as below. It can be broken down, nevertheless, into two different components just as defensibly, providing that the total remains unchanged $(= [1/a_{\overline{n}|}] \cdot P)$.

To illustrate in terms of Formula 5.3a, return on the investment is expressed as follows:

$$\frac{1}{a_{\overline{n}|}} \cdot P = iP + {}_idP$$

where

iP = return on the initial capital outlay
$\quad$ = Item A of Expression II, Table 4.1 on page 61
$\quad$ = MAR, in dollars per year.
${}_idP$ = return of the initial capital outlay
$\quad$ = Item B of Expression II, Table 4.1
$\quad$ = the depreciation annuity, in dollars per year.

Now, they say, let's evaluate return of the investment at the "straight-line" rate, $_0dP$ $(= P/L)$. We can then adjust the other term $(= iP)$ accordingly, and $1/a_{\overline{n}|} \cdot P$ remains unchanged. Just adjust iP by the difference between $_0dP$ and $_idP$, as follows:

$\frac{1}{a_{\overline{n}|}} \cdot P$ = return on the investment + return of the investment

$\quad = \qquad\qquad iP \qquad\qquad + \qquad\qquad {}_idP \qquad\qquad$ (Form Y)
$\quad = \qquad (i + {}_id - {}_0d)P \qquad + \qquad\qquad {}_0dP \qquad\qquad$ (Form X)

Those who prefer Form X point out that $(i + {}_id - {}_0d)P$ represents the gross income that would actually be reported in the income statement if percentage return on investors' committed capital were $i\%$, and if "straight-line" depreciation were used. They observe that when "straight-line" depreciation is used, gross income is always stated as a percentage of net plant; that is, a percentage of $(P_x - R_x)$,

where

$\qquad P_x$ = capital investment in service in Year x.
$\qquad R_x$ = depreciation reserve in Year x.
$P_x - R_x$ = net plant in Year x.

And, they add, all this is arithmetically sound because the difference between $_0d$ and $_id$ ($= {}_0d - {}_id$) represents the interim earnings on reserves, temporarily reinvested to earn $i\%$.

It must be granted that Form X is just as sound arithmetically as Form Y. Technically, there is no objection to Form X. However, a number of practical reasons why Form X is undesirable and well avoided arise from the confusion that is introduced by referring to component $(i + {}_id - {}_0d)\,P$ as "return on the capital investment."

The expression seems to suggest that the quantity $(i + {}_id - {}_0d)$ represents <u>percentage</u> return on the <u>initial</u> capital investment, but that is not true. It represents <u>gross income</u>, not return on the initial capital investment but on the initial capital investment <u>reduced by the amount of depreciation reserves</u> each year.

Innumerable unwary businessmen, teachers, estimators, and even authors of textbooks forget that <u>if depreciation expense is estimated as</u> $_0d \cdot P$, then associated <u>return is not</u> $i \cdot P$.

Table 6.1 illustrates the incorrect version of $1/a_{\overline{n}|}$ that appears repeatedly in the literature. For 10-year life and return at 6%, the annual figure is incorrectly placed at 16.00% while the correct figure is 13.59%. This is an error of about 18% in the evaluation of $1/a_{\overline{n}|}$.

The explanation is that if depreciation is placed at 1/life (= 10%, in this example), then the associated "return" component is not <u>minimum acceptable return</u> (= MAR, or 6% in this example), as we have carefully defined it, but <u>minimal gross income</u> (= mgi, or $i + {}_id - {}_0d$), which is 3.59%. Table 6.2 shows the amount of this differential for several values of life and MAR.

The incorrect version illustrated in Table 6.1 is one more example of the kinds of misunderstandings, resulting in bad decisions and

Table 6.1. A popular incorrect calculation of revenue requirements for capital recovery (= Return plus Depreciation).

Assuming 10-year life, zero net salvage, MAR = 6%

The Incorrect Version

Return at 6%	6.00%
Depreciation at the "straight-line" rate (= 1/10)	10.00
Incorrect total	16.00%

The correct calculation may be made by either Method X or Method Y, as follows:

Method X

Minimal gross income, mgi (= $i + {}_id - {}_0d$)	3.59%
Book charge for "straight-line" depreciation (= $_0d$)	10.00
Correct total	13.59%

Method Y

Revenue requirement for return, i (= MAR)	6.00%
Depreciation annuity (= $_6d$)	7.59
Correct total	13.59%

(<u>Note:</u> The error is $\dfrac{16.00 - 13.59}{13.59} = 17.73\%$)

Table 6.2. Values of $(_0d - _id)$ and mgi* for several values of MAR and Life.
(All in percent.)

Values of n (Service Life)	Values of i (MAR)	$1/a_{\overline{n}}$ $= i + _id$ (Formula 5.3a) $= mgi + _0d$	$_0d$ $= 1/n$ $= 1/\text{Life}$	$_id$ $= i/[(1 + i^n) - 1]$ (Formula 5.2a)	$_0d - _id$	Minimal Gross Income (mgi) $= i + _id - _0d$
5 years	0	20.00	20.00	20.00	0.00	0.00
5	6	23.74	20.00	17.74	2.26	3.74
5	10	26.38	20.00	16.38	3.62	6.38
10	0	10.00	10.00	10.00	0.00	0.00
10	6	13.59	10.00	7.59	2.41	3.59
10	10	16.27	10.00	6.27	3.73	6.27
25	0	4.00	4.00	4.00	0.00	0.00
25	6	7.82	4.00	1.82	2.18	3.82
25	10	11.02	4.00	1.02	2.98	7.02
50	0	2.00	2.00	2.00	0.00	0.00
50	6	6.34	2.00	0.34	1.66	4.34
50	10	10.09	2.00	0.09	1.91	8.09

*Mgi means minimal gross income, that is, MAR% of initial capital investment less depreciation reserve each year.

unnecessary financial loss, that grow out of inexact definitions of intent. Students can expect to encounter this particular misunderstanding at all levels of management. The same error in reasoning occurs repeatedly in technical papers and magazine articles. There are some who recognize the error but excuse it because, they say, after all, estimates of service life in years are apt to be inaccurate in any event. This is like recommending that all wild mushrooms be eaten without attempting to discard poisonous ones, because, after all, there are not many deadly varieties, and some of those are difficult to identify with assurance.

A good rule is to avoid Form X, even when correctly calculated as in Table 6.1, for fear of repeating that common incorrect version. Actually, Form X is useful in only one situation: in developing formulas for federal income tax, as will be discussed in Chapter 8. In all other cases, use Form Y.

The "Replacement Expense" Fallacy

Surely it must be apparent, from all this discussion, that it is not the purpose of depreciation charges to provide funds for replacement of plant. Said before, it bears repeating. Every capital outlay for replacement is just that — an outlay. Depreciation charges, made after the fact, recover that outlay during service life. Depreciation expense is not an outlay; refer again to Table 4.1, on page 61.

Exactly the same charges would be made for depreciation expense even if it were certain in advance that no replacement would be made.

If at the time of retirement the replacement is found to cost more than did the item it replaces, then the new capital outlay for the replacement is greater than otherwise. However, a new and independent capital outlay is called for at replacement, regardless of its amount. The accounting practice just described is set up to accomplish that exact intent. It is what the investor-owner demands and expects.

Arguments on this score, advocating some kind of price-level-adjusted or replacement-cost depreciation charge have appeared frequently in newspapers, magazines, and "letters to the editor" since the altercation between President Kennedy and the steel industry. They appear frequently in popular pleas for tax-tinkering legislation euphemistically known as "tax reform." Many of these arguments are extremely ingenious, and they have sometimes been put forward by top-rank authorities. Nevertheless, they have no merit. Some important considerations which are almost universally overlooked will be discussed in Chapter 8 and Appendix C; the student can then reach his own conclusions based on dispassionate reasoning. Here, again, is the result of being content with inexact definitions of one's own intent.

Definition of $\beta_i d$ [8]

So much for common misunderstandings that are related to the choice of a depreciation accounting method. Now let's turn attention to the matter of retirement dispersion.

It is first necessary to distinguish between group-basis and unit-basis methods of calculation, because this is related to the superprescript beta which is now added to the symbol for the depreciation annuity, $\beta_i d$.

The group-basis approach recognizes that not all retirements occur at the same age. Just as the average life expectancy of a man is about 69 years, some individuals will assuredly die before reaching age 69, while about half will live longer. It is impossible to predict with any worthwhile accuracy when any particular person will die. The best that can be done is to estimate the average probability. That same thing applies to depreciable plant; the best we can do is to base estimates on probable average service life.

In the "straight-line" group-basis method, the annual depreciation rate is 1/(Probable Average Life), adjusted for ultimate net salvage.

In the group-basis procedure, that percentage is multiplied by investment in service in each year, as in the foregoing simple example of depreciation accounting entries. Investment in service means the initial cost, installed, of the current survivors of the original installation. That is, as piecemeal retirements occur, the number of survivors and the related investment decrease gradually each year.

In the group-basis procedure, it is therefore necessary to keep

---

[8]Commonly called "dee-eye-beta."

right on depreciating survivors <u>after they have passed the age corresponding to average life</u>, until the last survivor is finally retired at age omega (ω is the standard symbol for age at retirement of the last survivor). Thus, depreciation expense charged to the longer-lived survivors offsets the fact that underaverage retirements do not recover their full initial cost. For the group as a whole, the full initial cost is eventually recovered.

This same principle operates in life insurance. Those who die at an early age collect their insurance at the time of their early death. These payments are provided by premiums paid by others who live past the average expectancy, and who continue paying until their death occurs at an advanced age.

The important point is that $(i + {}_{i}^{\beta}d)$, in percent, is multiplied each year by $P_{\overline{x}}$ (the surviving investment still in service in Year x); not by P_0, the initial capital investment (that is, the placement made "at the end of Year 0").

The unit-basis procedure operates differently. Of the several variations of the unit-basis method one charges "straight-line" depreciation at ${}_{0}d$ percent of P_0 as long as a <u>unit of property</u> lasts but not past <u>estimated average life</u>. If a unit is retired early, the undepreciated residual is charged to depreciation expense at the time of its early retirement.

For example, say an average life of 20 years is expected. Each property unit would be charged:

$$_{0}d \cdot P_0 = \frac{1}{20} \cdot \text{initial cost, installed}$$

in each year for 20 years and no longer. If a unit were retired at Age 7, the residual = 13/20 of the first cost, installed, would be charged to depreciation expense at that time.

The only way to develop a <u>constant</u> annual percentage charge for depreciation (in percent of investment currently in service), plus a <u>constant</u> annual percentage return (in percent of investment currently in service), is to make the annual depreciation charge ${}_{i}^{\beta}d \cdot P_{\overline{x}}$, where $P_{\overline{x}}$ is the average capital investment in service in each Year x. This is the Form Y expression, discussed on page 118.

As explained before, <u>the same</u> lifetime-levelized annual dollars for return plus depreciation would result from using the Form X expression $(mgi + {}_{0}d) \cdot P_{\overline{x}}$ on page 118. The important difference is that $mgi \cdot P_{\overline{x}}$ (= minimal gross income) <u>in each year</u> is smaller than $i \cdot P_{\overline{x}}$ because it is $i\%$ of $(P_{\overline{x}} - R_{\overline{x}})$; that is, $i\%$ of average capital investment in service <u>less the depreciation reserve</u>, in each Year x.

It is most convenient to have tables of ${}_{i}^{\beta}d$ for each average life and percentage MAR. For that reason, the tables of depreciation annuities are set up that way, and the calculations are made in that manner.

Our exact intent, then, is to develop values of ${}_{i}^{\beta}d$ for any given average life and MAR percentage, which will exactly recover initial capital investment within that life span (that is, the life span from the date of initial installation to date omega, when the last survivor is finally retired.)

In arithmetical notation, the accumulation is to be $^{\beta}_{i}d \cdot P_{\overline{x}}$ in each year, where $P_{\overline{x}}$ is the average capital investment in service in Year x. The present worth at the initial in-service date of these lifetime charges at times of piecemeal retirements for repayment of the initial investment:

$$^{\beta}_{i}d \sum_{x=0}^{x=\omega} v^{x} \cdot P_{\overline{x}} = \sum_{x=0}^{x=\omega} v^{x} \cdot \text{retirements}_{x}$$

where

v^{x} = present worth factors in Year x, per Formula 5.1a on page 98.

retirements$_{x}$ = retirements in Year x.

Solving for $^{\beta}_{i}d$:

$$^{\beta}_{i}d = \frac{\displaystyle\sum_{x=0}^{x=\omega} v^{x} \cdot \text{retirements}_{x}}{\displaystyle\sum_{x=0}^{x=\omega} v^{x} \cdot P_{\overline{x}}} \qquad \text{(Formula 6.1)}$$

Formula 6.1 is the basic definition of $^{\beta}_{i}d$.

Other ways to calculate $^{\beta}_{i}d$ include one of special interest because it permits a timesaving shortcut in computations. It may be developed as follows:

$$\text{Annual return plus depreciation} = iP_{\overline{x}} + ^{\beta}_{i}d \cdot P_{\overline{x}}$$

The present worth of such lifetime charges would be:

$$i \sum_{x=0}^{x=\omega} v^{x} \cdot P_{\overline{x}} + ^{\beta}_{i}d \sum_{x=0}^{x=\omega} v^{x} \cdot P_{\overline{x}} = P_{0}$$

That is, the present worth of lifetime annual revenue requirements for return plus depreciation are, by definition, equal to the initial capital investment. Each is the financial equivalency of the other.

The same expression may be rendered in terms of $y_{\overline{x}}$, which is the symbol for <u>percentage</u> of initial placement surviving in Year x (instead of $P_{\overline{x}}$, the surviving <u>dollars</u>), by substituting $y_{\overline{x}}$ in place of $P_{\overline{x}}$ in the foregoing equation. The initial placement is then 100%, or unity:

$$i \sum_{x=0}^{x=\omega} v^{x} \cdot y_{\overline{x}} + ^{\beta}_{i}d \sum_{x=0}^{x=\omega} v^{x} \cdot y_{\overline{x}} = 1$$

Solving for $^{\beta}_{i}d$:

$$\beta_i d = \frac{1 - i \sum\limits_{x=0}^{x=\omega} v^x \cdot y_{\overline{x}}}{\sum\limits_{x=0}^{x=\omega} v^x \cdot y_{\overline{x}}} = \frac{1}{\sum\limits_{x=0}^{x=\omega} v^x \cdot y_{\overline{x}}} - i \qquad \text{(Formula 6.2)}$$

To illustrate the usefulness of Formula 6.2, let's apply it to the data used in the foregoing simple example used to illustrate accounting entries. The foregoing "mathematician's shorthand" may look forbidding, but it describes a very simple tabulation.

Evaluation of $\beta_i d$

Table 6.3 shows how $\beta_i d$ is evaluated, per Formula 6.2, for plant having 10-year average life; half of the installation being retired at Age 8 and the remainder at Age 12. MAR is 6%, and there is no ultimate net salvage.

Table 6.3. Shortcut calculation of the depreciation annuity, $\beta_i d$

Annual survivors of the initial installation as described in the discussion of depreciation accounting entries, minimum acceptable return (MAR) at 6%.

$$\beta_i d = \frac{1}{\sum\limits_{x=0}^{x=\omega} v^x \cdot y_{\overline{x}}} - i \qquad \text{(Formula 6.2)}$$

1	2	3	4
Year	Present Worth Factors at $i = 6\%$	Percentage Survivors	Col. 2 x Col. 3
(x)	(v^x)	$(y_{\overline{x}})$	$(= v^x y_{\overline{x}})$
1	0.943 396	100%	0.943 396
2	.889 996	100	.889 996
3	.839 619	100	.839 619
4	.792 094	100	.792 094
5	.747 258	100	.747 258
6	.704 961	100	.704 961
7	.665 057	100	.665 057
8	.627 412	100	.627 412
9	.591 898	50	.295 949
10	.558 395	50	.279 198
11	.526 788	50	.263 394
12 (ω)	.496 969	50	.248 484

$$\sum_{x=0}^{x=12} v^x \cdot y_{\overline{x}} = 7.296\ 818$$

$$\beta_i d = \frac{1}{7.296\ 818} - 0.06 = 7.7046\%$$

Note: See Appendix A for a discussion of significant figures, desirable number of decimal places, and suggestions concerning rounding procedure.

In each year, the surviving plant still in service (here, for convenience, in percent of initial installation) is shown in Column 3; it is multiplied by the appropriate present worth factor (per Column 2), and the products are tabulated in Column 4.

Column 4 is summed; the total is $\sum\limits_{x=0}^{x=\omega} v^x \cdot y_{\overline{x}}$. The reciprocal of this total, less $i\%$, equals $\beta_i d$. The solution is $\beta_6 d = 7.7046\%$.

An interesting comparison can be made, as follows:

$_6d$ = the "straight-line" rate = $1/10$ =   10.000%.
$_6d$ = the annuity which ignores retirement dispersion =   7.5868%.
   (that is, Formula 5.2a on page 100, which assumes
   10-year life for all units)
$\beta_6 d$ = the annuity adjusted for retirement dispersion =   7.7046%

You will discover that these relative amounts are typical; $\beta_i d$ is greater than $_i d$, while $_6 d$ is greater than either. The amount of the difference depends upon average life, the type of dispersion (the pattern in which individual retirements are scattered about average life), and MAR.

Suppose we test this solution by calculating the annual revenue requirements that would result.

Table 6.4 shows the annual quantities: return at $iP_{\overline{x}}$; depreciation at $\beta_i d \cdot P_{\overline{x}}$; and their present worth at installation date.

Table 6.5 shows the "straight-line" results: gross income at $i(P_{\overline{x}} - R_{\overline{x}})$; depreciation at $_6 d \cdot P_{\overline{x}}$; and their present worth at installation date. The figures of Table 6.5 may be described as the <u>year-by-year</u> "straight-line" results.

Table 6.6 presents another version of the "straight-line results." Here, gross income in each year is shown at the lifetime-levelized

Table 6.4. Annual revenue requirements for return and depreciation. Average life = 10 years. 50% retired at Age 8; 50% at Age 12. Zero ultimate net salvage. MAR = 6%.

$\beta_i d = 7.7046\%$, per Table 6.3

1	2	3	4	5	6	7	8
	Present Worth Factors at 6%	Surviving Investment	Annual Return	Annual Depreciation	Present Worth of		
Year					Return	Depreciation	Total
x	v^x	$P_{\overline{x}}$	$iP_{\overline{x}}$	$\beta_i d \cdot P_{\overline{x}}$	Col. 2 x Col. 4	Col. 2 x Col. 5	Col. 6 + Col. 7
1	0.943 396	$1,000	$60.00	$77.05	$ 56.60	$ 72.69	$ 129.29
2	.889 996	1,000	60.00	77.05	53.40	68.57	121.97
3	.839 619	1,000	60.00	77.05	50.38	64.69	115.07
4	.792 094	1,000	60.00	77.05	47.53	61.03	108.56
5	.747 258	1,000	60.00	77.05	44.84	57.57	102.41
6	.704 961	1,000	60.00	77.05	42.30	54.32	96.62
7	.665 057	1,000	60.00	77.05	39.90	51.24	91.14
8	.627 412	1,000	60.00	77.05	37.64	48.34	85.98
9	.591 898	500	30.00	38.52	17.76	22.80	40.56
10	.558 395	500	30.00	38.52	16.75	21.51	38.26
11	.526 788	500	30.00	38.52	15.80	20.29	36.09
12	.496 969	500	30.00	38.52	14.91	19.14	34.05
				Totals	$437.81	$562.19	$1,000.00

Table 6.5. Annual revenue requirements for return and depreciation. Average life = 10 years.
50% retired at Age 8; 50% at Age 12. Zero ultimate net salvage. MAR = 6%.

$$_0d = \frac{1}{\text{Life}} = 10.00\%$$

1	2	3	4	5	6	7	8
	Present Worth Factors at 6%	Depreciation Reserve	Minimal Gross Income	Annual Depreciation	Present Worth of		
Year					Gross Income	Depreciation	Total
x	v^x	$R_{\overline{x}}$	$i(P_{\overline{x}} - R_{\overline{x}})$	$_0d \cdot P_{\overline{x}}$	Col. 2 x Col. 4	Col. 2 x Col. 5	Col. 6 + Col. 7
1	0.943 396	$ 0	$60.00	$100.00	$ 56.61	$ 94.34	$ 150.95
2	.889 996	100	54.00	100.00	48.06	89.00	137.06
3	.839 619	200	48.00	100.00	40.30	83.96	124.26
4	.792 094	300	42.00	100.00	33.27	79.21	112.48
5	.747 258	400	36.00	100.00	26.90	74.73	101.63
6	.704 961	500	30.00	100.00	21.15	70.50	91.65
7	.665 057	600	24.00	100.00	15.96	66.50	82.46
8	.627 412	700	18.00	100.00	11.29	62.74	74.03
9	.591 898	300	12.00	50.00	7.10	29.59	36.69
10	.558 395	350	9.00	50.00	5.03	27.92	32.95
11	.526 788	400	6.00	50.00	3.16	26.34	29.50
12	.496 969	450	3.00	50.00	1.49	24.85	26.34
				Totals	$270.32	$729.68	$1,000.00

percentage $(i + {_i}d - {_0}d)$ P, in the manner of Form X on page 118: gross income at $(i + {_i^\beta}d - {_0}d)P_{\overline{x}}$; depreciation at $_0d \cdot P_{\overline{x}}$; and their present worth at installation date.

Observe that all three versions are technically "correct." Each one carries out a slightly different exact intent of the estimator; that is all. It is failure to recognize this situation which leads to the improper conclusion that the matter is "controversial," and the lame excuse that the solution is elusive, loose, and inexact. Not so!

The annual gross income of Table 6.6 may be calculated in a

Table 6.6. Annual revenue requirements for return and depreciation. Average life = 10 years.
50% retired at Age 8; 50% at Age 12. Zero ultimate net salvage. MAR = 6%.

$$_0d = 10.0000; \quad {_i^\beta}d = 7.7046\%; \quad _0d - {_i^\beta}d = 2.2954\%$$

$$(i + {_i^\beta}d - {_0}d) = 3.7046\%$$

1	2	3	4	5	6	7	8
	Present Worth Factors at 6%	Surviving Investment	Levelized Gross Income	Annual Depreciation	Present Worth of		
Year					Gross Income	Depreciation	Total
x	v^x	$P_{\overline{x}}$	$(i + {_i^\beta}d - {_0}d) P_{\overline{x}}$	$_0d \cdot P_{\overline{x}}$	Col. 2 x Col. 4	Col. 2 x Col. 5	Col. 6 + Col. 7
1	0.943 396	$1,000	$37.046	$100.00	$ 34.95	$ 94.34	$ 129.29
2	.889 996	1,000	37.046	100.00	32.97	89.00	121.97
3	.839 619	1,000	37.046	100.00	31.11	83.96	115.07
4	.792 094	1,000	37.046	100.00	29.34	79.21	108.55
5	.747 258	1,000	37.046	100.00	27.68	74.73	102.41
6	.704 961	1,000	37.046	100.00	26.12	70.50	96.62
7	.665 057	1,000	37.046	100.00	24.64	66.50	91.14
8	.627 412	1,000	37.046	100.00	23.24	62.74	85.98
9	.591 898	500	18.523	50.00	10.96	29.59	40.55
10	.558 395	500	18.523	50.00	10.34	27.92	38.26
11	.526 788	500	18.523	50.00	9.76	26.34	36.10
12	.496 969	500	18.523	50.00	9.21	24.85	34.06
				Totals	$270.32	$729.68	$1,000.00

slightly different way, as mentioned before, by levelizing the lifetime
depreciation reserves, thus:

$$\text{Gross income} = (i + \tfrac{\beta}{i}d - {}_0d)P_{\overline{x}} = i \cdot P_{\overline{x}}(1 - \overline{R})$$

where $\overline{R}$ is the lifetime-levelized "straight-line" reserve in percent
of $P_{\overline{x}}$.

This device is particularly convenient in income tax studies and
therefore worth understanding exactly. The identity is readily demonstrated analytically; Table 6.7 shows the year-by-year calculation of $\overline{R}$,
and how it reproduces gross income per Form X.

Two general comments are of importance in connection with
Tables 6.4, 6.5, and 6.6:

1. For simplicity, zero ultimate net salvage has been assumed
here. If there were some finite salvage value, it would be realized
piecemeal as the piecemeal retirements occur. That is, each individual retirement would be associated with its own ultimate net salvage.

If positive net salvage is realized, quantity $(1 - c)$ will be less than
unity. The revenue requirement for depreciation will be <u>reduced by</u>

Table 6.7. Demonstration of the identity of two calculations of minimal gross
income. Average life = 10 years.   50% retired at Age 8; 50% at Age 12.
Zero ultimate net salvage. MAR = 6%.

$$(i + {}_id - {}_0d)P_{\overline{x}} = i \cdot P_x(1 - \overline{R}) \text{ in each year.}$$

1	2	3	4	5	6
	Present Worth	Surviving	Depreciation	Present Worth of	
Year	Factors at 6%	Investment	Reserve	Survivors	Reserves
x	v^x	$P_{\overline{x}}$	$R_{\overline{x}}$	$v^x \cdot P_{\overline{x}}$	$v^x R_{\overline{x}}$
1	0.943 396	$1,000	$ 0	$ 943.396	$ 0
2	.889 996	1,000	100	889.996	88.9996
3	.839 619	1,000	200	839.619	167.9238
4	.792 094	1,000	300	792.094	237.6282
5	.747 258	1,000	400	747.258	298.9032
6	.704 961	1,000	500	704.961	352.4805
7	.665 057	1,000	600	665.057	399.0342
8	.627 412	1,000	700	627.412	439.1884
9	.591 898	500	300	295.949	177.5694
10	.558 395	500	350	279.198	195.4382
11	.526 788	500	400	263.394	210.7152
12	.496 969	500	450	248.485	223.6361
			Totals	$7,296.819	$2,791.5168

$$\overline{R} = \frac{2{,}791.5168}{7{,}296.819} = 38.257\%$$

$$iP_x (1 - \overline{R}) = 6(1.00000 - 0.38257) = 3.7046\%$$

$$i + {}_id - {}_0d = 6.0000 + 7.7046 - 10.0000 = 3.7046\%$$

(from Table 6.6)

amounts received from the junkman. If ultimate net salvage is negative (such as when a building must be demolished at considerable expense, and the wreckage has no scrap value), then (1 - c) is greater than unity, and revenue requirements are increased thereby.

In either case, the present worth of lifetime revenue requirements for return plus depreciation equal: (1) the initial capital investment, installed, plus (2) the present worth of ultimate net salvage. If ultimate scrap value is positive, the present worth of lifetime revenue requirements for return plus depreciation is less than the initial purchase price of the facilities, installed.

2. Note that, with zero net salvage, the fact that present worth of lifetime return plus depreciation exactly equals initial purchase price does not prove that the correct value of MAR has been used.

Assigning any value whatever to $i\%$, and then calculating present worth by discounting at that same percentage "interest" rate, will always result in finding a present worth exactly equal to the initial investment. This observation, too, will be made use of in Chapter 10.

The basic principles illustrated by Tables 6.4-6.7 are essential to the solution of a number of perplexing problems, such as determination of equitable reimbursement for damaged, destroyed, or confiscated property; in questions arising from joint ownership of property; in establishing reasonable prices for sale or purchase of equipment that is used and usable; in intercompany transactions such as interconnection agreements between public utilities; or cooperative arrangements between governmental agencies and investor-owned corporations.

These same principles also provide a firm foundation for product-pricing policy and for rate making. To suggest their importance in rate making, consider the widely accepted doctrine that a "fair" rate-making policy for public utilities demands that current customers bear current costs of the service they are rendered.

Which of the four tables truly presents the current cost of depreciation, sometimes referred to as "actual" current cost? The answer must now be apparent: None of them.

Actual cost of depreciation is that single capital outlay made at the date of initial purchase. Every other version is some financial equivalency of that initial cost. This applies to the "straight-line" rate or to any other that may be used for purposes of the company's books. Book charges are arbitrary annual allocations of amounts expected to recover the initial capital outlay, adjusted for salvage, within service lifetime.

You can theorize that changes in the depreciation reserve accumulated with passage of time represent loss in value, and that this loss in value is a "current cost" which ought to be recovered currently in prices charged for company output. But that is a matter of the company's pricing policy, not to be confused with the analysis of current outlays actually made. It is failure to recognize this exact difference that has caused the pervasive confusion.

The Iowa Type Curves

Tables 6.5-6.7 showed how $\overset{\beta}{_i}d$ may be calculated for any one particular type of retirement dispersion. In actual experience, all sorts
of dispersion patterns are encountered, and they greatly affect the
value of $\overset{\beta}{_i}d$ for a given average life. You will find that a difference in
a dispersion pattern for one given life can affect $\overset{\beta}{_i}d$ more than a 50%
change in life! Yet most textbooks ignore this undeniable fact. It is
difficult to understand why. Here is one more example of bad estimating that results from accepting inexact definitions of one's own intent
when a good approximation of exact intent is conveniently at hand,
readily picked from a table.

A convenient codified system for identifying commonly encountered
patterns of retirement dispersion has been developed at the Engineering Experiment Station of Iowa State University (Ames). Other systems
are also in use, but the Iowa Type Curves are most convenient for the
present purpose, and the best known.

Each pattern is designated by a letter (S, L, or R) and a numerical
subscript (0 to 6), thus: R_2. The letter refers to the rate of retirements at each age, a plot of which resembles the normal probability
curve — retirements slow at first, increasing to a maximum rate near
average life, and then decreasing until the last survivor is retired. A
curve that is symmetrical with respect to the average-life axis is Type
S. If the mode (maximum rate of retirement) occurs before average
life is reached, it is left-moded (L). If the mode occurs after average
life is attained, it is right-moded (R).

If retirements occur at nearly the same constant rate at all ages,
a subscript near zero is added. At the other extreme, if retirements
all occur within a short period near average life (that is, a high rate
for a few years), the subscript approaches 6.

These patterns are completely general. The shape of curve depends upon retirement behavior, as influenced by the reasons for retirement. For any given type of equipment reasons for retirement may
vary widely from one company to the next. Thus, there is no good reason to regard any one pattern as being necessarily associated with any
one type of equipment.

A set of these "generalized" curves appears in Figures 6.1, 6.2,
and 6.3.

Tables of $\overset{\beta}{_i}d$

Tables 6.8-6.19 present values of $\overset{\beta}{_i}d$ for average lives from 5 to
60 years; for MAR at 5%, 6%, 7%, and 8%; and for all Iowa Type Curves
plus several intermediate types.[9]

---

[9]Programming and computation by William H. Caunt, Jr., of Public Service Electric &
Gas Company, Newark, N.J. The summation procedure described above was used for the
present purpose by request. Mr. Caunt has also made studies of annuities making use of
the integration procedure and has done extensive research in the matter of desirable treatment and estimation of retirement dispersion.

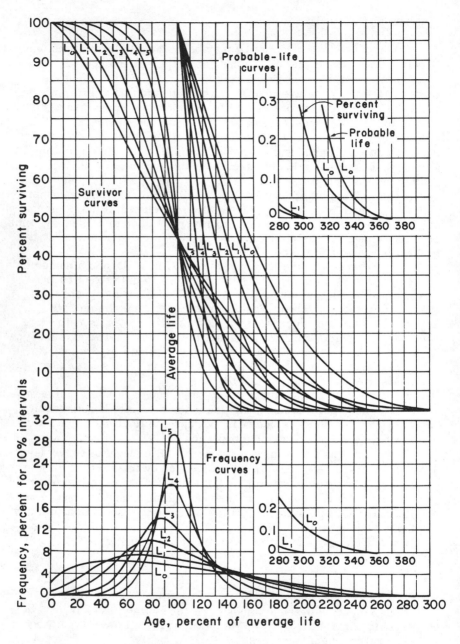

Fig. 6.1. Iowa Type curves: Left-moded mortality dispersions. (Reproduced from Iowa Engineering Experiment Station Bulletin 155 by Robley Winfrey)

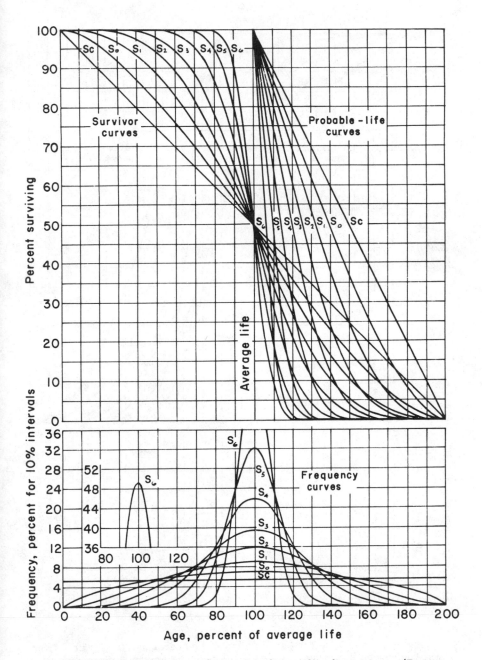

Fig. 6.2. Iowa Type curves: Symmetrical mortality dispersions. (Reproduced from Iowa Engineering Experiment Station Bulletin 155 by Robley Winfrey, with Type SC added)

131

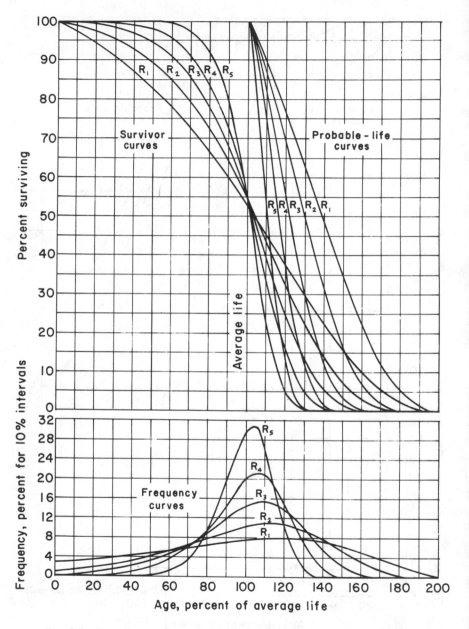

Fig. 6.3. Iowa Type curves: Right-moded dispersions. (Reproduced from Iowa Engineering Experiment Station Bulletin 155 by Robley Winfrey)

Table 6.8. $\beta_5 d$ for Iowa Type L probability. Present-worth group-basis depreciation annuities for left-moded dispersions, average lives from 5 to 60 years, and associated MAR of 5%.

Average Life (Years)	L_0	$L_{\frac{1}{2}}$	L_1	$L_{1\frac{1}{2}}$	L_2	L_3	L_4	L_5	Average Life (Years)
				Type of Retirement Dispersion					
5	19.12	18.95	18.79	18.67	18.56	18.38	18.24	18.16	5
6	15.71	15.55	15.39	15.28	15.16	14.98	14.85	14.78	6
7	13.29	13.13	12.97	12.85	12.74	12.56	12.42	12.35	7
8	11.48	11.32	11.16	11.05	10.93	10.75	10.61	10.54	8
9	10.08	9.91	9.75	9.64	9.53	9.34	9.20	9.14	9
10	8.95	8.79	8.63	8.52	8.41	8.22	8.09	8.02	10
11	8.04	7.88	7.72	7.60	7.49	7.31	7.17	7.11	11
12	7.28	7.12	6.96	6.84	6.73	6.55	6.42	6.35	12
13	6.64	6.48	6.32	6.20	6.09	5.91	5.78	5.71	13
14	6.09	5.93	5.78	5.66	5.55	5.37	5.23	5.17	14
15	5.62	5.46	5.31	5.19	5.08	4.90	4.77	4.70	15
16	5.21	5.05	4.90	4.78	4.67	4.49	4.36	4.29	16
17	4.85	4.69	4.54	4.42	4.31	4.13	4.00	3.93	17
18	4.53	4.37	4.22	4.10	3.99	3.81	3.68	3.62	18
19	4.25	4.09	3.94	3.82	3.71	3.53	3.40	3.34	19
20	3.99	3.83	3.68	3.56	3.45	3.28	3.15	3.09	20
21	3.76	3.61	3.45	3.34	3.22	3.05	2.92	2.86	21
22	3.56	3.40	3.25	3.13	3.02	2.85	2.72	2.66	22
23	3.37	3.21	3.06	2.94	2.83	2.66	2.54	2.47	23
24	3.20	3.04	2.89	2.77	2.66	2.49	2.37	2.31	24
25	3.04	2.88	2.73	2.62	2.51	2.34	2.22	2.15	25
26	2.90	2.74	2.59	2.47	2.36	2.20	2.08	2.01	26
27	2.76	2.61	2.46	2.34	2.23	2.07	1.95	1.89	27
28	2.64	2.48	2.34	2.22	2.11	1.95	1.83	1.77	28
29	2.53	2.37	2.22	2.11	2.00	1.84	1.72	1.66	29
30	2.42	2.27	2.12	2.01	1.90	1.74	1.62	1.56	30
31	2.32	2.17	2.02	1.91	1.80	1.64	1.53	1.47	31
32	2.23	2.08	1.93	1.82	1.71	1.55	1.44	1.38	32
33	2.14	1.99	1.85	1.74	1.63	1.47	1.36	1.30	33
34	2.06	1.91	1.77	1.66	1.55	1.40	1.29	1.23	34
35	1.99	1.84	1.70	1.59	1.48	1.33	1.21	1.16	35
36	1.92	1.77	1.63	1.52	1.41	1.26	1.15	1.09	36
37	1.85	1.70	1.56	1.45	1.35	1.20	1.09	1.03	37
38	1.79	1.64	1.50	1.39	1.29	1.14	1.03	.98	38
39	1.73	1.58	1.44	1.34	1.23	1.08	.98	.93	39
40	1.67	1.53	1.39	1.28	1.18	1.03	.93	.88	40
41	1.62	1.48	1.34	1.23	1.13	.98	.88	.83	41
42	1.57	1.43	1.29	1.18	1.08	.94	.84	.79	42
43	1.52	1.38	1.24	1.14	1.04	.90	.80	.75	43
44	1.48	1.34	1.20	1.10	1.00	.86	.76	.71	44
45	1.44	1.29	1.16	1.06	.96	.82	.72	.67	45
46	1.39	1.25	1.12	1.02	.92	.78	.69	.64	46
47	1.36	1.22	1.08	.98	.88	.75	.65	.60	47
48	1.32	1.18	1.05	.95	.85	.71	.62	.57	48
49	1.28	1.15	1.01	.91	.82	.68	.59	.55	49
50	1.25	1.11	.98	.88	.79	.65	.56	.52	50
51	1.22	1.08	.95	.85	.76	.63	.54	.49	51
52	1.19	1.05	.92	.83	.73	.60	.51	.47	52
53	1.16	1.02	.89	.80	.70	.58	.49	.45	53
54	1.13	1.00	.87	.77	.68	.55	.47	.42	54
55	1.10	.97	.84	.75	.65	.53	.45	.40	55
56	1.08	.94	.82	.72	.63	.51	.43	.38	56
57	1.05	.92	.80	.70	.61	.49	.41	.37	57
58	1.03	.90	.77	.68	.59	.47	.39	.35	58
59	1.00	.87	.75	.66	.57	.45	.37	.33	59
60	.98	.85	.73	.64	.55	.43	.36	.32	60

133

Table 6.9. $\beta_6 d$ for Iowa Type L probability. Present-worth group-basis depreciation annuities for left-moded dispersions, average lives from 5 to 60 years, and associated MAR of 6%.

Average Life (Years)	Type of Retirement Dispersion								Average Life (Years)
	L_0	$L_{\frac{1}{2}}$	L_1	$L_{1\frac{1}{2}}$	L_2	L_3	L_4	L_5	
5	18.97	18.76	18.57	18.43	18.30	18.08	17.91	17.81	5
6	15.55	15.36	15.17	15.03	14.89	14.67	14.51	14.42	6
7	13.13	12.93	12.74	12.60	12.46	12.24	12.08	12.00	7
8	11.31	11.12	10.92	10.79	10.65	10.43	10.27	10.19	8
9	9.91	9.71	9.52	9.38	9.25	9.03	8.86	8.78	9
10	8.78	8.59	8.40	8.26	8.13	7.91	7.75	7.67	10
11	7.88	7.68	7.49	7.35	7.22	7.00	6.84	6.76	11
12	7.12	6.93	6.74	6.60	6.46	6.25	6.09	6.00	12
13	6.48	6.29	6.10	5.96	5.82	5.61	5.45	5.37	13
14	5.94	5.75	5.56	5.42	5.28	5.07	4.91	4.83	14
15	5.47	5.28	5.09	4.95	4.82	4.61	4.45	4.37	15
16	5.07	4.87	4.69	4.55	4.41	4.20	4.05	3.97	16
17	4.71	4.52	4.33	4.19	4.06	3.85	3.69	3.62	17
18	4.39	4.20	4.02	3.88	3.74	3.54	3.39	3.31	18
19	4.11	3.92	3.74	3.60	3.47	3.26	3.11	3.03	19
20	3.86	3.67	3.49	3.35	3.22	3.01	2.87	2.79	20
21	3.63	3.45	3.26	3.13	2.99	2.79	2.65	2.57	21
22	3.43	3.24	3.06	2.93	2.79	2.59	2.45	2.37	22
23	3.25	3.06	2.88	2.74	2.61	2.41	2.27	2.20	23
24	3.08	2.89	2.71	2.58	2.45	2.25	2.11	2.04	24
25	2.92	2.74	2.56	2.43	2.29	2.10	1.96	1.89	25
26	2.78	2.60	2.42	2.29	2.16	1.97	1.83	1.76	26
27	2.65	2.47	2.29	2.16	2.03	1.84	1.70	1.63	27
28	2.53	2.35	2.18	2.04	1.91	1.73	1.59	1.52	28
29	2.42	2.24	2.07	1.94	1.81	1.62	1.49	1.42	29
30	2.32	2.14	1.97	1.84	1.71	1.52	1.39	1.33	30
31	2.22	2.04	1.87	1.74	1.62	1.43	1.31	1.24	31
32	2.13	1.96	1.79	1.66	1.53	1.35	1.22	1.16	32
33	2.05	1.87	1.71	1.58	1.45	1.28	1.15	1.09	33
34	1.97	1.80	1.63	1.50	1.38	1.20	1.08	1.02	34
35	1.90	1.73	1.56	1.43	1.31	1.14	1.02	.95	35
36	1.83	1.66	1.49	1.37	1.25	1.08	.96	.90	36
37	1.76	1.59	1.43	1.31	1.19	1.02	.90	.84	37
38	1.70	1.53	1.37	1.25	1.13	.96	.85	.79	38
39	1.65	1.48	1.32	1.20	1.08	.91	.80	.74	39
40	1.59	1.43	1.27	1.15	1.03	.87	.75	.70	40
41	1.54	1.38	1.22	1.10	.98	.82	.71	.66	41
42	1.49	1.33	1.17	1.05	.94	.78	.67	.62	42
43	1.45	1.28	1.13	1.01	.90	.74	.64	.58	43
44	1.40	1.24	1.09	.97	.86	.70	.60	.55	44
45	1.36	1.20	1.05	.93	.82	.67	.57	.52	45
46	1.32	1.16	1.01	.90	.79	.64	.54	.49	46
47	1.29	1.13	.98	.86	.75	.61	.51	.46	47
48	1.25	1.09	.95	.83	.72	.58	.48	.43	48
49	1.22	1.06	.91	.80	.69	.55	.46	.41	49
50	1.18	1.03	.88	.77	.67	.53	.43	.39	50
51	1.15	1.00	.86	.75	.64	.50	.41	.36	51
52	1.12	.97	.83	.72	.61	.48	.39	.34	52
53	1.09	.95	.80	.70	.59	.46	.37	.32	53
54	1.07	.92	.78	.67	.57	.44	.35	.31	54
55	1.04	.89	.75	.65	.55	.42	.33	.29	55
56	1.02	.87	.73	.63	.53	.40	.32	.27	56
57	.99	.85	.71	.61	.51	.38	.30	.26	57
58	.97	.83	.69	.59	.49	.36	.28	.25	58
59	.95	.81	.67	.57	.47	.35	.27	.23	59
60	.93	.79	.65	.55	.45	.33	.26	.22	60

Table 6.10. βd for Iowa Type L probability. Present-worth group-basis depreciation annuities for left-moded dispersions, average lives from 5 to 60 years, and associated MAR of 7%.

Average Life (Years)	L_0	$L_{\frac{1}{2}}$	L_1	$L_{1\frac{1}{2}}$	L_2	L_3	L_4	L_5	Average Life (Years)
			Type of Retirement Dispersion						
5	18.82	18.58	18.35	18.19	18.04	17.79	17.59	17.48	5
6	15.40	15.17	14.95	14.78	14.62	14.37	14.18	14.08	6
7	12.97	12.74	12.52	12.35	12.19	11.94	11.75	11.65	7
8	11.15	10.92	10.70	10.54	10.38	10.13	9.94	9.84	8
9	9.75	9.52	9.30	9.14	8.98	8.73	8.54	8.44	9
10	8.63	8.40	8.18	8.02	7.86	7.61	7.43	7.33	10
11	7.73	7.50	7.28	7.12	6.96	6.71	6.52	6.43	11
12	6.97	6.75	6.52	6.36	6.20	5.96	5.77	5.68	12
13	6.34	6.11	5.90	5.73	5.57	5.33	5.14	5.05	13
14	5.80	5.57	5.36	5.19	5.04	4.79	4.61	4.52	14
15	5.33	5.11	4.90	4.73	4.58	4.34	4.16	4.07	15
16	4.93	4.71	4.49	4.33	4.18	3.94	3.76	3.67	16
17	4.57	4.36	4.14	3.98	3.83	3.59	3.41	3.33	17
18	4.27	4.04	3.84	3.67	3.52	3.28	3.11	3.02	18
19	3.99	3.77	3.56	3.40	3.25	3.01	2.84	2.76	19
20	3.74	3.52	3.32	3.16	3.00	2.77	2.60	2.52	20
21	3.52	3.30	3.09	2.94	2.79	2.56	2.39	2.31	21
22	3.32	3.11	2.90	2.74	2.59	2.36	2.20	2.12	22
23	3.14	2.92	2.72	2.56	2.41	2.19	2.03	1.95	23
24	2.97	2.76	2.56	2.40	2.25	2.03	1.87	1.79	24
25	2.82	2.61	2.41	2.25	2.11	1.89	1.73	1.65	25
26	2.68	2.47	2.27	2.12	1.97	1.76	1.61	1.53	26
27	2.55	2.35	2.15	2.00	1.85	1.64	1.49	1.41	27
28	2.44	2.23	2.03	1.88	1.74	1.53	1.38	1.31	28
29	2.33	2.13	1.93	1.78	1.64	1.43	1.29	1.21	29
30	2.23	2.03	1.83	1.69	1.54	1.34	1.20	1.13	30
31	2.13	1.93	1.74	1.60	1.46	1.26	1.12	1.04	31
32	2.05	1.85	1.66	1.51	1.37	1.18	1.04	.97	32
33	1.97	1.77	1.58	1.44	1.30	1.11	.97	.90	33
34	1.89	1.70	1.51	1.37	1.23	1.04	.91	.84	34
35	1.82	1.63	1.44	1.30	1.16	.98	.85	.78	35
36	1.75	1.56	1.38	1.24	1.10	.92	.79	.73	36
37	1.69	1.50	1.32	1.18	1.05	.87	.74	.68	37
38	1.63	1.44	1.26	1.13	1.00	.82	.70	.63	38
39	1.58	1.39	1.21	1.08	.95	.77	.65	.59	39
40	1.52	1.34	1.17	1.03	.90	.73	.61	.55	40
41	1.48	1.29	1.12	.99	.86	.69	.57	.52	41
42	1.43	1.25	1.08	.94	.82	.65	.54	.48	42
43	1.38	1.20	1.03	.90	.78	.62	.51	.45	43
44	1.34	1.17	.99	.87	.74	.58	.48	.42	44
45	1.30	1.13	.96	.83	.71	.55	.45	.40	45
46	1.26	1.09	.92	.80	.68	.52	.42	.37	46
47	1.23	1.06	.89	.77	.65	.50	.40	.35	47
48	1.19	1.02	.86	.74	.62	.47	.37	.32	48
49	1.16	.99	.83	.71	.59	.45	.35	.30	49
50	1.13	.96	.80	.68	.57	.42	.33	.28	50
51	1.10	.93	.78	.66	.54	.40	.31	.27	51
52	1.07	.91	.75	.63	.52	.38	.29	.25	52
53	1.04	.88	.73	.61	.50	.36	.28	.23	53
54	1.02	.86	.70	.59	.48	.35	.26	.22	54
55	.99	.83	.68	.57	.46	.33	.25	.21	55
56	.97	.81	.66	.55	.44	.31	.23	.19	56
57	.95	.79	.64	.53	.43	.30	.22	.18	57
58	.93	.77	.62	.51	.41	.28	.21	.17	58
59	.90	.75	.60	.50	.39	.27	.20	.16	59
60	.88	.73	.58	.48	.38	.26	.19	.15	60

135

Table 6.11. $\frac{\beta}{8}d$ for Iowa Type L probability. Present-worth group-basis depreciation annuities for left-moded dispersions, average lives from 5 to 60 years, and associated MAR of 8%.

Average Life (Years)	Type of Retirement Dispersion								Average Life (Years)
	L_0	$L_{\frac{1}{2}}$	L_1	$L_{1\frac{1}{2}}$	L_2	L_3	L_4	L_5	
5	18.69	18.44	18.19	18.01	17.83	17.54	17.31	17.21	5
6	15.26	15.01	14.76	14.57	14.40	14.10	13.88	13.77	6
7	12.83	12.57	12.32	12.14	11.96	11.67	11.45	11.34	7
8	11.01	10.76	10.51	10.32	10.14	9.85	9.63	9.53	8
9	9.61	9.35	9.10	8.92	8.73	8.45	8.23	8.13	9
10	8.49	8.24	7.99	7.80	7.62	7.34	7.12	7.02	10
11	7.59	7.33	7.08	6.90	6.72	6.44	6.22	6.12	11
12	6.84	6.58	6.34	6.15	5.97	5.69	5.48	5.38	12
13	6.21	5.95	5.71	5.52	5.34	5.07	4.86	4.76	13
14	5.67	5.42	5.18	4.99	4.81	4.54	4.33	4.23	14
15	5.21	4.96	4.72	4.53	4.36	4.08	3.88	3.78	15
16	4.81	4.56	4.32	4.14	3.96	3.69	3.50	3.40	16
17	4.46	4.22	3.98	3.79	3.62	3.35	3.16	3.06	17
18	4.16	3.91	3.67	3.49	3.31	3.05	2.86	2.76	18
19	3.88	3.64	3.40	3.22	3.05	2.79	2.60	2.51	19
20	3.64	3.39	3.16	2.98	2.81	2.55	2.37	2.28	20
21	3.42	3.18	2.95	2.77	2.60	2.34	2.16	2.07	21
22	3.22	2.98	2.75	2.58	2.41	2.16	1.98	1.89	22
23	3.04	2.81	2.58	2.40	2.23	1.99	1.82	1.73	23
24	2.88	2.64	2.42	2.25	2.08	1.84	1.67	1.58	24
25	2.73	2.50	2.28	2.10	1.94	1.70	1.53	1.45	25
26	2.60	2.37	2.14	1.97	1.81	1.58	1.41	1.33	26
27	2.47	2.24	2.02	1.86	1.69	1.46	1.30	1.22	27
28	2.36	2.13	1.91	1.75	1.59	1.36	1.20	1.12	28
29	2.25	2.03	1.81	1.65	1.49	1.27	1.11	1.03	29
30	2.15	1.93	1.72	1.56	1.40	1.18	1.03	.95	30
31	2.06	1.84	1.63	1.47	1.31	1.10	.95	.88	31
32	1.98	1.76	1.55	1.39	1.24	1.03	.88	.81	32
33	1.90	1.68	1.48	1.32	1.17	.96	.82	.75	33
34	1.82	1.61	1.41	1.25	1.10	.90	.76	.69	34
35	1.76	1.54	1.34	1.19	1.04	.84	.71	.64	35
36	1.69	1.48	1.28	1.13	.98	.79	.66	.59	36
37	1.63	1.42	1.23	1.08	.93	.74	.61	.55	37
38	1.57	1.37	1.17	1.03	.88	.70	.57	.51	38
39	1.52	1.32	1.12	.98	.84	.65	.53	.47	39
40	1.47	1.27	1.08	.93	.79	.61	.50	.44	40
41	1.42	1.23	1.03	.89	.75	.58	.46	.41	41
42	1.38	1.18	1.00	.85	.72	.54	.43	.38	42
43	1.33	1.14	.95	.82	.68	.51	.40	.35	43
44	1.29	1.10	.92	.78	.65	.48	.38	.33	44
45	1.25	1.06	.88	.75	.62	.46	.35	.30	45
46	1.22	1.03	.85	.72	.59	.43	.33	.28	46
47	1.18	1.00	.82	.69	.56	.41	.31	.26	47
48	1.15	.97	.79	.66	.54	.38	.29	.24	48
49	1.12	.94	.76	.64	.51	.36	.27	.23	49
50	1.09	.91	.74	.61	.49	.34	.25	.21	50
51	1.06	.88	.71	.59	.47	.33	.24	.20	51
52	1.03	.86	.69	.57	.45	.31	.22	.18	52
53	1.00	.83	.66	.55	.43	.29	.21	.17	53
54	.98	.81	.64	.53	.41	.28	.20	.16	54
55	.95	.79	.62	.51	.39	.26	.18	.15	55
56	.93	.76	.60	.49	.38	.25	.17	.14	56
57	.91	.74	.58	.47	.36	.24	.16	.13	57
58	.89	.72	.57	.46	.35	.22	.15	.12	58
59	.87	.71	.55	.44	.33	.21	.14	.11	59
60	.85	.69	.53	.43	.32	.20	.14	.10	60

Table 6.12. $\overset{\beta}{_5}d$ for Iowa Type S probability. Present-worth group-basis depreciation annuities for symmetrical dispersions, average lives from 5 to 60 years, and associated MAR of 5%.

Average Life (Years)	SC	$S_{-\frac{1}{2}}$	S_0	$S_{\frac{1}{2}}$	S_1	$S_{1\frac{1}{2}}$	S_2	S_3	S_4	S_5	S_6	Average Life (Years)
					Type of Retirement Dispersion							
5	18.98	18.83	18.68	18.58	18.49	18.42	18.35	18.26	18.18	18.14	18.12	5
6	15.58	15.43	15.28	15.18	15.09	15.02	14.95	14.86	14.78	14.74	14.72	6
7	13.16	13.01	12.86	12.76	12.67	12.60	12.53	12.43	12.36	12.32	12.30	7
8	11.35	11.20	11.05	10.95	10.86	10.79	10.72	10.62	10.55	10.51	10.49	8
9	9.95	9.80	9.65	9.55	9.45	9.38	9.31	9.22	9.15	9.11	9.08	9
10	8.84	8.68	8.53	8.43	8.33	8.26	8.19	8.10	8.03	7.99	7.97	10
11	7.93	7.77	7.62	7.52	7.42	7.35	7.28	7.19	7.11	7.07	7.05	11
12	7.17	7.02	6.86	6.76	6.66	6.59	6.52	6.43	6.36	6.32	6.30	12
13	6.54	6.38	6.22	6.12	6.03	5.96	5.89	5.79	5.72	5.68	5.66	13
14	6.00	5.84	5.68	5.58	5.48	5.41	5.34	5.25	5.18	5.14	5.12	14
15	5.53	5.37	5.21	5.11	5.01	4.94	4.87	4.78	4.71	4.67	4.65	15
16	5.13	4.96	4.80	4.70	4.61	4.53	4.46	4.37	4.30	4.26	4.24	16
17	4.77	4.60	4.44	4.34	4.25	4.18	4.11	4.01	3.94	3.90	3.88	17
18	4.45	4.29	4.13	4.03	3.93	3.86	3.79	3.70	3.63	3.59	3.57	18
19	4.17	4.01	3.85	3.75	3.65	3.58	3.51	3.42	3.35	3.31	3.29	19
20	3.92	3.76	3.59	3.50	3.40	3.33	3.26	3.17	3.10	3.06	3.04	20
21	3.70	3.53	3.37	3.27	3.17	3.10	3.03	2.94	2.87	2.83	2.81	21
22	3.50	3.33	3.17	3.06	2.97	2.90	2.83	2.74	2.67	2.63	2.61	22
23	3.31	3.14	2.98	2.88	2.78	2.71	2.64	2.55	2.48	2.45	2.43	23
24	3.14	2.97	2.81	2.71	2.61	2.54	2.47	2.39	2.32	2.28	2.26	24
25	2.99	2.82	2.66	2.56	2.46	2.39	2.32	2.23	2.16	2.13	2.11	25
26	2.85	2.68	2.52	2.41	2.32	2.25	2.18	2.09	2.02	1.99	1.97	26
27	2.72	2.55	2.39	2.29	2.19	2.12	2.05	1.96	1.90	1.86	1.84	27
28	2.60	2.43	2.27	2.17	2.07	2.00	1.93	1.85	1.78	1.74	1.72	28
29	2.49	2.32	2.16	2.06	1.96	1.89	1.82	1.74	1.67	1.63	1.62	29
30	2.39	2.22	2.05	1.95	1.86	1.79	1.72	1.64	1.57	1.53	1.52	30
31	2.29	2.12	1.96	1.86	1.76	1.70	1.63	1.54	1.48	1.44	1.42	31
32	2.21	2.03	1.87	1.77	1.68	1.61	1.54	1.46	1.39	1.36	1.34	32
33	2.12	1.95	1.79	1.69	1.59	1.53	1.46	1.38	1.31	1.28	1.26	33
34	2.05	1.88	1.71	1.61	1.52	1.45	1.38	1.30	1.24	1.20	1.19	34
35	1.98	1.80	1.64	1.54	1.45	1.38	1.32	1.23	1.17	1.13	1.12	35
36	1.91	1.74	1.57	1.47	1.38	1.31	1.25	1.17	1.10	1.07	1.05	36
37	1.84	1.67	1.51	1.41	1.32	1.25	1.19	1.10	1.04	1.01	.99	37
38	1.79	1.61	1.45	1.35	1.26	1.19	1.13	1.05	.99	.95	.94	38
39	1.73	1.56	1.40	1.30	1.20	1.14	1.08	1.00	.93	.90	.89	39
40	1.68	1.50	1.34	1.25	1.15	1.09	1.03	.94	.88	.85	.84	40
41	1.63	1.45	1.29	1.20	1.10	1.04	.98	.90	.84	.81	.79	41
42	1.58	1.41	1.25	1.15	1.06	.99	.93	.85	.79	.76	.75	42
43	1.53	1.36	1.20	1.11	1.01	.95	.89	.81	.75	.72	.71	43
44	1.49	1.32	1.16	1.07	.97	.91	.85	.77	.72	.69	.67	44
45	1.45	1.28	1.12	1.03	.93	.87	.81	.74	.68	.65	.64	45
46	1.41	1.24	1.08	.99	.90	.84	.78	.70	.64	.62	.60	46
47	1.38	1.21	1.05	.95	.86	.80	.74	.67	.61	.58	.57	47
48	1.34	1.17	1.01	.92	.83	.77	.71	.64	.58	.55	.54	48
49	1.31	1.14	.98	.89	.80	.74	.68	.61	.55	.53	.51	49
50	1.28	1.11	.95	.86	.77	.71	.65	.58	.53	.50	.49	50
51	1.25	1.08	.92	.83	.74	.68	.62	.55	.50	.47	.46	51
52	1.22	1.05	.89	.80	.72	.66	.60	.53	.48	.45	.44	52
53	1.19	1.02	.87	.78	.69	.63	.57	.50	.45	.43	.42	53
54	1.16	1.00	.84	.75	.67	.61	.55	.48	.43	.41	.39	54
55	1.14	.97	.82	.73	.64	.59	.53	.46	.41	.39	.37	55
56	1.11	.95	.79	.71	.62	.56	.51	.44	.39	.37	.36	56
57	1.09	.93	.77	.68	.60	.54	.49	.42	.37	.35	.34	57
58	1.07	.91	.75	.66	.58	.52	.47	.40	.36	.33	.32	58
59	1.05	.88	.73	.64	.56	.50	.45	.39	.34	.32	.30	59
60	1.03	.86	.71	.62	.54	.49	.43	.37	.32	.30	.29	60

Table 6.13. $\overset{\beta}{_c}d$ for Iowa Type S probability. Present-worth group-basis depreciation annuities for symmetrical dispersions, average lives from 5 to 60 years, and associated MAR of 6%.

Average Life (Years)	SC	$S_{-\frac{1}{2}}$	S_0	$S_{\frac{1}{2}}$	S_1	$S_{1\frac{1}{2}}$	S_2	S_3	S_4	S_5	S_6	Average Life (Years)
5	18.80	18.62	18.43	18.32	18.21	18.12	18.04	17.93	17.84	17.79	17.76	5
6	15.40	15.21	15.03	14.91	14.80	14.72	14.63	14.52	14.43	14.38	14.36	6
7	12.98	12.79	12.61	12.49	12.38	12.29	12.21	12.10	12.01	11.96	11.93	7
8	11.17	10.98	10.80	10.68	10.56	10.48	10.40	10.29	10.20	10.15	10.12	8
9	9.77	9.58	9.39	9.28	9.16	9.08	8.99	8.88	8.79	8.75	8.72	9
10	8.66	8.47	8.28	8.16	8.05	7.96	7.88	7.77	7.68	7.63	7.61	10
11	7.75	7.56	7.37	7.25	7.14	7.05	6.97	6.86	6.77	6.72	6.70	11
12	7.00	6.81	6.62	6.50	6.38	6.30	6.21	6.10	6.02	5.97	5.95	12
13	6.37	6.18	5.99	5.87	5.75	5.67	5.58	5.47	5.38	5.34	5.31	13
14	5.84	5.64	5.45	5.33	5.21	5.13	5.04	4.93	4.85	4.80	4.78	14
15	5.38	5.18	4.99	4.87	4.75	4.66	4.58	4.47	4.38	4.34	4.31	15
16	4.97	4.78	4.58	4.46	4.34	4.26	4.18	4.07	3.98	3.93	3.91	16
17	4.62	4.42	4.23	4.11	3.99	3.91	3.82	3.71	3.63	3.58	3.56	17
18	4.31	4.11	3.92	3.80	3.68	3.60	3.51	3.40	3.32	3.27	3.25	18
19	4.04	3.84	3.64	3.52	3.41	3.32	3.24	3.13	3.05	3.00	2.98	19
20	3.79	3.59	3.40	3.28	3.16	3.07	2.99	2.88	2.80	2.76	2.73	20
21	3.58	3.37	3.18	3.05	2.94	2.85	2.77	2.66	2.58	2.54	2.52	21
22	3.38	3.17	2.98	2.86	2.74	2.65	2.57	2.47	2.39	2.34	2.32	22
23	3.20	2.99	2.80	2.67	2.56	2.48	2.39	2.29	2.21	2.16	2.14	23
24	3.03	2.83	2.63	2.51	2.40	2.31	2.23	2.13	2.05	2.00	1.98	24
25	2.88	2.68	2.48	2.36	2.25	2.17	2.08	1.98	1.90	1.86	1.84	25
26	2.75	2.54	2.35	2.23	2.11	2.03	1.95	1.85	1.77	1.73	1.70	26
27	2.62	2.42	2.22	2.10	1.99	1.91	1.83	1.72	1.64	1.60	1.58	27
28	2.51	2.30	2.11	1.99	1.87	1.79	1.71	1.61	1.53	1.49	1.47	28
29	2.40	2.20	2.00	1.88	1.77	1.69	1.61	1.51	1.43	1.39	1.37	29
30	2.30	2.10	1.90	1.78	1.67	1.59	1.51	1.41	1.34	1.30	1.28	30
31	2.21	2.01	1.81	1.69	1.58	1.50	1.42	1.32	1.25	1.21	1.19	31
32	2.13	1.92	1.73	1.61	1.50	1.42	1.34	1.24	1.17	1.13	1.11	32
33	2.05	1.84	1.65	1.53	1.42	1.34	1.26	1.17	1.10	1.06	1.04	33
34	1.97	1.77	1.57	1.46	1.35	1.27	1.19	1.10	1.03	.99	.97	34
35	1.91	1.70	1.51	1.39	1.28	1.20	1.13	1.04	.96	.93	.91	35
36	1.84	1.64	1.44	1.33	1.22	1.14	1.07	.97	.91	.87	.85	36
37	1.78	1.58	1.38	1.27	1.16	1.08	1.01	.92	.85	.81	.80	37
38	1.72	1.52	1.33	1.21	1.11	1.03	.96	.87	.80	.76	.75	38
39	1.67	1.47	1.27	1.16	1.05	.98	.91	.82	.75	.72	.70	39
40	1.62	1.42	1.22	1.11	1.01	.93	.86	.77	.71	.67	.66	40
41	1.57	1.37	1.18	1.07	.96	.89	.82	.73	.67	.63	.62	41
42	1.53	1.32	1.13	1.03	.92	.85	.78	.69	.63	.59	.58	42
43	1.48	1.28	1.09	.98	.88	.81	.74	.65	.59	.56	.54	43
44	1.44	1.24	1.05	.95	.84	.77	.70	.62	.56	.53	.51	44
45	1.40	1.21	1.02	.91	.81	.74	.67	.59	.53	.49	.48	45
46	1.37	1.17	.98	.88	.77	.70	.64	.55	.50	.47	.45	46
47	1.33	1.14	.95	.84	.74	.67	.61	.53	.47	.44	.42	47
48	1.30	1.11	.92	.81	.71	.64	.58	.50	.44	.41	.40	48
49	1.27	1.07	.89	.78	.68	.62	.55	.47	.42	.39	.37	49
50	1.24	1.04	.86	.76	.66	.59	.53	.45	.39	.37	.35	50
51	1.21	1.02	.83	.73	.63	.57	.50	.43	.37	.35	.33	51
52	1.18	.99	.81	.70	.61	.54	.48	.40	.35	.33	.31	52
53	1.16	.96	.78	.68	.58	.52	.46	.38	.33	.31	.29	53
54	1.13	.94	.76	.66	.56	.50	.44	.37	.31	.29	.28	54
55	1.11	.92	.74	.64	.54	.48	.42	.35	.30	.27	.26	55
56	1.08	.90	.71	.62	.52	.46	.40	.33	.28	.26	.25	56
57	1.06	.87	.70	.60	.50	.44	.38	.31	.27	.24	.23	57
58	1.04	.85	.68	.58	.49	.42	.37	.30	.25	.23	.22	58
59	1.02	.83	.66	.56	.47	.41	.35	.28	.24	.22	.21	59
60	1.00	.81	.64	.54	.45	.39	.34	.27	.23	.20	.19	60

Table 6.14. $\frac{\beta}{7}d$ for Iowa Type S probability. Present-worth group-basis depreciation annuities for symmetrical dispersions, average lives from 5 to 60 years, and associated MAR of 7%.

Average Life (Years)	SC	$S_{-\frac{1}{2}}$	S_0	$S_{\frac{1}{2}}$	S_1	$S_{1\frac{1}{2}}$	S_2	S_3	S_4	S_5	S_6	Average Life (Years)
					Type of Retirement Dispersion							
5	18.64	18.42	18.20	18.07	17.94	17.84	17.74	17.61	17.50	17.45	17.41	5
6	15.23	15.00	14.79	14.65	14.52	14.42	14.33	14.20	14.09	14.03	14.01	6
7	12.80	12.58	12.37	12.23	12.10	12.00	11.90	11.77	11.66	11.61	11.58	7
8	11.00	10.78	10.56	10.42	10.28	10.19	10.09	9.96	9.85	9.80	9.77	8
9	9.60	9.38	9.16	9.02	8.88	8.79	8.69	8.56	8.45	8.40	8.37	9
10	8.49	8.27	8.05	7.91	7.77	7.67	7.57	7.44	7.34	7.29	7.26	10
11	7.59	7.37	7.14	7.00	6.87	6.77	6.67	6.54	6.44	6.38	6.36	11
12	6.85	6.62	6.40	6.26	6.12	6.02	5.92	5.79	5.69	5.64	5.61	12
13	6.23	5.99	5.77	5.63	5.49	5.39	5.30	5.17	5.07	5.01	4.98	13
14	5.70	5.46	5.24	5.10	4.96	4.86	4.76	4.63	4.53	4.48	4.45	14
15	5.24	5.00	4.78	4.64	4.50	4.40	4.31	4.18	4.08	4.03	4.00	15
16	4.84	4.61	4.38	4.24	4.10	4.01	3.91	3.78	3.68	3.63	3.60	16
17	4.50	4.26	4.03	3.89	3.76	3.66	3.56	3.44	3.34	3.29	3.26	17
18	4.19	3.96	3.73	3.59	3.45	3.35	3.26	3.13	3.04	2.98	2.96	18
19	3.92	3.69	3.46	3.32	3.18	3.09	2.99	2.87	2.77	2.72	2.69	19
20	3.69	3.45	3.22	3.08	2.94	2.85	2.75	2.63	2.53	2.48	2.46	20
21	3.47	3.23	3.00	2.86	2.73	2.63	2.54	2.41	2.32	2.27	2.25	21
22	3.28	3.04	2.81	2.67	2.53	2.44	2.34	2.22	2.13	2.08	2.06	22
23	3.10	2.86	2.63	2.49	2.36	2.26	2.17	2.05	1.96	1.91	1.89	23
24	2.94	2.70	2.47	2.33	2.20	2.11	2.01	1.90	1.81	1.76	1.73	24
25	2.80	2.56	2.33	2.19	2.06	1.96	1.87	1.76	1.67	1.62	1.60	25
26	2.67	2.43	2.20	2.06	1.93	1.84	1.74	1.63	1.54	1.49	1.47	26
27	2.55	2.31	2.08	1.94	1.81	1.72	1.63	1.51	1.43	1.38	1.36	27
28	2.43	2.19	1.97	1.83	1.70	1.61	1.52	1.41	1.32	1.28	1.25	28
29	2.33	2.09	1.87	1.73	1.60	1.51	1.42	1.31	1.22	1.18	1.16	29
30	2.24	2.00	1.77	1.64	1.51	1.42	1.33	1.22	1.14	1.09	1.07	30
31	2.15	1.91	1.68	1.55	1.42	1.33	1.25	1.14	1.06	1.01	.99	31
32	2.07	1.83	1.60	1.47	1.34	1.26	1.17	1.06	.98	.94	.92	32
33	1.99	1.75	1.53	1.40	1.27	1.18	1.10	.99	.91	.87	.85	33
34	1.92	1.68	1.46	1.33	1.20	1.12	1.03	.93	.85	.81	.79	34
35	1.85	1.62	1.40	1.27	1.14	1.05	.97	.87	.79	.75	.74	35
36	1.79	1.56	1.33	1.20	1.08	1.00	.91	.81	.74	.70	.68	36
37	1.73	1.50	1.28	1.15	1.03	.94	.86	.76	.69	.65	.64	37
38	1.68	1.44	1.22	1.10	.98	.89	.81	.72	.64	.61	.59	38
39	1.63	1.40	1.17	1.05	.93	.85	.77	.67	.60	.57	.55	39
40	1.58	1.35	1.13	1.00	.88	.81	.73	.63	.56	.53	.51	40
41	1.53	1.30	1.09	.96	.84	.76	.69	.59	.53	.49	.48	41
42	1.49	1.26	1.04	.92	.80	.73	.65	.56	.49	.46	.44	42
43	1.45	1.22	1.00	.88	.77	.69	.62	.53	.46	.43	.41	43
44	1.41	1.18	.97	.85	.73	.66	.58	.49	.43	.40	.39	44
45	1.37	1.15	.93	.82	.70	.63	.55	.47	.40	.37	.36	45
46	1.34	1.11	.90	.78	.67	.60	.52	.44	.38	.35	.34	46
47	1.30	1.08	.87	.75	.64	.57	.50	.41	.36	.33	.31	47
48	1.27	1.05	.84	.73	.61	.54	.47	.39	.33	.31	.29	48
49	1.24	1.02	.81	.70	.59	.52	.45	.37	.31	.29	.27	49
50	1.21	.99	.79	.67	.56	.50	.43	.35	.29	.27	.25	50
51	1.19	.97	.76	.65	.54	.47	.41	.33	.28	.25	.24	51
52	1.16	.94	.74	.63	.52	.45	.39	.31	.26	.23	.22	52
53	1.13	.92	.72	.61	.50	.43	.37	.29	.24	.22	.21	53
54	1.11	.90	.69	.59	.48	.41	.35	.28	.23	.20	.19	54
55	1.09	.87	.67	.57	.46	.40	.33	.26	.21	.19	.18	55
56	1.06	.85	.65	.55	.45	.38	.32	.25	.20	.18	.17	56
57	1.04	.83	.63	.53	.43	.37	.30	.23	.19	.17	.16	57
58	1.02	.81	.62	.51	.41	.35	.29	.22	.18	.16	.15	58
59	1.00	.79	.60	.50	.40	.34	.28	.21	.17	.15	.14	59
60	.98	.78	.58	.48	.38	.32	.26	.20	.16	.14	.13	60

139

Table 6.15. $^\beta_8 d$ for Iowa Type S probability. Present-worth group-basis depreciation annuities for symmetrical dispersions, average lives from 5 to 60 years, and associated MAR of 8%.

Average Life (Years)	SC	$S_{-\frac{1}{2}}$	S_0	$S_{\frac{1}{2}}$	S_1	$S_{1\frac{1}{2}}$	S_2	S_3	S_4	S_5	S_6	Average Life (Years)
5	18.48	18.25	18.02	17.86	17.71	17.60	17.49	17.34	17.22	17.15	17.13	5
6	15.06	14.82	14.59	14.43	14.28	14.17	14.06	13.91	13.79	13.72	13.69	6
7	12.64	12.40	12.16	12.00	11.85	11.73	11.62	11.47	11.35	11.29	11.26	7
8	10.84	10.59	10.35	10.19	10.03	9.92	9.81	9.66	9.54	9.48	9.44	8
9	9.45	9.19	8.95	8.79	8.63	8.52	8.41	8.26	8.14	8.08	8.05	9
10	8.34	8.09	7.84	7.68	7.52	7.41	7.30	7.15	7.03	6.97	6.94	10
11	7.45	7.19	6.94	6.78	6.62	6.51	6.40	6.25	6.13	6.07	6.04	11
12	6.71	6.45	6.20	6.04	5.88	5.77	5.65	5.51	5.39	5.33	5.30	12
13	6.09	5.83	5.57	5.41	5.26	5.14	5.03	4.89	4.77	4.71	4.68	13
14	5.57	5.30	5.05	4.89	4.73	4.62	4.51	4.36	4.25	4.19	4.16	14
15	5.12	4.85	4.59	4.43	4.28	4.16	4.05	3.91	3.80	3.74	3.71	15
16	4.73	4.46	4.20	4.04	3.89	3.77	3.66	3.52	3.41	3.35	3.32	16
17	4.39	4.12	3.86	3.70	3.55	3.43	3.32	3.18	3.07	3.02	2.99	17
18	4.09	3.82	3.56	3.40	3.25	3.14	3.03	2.89	2.78	2.72	2.69	18
19	3.83	3.56	3.30	3.14	2.98	2.87	2.76	2.63	2.52	2.46	2.44	19
20	3.59	3.32	3.06	2.90	2.75	2.64	2.53	2.39	2.29	2.23	2.21	20
21	3.38	3.11	2.85	2.69	2.54	2.43	2.33	2.19	2.09	2.03	2.00	21
22	3.20	2.92	2.66	2.50	2.35	2.24	2.14	2.01	1.90	1.85	1.82	22
23	3.03	2.75	2.49	2.34	2.18	2.08	1.97	1.84	1.74	1.69	1.66	23
24	2.87	2.60	2.34	2.18	2.03	1.93	1.82	1.69	1.59	1.54	1.52	24
25	2.73	2.46	2.20	2.04	1.89	1.79	1.69	1.56	1.46	1.41	1.39	25
26	2.60	2.33	2.07	1.92	1.77	1.67	1.56	1.44	1.34	1.29	1.27	26
27	2.48	2.21	1.95	1.80	1.65	1.55	1.45	1.33	1.23	1.19	1.16	27
28	2.38	2.11	1.85	1.70	1.55	1.45	1.35	1.23	1.14	1.09	1.07	28
29	2.28	2.01	1.75	1.60	1.46	1.36	1.26	1.14	1.05	1.00	.98	29
30	2.18	1.92	1.66	1.51	1.37	1.27	1.17	1.05	.97	.92	.90	30
31	2.10	1.83	1.58	1.43	1.29	1.19	1.10	.98	.89	.85	.83	31
32	2.02	1.75	1.50	1.35	1.21	1.12	1.02	.91	.82	.78	.76	32
33	1.95	1.68	1.43	1.28	1.14	1.05	.96	.84	.76	.72	.70	33
34	1.88	1.61	1.36	1.22	1.08	.99	.90	.79	.71	.66	.64	34
35	1.81	1.55	1.30	1.16	1.02	.93	.84	.73	.65	.61	.59	35
36	1.75	1.49	1.24	1.10	.97	.88	.79	.68	.61	.57	.55	36
37	1.70	1.44	1.19	1.05	.92	.83	.74	.64	.56	.52	.51	37
38	1.65	1.39	1.14	1.00	.87	.78	.70	.59	.52	.48	.47	38
39	1.60	1.34	1.09	.96	.83	.74	.65	.55	.48	.45	.43	39
40	1.55	1.29	1.05	.92	.78	.70	.62	.52	.45	.41	.40	40
41	1.50	1.25	1.01	.88	.75	.66	.58	.48	.42	.38	.37	41
42	1.46	1.21	.97	.84	.71	.63	.55	.45	.39	.35	.34	42
43	1.42	1.17	.93	.80	.68	.60	.52	.42	.36	.33	.31	43
44	1.38	1.14	.90	.77	.65	.57	.49	.40	.34	.30	.29	44
45	1.35	1.10	.87	.74	.62	.54	.46	.37	.31	.28	.27	45
46	1.32	1.07	.84	.71	.59	.51	.44	.35	.29	.26	.25	46
47	1.28	1.04	.81	.68	.56	.49	.41	.33	.27	.24	.23	47
48	1.25	1.01	.78	.66	.54	.46	.39	.31	.25	.23	.21	48
49	1.22	.98	.75	.63	.51	.44	.37	.29	.23	.21	.20	49
50	1.19	.96	.73	.61	.49	.42	.35	.27	.22	.19	.18	50
51	1.17	.93	.71	.59	.47	.40	.33	.26	.20	.18	.17	51
52	1.14	.91	.68	.57	.45	.38	.32	.24	.19	.17	.16	52
53	1.12	.88	.66	.55	.43	.37	.30	.23	.18	.16	.14	53
54	1.09	.86	.64	.53	.42	.35	.28	.21	.17	.14	.13	54
55	1.07	.84	.62	.51	.40	.33	.27	.20	.15	.13	.12	55
56	1.05	.82	.60	.49	.38	.32	.26	.19	.14	.12	.12	56
57	1.03	.80	.59	.48	.37	.31	.24	.18	.14	.12	.11	57
58	1.01	.78	.57	.46	.36	.29	.23	.17	.13	.11	.10	58
59	.99	.77	.55	.45	.34	.28	.22	.16	.12	.10	.09	59
60	.97	.75	.54	.43	.33	.27	.21	.15	.11	.09	.08	60

140

Table 6.16. $\beta_5 d$ for Iowa Type R probability. Present-worth group-basis depreciation annuities for right-moded dispersions, average lives from 5 to 60 years, and associated MAR of 5%.

Average Life (Years)	Type of Retirement Dispersion									Average Life (Years)
	$R_{\frac{1}{2}}$	R_1	$R_{1\frac{1}{2}}$	R_2	$R_{2\frac{1}{2}}$	R_3	R_4	R_5	SQ	
5	18.83	18.67	18.56	18.46	18.38	18.30	18.21	18.15	18.10	5
6	15.43	15.28	15.17	15.06	14.98	14.90	14.81	14.75	14.70	6
7	13.00	12.85	12.74	12.64	12.56	12.48	12.39	12.33	12.28	7
8	11.20	11.04	10.94	10.83	10.75	10.67	10.58	10.52	10.47	8
9	9.80	9.65	9.53	9.43	9.35	9.27	9.18	9.11	9.07	9
10	8.68	8.53	8.41	8.30	8.23	8.15	8.06	8.00	7.95	10
11	7.77	7.61	7.50	7.40	7.32	7.24	7.15	7.08	7.04	11
12	7.01	6.86	6.75	6.64	6.56	6.48	6.39	6.33	6.28	12
13	6.38	6.22	6.11	6.00	5.92	5.85	5.75	5.69	5.65	13
14	5.84	5.68	5.57	5.46	5.38	5.30	5.21	5.15	5.10	14
15	5.37	5.21	5.10	4.99	4.91	4.83	4.74	4.68	4.63	15
16	4.96	4.81	4.69	4.58	4.50	4.43	4.33	4.27	4.23	16
17	4.61	4.45	4.34	4.23	4.15	4.07	3.98	3.91	3.87	17
18	4.29	4.13	4.02	3.91	3.83	3.75	3.66	3.60	3.55	18
19	4.01	3.85	3.74	3.63	3.55	3.47	3.38	3.32	3.27	19
20	3.76	3.60	3.49	3.38	3.30	3.22	3.13	3.07	3.02	20
21	3.53	3.38	3.26	3.15	3.07	3.00	2.90	2.84	2.80	21
22	3.33	3.17	3.06	2.95	2.87	2.79	2.70	2.64	2.60	22
23	3.15	2.99	2.88	2.77	2.69	2.61	2.52	2.46	2.41	23
24	2.98	2.82	2.71	2.60	2.52	2.44	2.35	2.29	2.25	24
25	2.83	2.67	2.56	2.45	2.37	2.29	2.20	2.14	2.10	25
26	2.69	2.53	2.42	2.31	2.23	2.15	2.06	2.00	1.96	26
27	2.56	2.40	2.29	2.18	2.10	2.02	1.93	1.87	1.83	27
28	2.44	2.28	2.17	2.06	1.98	1.90	1.81	1.75	1.71	28
29	2.33	2.17	2.06	1.95	1.87	1.79	1.70	1.64	1.60	29
30	2.23	2.07	1.96	1.85	1.77	1.69	1.60	1.54	1.51	30
31	2.13	1.98	1.87	1.76	1.68	1.60	1.51	1.45	1.41	31
32	2.04	1.89	1.78	1.67	1.59	1.51	1.42	1.37	1.33	32
33	1.96	1.81	1.70	1.59	1.51	1.43	1.34	1.29	1.25	33
34	1.89	1.73	1.62	1.51	1.44	1.36	1.27	1.21	1.18	34
35	1.82	1.66	1.55	1.44	1.37	1.29	1.20	1.14	1.11	35
36	1.75	1.60	1.49	1.38	1.30	1.22	1.14	1.08	1.04	36
37	1.69	1.53	1.42	1.32	1.24	1.16	1.08	1.02	.98	37
38	1.63	1.48	1.37	1.26	1.18	1.11	1.02	.96	.93	38
39	1.57	1.42	1.31	1.21	1.13	1.05	.97	.91	.88	39
40	1.52	1.37	1.26	1.15	1.08	1.00	.92	.86	.83	40
41	1.47	1.32	1.21	1.11	1.03	.96	.87	.82	.78	41
42	1.42	1.28	1.17	1.06	.99	.91	.83	.77	.74	42
43	1.38	1.23	1.12	1.02	.94	.87	.79	.73	.70	43
44	1.34	1.19	1.08	.98	.90	.83	.75	.69	.66	44
45	1.30	1.15	1.05	.94	.87	.79	.71	.66	.63	45
46	1.26	1.12	1.01	.91	.83	.76	.68	.63	.59	46
47	1.22	1.08	.97	.87	.80	.73	.64	.59	.56	47
48	1.19	1.05	.94	.84	.77	.69	.61	.56	.53	48
49	1.16	1.02	.91	.81	.74	.67	.59	.53	.50	49
50	1.13	.99	.88	.78	.71	.64	.56	.51	.48	50
51	1.10	.96	.85	.75	.68	.61	.53	.48	.45	51
52	1.07	.93	.83	.73	.66	.59	.51	.46	.43	52
53	1.04	.91	.80	.70	.63	.56	.48	.44	.41	53
54	1.02	.88	.78	.68	.61	.54	.46	.41	.39	54
55	.99	.86	.76	.66	.59	.52	.44	.39	.37	55
56	.97	.84	.73	.64	.57	.50	.42	.38	.35	56
57	.95	.81	.71	.62	.55	.48	.40	.36	.33	57
58	.93	.79	.69	.60	.53	.46	.39	.34	.31	58
59	.91	.77	.67	.58	.51	.44	.37	.32	.30	59
60	.89	.75	.66	.56	.49	.43	.35	.31	.28	60

Table 6.17. $_6^\beta d$ for Iowa Type R probability. Present-worth group-basis depreciation annuities for right-moded dispersions, average lives from 5 to 60 years, and associated MAR of 6%.

Average Life (Years)	Type of Retirement Dispersion									Average Life (Years)
	$R_{\frac{1}{2}}$	R_1	$R_{1\frac{1}{2}}$	R_2	$R_{2\frac{1}{2}}$	R_3	R_4	R_5	SQ	
5	18.62	18.43	18.30	18.18	18.08	17.99	17.88	17.81	17.74	5
6	15.21	15.03	14.90	14.77	14.67	14.58	14.47	14.39	14.34	6
7	12.79	12.60	12.47	12.34	12.24	12.15	12.05	11.97	11.91	7
8	10.98	10.79	10.66	10.53	10.44	10.34	10.24	10.16	10.10	8
9	9.58	9.40	9.26	9.13	9.04	8.94	8.83	8.76	8.70	9
10	8.47	8.28	8.15	8.01	7.92	7.83	7.71	7.64	7.59	10
11	7.56	7.37	7.24	7.11	7.01	6.92	6.81	6.73	6.68	11
12	6.81	6.62	6.49	6.35	6.26	6.17	6.06	5.98	5.93	12
13	6.18	5.99	5.86	5.72	5.63	5.54	5.43	5.35	5.30	13
14	5.64	5.45	5.32	5.19	5.09	5.00	4.88	4.81	4.76	14
15	5.18	4.99	4.85	4.72	4.63	4.53	4.42	4.35	4.30	15
16	4.78	4.59	4.45	4.32	4.23	4.13	4.02	3.95	3.90	16
17	4.43	4.24	4.10	3.97	3.87	3.78	3.67	3.60	3.54	17
18	4.12	3.93	3.79	3.66	3.56	3.47	3.36	3.29	3.24	18
19	3.84	3.65	3.52	3.39	3.29	3.20	3.09	3.01	2.96	19
20	3.60	3.41	3.27	3.14	3.05	2.95	2.84	2.77	2.72	20
21	3.38	3.19	3.05	2.92	2.83	2.73	2.62	2.55	2.50	21
22	3.18	2.99	2.86	2.72	2.63	2.53	2.43	2.35	2.30	22
23	3.00	2.81	2.68	2.55	2.45	2.36	2.25	2.18	2.13	23
24	2.84	2.65	2.52	2.38	2.29	2.19	2.09	2.02	1.97	24
25	2.69	2.50	2.37	2.24	2.14	2.05	1.94	1.87	1.82	25
26	2.55	2.37	2.23	2.10	2.01	1.91	1.81	1.74	1.69	26
27	2.43	2.24	2.11	1.98	1.88	1.79	1.69	1.62	1.57	27
28	2.32	2.13	2.00	1.87	1.77	1.68	1.57	1.50	1.46	28
29	2.21	2.03	1.89	1.76	1.67	1.58	1.47	1.40	1.36	29
30	2.11	1.93	1.80	1.67	1.57	1.48	1.38	1.31	1.26	30
31	2.02	1.84	1.71	1.58	1.49	1.40	1.29	1.22	1.18	31
32	1.94	1.76	1.62	1.50	1.40	1.31	1.21	1.14	1.10	32
33	1.86	1.68	1.55	1.42	1.33	1.24	1.14	1.07	1.03	33
34	1.79	1.61	1.48	1.35	1.26	1.17	1.07	1.00	.96	34
35	1.72	1.54	1.41	1.28	1.19	1.10	1.00	.94	.90	35
36	1.66	1.48	1.35	1.22	1.13	1.04	.94	.88	.84	36
37	1.60	1.42	1.29	1.17	1.08	.99	.89	.83	.79	37
38	1.54	1.37	1.24	1.11	1.02	.94	.84	.77	.74	38
39	1.49	1.32	1.19	1.06	.97	.89	.79	.73	.69	39
40	1.44	1.27	1.14	1.02	.93	.84	.74	.68	.65	40
41	1.39	1.22	1.09	.97	.89	.80	.70	.64	.61	41
42	1.35	1.18	1.05	.93	.84	.76	.66	.60	.57	42
43	1.31	1.14	1.01	.89	.81	.72	.63	.57	.53	43
44	1.27	1.10	.98	.85	.77	.69	.59	.54	.50	44
45	1.23	1.07	.94	.82	.74	.65	.56	.50	.47	45
46	1.20	1.03	.91	.79	.70	.62	.53	.47	.44	46
47	1.16	1.00	.88	.76	.68	.59	.50	.45	.41	47
48	1.13	.97	.85	.73	.65	.57	.48	.42	.39	48
49	1.10	.94	.82	.70	.62	.54	.45	.40	.37	49
50	1.07	.91	.79	.68	.60	.52	.43	.37	.34	50
51	1.04	.89	.77	.65	.57	.49	.41	.35	.32	51
52	1.02	.86	.74	.63	.55	.47	.39	.33	.30	52
53	.99	.84	.72	.61	.53	.45	.37	.32	.29	53
54	.97	.81	.70	.59	.51	.43	.35	.30	.27	54
55	.95	.79	.68	.57	.49	.41	.33	.28	.25	55
56	.92	.77	.66	.55	.47	.40	.31	.26	.24	56
57	.90	.75	.64	.53	.45	.38	.30	.25	.22	57
58	.88	.74	.62	.51	.44	.36	.28	.24	.21	58
59	.87	.72	.61	.50	.42	.35	.27	.22	.20	59
60	.85	.70	.59	.48	.41	.33	.26	.21	.19	60

142

Table 6.18. $\beta_7 d$ for Iowa Type R probability. Present-worth group-basis depreciation annuities for right-moded dispersions, average lives from 5 to 60 years, and associated MAR of 7%.

Average Life (Years)	Type of Retirement Dispersion									Average Life (Years)
	$R_{\frac{1}{2}}$	R_1	$R_{1\frac{1}{2}}$	R_2	$R_{2\frac{1}{2}}$	R_3	R_4	R_5	SQ	
5	18.42	18.20	18.05	17.90	17.78	17.68	17.55	17.47	17.39	5
6	15.01	14.79	14.64	14.48	14.37	14.26	14.13	14.05	13.98	6
7	12.58	12.36	12.21	12.06	11.94	11.84	11.71	11.62	11.56	7
8	10.77	10.55	10.40	10.24	10.14	10.03	9.90	9.81	9.75	8
9	9.38	9.16	9.00	8.85	8.74	8.63	8.50	8.41	8.35	9
10	8.27	8.05	7.89	7.74	7.63	7.52	7.39	7.30	7.24	10
11	7.37	7.15	6.99	6.84	6.73	6.62	6.48	6.40	6.34	11
12	6.62	6.40	6.25	6.09	5.98	5.87	5.74	5.65	5.59	12
13	6.00	5.78	5.62	5.46	5.35	5.24	5.11	5.03	4.97	13
14	5.47	5.25	5.09	4.93	4.82	4.71	4.58	4.50	4.43	14
15	5.01	4.79	4.63	4.48	4.36	4.25	4.13	4.04	3.98	15
16	4.61	4.40	4.24	4.08	3.97	3.86	3.73	3.65	3.59	16
17	4.27	4.05	3.89	3.74	3.62	3.51	3.39	3.30	3.24	17
18	3.97	3.75	3.59	3.43	3.32	3.21	3.08	3.00	2.94	18
19	3.70	3.48	3.32	3.17	3.05	2.94	2.82	2.73	2.68	19
20	3.46	3.24	3.08	2.93	2.82	2.71	2.58	2.50	2.44	20
21	3.24	3.03	2.87	2.71	2.60	2.49	2.37	2.29	2.23	21
22	3.05	2.83	2.68	2.52	2.41	2.30	2.18	2.10	2.04	22
23	2.88	2.66	2.50	2.35	2.24	2.13	2.01	1.93	1.87	23
24	2.72	2.50	2.35	2.19	2.08	1.98	1.85	1.77	1.72	24
25	2.58	2.36	2.20	2.05	1.94	1.84	1.71	1.63	1.58	25
26	2.44	2.23	2.08	1.93	1.82	1.71	1.59	1.51	1.46	26
27	2.32	2.11	1.96	1.81	1.70	1.59	1.47	1.39	1.34	27
28	2.21	2.00	1.85	1.70	1.59	1.49	1.37	1.29	1.24	28
29	2.11	1.90	1.75	1.60	1.49	1.39	1.27	1.19	1.14	29
30	2.02	1.81	1.66	1.51	1.40	1.30	1.18	1.11	1.06	30
31	1.93	1.73	1.57	1.43	1.32	1.22	1.10	1.03	.98	31
32	1.85	1.65	1.50	1.35	1.25	1.14	1.03	.95	.91	32
33	1.78	1.58	1.43	1.28	1.18	1.07	.96	.89	.84	33
34	1.71	1.51	1.36	1.21	1.11	1.01	.90	.82	.78	34
35	1.64	1.44	1.30	1.15	1.05	.95	.84	.77	.72	35
36	1.58	1.39	1.24	1.10	.99	.90	.78	.71	.67	36
37	1.53	1.33	1.18	1.04	.94	.84	.73	.67	.62	37
38	1.47	1.28	1.13	.99	.89	.80	.69	.62	.58	38
39	1.43	1.23	1.09	.95	.85	.75	.64	.58	.54	39
40	1.38	1.19	1.04	.91	.81	.71	.60	.54	.50	40
41	1.33	1.14	1.00	.86	.77	.67	.57	.50	.47	41
42	1.29	1.11	.96	.83	.73	.64	.53	.47	.43	42
43	1.25	1.07	.93	.79	.70	.60	.50	.44	.40	43
44	1.22	1.03	.89	.76	.67	.57	.47	.41	.38	44
45	1.18	1.00	.86	.73	.64	.54	.44	.38	.35	45
46	1.15	.97	.83	.70	.61	.52	.42	.36	.33	46
47	1.12	.94	.80	.67	.58	.49	.39	.34	.30	47
48	1.09	.91	.78	.65	.56	.47	.37	.31	.28	48
49	1.06	.88	.75	.62	.53	.44	.35	.29	.26	49
50	1.03	.86	.73	.60	.51	.42	.33	.28	.25	50
51	1.00	.83	.70	.58	.49	.40	.31	.26	.23	51
52	.98	.81	.68	.56	.47	.38	.29	.24	.21	52
53	.96	.79	.66	.54	.45	.37	.28	.23	.20	53
54	.93	.77	.64	.52	.43	.35	.26	.21	.19	54
55	.91	.75	.62	.50	.42	.33	.25	.20	.17	55
56	.89	.73	.61	.48	.40	.32	.23	.19	.16	56
57	.87	.71	.59	.47	.39	.31	.22	.17	.15	57
58	.85	.69	.57	.45	.37	.29	.21	.16	.14	58
59	.84	.68	.56	.44	.36	.28	.20	.15	.13	59
60	.82	.66	.54	.43	.35	.27	.19	.14	.12	60

143

Table 6.19. $\beta_8 d$ for Iowa Type R probability. Present-worth group-basis depreciation annuities for right-moded dispersions, average lives from 5 to 60 years, and associated MAR of 8%.

Average Life (Years)	$R_{\frac{1}{2}}$	R_1	$R_{1\frac{1}{2}}$	R_2	$R_{2\frac{1}{2}}$	R_3	R_4	R_5	SQ	Average Life (Years)
				Type of Retirement Dispersion						
5	18.23	17.98	17.82	17.65	17.53	17.42	17.27	17.17	17.05	5
6	14.81	14.57	14.40	14.23	14.11	13.99	13.84	13.74	13.63	6
7	12.39	12.14	11.97	11.80	11.67	11.55	11.41	11.31	11.21	7
8	10.58	10.33	10.16	9.99	9.86	9.74	9.59	9.49	9.40	8
9	9.19	8.94	8.76	8.59	8.47	8.34	8.20	8.10	8.01	9
10	8.09	7.84	7.66	7.48	7.36	7.23	7.09	6.99	6.90	10
11	7.14	6.94	6.76	6.59	6.46	6.34	6.19	6.09	6.01	11
12	6.45	6.20	6.02	5.85	5.72	5.59	5.45	5.35	5.27	12
13	5.83	5.58	5.40	5.23	5.10	4.97	4.83	4.73	4.65	13
14	5.31	5.06	4.88	4.70	4.57	4.45	4.30	4.20	4.13	14
15	4.86	4.61	4.43	4.25	4.12	4.00	3.85	3.76	3.68	15
16	4.47	4.22	4.04	3.86	3.74	3.61	3.47	3.37	3.30	16
17	4.13	3.88	3.70	3.53	3.40	3.27	3.13	3.03	2.96	17
18	3.83	3.58	3.40	3.23	3.10	2.98	2.83	2.74	2.67	18
19	3.57	3.32	3.14	2.97	2.84	2.72	2.57	2.48	2.41	19
20	3.34	3.09	2.91	2.74	2.61	2.49	2.34	2.25	2.19	20
21	3.13	2.88	2.70	2.53	2.40	2.28	2.14	2.05	1.98	21
22	2.94	2.70	2.52	2.34	2.22	2.10	1.96	1.87	1.80	22
23	2.77	2.53	2.35	2.18	2.06	1.93	1.79	1.70	1.64	23
24	2.62	2.38	2.20	2.03	1.91	1.79	1.65	1.56	1.50	24
25	2.48	2.24	2.06	1.89	1.77	1.65	1.52	1.43	1.37	25
26	2.35	2.12	1.94	1.77	1.65	1.53	1.40	1.31	1.25	26
27	2.24	2.00	1.83	1.66	1.54	1.42	1.29	1.20	1.14	27
28	2.13	1.90	1.73	1.56	1.44	1.32	1.19	1.10	1.05	28
29	2.03	1.80	1.63	1.47	1.35	1.23	1.10	1.02	.96	29
30	1.94	1.72	1.54	1.38	1.26	1.15	1.02	.93	.88	30
31	1.86	1.63	1.46	1.30	1.18	1.07	.94	.86	.81	31
32	1.78	1.56	1.39	1.23	1.11	1.00	.87	.79	.75	32
33	1.71	1.49	1.32	1.16	1.05	.94	.81	.73	.69	33
34	1.65	1.43	1.26	1.10	.99	.88	.75	.68	.63	34
35	1.59	1.37	1.20	1.05	.93	.82	.70	.63	.58	35
36	1.53	1.31	1.15	.99	.88	.77	.65	.58	.53	36
37	1.47	1.26	1.10	.94	.83	.73	.61	.54	.49	37
38	1.42	1.21	1.05	.90	.79	.68	.57	.50	.45	38
39	1.38	1.17	1.01	.86	.75	.64	.53	.46	.42	39
40	1.33	1.12	.97	.82	.71	.61	.49	.43	.39	40
41	1.29	1.08	.93	.78	.68	.57	.46	.39	.36	41
42	1.25	1.05	.89	.75	.64	.54	.43	.37	.33	42
43	1.21	1.01	.86	.71	.61	.51	.40	.34	.30	43
44	1.18	.98	.83	.68	.58	.48	.38	.31	.28	44
45	1.14	.95	.80	.66	.56	.46	.35	.29	.26	45
46	1.11	.92	.77	.63	.53	.43	.33	.27	.24	46
47	1.08	.89	.75	.60	.51	.41	.31	.25	.22	47
48	1.05	.86	.72	.58	.48	.39	.29	.23	.20	48
49	1.03	.84	.70	.56	.46	.37	.27	.22	.19	49
50	1.00	.82	.68	.54	.44	.35	.26	.20	.17	50
51	.98	.79	.65	.52	.43	.34	.24	.19	.16	51
52	.95	.77	.63	.50	.41	.32	.23	.18	.15	52
53	.93	.75	.62	.48	.39	.30	.21	.16	.14	53
54	.91	.73	.60	.47	.38	.29	.20	.15	.13	54
55	.89	.71	.58	.45	.36	.28	.19	.14	.12	55
56	.87	.70	.56	.44	.35	.26	.18	.13	.11	56
57	.85	.68	.55	.42	.34	.25	.17	.12	.10	57
58	.83	.66	.53	.41	.32	.24	.16	.11	.09	58
59	.82	.65	.52	.40	.31	.23	.15	.11	.09	59
60	.80	.63	.51	.39	.30	.22	.14	.10	.08	60

144

Values of $\overset{\beta}{i}d$ selected from these tables are to be adjusted for ultimate net salvage by applying the multiplier $(1 - c)$, where $c =$ ultimate
net salvage in percent of initial capital cost, installed. Interpolations
may be made for intermediate percentages MAR.

Tabulated values were calculated by the IBM 650 computer in the
manner of Table 6.4, assuming annual survivors $(y_{\overline{x}})$ to be the arithmetical mean of successive year-end values picked from the Iowa Type
Curves (Figures 6.1, 6.2, 6.3). This amounts to converting the smooth
Type Curves into equivalent step curves, half of the retirements for
each year occurring on the first day of the year and the other half on
the last day of the year.

Although this is a good approximation, it is nevertheless an approximation. Probably the behavior of actual piecemeal retirements,
in most cases, is as closely represented by a step curve as by the
smooth Type Curve; irregular annual retirements are substantially
always the rule. Accordingly, the approximation is more than adequate. However, it does make use of simple interest for periods of
less than one year, together with compound interest for longer periods,
which cannot be said to be the analyst's exact intent. In certain theoretical problems, the precise figures might be of concern. Before
recommending the tabulated figures for ordinary purposes, studies
were made of the differentials by William H. Caunt, Jr.

Table 6.20 illustrates the calculation of $\overset{\beta}{6}d$ for 10, R_1 (that is, for
10-year probable average life, Type R_1 is the probable type of dispersion).

A few examples illustrating use of the tables follow.
$\overset{\beta}{i}d$ for 24-year average life, Type L_0 dispersion, MAR 7%, zero
ultimate net salvage, per Table 6.10:

$$\overset{\beta}{7}d = 2.97\% \tag{1}$$

Adjusted for 10% ultimate net salvage:

$$\overset{\beta}{7}d (1 - c) = 2.97 \times 0.90 = 2.67\% \tag{2}$$

$\overset{\beta}{i}d$ for 36-year average life, Type L_0, MAR 7%, zero salvage:

$$\overset{\beta}{7}d = 1.75\% \tag{3}$$

The 50% increase in life changes the annuity by:

$$2.97 - 1.75 = 1.22\%; \quad 1.22/2.97 = 41\%.$$

For 24-year life, Type SQ (no dispersion), MAR 7%, per Table
6.18:

$$_7d = 1.72\% \tag{4}$$

This is almost identical with $\overset{\beta}{7}d$ for a 50% greater life, per (3).
The difference in type of dispersion is as important as the 50% difference in life.

These examples emphasize that is is not safe to ignore effects of
the type of retirement dispersion.

Table 6.20. Shortcut calculation of the depreciation annuity, $\overset{\beta}{i}d$.
10-year average life. Iowa Type R_1 dispersion. MAR = 6%.

$$\overset{\beta}{i}d = \frac{1}{\displaystyle\sum_{0}^{20} v^x \cdot y_{\overline{x}}} - i$$

1	2	3	4
	Present Worth Factors	Percentage Survivors per Iowa Type Curve	Col. 2 x Col. 3
Year			
x	v^x	$y_{\overline{x}}$	$v^x \cdot y_{\overline{x}}$
1	0.943 396	98.6	93.0188
2	.889 996	95.7	85.1726
3	.839 619	92.4	77.5808
4	.792 094	88.8	70.3379
5	.747 258	84.8	63.3675
6	.704 961	80.3	56.6084
7	.665 057	75.2	50.0123
8	.627 412	69.6	43.6679
9	.591 898	63.4	37.5263
10	.558 395	56.5	31.5493
11	.526 788	49.1	25.8653
12	.490 909	41.4	20.5745
13	.468 839	33.6	15.7530
14	.442 301	26.0	11.4998
15	.417 265	18.9	7.8863
16	.393 646	12.7	4.9993
17	.371 364	7.5	2.7852
18	.350 344	3.8	1.3313
19	.330 513	1.4	0.4627
20	.311 805	0.3	0.0935

$$\sum_{0}^{20} v^x \cdot y_{\overline{x}} = 700.0927\%$$

Per above formula:

$$\overset{\beta}{6}d = \frac{1}{7.000\ 927} - 6.000\ 000 = 8.283\ 823\%$$

Application to Single Units of Property

It is impossible to foresee the date at which a property unit will be retired. The best we can do is to estimate probable average service life.

The bell-shaped curves at the bottom of Figures 6.1, 6.2, and 6.3 show rates of retirement at every age for the Iowa Type Curves. They reflect the probability of retirement, at each age, for a single unit of property.

The following discussion will illustrate:

1. That the annuity for a given probable life is not the same as for the identical life certain;

2. How much the disparity amounts to, in a typical case; and
3. The reasoning that demands recognition of correct (exactly intended) arithmetic in estimating the depreciation annuity for
   single units of property.

Suppose we are asked to estimate $_i^\beta d$ for a single property unit to
be used for making fissionable products. We have no experience to
guide us, because this equipment is the first ever built of its kind.
However, in the opinion of those best qualified to judge, we can write
down these "educated opinions":

a. It will almost certainly have a life of 20 years or more.
b. It will almost certainly be retired by Age 40, if not sooner.
c. There is just about an equal probability of its serving for 20,
   30, or 40 years.

If we must settle for a single most likely life, it is $(20 + 30 + 40)/3$
= 30 years, probable life. This is equivalent to saying that out of a
large number of similar units, we would expect all to serve for 20
years, about two-thirds to serve for another 10 years, and the remainder to serve for 40 years. It is not equivalent to saying that out of a
large number, we would expect all to last exactly 30 years. This is
important, because the calculations must carry out the exact intent.

Table 6.21 shows how to calculate $_i^\beta d$, in the manner of Tables 6.3
and 6.20 to carry out our exact intent. Assuming MAR = 6%, and before considering effects of salvage, $_6^\beta d$ is 1.45%.

Compare this with two other figures:

$$_0 d = \frac{1}{30} = 3.33\% \quad \text{(the "straight-line" rate)}$$

$$_6 d = \frac{i}{(1 + i)^n - 1} = 1.26\% \quad \text{(Formula 5.2a on page 100,}$$
$$\text{ignoring retirement dispersion)}$$

Ignoring retirement in this example would introduce an error of $(1.45$
$- 1.26)/1.45 = 13\%$. This error would also enter into the estimate of
income tax.

Accordingly, it is essential that the factor of probability or uncertainty be taken into account in estimates of the revenue requirement
for depreciation. This applies even when estimating $_i^\beta d$ for a single
property unit, which is necessarily retired "All at once and nothing
first/Just as bubbles do when they burst." It is not a matter of economic theory. It is a matter of using the arithmetic that carries out
one's own exact intent. More will be said on this subject in Chapter 7.

The material of this chapter makes it abundantly evident that in
order to make reasonable estimates of revenue requirements for depreciation, it is essential to make reasonable estimates of: (a) probable average life; and (b) the probable pattern of individual retirements,
before and after the age corresponding to probable average life. Procedures for making such estimates are described in Chapter 7.

Table 6.21. The depreciation annuity for a single property unit.
Probable average life = 30 years. Equal probability of
retirement at 20, 30, or 40 years.*

1	2	3	4	5
Period in Years	Probability of Retirement at Beginning of Period, in %	Probable Survivors in Period	Present Worth Factors at 6%	Present Worth of Probable Survivors (Col. 3 x Col. 4)
1-20	0	100	11.4699*	11.4699
21-30	33-1/3	66-2/3	2.2949	1.5299
31-40	33-1/3	33-1/3	1.2815	0.4272
After 40	33-1/3	0	1.6204	0.0000
Totals	100.0%		16.6667	13.4270

$$\beta_i d = \frac{1}{13.4270} - 6\% = 1.45\%$$

*Σ (Probable survivors x Present worth factors) = (Probable survivors) x Σ (Present worth factors), when probable survivors are constant throughout the period.

$\sum\limits_{x=m}^{x=n}$ (Present worth factors) may be expressed for the period $m = 1/1/31$ to $n =$ 12/31/40, for example, as: $a_{\overline{40}|} - a_{\overline{30}|}$ where $a_{\overline{n}|} =$ present worth of an annuity of $1 for n years.

Résumé

I. Depreciation expense is the accountant's regular periodic charge made to recover the initial capital investment in depreciable assets (adjusted for ultimate net salvage) within their anticipated service life.

II. The annual revenue requirement to recover that single initial capital outlay is the level annuity, in percent of capital investment in service each year. This service lifetime depreciation annuity (together with return at i = MAR) is the financial equivalency of that single actual outlay.

III. The annual revenue requirement for depreciation does not represent loss in value. It is purely an amortization rate.

IV. The depreciation annuity, $_i dP$, is associated with the revenue requirement for return on the capital investment currently in service, iP, where i = MAR.

V. Annual revenue requirements for capital recovery, meaning return on and of the capital investment, are thus:

$$\frac{1}{a_{\overline{n}|}} \cdot P = iP + {}_i dP \qquad \text{(Form Y)}$$

VI. Some may desire to express the annual revenue requirement for depreciation as $_0 dP$, where $_0 d$ is the "straight-line" rate = 1/life. In such case, the related revenue requirement for return is minimal gross income, or $(i + {}_i d - {}_0 d)P$, where i = MAR.

Annual revenue requirements for capital recovery are then:

$$\frac{1}{a_{\overline{n}|}} \cdot P = (i + {}_id - {}_0d)P + {}_0dP \qquad \text{(Form X)}$$

This form should be avoided. Although technically beyond reproach, it invites misunderstandings.

VII. The quantity $(i + {}_id - {}_0d)P$ is identified as minimal gross income, when i = MAR. Its behavior is of interest in income tax calculations.

VIII. Two adjustments to ${}_id$ must be made, in practice:

1. The adjustment for ultimate net salvage, by multiplying ${}_id$ by $(1 - c)$, where c = ultimate net salvage, in percent of initial cost, installed, decimally expressed; and

2. The adjustment for retirement dispersion, or the probability that retirements will not occur at any single predictable date.

XI. The arithmetical definition of ${}_i^\beta d$, the revenue requirement for depreciation adjusted for effects of uncertainty, is:

$$ {}_i^\beta d = \frac{\displaystyle\sum_{x=0}^{x=\omega} v^x \cdot \text{retirements}_x}{\displaystyle\sum_{x=0}^{x=\omega} v^x \cdot P_{\overline{x}}} \qquad \text{(Formula 6.1)}$$

X. Another expression for ${}_i^\beta d$ which facilitates calculations, is:

$$ {}_i^\beta d = \frac{1}{\displaystyle\sum_{x=0}^{x=\omega} v^x \cdot y_x} - i \qquad \text{(Formula 6.2)}$$

XI. Tables of ${}_i^\beta d$ for lives from 5 to 60 years, for numerous types of dispersion (Iowa Type Curves) and for MAR at 5%, 6%, 7%, and 8%, permit easy evaluation of the revenue requirement for depreciation. The tables were prepared in the manner of Formula 6.2.

XII. It is essential that retirement dispersion, representing the effects of uncertainty as to probable date of retirement, be recognized, even in estimates of depreciation for a single unit of property.

XIII. All the conclusions reached in this chapter flow directly from the establishment of the estimator's exact intent, and use of the particular arithmetic which will carry out that intent. In order to comprehend this situation and to eliminate the confusion that is so prevalent, it is important to become familiar with the actual accounting for depreciation, particularly with the accounting in connection with depreciation reserves.

XIV. The revenue requirement for depreciation is a function of:

a. Initial capital investment in the depreciable facilities, installed;

   b. Ultimate net salvage;
   c. Probable average service life;
   d. The pattern of probable individual retirements scattered about the average; and
   e. Minimum acceptable return (MAR).

   XV. The lifetime-levelized revenue requirement for depreciation, called Method Y, is <u>not</u> a function of:

   a. The depreciation accounting method, be it "straight-line," sinking fund, SYD, DRDB, or any other method;
   b. Estimated service life used by the firm for book purposes;
   c. Cost of replacements;
   d. Amounts in the depreciation reserve at date of retirement; or
   e. Whether group-basis or unit-basis be used for book purposes.

   XVI. The depreciation annuity is <u>never</u> correctly estimated, in advance, as $i/[(1 + i)^n - 1]$. Such an estimate can be in error by as much as 50%, or more. This is perhaps the most important fact developed in this chapter. The only defensible estimate necessarily recognizes probability of service life, as in the computations of Tables 6.8-6.19.

   XVII. A reference worth consulting is: Paul H. Jeynes, "The Depreciation Annuity," <u>Transactions of the American Institute of Electrical Engineers</u>, Vol. 75, part III, 1956 (February, 1957 section), page 1398.

Problems

1. This chapter deals with only one aspect of depreciation, that is, the revenue requirement for depreciation. What other aspects might conceivably enter into corporate financial problems?

(Hint: Mergers, dissolution, insurance, good faith.)

2. Cite several situations which demonstrate the futility of expecting any arithmetical formula to reflect "loss in value" with worthwhile accuracy.

(Hint: Corporate parallels to personal experience such as the family car; a new house in a deteriorating neighborhood; wartime scarcities; confiscation of buildings on land needed for superhighways; sentimental versus intrinsic value.)

3. Explain why it is so important to distinguish exactly between an expense and an outlay.

4. Calculate and plot the ratio of depreciation reserve to plant in service, at each year end, throughout the whole service lifetime (average = 10 years), for an initial group having retirement dispersion of: (a) Type SQ; (b) Type SC; (c) Type S_2; (d) Type L_0. Assume zero ultimate net salvage and "straight-line" group-basis depreciation accounting.

5. Repeat Problem 4, assuming 20% ultimate net salvage; (a) positive, and (b) negative. Comment on the departure of the results from those of Problem 4.

6. Suppose that at the end of Year 5 you decided that average life was going to turn out to be 20 years, instead of 10, in Problem 4(a). How would you proceed? How about the same situation in Problem 4(b)?

7. In your own words, explain why it is absolutely essential to select the appropriate annual return on an investment, in dollars per year, that is consistent with your stipulation of a depreciation method.

8. Why not defer all provision for annual depreciation expense until the date of actual piecemeal retirements, and make the charge to depreciation expense when and as the partial retirements of the original group occur?

9. At the beginning of this chapter it was said that only three of the several components that make total revenue requirements of a project are directly proportional to capital investment in plant.

    a. Does that apply to Form X? Explain.

    b. List several other components of total revenue requirements of a project, and explain why they are not ordinarily directly proportional to capital investment in the project.

10. a. Assuming use of "straight-line" depreciation, is it ever possible for the depreciation reserve to be a negative figure? Explain.

    b. Why the quotation marks around the words "straight-line"?

11. Repeat the calculations of Table 6.1 assuming 20-year life and 10% ultimate net salvage. Discuss results of your calculations.

12. Repeat the calculations of Table 6.2 assuming 10-year life and 20% ultimate net salvage. Discuss results of your calculations.

13. Repeat Problem 12, assuming Type R_1 dispersion.

14. Draw an arbitrary survivor curve of your own choice—not an Iowa Type—for a short average life (say four or five years). Calculate the value of $_i^\beta d$ for $i = 6\%$, using first Formula 6.1 on page 123, and then Formula 6.2 on page 124.

    a. With ultimate net salvage = zero.

    b. With ultimate net salvage = 20%.

(Hint: More than one way can be used to do part b. Select the simplest.)

15. Repeat Tables 6.4, 6.5, 6.6, and 6.7, assuming 20% ultimate net salvage. Discuss the results of your calculations.

16. Assuming 10-year life, Type SQ dispersion, zero ultimate net salvage, and MAR at 6%, prepare three tabulations of (a) return on the investment, and (b) return of the investment, using: "straight-line" depreciation; 100% recovery of

the investment at the end of Year 1; no charge for depreciation until the end of Year 10, when a charge of 100% is made.

Calculate the present worths of the annual revenue requirements for capital recovery. What do the results demonstrate?

17. Using your own original assumptions, prepare Examples (1), (2), (3), and (4) (beginning on page 145) to illustrate the same points.

18. Explain in your own words why the depreciation annuity is, in practice, always correctly estimated at a figure greater than $i/[(1+i)^n-1]$, even for a single unit of property.

19. a. Why is the annual revenue requirement for depreciation independent of estimated life used for purposes of book depreciation by the accountants?

b. Why is the annual revenue requirement for depreciation independent of the cost of replacements?

c. Why is the annual revenue requirement for depreciation independent of the accountant's estimate of ultimate net salvage?

(Hint: The question is "Why is the annual revenue requirement...?"; not, "Why is the estimated depreciation annuity...?")

20. a. Why is the lifetime-levelized revenue requirement for depreciation not a function of the amounts in the depreciation reserve at the date of retirement, as stated in the Résumé, Item XV (d)?

b. Would this still be the same if you were referring to a single unit of property with its own reserve?

21. What is the exact distinction between the symbols $_id$ and $_i^\beta d$?

(Note: Actually, the complete version of $_id$ is $_i^\alpha d$—superprescript alpha, instead of beta.)

22. In general, is it economic to pay twice as much for alternative equipment that is the same in all respects except that it has double service life? Suggest a simple example to illustrate the principle involved.

23. A stamping press cost $30,000, installed, as follows:

Cost of the machine, delivered	$20,000
Foundations	7,000
Installation cost (labor)	3,000

At various times during its service life of 28 years, small repairs were made and charged to maintenance expense. Total cost of these repairs was:

Materials	$1,200
Labor	1,500

No salvage was realized at the time of making these repairs. At Age 28, the press was sold for junk. It cost $800 to remove it and truck it to the junkyard. The junkman paid $500 for it, delivered to him.

What percentage net scrap value was realized?

24. In many of the tabulations in this chapter it is assumed that gross income from a particular installation decreases as depreciation reserves accumulate. How do you reconcile this assumption with the practical observation that a given project or machine often supplies a variable annual output; sometimes even a growing annual output and increasing gross income as a new installation is gradually loaded up to its full capacity?

25. Some writers regard the depreciation annuity as strictly correct "only if depreciation reserves are invested in plant without delay." This concern over delay in making use of funds suggests that those writers have overlooked two essential characteristics of the revenue requirement for return. Explain.

26. Referring to Tables 6.8-6.18, what is the depreciation annuity for:

	Life	Dispersion Type	Return	Salvage
a.	30 years	SC	6%	0
b.	30	SQ	6%	0
c.	40	R_1	5%	+25%
d.	40	R_1	5%	-25%
e.	60	SC	7%	0
f.	60	SQ	7%	0

27. Answer the following questions by reference to Figures 6.1, 6.2, 6.3:

a. What percentage of the initial installation is still in service at Age 30 if mortality characteristics are:

1. 30, SC   4. 30, L_0
2. 15, SC   5. 30, R_5
3. 60, SC   6. 30, $R_{1/2}$

b. What is the remaining life expectancy:

1. At Age 30, for 30, SC?
2. At Age 60, for 30, SC?
3. At Age 60, for 30, L_0 ?
4. At Age 30, for 60, $R_{1/2}$?
5. At Age 30, for 30, SQ?
6. At Age 60, for 30, SQ?

28. In Problem 27, no mention was made of rate of return. Why?

29. All textbooks emphasize the importance of obsolescence as a factor in depreciation. Yet nothing whatever is said in Problem 26 concerning the assumptions to be made about obsolescence. Since the depreciation annuity is the only revenue requirement allowance for depreciation, exactly how does recognition for obsolescence enter into estimates of revenue requirements? Or doesn't it?

30. During World War II, used automobiles could sometimes be sold for several times their original cost. Suppose trucks had 10-year life, Type S_8 dispersion, and 110% net salvage. What is the depreciation annuity? Since salvage is greater than first cost, would any allowance at all be made for return in such cases?

31. The owner of a marina bought ten small boats to rent to the public daily or weekly. He expects to lose one each year, mostly from abuse, accidents, or inexpert handling. Draw the curve of retirement rate and the survivor curve.

A nearby yacht club has a number of members who own similar boats. Average service life is the same. However, almost none are scrapped; mostly they are well kept, expertly handled, and finally traded in for newer models or larger boats. Few give their first owners less than four years of service; few are kept for more than six years. Draw a curve of retirement rate and a survivor curve to illustrate this situation.

Select a value of $_6^\beta d$ appropriate for each.

Consider the replacement, at the beginning of Year 2, of the first marina boat to be retired. Being a single property unit, it will have to be retired at once when it goes. At what age will it probably be retired? What is the appropriate $_6 d$? Discuss the whole problem.

32. A review of textbooks, manuals, and courses designed to prepare engineers for examinations for professional engineers' license reveals that substantially all concentrate mostly on two subjects: (a) interest formulas and their applications and (b) depreciation methods.

Statements similar to those listed below, repetitiously encountered in such literature and curricula, typify the level of understanding at which these subjects are presented.

Assuming that such texts and courses do equip engineers to pass the examinations, comment on the value of such certification. For an interesting comment on this situation, see "Engineering Economics and Practice," a book review by Arthur Lesser, Jr., in The Engineering Economist, Fall, 1965, p. 28. Illustrate by referring to each item.

a. The value of one dollar varies with respect to time; if the interest rate were zero, no such variation would occur.

b. Capital recovery is the income equal to the amount of money invested in an asset.

c. Each individual situation dictates the particular method of depreciation that is appropriate.

d. "Straight-line" depreciation is accompanied by average interest on unrecovered capital.

e. The sinking-fund method assumes that an equal amount will be deposited in a sinking fund at each year end.

f. A project involving above-average risk may justify use of a higher interest rate in calculating sinking-fund depreciation.

g. The declining-balance method of depreciation is desirable because it is conservative. The sum-of-years'-digits method accomplishes a similar result, but has the advantage that value of an asset can be reduced to zero.

Not one of the sources reviewed mentioned MAR, nor discussed the interest rate that is appropriate for use in calculations of equivalency.

7

. . . . . Estimates of . . .
Probable Life

Nature of the Problem

Estimates of probable service life and type of retirement dispersion[1] influence three details of the determination of profitability or economic choice:

1. Estimates of the revenue requirement for depreciation;
2. Estimates of the revenue requirement for taxes (mainly income taxes, but taxes on gross receipts are affected, in turn, by depreciation and income tax); and
3. Calculations of financial equivalencies (present worth, levelized annuities, and so forth).

This discussion of procedures for estimating probable service life will emphasize two aspects of a disciplined approach that are commonly ignored with unfortunate results that can be ruinous.

First, these are estimates of future service life. Statistical analyses of past experience are only a means to that end. Appraisals of future probabilities depend upon educated judgment, and analyses of past history are what make that judgment "educated"; otherwise we would be only guessing. It is not, and must not be, blindly assumed that the future will duplicate the past.

Second, the importance of probable deviation of individual retirements from the average will be emphasized. Allowance must be made for retirement dispersion if the analyst's own exact intent is to be carried out. Ignoring dispersion, as most people attempt to do, can result in disastrously unsound decisions, as will be shown later on; an unnecessary and undeniable arithmetical error is introduced that could have been easily avoided. The following simple example shows that failing to allow for dispersion can be about as important as a 50% error in estimating service life; the percentage error is still greater for longer-lived plant:

---

[1]The comprehensive term which contemplates both (a) average service life and (b) the pattern of retirement "scatter" about average life is probable mortality characteristics. That expression will sometimes be found useful.

155

Effect of Overestimating Life by 50%

MAR at 7%. Actual Life, 20 Years; Overestimated at 30 Years

Correct estimate of $_7d$ (20 years; Table 6.18, on page 143) = 2.44%
Incorrect estimate of $_7d$ (30 years; Table 6.18)   = 1.06%

$$\text{Error of estimate} = \frac{2.44 - 1.06}{2.44} = 56.5\%$$

Effect of Ignoring Retirement Dispersion

MAR at 7%. Average Life, 20 Years; Actual Dispersion Type L_0

Correct estimate of $^\beta_7d$ (20 years; Type L_0;
   Table 6.10 on page 135)   = 3.74%
Incorrect estimate (20 years; no dispersion, or Type SQ) = 2.44%
(per Table 6.18)

$$\text{Error of estimate} = \frac{3.74 - 2.44}{2.44} = 53.3\%$$

The General Approach

A disciplined approach makes use of probability theory, directly opposed to the despairing philosophy of "uncertainty."

Standard accounting practice classifies depreciable assets by categories according to their nature or function. This is the basis for standard classification of plant accounts. To great extent, equipment within each such grouping is exposed to more or less similar and consistent behavior of reasons for retirement. For example, buildings are not placed in the same account with automobiles; they do not perform the same function and are not exposed to the same reasons for retirement.

Each such group is subject to more than one reason for retirement; the major reasons can be recognized and anticipated to a degree. Retirements for some such reasons are random in occurrence, such as accidental damage. Others are fairly predictable, reflecting effects of wear and tear. Still others can be firmly expected but are less certain as to timing, such as obsolescence. Within any one category of plant, the combined effect of all these forces can be expected to exhibit a reasonably high degree of consistency as time goes on. Thus, a semblance of a natural law is at work, progressive with age in an orderly way; the older the asset, the less its resistance to these forces. This amounts to perceiving a probable relation between (a) aging of the asset, and (b) its influence on the decision to retire. Analyzing this situation consists of observing this effect, proposing an explicit probable relation between age and rate of retirement, and proceeding to test the probability of that working hypothesis.

Appropriate data are first classified by categories, to the best of

the analyst's ability, attempting to recognize reasons for ultimate retirement. Plant accounts provide one source of information; other
plant-record data are often at hand particularly if a CPR system ("continuing plant record" system) is maintained by the company or if "history cards" are available.

The "single law of chance" that is operative (that is, the working
hypothesis just described) is conveniently expressed by means of a
curve representing rate of retirement — or alternatively, survivors resulting from such retirements — at each age. The Iowa Type Curves,
described in Chapter 6, are invaluable for this purpose. They are
perfectly abstract patterns not related to any particular kind of assets
or to any particular reason for retirement.

If tests show that past behavior of retirements, within a prese-
lected category of plant, do indicate that this hypothesized "law" has
operated with great consistency, then two statements can be made:

1. There is good reason to extend that hypothesis into the future.
2. There is good reason to challenge any other estimate of the
   future, unless it is supported by equally good reasons for denying this tentative "law," or modifying it.

This, in brief, is the statistically and technically sound procedure
sometimes derided by the ignorant as "assuming that past history repeats itself."[2] The whole process is one of denying that the future is
completely uncertain, by recognizing strong probabilities and apprais-
ing the likelihood of departures therefrom.

There are, of course, limits to the helpfulness of inferences based
on brief experience, with limited amounts of assets, and under changing conditions as to basic reasons for retirement. But all that has no
bearing on the appropriate nature of the arithmetic used in the analysis;
it simply reflects upon the significance of findings. Hence, the observation that although the statistical methods described herein are universally applicable to any kind of equipment, they must be applied and
interpreted intelligently. One important essential is that the recorded
data must truly represent actual experience before they are worthy of
analysis.[3] It may seem queer that such a warning should be necessary,
but that simple precaution has been so often disregarded as to demand
further attention.

Three steps are involved in estimating probable life:

1. Scrutiny and preparation of the raw data;
2. Statistical analysis of past and current experience; and
3. Appraisal of the future.

---

[2]Patrick Henry's famous comment is pertinent:
"I have but one lamp by which my feet are guided, and that is the lamp of experience.
I know no way of judging of the future but by the past."
From a speech in the Virginia Convention, in March, 1775.
[3]The principle involved has been christened GIGO, meaning "garbage in, garbage out."

Preparatory Scrutiny of Raw Data

It is often pointed out that the problem of estimating service life of equipment closely resembles that of estimating human life expectancy. It is true that statistical procedures for analyzing past experience lean heavily on methods developed by life insurance actuaries. However, one important difference between analyses of human mortality experience and studies of equipment behavior is that vital statistics recorded by every municipality provide a record of the cause of death. It is most unusual, however, to encounter accurate records of the exact cause of plant retirements. And the whole basis for anticipating future retirement behavior rests upon predictions of future <u>reasons for retirement</u>.

This book opened with mention of the essential variability of such statistics. Statistical analyses of average life of equipment, in past experience, are of limited value unless accompanied by studies of the forces which accounted for such results. It is the forecast of the probable impact of these forces that is essential.

For some kinds of property, it may be company practice to keep history cards or similar records which reveal the dates of initial acquisition and final retirement. But for some property units such as motors, pumps, piping, electrical wiring, conduits, plumbing, shelving, and so forth, no information may be available beyond the record of dollar additions and retirements in the capital accounts. Such records are sometimes known as "mass accounts," to distinguish them from "location property."

Of course, the first consideration when having recourse to "mass accounts" is to be sure that the equipment in question is in fact charged to the capital accounts and not to maintenance expense. The accountant supplies the authority for this decision. He defines, as <u>units of property</u>, the items that are to be treated as capital investment. He also defines <u>retirement units</u> as the items whose initial cost is to be charged to the depreciation reserve when retired. Retirement units are not necessarily identical with units of property, though usually they are substantially alike. Some industries may have their own special nomenclature for units of property and retirement units, but their significance is the same.

The first step, then, is to examine available records to discover whether any worthwhile inferences can be drawn from recorded history. Three considerations demand special attention:

1. <u>The Number of Retirements to Date</u>. Long-lived facilities, such as buildings, cranes, freight cars, steelwork, and heavy machinery, sometimes provide such a small amount of retirement data, in proportion to the total amount of such plant in service, that it is hardly worth analyzing.

This difficulty is not confined to long-lived plant. For example, at present little experience has been had with respect to atomic-fission plants, jet aircraft, or aluminum siding for buildings. The few

retirements to date may not indicate a long probable life. They are
new departures; and early retirement of new departures frequently are
caused by obsolescence — by early development of greatly improved
replacements.

Thus, appropriate statistical methods must permit analysis of restricted periods of experience (limited "eras" or recent "vintages"),
without introducing unwitting arithmetical errors. For example, care
must be taken to recognize and avoid the principle represented by the
"graveyard" or "tombstone" method of making wrong estimates. This
consists in estimating average life of retirements to date, ignoring the
longer life of units of the same age not yet retired. Since retirements
to date represent mostly infant mortality, average life can be grossly
underestimated.

2. The Quality of The Records. The books of account are not kept
primarily for purposes of life analysis. Two aspects of the dollar records sometimes make them quite unsuitable for the purpose unless extensive corrections and alterations are made:

a. Heterogeneity. It is unwise to jump to the conclusion that all
items recorded in a single account are thereby apt to have about the
same service life. For example, a single account may include relatively long-lived heavy or special-purpose trucks, shorter-lived panel
delivery wagons, and still shorter-lived passenger cars.

The appropriate procedure in such case is to segregate the data,
if possible, by types of plant more likely to have consistent mortality
behavior.

b. Accounting adjustments. Although accountants ordinarily pursue a consistent policy with respect to classification of assets by accounts, borderline cases sometimes introduce confusion. For example,
shelving, counters, gratings, fire-fighting equipment, and so forth, may
sometimes be classified as furniture (short-lived), sometimes as part
of the building (long-lived). The obvious remedy here is a review and
reclassification of both additions and retirements, if feasible.

Another kind of problem arises from the standard accounting procedure of "closing the books" at the end of the accounting period. Any
bookkeeping errors subsequently discovered are made by means of
journal entries at a later date; corrections in the "closed" books are
not permissible. Journal entries of this sort have been facetiously described as insuring that the record will be incorrect both before and
after the adjustment is made. That is, the correction maintains the
correct balance by reversing the original entries; thus, a nonexistent
retirement is recorded at an early date, and a nonexistent new addition
is placed on the books.

Disturbing entries of this kind are of the greatest variety; in general, they are caused by entries made at some date to adjust for a condition found to have existed at some other date, as just described. The
faulty condition may relate to content, amount, age, or classification.
It may be a simple arithmetical error or a misinterpretation of accounting instructions. It may result from discovery that items of plant

presumed retired, per the records, are actually still in service; or that items still in service, per the records, actually were retired some time ago (commonly called "*o*'s and *u*'s," meaning overs and unders). To adjust for life-analysis purposes, it is necessary to remove the adjusting entries, correct if necessary, and reinsert them in the year in which the physical transaction actually took place.

3. Price-level changes. Some statistical procedures for life analysis of mass accounts depend upon relations between annual retirements and either plant additions or plant balances. Steadily rising price levels mean that retirements are largely composed of items whose original cost was less than the current unit cost of similar equipment. Resultant ratios of retirements to additions or to balances are then apt to overstate average life. This difficulty is not experienced if the analysis can be based on number of units rather than on dollars, even though still done en masse. Except for quite long-lived plant, it has been found in practice to be a less serious problem than might be imagined.

Actuarial Methods

Having secured information worthy of statistical analysis, three general methods for inquiring into average life and type of dispersion may be employed:

1. Actuarial methods;
2. Turnover methods; and
3. Simulated-plant-record methods.

The actuarial methods require a knowledge of age of units at the date of retirement, plus certain information concerning the ages of units still in service. Several procedures have been suggested for handling the data. The two most used are: (a) the original-group analysis, and (b) the annual-rate analysis.

Either method may be used to produce a survivor curve and/or retirement-frequency curve that is deemed characteristic of past experience. Average life may be calculated by plotting the data and finding the area enclosed, in the manner of Table 7.1.

Alternatively, average life may be calculated from the retirement-frequency curve by the method of moments. That is, the percentage retirement rate at each age is multiplied by that age in years; the sum of those products is then divided by the sum of $y_{\overline{x}}$'s, or $\sum\limits_{x=0}^{x=\omega} y_{\overline{x}}$.

The original-group analysis consists in determining and plotting survivors in each year x $(= {_tY_x})$ out of a given original placement $(= {_tA})$ in one year, indicated at time t. These additions in a given year are known as a "vintage."

Instead of plotting a separate curve for each vintage, results for

Table 7.1. "Straight-line" depreciation, group basis.
10-year average life, Type R_1 dispersion, zero net salvage.

1	2	3	4	5	6	7	8
	Survivors			Retire-ments	Depre-ciation	Reserve at End of Year	
Year	First of Year	End of Year	Mean Survivors	During Year	at 10% of Col.4	Total	In % of Col. 3
1	100.0	97.3	98.6	2.70	9.86	7.16	7.36
2	97.3	94.1	95.7	3.20	9.57	13.53	14.38
3	94.1	90.7	92.4	3.40	9.24	19.37	21.36
4	90.7	86.9	88.8	3.80	8.88	24.45	28.14
5	86.9	82.7	84.8	4.20	8.48	28.73	34.74
6	82.7	77.9	80.3	4.80	8.03	31.96	41.03
7	77.9	72.6	75.2	5.30	7.52	34.18	47.08
8	72.6	66.7	69.6	5.90	6.96	35.24	52.83
9	66.7	60.1	63.4	6.60	6.34	34.98	58.20
10	60.1	52.9	56.5	7.20	5.65	33.43	63.19
11	52.9	45.3	49.1	7.60	4.91	30.74	67.86
12	45.3	37.5	41.4	7.80	4.14	27.08	72.21
13	37.5	29.7	33.6	7.80	3.36	22.64	76.23
14	29.7	22.3	26.0	7.40	2.60	17.84	80.00
15	22.3	15.6	18.9	6.70	1.89	13.03	83.53
16	15.6	9.8	12.7	5.80	1.27	8.50	86.73
17	9.8	5.3	7.5	4.50	0.75	4.75	89.62
18	5.3	2.3	3.8	3.00	0.38	2.13	92.61
19	2.3	0.6	1.4	1.70	0.14	0.57	95.00
20	0.6	0.0	0.3	0.60	0.03	0.00	100.00
	Total		1000.0				

Divided by initial placement of 100 = $\frac{1,000}{100}$ = 10-year life.

several vintages may be combined in a single curve. That is, survivors at Age 1 for all vintages may be expressed as a percentage of all initial placements except the current year's (which are not yet one year old); survivors two years old for all vintages may be expressed as a percentage of all initial placements except for this year and the previous year (not yet two years old); and so on.

It is possible that "stub" curves may result, if no placements are old enough to be completely retired. In such case, the stub curve must be extrapolated in some manner to permit calculation of average life as just described. The Iowa Type Curves provide a convenient means of extrapolation, by matching the type most nearly representing the partial plot.

It will be apparent that:

1. A large number of vintages will contribute to points plotted for early years of life. If a stub curve is the result, only one vintage (last year's) will contribute to the oldest age plotted.
2. The familiar dilemma arises: Which is more informative, a small amount of recent experience, or a large amount of ancient history?

For such reasons, no statistical analysis is possible without relying to some extent on judgment.

The original-group analysis yields an observed survivorship characteristic that may be expressed as:

$$y_x = \frac{\displaystyle\sum_{t=1}^{t=k} {}_tY_x}{\displaystyle\sum_{t=1}^{t=k} {}_tA}$$

where

y_x = survivors of a unit radix at Age x.

t = time, in years (to identify survivors Y_x as related to additions ${}_tA$).

k = time of the last year of record (= ω, if data are available to date of retirement of last survivor).

x = age, in years.

Y_x = survivors at Age x.

A = additions in calendar year.

Since it is convenient to treat additions as though made at midyear, the summation would be more meticulously described as from Year x to Year $t = k - (x - 1/2)$.

The related retirements-frequency distribution is:

$$f_x = \frac{\displaystyle\sum_{t=1}^{t=k} {}_tF_x}{\displaystyle\sum_{t=1}^{t=k} {}_tA}$$

where ${}_tF_x$ means retirements in Year x out of additions ${}_tA$.

The estimated type of dispersion may be obtained by matching the resultant plot against the Iowa Type Curves.

The annual-rate analysis proceeds on the hypothesis that there is a characteristic rate of retirement, at each age, in percent of the units in service at the beginning of each year. Thus, survivors and retirements are not expressed as a percentage of initial placements but as a percentage of survivors of the previous age-year.

As in the case of the original-group analysis, the data to be analyzed may include all information of record to date; or it may be restricted to any specified "additions era"; or to any desired "retirement era." The meaning of "addition era" is no doubt obvious. The term "retirements era" means that survivors and retirements therefrom for the stipulated period, and additions only of vintages represented by such survivors, are to be included in the analysis.

The annual-rate analysis yields an observed survival ratio as follows:

$$P_x = \frac{\displaystyle\sum_{t=1}^{t=k} {}_tY_x}{\displaystyle\sum_{t=1}^{t=k} {}_tY_x}$$

That is, the result is a percentage of survivors at the beginning of the same year. A survivor curve may be calculated by starting with initial survivors of unity, and multiplying by P_1 to obtain y_1. Then y_1 is multiplied by P_2 to obtain y_2; y_2 is multiplied by P_3 to obtain y_3; and so on. Average life is calculated from the completed survivor curve in the same manner as for the original-group method.

The periodic frequency-probability characteristic, using the annual-rate method, is

$$q_x = \frac{\displaystyle\sum_{t=1}^{t=k} {}_tF_x}{\displaystyle\sum_{t=1}^{t=k} {}_tY_x - 1}$$

Tables 7.2 and 7.3 show how data may be compiled for analyses of this kind. They are taken from Methods of Estimating Utility Plant Life, a report of the Engineering Subcommittee of the Depreciation Accounting Committee, Edison Electric Institute, 1952; publication No. 51-23. Although prepared particularly for use by public utilities, the procedures described therein apply just as well to any kind of business, as mentioned before. This report describes these statistical methods in greater detail and includes helpful suggestions for smoothing and extrapolating data.

Turnover Methods

If available data do not reveal ages at retirement, as is necessary for application of the actuarial methods, it still may be possible to estimate average life realized by analysis of the annual additions, retirements, and balances in service. Among the procedures developed for this purpose are:

1. The turnover-period method;
2. The half-cycle ratio method;
3. The asymptotic method; and
4. The geometric mean method.

None of these reveals the type of retirement dispersion, though it is possible to make approximations by comparing simultaneous analyses made by the turnover-period and half-cycle ratio methods, each

Table 7.2. Mortality data sheet. Electric meters (in physical units).

Vintage Retirements during age year, $F(x)$
Vintage Survivors at end of age year, $Y(x)$

Column key: B = Balance end of year; R = Retirements during year; A = Additions during year. Each age-column cell is given as $F(x)$ / $Y(x)$ (top value = retirements during the age year, bottom value = survivors at end of age year); "-" denotes none.

Year (Vintage) of year	B	R	A	0.5	1.5	2.5	3.5	4.5	5.5	6.5	7.5	8.5	9.5	10.5	11.5	12.5	13.5	14.5	15.5	16.5	17.5	18.5	19.5	20.5	21.5	22.5	23.5	24.5	25.5	26.5	27.5	28.5	29.5	30.5	31.5	32.5	33.5	34.5
1905	65	-	65	-/65	-/65	-/65	-/65	-/65	-/65	-/65	-/65	-/65	-/65	4/61	2/59	-/59	1/58	-/58	-/58	-/58	-/58	-/58	3/55	-/55	4/51	2/49	2/47	3/44	6/38	2/36	4/32	2/30	1/29	3/26	10/16	10/6	5/1	-/1
1906	163	-	98	-/98	1/97	-/97	-/97	-/97	-/97	-/97	-/97	-/97	-/97	-/97	-/97	1/96	-/96	1/95	-/95	-/95	3/92	-/92	-/92	11/81	6/75	8/67	5/62	7/55	1/54	7/47	-/47	3/44	12/32	12/20	10/10	3/7	2/5	
1907	514	1	352	-/352	1/351	-/351	-/351	-/351	-/351	-/351	1/350	-/350	-/350	-/350	1/349	2/347	2/345	6/339	1/338	2/336	3/333	1/332	30/302	21/281	13/268	24/244	13/231	14/217	20/197	3/194	14/180	39/141	46/95	34/61	33/28	20/8		
1908	638	1	125	-/125	-/125	-/125	-/125	-/125	-/125	-/125	1/124	-/124	-/124	-/124	3/121	3/118	-/118	-/118	2/116	1/115	1/114	5/109	3/106	6/100	3/97	4/93	5/88	5/83	3/80	5/75	12/63	22/41	16/25	15/10	9/1			
1909	769	-	131	-/131	-/131	-/131	1/130	-/130	-/130	-/130	-/130	-/130	1/129	-/129	1/128	-/128	3/125	-/125	2/123	-/123	6/117	8/109	1/108	6/102	6/96	3/93	5/88	2/86	2/84	6/78	30/48	27/21	12/9	4/5				
1910	828	-	59	-/59	-/59	-/59	-/59	1/58	1/57	-/57	-/57	-/57	-/57	-/57	-/57	-/57	2/55	-/55	1/54	-/54	-/54	3/51	7/44	-/44	2/42	2/40	-/40	7/33	3/30	8/22	14/8	3/5						
1911	938	-	110	-/110	-/110	1/109	-/109	-/109	-/109	-/109	-/109	-/109	3/106	-/106	-/106	1/105	-/105	-/105	6/99	5/94	5/89	6/83	6/77	7/70	2/68	3/65	2/63	10/53	20/33	14/19	11/8	3/5						
1912	1019	1	82	-/82	-/82	-/82	-/82	-/82	-/82	-/82	-/82	1/81	-/81	-/81	-/81	2/79	-/79	8/71	6/65	2/63	3/60	2/58	2/56	4/52	3/49	3/46	5/41	12/29	13/16	12/4	3/1							
1913	1120	1	102	-/102	1/101	-/101	-/101	-/101	-/101	-/101	2/99	-/99	-/99	-/99	-/99	-/99	-/99	8/91	6/85	5/80	4/76	-/76	11/65	2/63	6/57	6/51	6/45	37/8	5/3								
1914	1280	3	163	-/163	1/162	-/162	1/161	-/161	-/161	-/161	1/160	-/160	2/158	1/157	1/156	2/154	-/154	2/152	1/151	-/151	2/149	-/149	1/148	1/147	4/143	3/140	2/138	11/127	14/113								
1915	1475	7	202	-/202	-/202	-/202	-/202	-/202	-/202	-/202	-/202	-/202	1/201	-/201	3/198	1/197	1/196	4/192	2/190	2/188	-/188	2/186	-/186	3/183	1/182	1/181	3/178	12/166									
1916	1790	3	318	1/317	-/317	-/317	-/317	1/316	-/316	-/316	-/316	-/316	-/316	1/315	-/315	1/314	-/314	2/312	2/310	1/309	-/309	1/308	5/303	1/302	1/301	11/290	10/280										
1917	1937	1	148	-/148	-/148	-/148	-/148	-/148	1/147	-/147	1/146	-/146	-/146	-/146	1/145	-/145	-/145	-/145	1/144	1/143	-/143	3/140	3/137	2/135	5/130												
1918	2002	2	67	-/67	1/66	-/66	-/66	1/65	1/64	1/63	-/63	-/63	-/63	1/62	-/62	-/62	-/62	-/62	-/62	-/62	1/61	3/58	1/57	1/56	2/54												
1919	2275	10	283	2/281	3/278	-/278	1/277	2/275	1/274	-/274	-/274	-/274	-/274	-/274	-/274	3/271	-/271	-/271	-/271	1/270	3/267	1/266	6/260	6/254													
1920	2714	18	457	1/456	-/456	-/456	3/453	-/453	1/452	-/452	2/450	-/450	1/449	-/449	2/447	2/445	2/443	-/443	5/438	5/433	5/428	16/412	8/404														

Year	n	Total																																			
1921	7	3209	502	⁻502	¹501	⁴497	⁻497	¹497	¹496	¹496	¹495	¹495	¹495	⁻494	⁻494	¹493	³490	²488	²486	⁷479	⁸471																	
1922	4	3842	637	⁻637	¹636	⁻636	⁻636	¹636	¹635	¹635	¹634	⁻633	¹633	¹633	¹632	⁻632	²632	⁻632	¹⁴618	⁴614																		
1923	27	4373	558	⁻558	⁻558	¹558	¹557	¹557	¹556	¹555	¹555	²554	²554	²553	²553	¹²551	¹³538	⁴534																			
1924	15	4984	626	⁻626	¹626	¹625	⁻625	²624	²624	¹622	⁻622	²620	¹619	³617	¹²614	³602	³599																				
1925	6	5675	697	⁻697	⁻697	¹696	⁻696	²694	⁻694	⁻694	²694	¹693	¹⁴693	¹⁴679	²677																							
1926	80	6310	715	²713	¹712	⁻712	¹711	¹710	⁻710	²709	³709	³706	¹⁸704	¹⁸686	³683																							
1927	68	6870	628	⁻628	⁻628	²626	²624	¹623	¹622	⁻621	⁷621	⁷620	¹²608	¹607																								
1928	57	7407	594	⁻594	¹593	⁻593	²593	¹592	⁶591	⁶591	⁷591	⁷584	²582																									
1929	67	7791	451	⁻451	¹450	²448	⁻448	¹448	⁴447	⁶447	³441	³438																										
1930	57	8031	297	⁻297	⁻297	¹297	⁻296	¹296	⁴295	⁶295	³289	³286																										
1931	55	8233	257	⁻257	⁻257	¹257	⁻256	¹256	²255	⁴251	¹250																											
1932	68	8271	106	⁻106	⁻106	²106	⁻106	²106	⁵104	⁻104																												
1933	30	8600	359	⁻359	¹359	⁴358	⁴357	²355	⁵350	⁻350																												
1934	50	8883	333	⁻333	⁻333	⁴333	⁴333	⁴329	⁻329																													
1935	128	9284	529	¹528	¹528	¹528	⁻527	⁻527																														
1936	197	9326	239	⁻239	⁻239	⁻239	⁻239																															
1937	197	9578	449	⁻449	¹448	⁻448	⁻448																															
1938	279	9671	372	⁻372	⁻372	⁻372																																
1939	136	10030	495	¹494																																		
Total	1576		11606	11598	11092	11109	10708	10248	9993	9450	9111	8743	8630	8360	8050	7578	6956	6322	5586	4856	4212	3630	2953	2400	1925	1613	1487	1301	901	648	476	387	286	190	122	55	21	6	1

165

Table 7.3. Summations and observed ratios. (For complete and restricted use of Table 7.2 mortality data, for each age x.)

	0.5	1.5	2.5	3.5	4.5	5.5	6.5	7.5	8.5	9.5	10.5	11.5	12.5	13.5	14.5	15.5	16.5	17.5	18.5	19.5	20.5	21.5	22.5	23.5	24.5	25.5	26.5	27.5	28.5	29.5	30.5	31.5	32.5	33.5	34.5	Aver Life $E_y(x)$
SUMMATIONS (with limits as indicated below)																																				
Complete Data																																				
Lower limit is 1905, upper limit is 1939 less (x − 0.5)																																				
Survivors, end of year, Y(x)	11598	11092	10708	10248	9993	9450	9111	8743	8630	8360	8050	7578	6956	6322	5586	4856	4212	3520	2953	2400	1925	1613	1487	1301	901	648	476	367	286	190	122	55	21	6	1	
Additions, A(t)	11066	11111	10739	10290	10101	9522	9189	8830	8724	8467	8170	7719	7125	6497	5782	5085	4459	3601	3264	2762	2305	2022	1955	1807	1489	1287	1124	1022	940	830	771	640	515	163		
Survivors, first of year, Y(x−1)	11606	11104	10720	10260	10009	9466	9121	8761	8639	8380	8074	7612	6996	6349	5639	4909	4257	3678	3016	2482	1996	1671	1559	1359	1021	735	535	415	386	281	190	117	54	13	1	
Additions Eras																																				
Lower limit is lower era limit, upper limit is upper era limit or 1939 less (x − 0.5) whichever is less																																				
1905-1914																																				
Survivors, end of year, Y(x)	1287	1283	1282	1280	1279	1278	1278	1273	1272	1267	1261	1253	1243	1237	1209	1184	1169	1141	1112	1053	995	946	888	843	735	648	476	367	286	190	122	55	21	6	1	
Additions, A(t)	1287	1287	1287	1287	1287	1287	1287	1287	1287	1267	1261	1253	1287	1237	1287	1287	1287	1287	1287	1287	1287	1287	1287	1287	1287	1287	1124	1022	940	830	771	640	515	163		
Survivors, first of year, Y(x−1)	1287	1287	1283	1282	1280	1279	1278	1278	1273	1272	1267	1261	1253	1243	1237	1209	1184	1169	1141	1112	1053	995	946	888	843	735	535	415	386	281	190	117	54	13	1	
1915-1939																																				
Survivors, end of year, Y(x)	10311	9809	9426	8968	8714	8172	7833	7470	7358	7093	6789	6325	5713	5085	4377	3672	3043	2689	1841	1347	930	667	599	458	166											
Additions, A(t)	10319	9824	9452	9003	8764	8235	7902	7543	7437	7180	6883	6432	5838	5210	4495	3798	3172	2614	1977	1475	1018	735	668	520	202											
Survivors, first of year, Y(x−1)	10319	9817	9437	8978	8729	8187	7843	7483	7366	7108	6807	6351	5743	5106	4402	3700	3073	2609	1875	1370	943	676	613	471	178											
Retirements Eras																																				
Lower limit is lower era limit less (x−0.5), upper limit is upper era limit less (x−0.5)																																				
1920-1929																																				
Survivors, end of year, Y(x)	5862	5686	5150	4667	4267	3769	3302	2840	2286	1894	1498	1347	1396	1593	1343	1184	1018	829	707	619	491	360	109	44												
Additions, A(t)	5865	5697	5170	4690	4293	3798	3335	2879	2324	1932	1534	1382	1440	1644	1424	1287	1124	940	830	771	640	515	163	65												
Survivors, first of year, Y(x−1)	5865	5692	5158	4672	4273	3773	3306	2847	2287	1900	1502	1353	1406	1598	1375	1209	1033	838	746	663	517	394	116	47												
1930-1939																																				
Survivors, end of year, Y(x)	3434	3390	3609	3782	4245	4403	4692	4889	5412	5643	5791	5605	5057	4575	4185	3672	3194	2124	1693	1306	1122	1127	1192	857												
Additions, A(t)	3436	3392	3614	3793	4269	4437	4730	4929	5460	5697	5865	5170	5085	4690	4293	3798	3335	2324	1932	1534	1382	1440	1644	1424												
Survivors, first of year, Y(x−1)	3436	3391	3612	3787	4254	4414	4698	4898	5420	5657	5806	5627	5085	4595	4206	3700	3224	2162	1736	1333	1154	1165	1243	974												
1920-1939																																				
Survivors, end of year, Y(x)	9296	9076	8759	8449	8512	8172	7994	7729	7698	7537	7289	6952	6453	6168	5528	4856	4212	2953	2400	1925	1613	1487	1301	901												
Additions, A(t)	9301	9089	8784	8483	8562	8235	8065	7808	7784	7637	7399	7079	6610	6334	5085	1287	4459	3264	2762	2305	2022	1955	1807	1489												
Survivors, first of year, Y(x−1)	9301	9083	8770	8459	8527	8187	8004	7745	7707	7557	7308	6980	6491	6193	5581	4909	4257	3016	2482	1996	1671	1559	1359	1021												
SURVIVAL RATIOS, p(x) − ΣY(x)/ΣY(x−1)																																				
Annual Rate Method																																				
Complete Data	.9993	.9989	.9989	.9988	.9984	.9983	.9989	.9979	.9990	.9976	.9970	.9955	.9943	.9957	.9906	.9892	.9894	.9869	.9791	.9670	.9644	.9653	.9538	.9573	.9825	.8816	.8897	.8147	.7409	.6762	.6421	.4701	.3889	.4615	1.000	
Additions Eras																																				
1906-1914	1.000	.9969	.9961	.9946	.9938	.9930	.9930	.9891	.9845	.9798	.9736	.9658	.9611	.9394	.9200	.9083	.8866	.8640	.8182	.7731	.7350	.6900	.6550	.6351	.5711	.5035	.4235	.3787	.3043	.2289	.1582	.0859	.0408	.0368	.0154	
1915-1939	.9992	.9992	.9988	.9989	.9983	.9982	.9982	.9989	.9979	.9974	.9959	.9948	.9902	.9902	.9573	.9924	.9520	.9819	.9832	.9867	.9772	.9724	.9326													
Retirements Eras																																				
1920-1929	.9995	.9989	.9989	.9984	.9986	.9979	.9989	.9988	.9975	.9982	.9955	.9937	.9920	.9956	.9767	.9793	.9746	.9707	.9707	.9336	.9497	.9137	.9362													
1930-1939	.9994	.9997	.9994	.9979	.9979	.9977	.9982	.9975	.9974	.9961	.9974	.9961	.9945	.9956	.9744	.9707	.9612	.9024	.9752	.9797	.9723	.9674	.9590	.8799												
1920-1939	.9995	.9992	.9987	.9988	.9982	.9982	.9988	.9979	.9974	.9974	.9960	.9941	.9941	.9905	.9892	.9824	.9669	.9791	.9670	.9644	.9653	.9538	.9573	.9825												
SURVIVOR RATIOS, y(x)																																				
Original Group Method, ΣY(x)/ΣA(t)																																				
Complete Data	.9993	.9983	.9971	.9959	.9943	.9924	.9901	.9901	.9892	.9874	.9853	.9817	.9763	.9731	.9661	.9550	.9446	.9305	.9047	.8689	.8351	.7977	.7606	.7200	.6051	.5035	.4235	.3787	.3043	.2289	.1582	.0859	.0408	.0368	.0154	25.3
Additions Eras																																				
1905-1914	1.000	.9969	.9961	.9946	.9938	.9930	.9930	.9891	.9845	.9798	.9736	.9658	.9611	.9394	.9200	.9083	.8866	.8640	.8182	.7731	.7350	.6900	.6550	.6351	.5711	.5035	.4235	.3787	.3043	.2289	.1582	.0859	.0408	.0368	.0154	24.8
1915-1939	.9992	.9985	.9972	.9960	.9943	.9923	.9920	.9891	.9863	.9803	.9765	.9747	.9694	.9690	.9431	.9200	.9057	.9434	.9139	.9763	.8514	.7626	.8967	.8808	.6018	.5035	.4235	.3787	.3043	.2289	.1582	.0859	.0408	.0368	.0154	25.5
Retirements Eras																																				
1920-1929	.9995	.9981	.9961	.9951	.9939	.9924	.9919	.9912	.9874	.9891	.9821	.9761	.9755	.9689	.9748	.9668	.9577	.8763	.9434	.9577	.8119	.8351	.7977	.7606	.7251	.6018	.5035	.4235	.3767	.3043	.1582	.0859	.0408	.0368	.0154	25.3
1930-1939	.9994	.9994	.9967	.9972	.9960	.9944	.9923	.9912	.9899	.9890	.9821	.9762	.9738	.9669	.9550	.9446	.9305	.9047	.8689	.8351	.7977	.7606	.7200	.6051	.7200	.6051	.5035	.4235	.3767	.2289	.1582	.0859	.0408	.0368	.0154	25.5
1920-1939	.9995	.9986	.9972	.9960	.9972	.9926	.9913	.9899	.9890	.9821	.9821	.9762	.9738	.9669	.9550	.9446	.9305	.9269	.9075	.8689	.8351	.7977	.7606	.6051	.6051	.5035	.4235	.3767	.3043	.2289	.1582	.0859	.0408	.0368	.0154	25.3
Annual Rate Method, p(x)/y(x−1)																																				
Complete Data	.9993	.9982	.9971	.9959	.9943	.9932	.9915	.9915	.9884	.9860	.9830	.9786	.9730	.9688	.9597	.9493	.9392	.9075	.8776	.8464	.8170	.7793	.7460	.6583	.5804	.5164	.4207	.3117	.2108	.1354	.0637	.0248	.0114	.0114	.0114	25.5
Additions Eras																																				
1905-1914	1.000	.9969	.9961	.9945	.9937	.9929	.9929	.9894	.9844	.9797	.9735	.9657	.9611	.9394	.9200	.9083	.8865	.8640	.8181	.7730	.7460	.7793	.6899	.6549	.5710	.5034	.4479	.3669	.2704	.1828	.1174	.0552	.0215	.0099	.0099	24.6
1915-1939	.9992	.9984	.9972	.9961	.9944	.9926	.9913	.9896	.9885	.9891	.9821	.9747	.9652	.9521	.9689	.9463	.9267	.9133	.8699	.8638	.8186	.7642	.7258	.6632	.6232	.5834										
Retirements Eras																																				
1920-1929	1.000	.9969	.9984	.9972	.9961	.9957	.9943	.9932	.9920	.9889	.9859	.9832	.9720	.9689	.9485	.9409	.9239	.9084	.8959	.8840	.8632	.8400	.7834													
1930-1939																																				

adjusted for rate of growth and trial assumptions as to retirement pattern. Because superior procedures are available, the turnover methods
are employed mostly for obtaining "some idea" as to the average life
with minimum effort. They are useful for making the trial assumption
involved in the simulation approach to be described. See the Edison
Electric Institute report mentioned for further information concerning
the turnover methods.

Simulation Methods

The simulated-plant-record method developed by Alex E. Bauhan
(of Public Service Electric and Gas Company, Newark, N.J., and formerly Chairman of the EEI Depreciation Accounting Committee) is a
trial-and-error procedure which is widely used now that electronic
computers have become generally available. Two minor variations of
the approach here described are less often used to date. The indicated-
renewals version has some advantages which may be worth considering
if tabulations of the renewal function (to be discussed) are available for
various lives and dispersion patterns. The data required are records
of actual annual additions over a long period of years, plus annual retirements or plant balances to date.

A trial assumption is first made as to average life and type of dispersion; the turnover methods are useful for this purpose. Survivor
tables, such as are available for the Iowa Type Curves, are prepared
for that assumed life and dispersion pattern. The known additions of a
particular year are multiplied by the successive survivorship percentage, and the presumed annual survivors of that particular vintage are
set down, year by year. Additions in the following year are converted
into presumed survivors in that same manner and tabulated year by
year. The same thing is done for every vintage of additions, up to the
present. Survivors of all vintages are added up in each year to find
presumed plant balances in each year. These presumed balances,
which would result from the known additions and the assumed life are
then compared with reported annual balances.

Deviations of presumed balances from reported balances provide
the basis for a second trial assumption as to average life and type of
dispersion. A major contribution of Bauhan was the means for minimizing the number of reported balances in this manner. The "best fit"
is discovered by seeking the least sum of squared differences between
computed and reported balances, respectively.

A "conformance index" permits rating the degree of success with
which reported balances are reproduced by computed values, in terms
of excellent, good, fair, or poor. A separate "retirement experience
index" may be applied to decide whether the records supply enough information over a sufficient period, in terms of apparent average life,
to be a dependable representation of the actual situation.

The simulation principle is so simple, and its application so obvious, that examples are not felt to be necessary here. A detailed description of procedures using desk-type calculators appears in the Edison Electric Institute report mentioned above. It includes suggested forms and describes in greater detail the conformance and retirements-experience indices.[4]

A more sensitive indicator may be useful in application to well-behaved data, obtainable by matching calculated annual retirements (instead of plant balances) against reported annual retirements. These calculations may start with known annual gross additions (the Indicated Retirements Method[5]), or with known annual net additions (the Indicated Annual Renewals Method[6]). The latter makes use of the concept of a continuing plant, mentioned before and to be discussed later in more detail, and has some advantages under certain special conditions.

Nowadays, the simulation procedure is carried out by means of digital computers. Again, the AGA-EEI Depreciation Accounting Committees have made significant contributions to the art. For the benefit of those to whom their material is available, a few typical references are footnoted.[7] Great strides have been taken toward near-automation of tests for conformance, selection of successive patterns for trial, observation of trends, minimization of operations, and so forth. It is regrettable that so little on this subject appears in the literature of managerial accounting.

Assessing the Future

It is common knowledge that relatively little property is retired primarily because it is worn out. More often it is "fired," for a variety of reasons: it is inadequate; repairs are excessive as to their cost or because of the "down time" involved; more efficient replacements are economically justified; automation is desirable; demand for the product has fallen off; fire or other accident has damaged it; space requirements are excessive.

Some companies have a policy of retiring passenger automobiles when only one year old. The reasons are that their salesmen run up tremendous mileages in one year, turn-in values are high, and it is felt that the smarter appearance of an always-new fleet is worth paying

---

[4]A description of the method was also published by its author:

Alex E. Bauhan, "Simulated Plant-Record Method of Life Analysis of Utility Plant for Depreciation Accounting Purposes," Land Economics (May, 1964).

[5]Henry R. Whiton, "The Indicated Retirement Approach to the Simulated Plant-Record Method of Estimating Lives of Mass Accounts of Utility Property for Depreciation Accounting Purposes," Proceedings of the AGA-EEI National Accounting Conference, 1947 (mimeo.).

[6]Paul H. Jeynes, "Indicated Renewals," Proceedings of the AGA-EEI National Accounting Conference, 1947 (mimeo.).

[7]More or less typical contributions are H. Frank Carey (Long Island Lighting Company), "Machine Calculation of Depreciation Account and Reserve Requirements by a Modified Fisher Method," Nov. 18, 1965 (mimeo.); and Roy H. Berglund (Northern States Power Company), "Machine Calculations of Trends in Average Life of Utility Plant," Proceedings of the National Conference of Electric and Gas Utility Accountants, April, 1966 (mimeo.).

something for. Other companies find that the minimum cost of passenger cars, in their experience, dictates a six-year life, on the average, and minimized cost is the controlling factor. Such policy decisions are not permanent; they may change with a change in administration.

Before World War II, some large users of electrical equipment such as motors and transformers had advantageous exchange-sales agreements with manufacturers of such equipment. Turn-in allowances were so high that it did not pay to make any but minor repairs. Accordingly, average life was relatively short; annual maintenance expense was nearly nothing. When such agreements were terminated, the companies set up their own repair shops. Average life increased substantially, at the expense of repair costs. Although the equipment was of substantially the same nature as before, used for the same purposes, one important reason for retirement had changed.

Sometimes a choice of equipment to be used for the same purpose is available. Laborsaving devices may be available at a price which makes them desirable under certain temporary conditions and not justifiable under other conditions. As a result, age at retirement and replacement may depend on forces that vary from time to time.

Studies of relative economy, such as discussed in this book, may reveal that the company's policies with respect to retirement and/or replacement could be improved upon. Again, a change in probable average life in the future is likely; a reason for retirement is altered.

If the foregoing observations have a negative flavor, it is because they deal with exceptions to the general rule that, by and large, the future is not apt to depart drastically from past experience without warning. The overwhelming preponderance of evidence shows that average life in the recent past has approximated that of still earlier generations; that current experience is pretty much the same for both; and that we have every reason to believe that, within a single company, the future will be much like the present.

It is probable that average life experienced by two different companies for the same kind of equipment will differ somewhat, owing to differences in company policy, different geographical locations, different local habits, different uses of similar equipment, and so forth. Nevertheless, some lower degree of consistency is usually found from year to year between separate individual companies.

One bit of reassuring evidence to this effect is that common experience of many companies is consistent enough so that the Internal Revenue Service has been willing to suggest average lives (for all kinds of equipment) which it is willing to accept as reasonable estimates in calculations of federal income tax. These proposed lives, presented in the bureau's Bulletin F, do not prescribe estimates that must be used; they are simply values which the bureau will accept in the absence of better evidence by the taxpayer as to the average life of such assets. General experience with similar equipment is consistent enough to justify the IRS application.

For short-lived plant, evidence as to average-life behavior

accumulates rapidly. An abundance of recent experience for analysis by any or all of the statistical methods described has accumulated. Average life and type of dispersion can be established by additions vintages, or by retirements vintages, in order to observe any trends with passage of time. Because there is so much recent experience, it is easier to review the causes of retirement which account for the observed results, including trends. There is a firm basis for predictions of the future, and predictions do not need to be projected so far into the future for short-lived plant.

On the other hand, estimates for long-lived plant have their bright side, too. If there is a paucity of actual retirement experience for long-lived plant, particularly for a young company which does not yet have old property of any description, surely it is obvious that $\beta_i d$ must be relatively small (it decreases fast with increasing life; see Tables 6.8-6.19, on pages 133-144). And the smaller $\beta_i d$ is, the smaller is the importance of great accuracy in its estimate.

Heterogeneous Accounts Versus Single Units

Quite often the major source of information as to probable life is the books of account. And quite often facilities having widely different mortality characteristics are grouped in a single account, for reasons which are completely unrelated to the present problem.

For example, retirements of electric generating plant may be made up of two distinctly different components, so far as typical average life is concerned:

1. More or less regularly occurring small replaceable items such as pumps, motors, valves, fans, flues, piping, circuit breakers, instruments and meters, control equipment, heat exchangers, fuel-handling and ash-disposal equipment, and conveyors; or
2. Very infrequent withdrawal of major items such as turbo-generator units (with or without associated boilers), condensers, circulatory pumps, fuel-preparation equipment, stacks, and electrical equipment.

As a result, it is sometimes difficult to establish any such simple pattern of retirement dispersion as reflected by the Iowa Type Curves. The smaller frequent renewals settle down to a nearly constant rate of retirement, on which is superimposed the larger infrequent retirements of the major components. The only practicable solution is to identify gross additions of each component separately, as closely as possible, and estimate a different pattern for each.

In this connection, it may be helpful to point out that the survivor curve applicable to single property units may be thought of as a rectangle (Type SQ) in every case; the probability is expressed by the relative weight given to the width of the figure. For example, for 30-year average life and Type R probability, probable survivor curves might be described as follows:

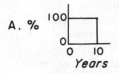

A. %

Most unlikely. Very small chance of retirement up to Age 10.

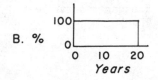

B. %

Faintly possible. Some chance of retirement between Ages 10 and 20.

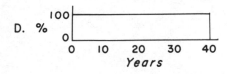

C. %

The most likely. About a 50/50 chance that this is the closest approximation of the six proposed.

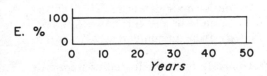

D. %

More likely than B, but less likely than C.

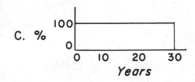

E. %

Nearly as unlikely as A; retirement fairly sure to occur by Age 40.

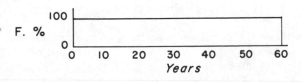

F. %

Most unlikely; but has to be mentioned as an outside possibility.

The combined probability of these six Type SQ curves may then be expressed as the single Type R_1 curve below, and the probable annuity $(\overset{\beta}{_i}d)$ computed accordingly:

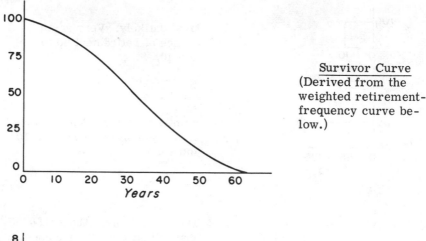

Survivor Curve
(Derived from the
weighted retirement-
frequency curve be-
low.)

Retirement-Frequency
Curve
(Weighted result of A,
B, C, D, E, F, above.)

Self-Contradictions

One common source of indefensibly erroneous estimates of depreciation and related income taxes often escapes detection. It results
from a self-contradiction unwittingly made by the estimator himself in
deciding upon the study period he will adopt in comparing alternative
proposals.

Quite often, the competing proposals to be evaluated contemplate
installation of different kinds of plant; average life of Plan A facilities
may differ substantially from the average life of facilities in Plan B.
Also, each plan may be made up of several kinds of equipment having
different lives.

In Chapter 5, we discussed the problem of settling upon a period of
study when this situation is encountered. Ordinarily, as the result of
retirement dispersion, there is no one date at which all facilities will
simultaneously reach the end of their predicted life. As a result, selecting any finite date whatever for the end of the study period necessarily means that for some or all of the facilities the depreciation annuity used to calculate annual revenue requirements cannot be correct.
Annual income taxes must also be incorrectly estimated. The only
situation where this difficulty does not arise is when the two proposals

under comparison are made up of plant having identical probable lives and identical types of dispersion.

A practical means for handling this awkward problem will be discussed in Chapter 10. But first let's see how serious it can be.

Most analysts seek to avoid the difficulty by adopting an evasive tactic. They estimate revenue requirements in <u>dollars per year</u> for each proposal, and base their decision on that comparison without stipulating any end point. This is convenient, but it is manifestly an incompetent solution unless two predictions can be firmly made:

1. As retirements occur, they will be replaced immediately <u>in kind</u> forever. That is, the replacement will be property having exactly the same probable life and type of dispersion as the units replaced, forever.
2. Price per unit of replacements will remain identical, forever, with price per unit of the initial placements.

It is substantially impossible to make any such firm long-term predictions. Therefore, this usual approach is quite amateurish in the absence of some further inquiry into the quantitative importance of the deviations from that hypothetical situation that can be reasonably predicted. For the moment, we are concerned with the self-contradiction commonly arising from any other approach, such as the "coterminate date" assumption.

Suppose we estimate return and depreciation for Plan A and Plan B as follows:

An Estimate of Annual Revenue Requirements

Plan A: 20-year life; zero net salvage; capital investment $100,000.

Plan B: 25-year life; zero net salvage; capital investment $125,000.

Minimum acceptable return = 6%.

(Here, for simplicity, we assume life to be 100% predictable, and taxes are ignored.)

Annual Revenue Requirements

	Plan A	Plan B
Minimum acceptable return	6.00%	6.00%
Depreciation	2.72	1.82
Total	8.72%	7.82%
Multiplied by the capital investment	x 100,000	x 125,000
Annual revenue requirements	$8,720/year	$9,775/year

The simple comparison of annual revenue requirements suggests that Plan A is superior, as indeed it would be if one could firmly predict the two basic conditions above would hold true forever. But, being unwilling to hazard such a dubious prediction, say the estimator decides to propose instead a 20-year period of study. But if he assumes a coterminous date at the end of Year 20, then Plan B annual revenue requirements are seriously in error. A 25-year life is impossible.

Well, then, let's consider a coterminous date at the end of Year 25 — the life of the longer-lived alternative. In such case, the equipment of Plan A would need replacement at Age 20, and the replacement would have a life of only 5 years. The comparison would then be as follows:

Plan A. 20 years at $8,720 per year, as above, plus
          5 years at $23,740 per year, as follows:
              Return   6.00%
              Depreciation   17.74% (5-year life)
                              23.74%
              x 100,000
              $ 23,740/year for 5 years

Plan B. 25 years at 9,775 per year, as before.
          Which plan is now superior?

Plan A: 100,000 x 1.000000 = $100,000
         100,000 x 0.311805 =   31,180
             Plan A, total $131,180

Plan B: 125,000 x 1.000000 = $125,000

Plan B is now superior. If any chance exists of an <u>actual</u> terminal date at Year 25, this possibility cannot be ignored.

For plant having probable average life of 15-30 years or more and likely to be replaced at least once, or for plant having a probable life in excess of 30 years even though replacement may not be reasonably certain, the rational solution is to base the comparison on the present worth of all future revenue requirements (PWAFRR), mentioned before and to be discussed in Chapter 10. In such case, the effect of the terminal date on the probable-life estimate can be safely ignored. Otherwise, <u>it is necessary to consider the effect of the presumed terminal date on the life estimates of replacements</u> if the awkward self-contradiction is to be eliminated. This is particularly important if the coterminous date assumption is deliberately adopted, which is not recommended if it can possibly be avoided. Chapter 10 discusses the disciplined solution (Continuing Plant).

Résumé

     I. Less difficulty is encountered in making reasonable life estimates than is generally appreciated.

     II. Because life estimates are predictions of future retirement dates, the only figure possible of estimate is <u>probable average</u> life.

III. The expression <u>probable average</u> life firmly recognizes the likelihood of actual retirements occurring before and after the average date. The pattern of this "scatter" of retirements is known as <u>retirement dispersion</u>.

IV. It is essential that the arithmetical effect of retirement dispersion be recognized in:

a. Estimating probable average life;
b. Computing the depreciation annuity which corresponds to probable average life;
c. Computing depreciation reserves which result from a given average life; and
d. Computing income taxes related to a given average life.

V. The process of estimating probable life <u>does not</u> rest on the assumption that future events will repeat the past. Two steps are always involved:

a. The survey of past experience; observation of average lives realized; and the reasons for retirements which brought about that result.
b. Consideration for current events and future trends in the events which will affect future retirement dates.

VI. A number of statistical methods for analysis of past experience are well established. They are applicable to any kind of plant for which the necessary information is available.

VII. Several reasons for having confidence in the possibility of making dependable estimates are important. One reason is the limited range of retirement-dispersion patterns ordinarily encountered. Another is the fact that the accuracy of life estimates influences the present worth of revenue requirements other than return and depreciation only (that is, income tax, other taxes, operation and maintenance, and so forth).

VIII. Before applying analytical methods to available data, the data must be scrutinized to insure that they are worthy of analysis. Several common sources of misinformation can be detected and corrected.

IX. The most useful methods of analysis are:

a. Actuarial methods
    (1) Original-group
    (2) Annual-rate
b. Turnover methods
    (1) Half-cycle ratio
    (2) Geometric mean
c. Simulated-plant-record methods.

X. The so-called Graveyard or Tombstone Method is to be avoided. This procedure looks to "average age at retirement" as the index to probable average life.

XI. The Iowa Type Curves provide a convenient means for classifying retirement-dispersion patterns. Other systems have been proposed but they are less well known.

XII. A valuable "feel" for the importance of the several important contributing factors in estimating life may be developed by setting up simple models to test their relative quantitative importance.

XIII. Errors in estimating life of short-lived plant result in large percentage errors in the estimate of revenue requirements. However, short-lived plant produces so much information as to lives currently experienced that large errors are unlikely. Longer-lived plant produces a smaller mass of information, but errors in estimating life produce much smaller percentage errors in the estimate of revenue requirements.

XIV. Ignoring effects of probability (retirement dispersion) results in underestimates of revenue requirements for depreciation and taxes. If no information whatever is available to suggest the probable pattern of retirement dispersion, an arbitrary selection of Type R_1 or S_2 is recommended. Such an arbitrary selection is far better than ignoring it altogether (as is common practice), which commonly introduces an unforgivable error around 4% of estimated minimum revenue requirements.

XV. As noted at the end of Chapter 6, the depreciation annuity is never correctly estimated at the so-called sinking-fund rate, $i/[(1 + i)^n - 1]$, which is always an underestimate.

XVI. It is important to recognize effects of probability, as represented by retirement-dispersion patterns, even when estimating service life for a single unit which obviously must be retired all at once.

XVII. Self-contradictions introduced by arbitrary assumptions concerning a terminal date for the cost comparison can be readily avoided.

XVIII. Among the few helpful references on this subject of service-life estimates are the following:

a. Engineering Subcommittee, Depreciation Accounting Committee, Edison Electric Institute, New York, Methods of Estimating Utility Plant Life (No. 51-23, 1951).

b. Anson Marston, Robley Winfrey, and Jean C. Hempstead, Engineering Valuation and Depreciation, 2nd ed. (Iowa State University Press, Ames, 1964).

Problems

1. What is the difference between $\bar{R}$ (which could also be written $\bar{R}_x$), and $R_{\bar{x}}$? Why is the distinction so important?

2. Since investors' committed capital is represented by net plant, and the purpose of depreciation charges is to "keep busy" that investment, why not depreciate net plant only rather than gross plant? Explain in detail.

3. Cite reasons, drawn from your own experience, why it cannot be expected that average life of equipment bought today will necessarily duplicate past experience with similar equipment.

4. Nonregulated companies ordinarily "plow back" some part of their earnings into the business. Can a regulated public utility do the same? Explain.

5. A well-known textbook points out that sinking funds are sometimes established to guarantee repayment of the face value of bonds at maturity, and that in such cases part of depreciation charges are so invested annually. Do you concur? Explain.

6. Can you imagine any conditions which might justify estimating MAR at 7% for one alternative and at some other percentage for a competing proposal? Explain fully.

7. Suppose that over the past few years a company had adopted price-level-adjusted depreciation, in place of depreciating actual original cost. Assuming that all other items of operating revenue deductions remained the same, in what direction would the following items change by the end of the period, and why:

    a. Capital stock and long-term debt
    b. Earned surplus
    c. Plant
    d. Depreciation reserves
    e. Accounts payable
    f. Materials and supplies

(For example, materials and supplies would not change, because that account is not related to the change in policy.)

8. Place T (true) or F (false), as appropriate, before each of the following statements:

    a. Net salvage affects the survivor pattern of a group of plant installations.
    b. The survivor pattern of a group of plant installations affects the average life of the group.
    c. The plant survivor pattern does not affect the associated reserve balance when the "straight-line" rate is used.
    d. The plant survivor pattern does not affect the associated retirement pattern.
    e. Net salvage does not affect the survivor pattern.
    f. Net salvage affects the periodic depreciation accruals in dollars.
    g. Net salvage does not affect the present worth of revenue requirements for capital recovery.
    h. Net salvage affects average life.
    i. For a particular survivor pattern plotted against years of service life only one average life figure exists.
    j. For a given average life only one survivor pattern exists.
    k. The present worth of mean annual survivors of a group of plant units is affected by anticipated ultimate net salvage.
    l. In addition to other factors, net plant in Year x is affected by the summation of retirements from Year 0 through Year x.
    m. Using Method Y on page 118 for tabulating annual revenue requirements for capital recovery, net salvage affects the dollars of return.

n. Using Method X on page 118 for tabulating annual revenue requirements for capital recovery, net salvage affects the annual dollars for
both return and depreciation.

o. Survivors at the end of Year x may be represented by the expression:

$$y_0 - \sum_0^x (1 - c) \cdot \text{retirements.}$$

p. If net salvage is zero, then net plant is determined solely by the expression: $y_0 - \sum_0^x {_0}d\, y_x$.

q. Assuming zero net salvage, the present worth of lifetime capital
recovery costs equals the initial investment only when the "interest
rate" is MAR.

r. The lifetime present worth of capital recovery costs always equals
the lifetime present worth of revenue requirements for capital recovery.

s. If $i = 6\%$, ${_i^\beta}d\,(1 - c)$ is always less than ${_0}d\,(1 - c)$.

t. ${_i^\beta}d(1 - c)$ is not affected by the interest rate.

u. The depreciated cost of plant is affected by net salvage.

v. If $i = 6\%$, the Method X lifetime-levelized percentage for return is
always less than the Method Y percentage return.

w. Percent condition at the end of Year x is the ratio of the unrecovered
portion of the investment in the original group of plant to the total investment in the original group.

x. If $\bar{y}_x$ represents the mean annual survivors of a group of plant units;
v^x represents the corresponding present worth factors; and ${_0}d(1 - c)$
represents the annual "straight-line" accrual rate; then:

$$\sum_0^\omega {_0}d(1 - c)\, v^x\, \bar{y}_x \Big/ \sum_0^\omega v^x \bar{y}_x \text{ represents the depreciation annuity,} {_i^\beta}d(1 - c).$$

y. $i \sum_0^\omega v^x\, (\bar{y}_x - \text{Reserve}) + {_0}d(1 - c) \sum_0^\omega v^x \bar{y}_x \Big/ \sum_0^\omega v^x \bar{y}_x$ equals $i + {_i^\beta}d(1 - c)$.

z. A company's income taxes are affected by the type of retirement dispersion as well as by average service life of its plant units. (Possibly this question is "unfair" since income tax is first treated in the
next chapter; but a thoughtful student should be able to answer.)

9. Illustrate use of the simulated-plant-record method of analysis by applying it to synthetic data prepared by yourself, as follows:

a. Assume an average life of 5 years, Type SQ (for simplicity).

b. Prepare a table of mean annual survivors.

c. Starting with an installation of 1,000 units at the beginning of Year 1,
prepare a table of gross annual additions for the next 20 years, assuming approximately 5% annual growth (that is, of additions).

d. Calculate the annual plant balances that would result, using the
simulated-plant-record procedure.

e. Now introduce some deliberate annual variability, by increasing the
annual balances slightly in some years, decreasing them in the following year in each case by the same amount.

f. Assuming that all the analyst knows is: (1) annual additions, per
item c, and (2) annual plant balances, per item e, show how he would
estimate mortality characteristics of the account, arriving at approximately 5, SQ.
(Note: To minimize the number of trials, investigate 4, SQ, 5,
SQ, and 6, SQ only, for purposes of this problem.)

10. List the important reasons why you can expect to make life estimates
adequate for the intended purpose by methods described in this chapter.

11. Of all white male babies born alive in the United States, approximately

50% can expect to be still living at age 70. Almost none can hope to live past age 95. Without referring to tables, approximately what is their life expectancy at age 70?

12. Why is it worthwhile understanding such terms as "additions era" and "retirements era" before attempting to make economic studies?

13. The question is often asked whether analyses of past mortality experience should be based on property units or on dollars of capital investment retired. Describe the nature of studies you would suggest to inquire into the matter.

14. Explain how interim replacements (sometimes called interim renewals) affect the value of $_i^\beta d$. Illustrate with a simple example. (Careful!)

15. What is the major distinction between R, S, and L Type curves? For a given life and MAR, which type would you expect to produce the smaller value of $_i^\beta d$ (aside from drawing conclusions from tables of $_i^\beta d$)?

16. Philosophers have long warned that deductive reasoning has its limitations. For example, how can anyone prove that the sun will rise again tomorrow? By that same token, how can anyone prove that past mortality experience has any bearing at all on future mortality experience for the same kind of assets?

In view of this difficulty, what are your reasons for having any confidence in estimates of service life made in the manner described in this chapter.

17. In rebuttal of Patrick Henry's viewpoint (footnote, page 157) the following assertion by Edmund Burke might be quoted: "You can never plan the future by the past."

Would you say that this mutual contradiction just proves the futility of trying to establish principles by majority opinion? Or does some interpretation of both statements reveal them to be complementary, each supporting the other? (Hint: Refer to the opening paragraphs of Chapter 1.)

18. A useful device often employed by economists is to postulate a hypothetical set of conditions and to analyze economic behavior of a problem if such conditions were to prevail. Such behavior is said to be "under certainty." They then introduce probable deviations from that certainty which might reasonably be expected in the light of practical experience, and reexamine results. This is known as recognizing "real world" situations.

Explain why this approach is particularly well suited to the analytical approach described on page 173: the hypothetical replacement-in-kind pattern.

19. Explain in your own words:
    a. Why it is essential to make allowance for retirement dispersion in estimating the depreciation annuity for a single property unit, which necessarily must be retired all at once, and therefore cannot have any retirement dispersion.
    b. Why it is preferable by far to assume some, even though 100% arbitrary, type of dispersion other than SQ, when estimating the depreciation annuity for a plant of a new kind, for which there is no experience whatever to serve as a guide to the probable retirement pattern?

20. a. Bring to class a stick of any convenient length; say about 21 inches long. Have each member of the class write down his independent estimate of its length, to the nearest half or quarter inch. Collect the estimates, and plot the frequency curve (that is, the number of estimates at each interval of length). Calculate and show the mean, mode, and average estimates. Then measure the stick, and indicate its actual length on the curve. Finally, draw up the curve corresponding to the survivor curve.
    b. Suppose that each member of the class, instead of submitting an estimate of length, submitted a stick whose length corresponded to his estimate. You would then have a collection of sticks of various but determinate lengths. Suppose you then plotted the resultant frequency

curve, indicating the mean, mode, and average length of the sticks. Would this reproduce the previous curve exactly?

Explain how these experiments illustrate the phenomenon of retirement dispersion, applied to a group of life objects and to a single object.

c. Suppose you tossed ten coins a large number of times (more than 30), keeping a record each time of the number of heads and tails. What percentage of the time would you expect to get five heads and five tails? Try it, and see. Discuss how an uninformed sucker might be taken by betting on the result. What bearing does this have on the matter of estimating the depreciation annuity?

8

• • • • • Income Taxes • •

A Unique Problem

The Diagrams of Intent on page 190 make it clear that a company's income tax payments have two distinct components:

T = the <u>revenue requirement</u> for income tax
   = the <u>tax on taxable portion</u> of MAR.
T' = income tax on <u>Profit Incentive</u>
   = the <u>tax on earnings</u> in excess of MAR.

Only the first, the revenue requirement for income tax, enters into economic comparisons.

Two other observations are also important:

1. Income tax is an expense, like outlays for payrolls, repairs, materials and supplies, or real estate taxes. Income tax is not income. The <u>amount</u> of income tax due depends upon the amount of the firm's income. But there is no more sense in discussing "earnings before income tax" than there is in discussing "earnings before repairs." That is a good deal like discussing "earned runs before the first inning"; it suggests ignorance of rules of the game.

2. Income taxes are a matter of law. Laws do not necessarily conform to economic principles or to common sense. Thus, the first essential is to become acquainted with exact provisions of the tax law and with details of its administration by the Treasury Department.

Having become familiar with such details, we will discover that it is perfectly feasible to develop expressions for income taxes, both T and T', that will result from any combination of the numerous variables involved. The formulas may appear a little complicated on first inspection, but actually they are quite easily evaluated.

Because the exact behavior of income taxes is so complicated and depends upon such a large number of variables whose behavior is not well understood by most people, it could be expected that the literature on this subject would be impressively low grade, unhelpful, and misleading to the point of working serious mischief. A large volume of such unsound opinion has been so widely circulated that it seems desirable to devote some space to a discussion of its faults and dangers. This critique is largely contained in Appendix C, though occasional references to unsound opinions are scattered throughout the text of this chapter wherever appropriate.

Two Basic Formulas, Plus "Liberalization"

Basic Formula 8.1 permits calculation of $T\%$ (= the lifetime-levelized revenue requirement for federal income tax) in percent of capital investment. It is described as "basic" because it assumes use of "straight-line" depreciation for both books and for tax depreciation purposes. It applies to depreciable assets installed before 1954, which are not eligible for liberalized-depreciation benefits.

Basic Formula 8.2 permits calculation of $T'\%$ (= the tax on Profit Incentive). It consists simply in applying the statutory tax rate (t), currently 48%, to the amount of Profit Incentive, since T' is not affected at all by deductible depreciation, by interest on debt, liberalized depreciation, investment credit, or "guidelines."

Formula 8.3 allows for effects of liberalized depreciation on T, but not for investment credit. It applies to assets that are not eligible for the investment credit.

Formula 8.4 allows for effects of both liberalized depreciation and investment credit on T, and is applicable to assets eligible for both.

We will first present the four formulas and give examples of their evaluation. After that, their derivation will be explained in detail, and attention will be given to a number of related matters such as "guidelines," optional depreciation methods (sum-of-years'-digits and double-rate declining-balance), and optional methods of accounting ("flow-through" versus "normalization").

Basic Formula 8.1
Annual Revenue Requirement for Federal Income Tax
("Straight-Line" Depreciation for Books and for Taxes)

$$T\% = \frac{t}{1 - t} (i + {}_i^\beta d - {}_0 d) (1 - \frac{Bb}{i}) \qquad \text{(Formula 8.1)}$$

where

t = statutory rate as a decimal fraction of taxable income. At present, t = 48% of taxable income in excess of \$25,000 annually.

i = minimum acceptable return (MAR), in %.

${}_i^\beta d$ = the depreciation annuity, in % (see Chapter 6).

${}_0 d$ = "straight-line" depreciation rate, in %, or 100/life.

B = fraction of debt in the company's "investors' committed capital," that is, expressed as a decimal. Thus, for 20% debt, B = 0.20.

b = average interest rate on outstanding debt, in %.

Adjusted for ultimate net salvage at $c\%$ (to be expressed decimally), Basic Formula 8.1 becomes:

$$T\% = \frac{t}{1 - t}\left[i + {}_i^\beta d \, (1 - c) - {}_0 d \, (1 - c)\right] (1 - \frac{Bb}{i})$$

Note particularly that Formula 8.1 expresses the tax payable on earnings equal to MAR only, adjusted for the deductible interest component.

One ordinarily expects that company earnings will exceed MAR by a margin described herein as the Profit Incentive. Of course, an income tax is payable on that Profit Incentive, as shown at the bottom of the Diagram of Intent. This tax is separately computed by Basic Formula 8.2, which follows.

Basic Formula 8.2
Federal Income Tax on Profit Incentive
(Tax Payable in Excess of the Revenue Requirement for Income Tax)

$$T'\% = \frac{t}{1 - t} \text{ (Profit Incentive)} \qquad \text{(Formula 8.2)}$$

where

t = statutory rate as a decimal fraction of taxable income. At present, t = 48% of taxable income in excess of $25,000 annually.

Profit Incentive = annual earnings in excess of minimum acceptable return (MAR). In other words, annual revenues less annual revenue requirements and less T'; all expressed as a percentage of the initial cost, installed, or plant currently in service each year.

If desired, Profit Incentive may be expressed in dollars instead of in percent; in such case, T' is obtained in dollars. T' is not a component of minimum revenue requirements; it is not involved in economic comparisons. The company's total obligations for federal income tax = $T + T'$.

Liberalized Depreciation; Investment Credit

Most companies practice liberalized depreciation; that is, they take advantage of the law permitting larger deductible depreciation than book depreciation, which usually was "straight-line," in calculating tax obligations. All are obliged to accept the investment credit. Basic Formula 8.1 left these adjustments for later consideration, for reasons noted.

Formula 8.3
Revenue Requirement for Federal Income Tax
as Affected by Liberalized Depreciation
(Assuming "Flow-Through" Accounting)[1]

$$T\% = \frac{t}{1-t}\left[(i + \tfrac{\beta}{i}d - d')(1 - \frac{Bb}{i}) - (d_t - d')\right] \quad \text{(Formula 8.3)}$$

where all symbols are the same as in Formula 8.1, except:

d' = the book-depreciation annuity ($= {}_0d$, for "straight-line").
d_t = the tax-depreciation annuity, per Figure 8.1a,b,c.

As in Basic Formula 8.1, adjustment for ultimate net salvage is made by multiplying $\tfrac{\beta}{i}d$, d', and d_t by $(1 - c)$, where c is percentage net salvage expressed decimally.[2]

Formula 8.4 presents the expression for lifetime-levelized tax as affected by liberalized depreciation plus investment credit (1964 allowance). The investment credit is 7% of eligible new capital investment in the year of its placement, except for certain public utilities which are granted a 3% credit (that is, three-sevenths of the nonutility allowance). Since the credit is effective at the end of that first year of service life, it may be converted into a lifetime equivalent annuity as follows:

$$IC \text{ (in dollars)} = \frac{k(i + \tfrac{\beta}{i}d)}{1 + i} \cdot P_0$$

where k is 7% or 3%, as appropriate, and P_0 is the new capital investment. Here, $\tfrac{\beta}{i}d$ is not to be adjusted for salvage. However, the effect of IC on $T\%$ is not so simple as you might expect on first thought.

Formula 8.4
Revenue Requirement for Federal Income Tax
as Affected by Liberalized Depreciation and the Investment Credit
(Assuming "Flow-Through" Accounting)

$$T\% = \frac{t}{1-t}\left[(i + \tfrac{\beta}{i}d - d')(1 - \frac{Bb}{i}) - (d_t - d') - IC\right] - IC \quad \text{(Formula 8.4)}$$

---

[1]We can assume that the company practices "flow-through" accounting unless it specifically "normalizes" tax deferrals. Few companies other than certain public utilities "normalize."

[2]For SYD and DRDB depreciation, applying the factor $(1 - c)$ is only an approximation of the exact adjustment for salvage. However, it is a close approximation except in cases of exceptionally large percentage salvage and unusually short life. For an illustration of the exact adjustment, Type SQ dispersion, see Example 4, Chapter 12 (page 365). For types of dispersion other than SQ, the exact calculation calls for computation of unrecovered balances year by year, as affected by salvage, to find the adjusted depreciation expense each year from which the lifetime-levelized annuity is found, as in Appendix C (Tables C.1, C.2, and C.3).

where all symbols are the same as in Formula 8.3, and IC represents the investment credit as evaluated in the preceding paragraph.

Figures 8.1a, b, and c are plots of the depreciation annuity for sum-of-years'-digits (SYD) or double-rate-declining-balance (DRDB) depreciation; for lives from 1 to 60 years; for MAR at 6%, 7%, and 8%, respectively; and for extreme types of dispersion SC and SQ.[3] Annuities for other conditions may be obtained by interpolation. For Iowa Type dispersions having subscripts near zero the annuity will lie near the SC curves; for subscripts near 6 it will lie nearer the SQ curves.

Note that the revenue requirement for income tax, $T\%$, is reduced by almost double k (7% or 3%) times the new investment, for the same MAR after taxes, which is the only meaningful way to express MAR.

Quantitative Effects

The magnitude of the tax reduction that can be realized by taking advantage of permissive liberalized depreciation and mandatory investment credit provisions of the law does not appear to be generally appreciated. A few sample calculations will illustrate the point.

A. Basic Formula 8.1 (for MAR = 6%; $t = 48\%$)

1. Effect of Service Life

   (a) Probable life = 10, R_1. Zero net salvage; no deductible interest.

   $$T\% = \frac{0.48}{0.52} (6.00 + 8.28 - 10.00)(1 - 0) = 3.95\%$$

   (b) Probable life = 40, R_1. Zero net salvage; no deductible interest.

   $$T\% = \frac{0.48}{0.52} (6.00 + 1.27 - 2.50)(1 - 0) = 4.40\%$$

2. Effect of Deductible Interest

   (a) Same as 1(a); but 50% debt at 4% interest.

   $$T\% = \frac{0.48}{0.52} (6.00 + 8.28 - 10.00)(1 - \frac{0.50 \times 4}{6}) = 2.63\%$$

   (b) Same as 1(b); but 50% debt at 4% interest.

   $$T\% = \frac{0.48}{0.52} (6.00 + 1.27 - 2.50)(1 - \frac{0.50 \times 4}{6}) = 2.94\%$$

3. Effect of Change in Statutory Tax Rate (t)

   (a) Same as 1(a); but 52% tax rate.

   $$T\% = \frac{0.52}{0.48} (6.00 + 8.28 - 10.00)(1 - 0) = 4.64\%$$

   (b) Same as 1(b); but 52% tax rate.

   $$T\% = \frac{0.52}{0.48} (6.00 + 1.27 - 2.50)(1 - 0) = 5.17\%$$

---

[3]These evaluations of d_t are based on the special studies and calculations made by William G. Michaelson, Public Service Electric & Gas Company, Newark, N.J.

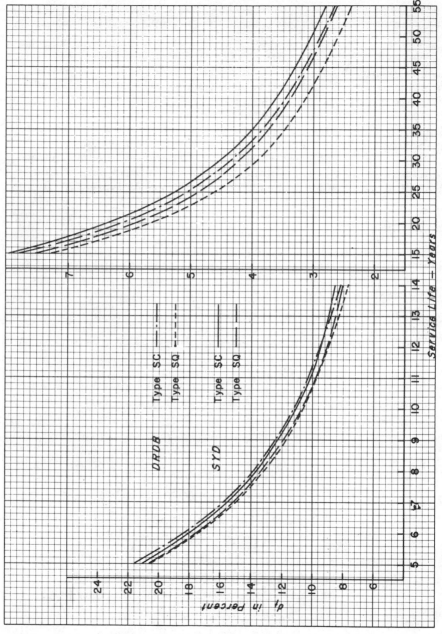

Fig. 8.1a. Values of d_i; MAR at 6%. For two extreme types of dispersions. (For further details, see Appendix C.)

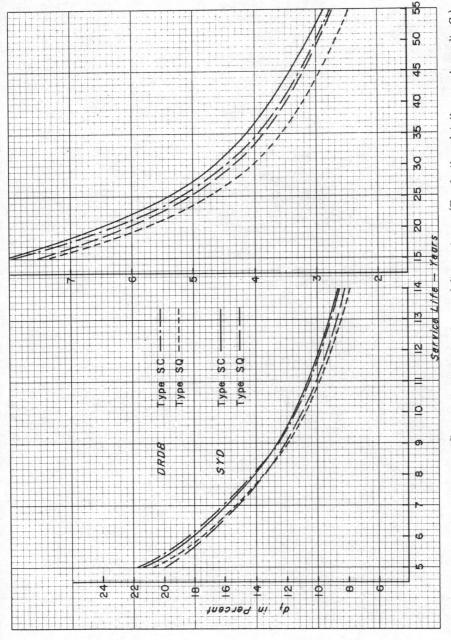

Fig. 8.1b. Values of d_t; MAR at 7%. For two extreme types of dispersions. (For further details, see Appendix C.)

187

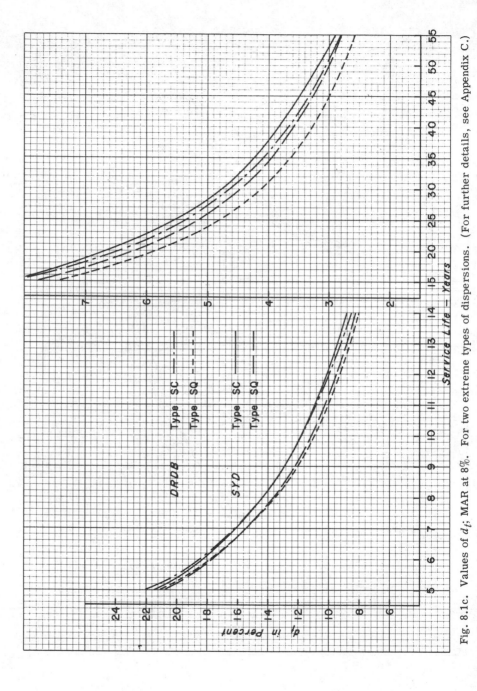

Fig. 8.1c. Values of d_t; MAR at 8%. For two extreme types of dispersions. (For further details, see Appendix C.)

B. Formula 8.3, Liberalized Depreciation
  (a) Same as A, 1(a); but DRDB for tax depreciation ("straight-line" for books).

$$T\% = \frac{0.48}{0.52}\left[(6.00 + 8.28 - 10.00)(1 - 0) - (11.05 - 10.00)\right] = 2.98\%$$

  (b) Same as A, 1(b); but DRDB for tax depreciation ("straight-line" for books).

$$T\% = \frac{0.48}{0.52}\left[(6.00 + 1.27 - 2.50)(1 - 0) - (3.32 - 2.50)\right] = 3.65\%$$

C. Formula 8.4, Liberalized Depreciation and Investment Credit
  (a) Same as B(a), but with 7% investment credit.

$$T\% = \frac{0.48}{0.52}\left[(6.00 + 8.28 - 10.00)(1 - 0) - (11.05 - 10.00) - 0.94\right]$$
$$- 0.94 = 1.17\%$$

  (b) Same as B(b), but with 7% investment credit.

$$T\% = \frac{0.48}{0.52}\left[(6.00 + 1.27 - 2.50)(1 - 0) - (3.32 - 2.50) - 0.48\right]$$
$$- 0.48 = 2.72\%$$

D. Zero Revenue Requirement for Tax; Formula 8.4 with Large Debt
  (a) Same as C(a), but with 50% debt at 3.58% interest.

$$T\% = \frac{0.48}{0.52}\left[(6.00 + 8.28 - 10.00)(1 - \frac{0.50 \times 3.58}{6.00})\right.$$
$$\left. - (11.05 - 10.00) - 0.94\right] - 0.94 = 0$$

All the foregoing are calculations of the revenue requirement (= T) for federal income tax; they are not calculations of the total income tax payable (= $T + T'$) on earnings of the project. This distinction is most important. It is overlooked by all methods of analysis other than MRRD.

Economic comparisons must be made by looking at revenue requirements only, as indicated by the shaded portion of the Diagram of Intent; not by comparing revenues. And revenue requirements of a project include T, but not T'. It is perfectly possible for the revenue requirement T to be zero, as illustrated by the foregoing Example D. In such case, income tax does not enter into the economic comparison at all, even though the company may be paying a tax T' on earnings in excess of MAR. This fact is overlooked by all methods of analysis other than MRRD. That is one important reason why MRRD must not be described as "the Annual Cost Method with return pegged at MAR." Return is not pegged at MAR in the Minimum Revenue Requirements Discipline. Return is recognized as MAR plus Profit Incentive, and Profit Incentive is not "pegged" at anything. Figure 8.2 illustrates the situation.

The economic choice between the two alternative proposals is identified by its smaller revenue requirements (the shaded area) out of the larger identical revenues from identical sales which are tentatively

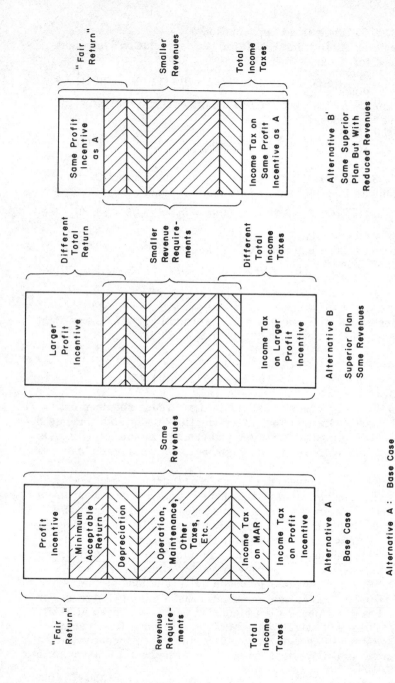

Fig. 8.2. Diagram of Intent.

190

hypothesized for purposes of this identification. Once having identified the superior alternative and the amount of its superiority in this manner, the disposition of benefits obtained by adopting the superior choice is another matter; it is a separate managerial problem in pricing. Management may, if desired, maintain prices and revenues at the tentatively hypothesized level. Or, if felt desirable and necessary, prices and revenues for that same output may be reduced, and some or all of the benefit thus be passed on to consumers, while MAR remains at its original level.[4] The point is that determination of the economic choice is not affected by this subsequent pricing decision.

Consequently, the magnitude of Profit Incentive and the tax (T') on Profit Incentive play no part in identification of the economic choice. Since the amount of T' is affected by the subsequent pricing decision, it is essential that T' be excluded from the process of making the economic comparison.

Service Life and Taxes

The sample calculations demonstrate that $T\%$ is affected importantly by service life. Percentage income tax is smallest for lives near 10 years, greater for shorter and longer lives. It must also be recognized that the estimate of probable taxes is a function of the probable depreciation annuity $\frac{\beta}{i}d$ (from Tables 6.8-6.19, pages 133 to 144). This factor has been introduced in Formulas 8.1, 8.3, and 8.4. An associated problem, however, cannot be disposed of in that manner.

Formulas 8.1, 8.3, and 8.4 evaluate percentage tax. The question is, "Percentage of what?" The answer is, "Percentage of $P_{\overline{x}}$, the portion of the initial capital investment P_0 that is still in service in each Year x."

Accordingly, the probable tax is not $T\%$ of the initial cost of a single installation (P_0) in each year unless replacements are made as retirements occur, so that 100% of the original capital investment is kept in service in every future year. But present worth of $T\% \times P_0$, indefinitely, is obviously greater than the present worth of $T\% \times P_x$ for one lifetime of a single installation.

This phenomenon was discussed before in connection with the revenue requirement for capital recovery (return plus depreciation). It is necessary for the analyst to state his exact intention, whether he means to calculate $T\% \times P_x$ for a single initial installation, or the larger figure $T\% \times P_0$, for a plant maintained by reason of capital investments in the single initial placement plus replacements.

The usual solution, adopted by reason of failing to see the problem, is to make the unreasonable assumption that service life can be predicted with 100% certainty (as if in retrospect), so that the initial

---

[4]It is possible, of course, that reducing prices might increase sales and revenues, which is the reason for emphasizing the proviso "for that same output."

capital investment P_0 remains in service without replacements for exactly one service life. The error in the resultant estimate of taxes is
not as serious as the error in estimating the revenue requirement for
depreciation, which can be as much as 50%. For important decisions,
though, the lifetime tax actually paid could be quite far removed from
the usual careless estimate.

This subject will be explored further in Chapter 10 and Appendix
C: "Behavior of T, Continuing Plant."

Opinions and Misconceptions

Before embarking upon derivation of Basic Formulas 8.1 and 8.2,
together with Formulas 8.3 and 8.4, it seems wise to call brief attention
to a number of widely accepted misconceptions concerning income
taxes. These misunderstandings are so generally and uncritically accepted as the basis for action, and often so plausible on superficial
consideration, that they are responsible for uncounted decisions that
have been costly and wasteful. For this reason, a presentation of the
subject of taxes that describes only the appropriate arithmetic is inadequate for the student's purpose.

The most serious fallacy in unsound practices is a misconception
of public utility income taxes. Applied to the exceptionally large capital investments that are typical of public utilities, this particular error
is especially grave. That is, it is widely believed that income taxes
paid by public utilities differ somehow from those paid by nonregulated
("competitive") industry. This is quite untrue. Formulas 8.1, 8.2, 8.3,
and 8.4 apply in exactly the same way to both public utilities and nonregulated industry. It is important that the student perceive the source
of this misunderstanding, because it illustrates forcefully how a whole
series of wrong conclusions can flow from one apparently minor departure from an exact definition of intent.

The culprit in this case is the "small" departure from the analyst's
exact intent that is inherent in the Annual Cost Method. It is asserted
(incorrectly, but the Annual Cost reasoning permits no other interpretation) that the utility's "fair rate of return on rate base" represents
the company's cost of capital, "interest rate," or otherwise described
rate of return to be used in its economy studies. Such a view defies a
basic principle upon which the whole system of public utility regulation
depends. It ignores the margin of Profit Incentive, which is even more
important to public utilities than to nonregulated industry. "Fair return" equals MAR plus a regulated "fair" Profit Incentive.[5] It is this
margin of Profit Incentive only that is regulable; MAR is established
by investors themselves, who supply the capital.

---

[5]See:
    Ellsworth Nichols and Francis X. Welch, "Zone of Reasonableness Above Confiscation
Point," Ruling Principles of Utility Regulation, Rate of Return, Supplement A (Public Utilities Reports, Inc., Washington, D.C., 1964), p. 20.

The unsound Annual Cost reasoning leads to several other conclusions concerning taxes for public utilities that are indefensible: that the tax depends on the nature of rate regulation to be expected; that it is a function of rate base; that it depends on the ratio of rate base to book value; that it depends on the special assumption that the amount of debt associated with any particular asset can be identified; and that it depends on the special assumption that the ratio of interest on debt to total return will remain constant throughout service life. None of these is unqualifiedly true.

Further mischief (of a little different nature) done by Annual Cost reasoning is discussed in Chapters 11 and 14. For the moment, though, we will confine our attention to tax aspects of the situation, and correct the above misunderstandings by a series of statements. Students of MRRD probably will regard them as rather obvious truisms, but they are direct contradictions of unsound beliefs held by those who have not yet perceived the inherent shortcomings of the Annual Cost reasoning:

1. The revenue requirement for income tax to be used in economy studies is calculated in exactly the same manner for public utilities as for nonregulated enterprises. "Fair return" and "rate base" are no part of the calculation.

2. The revenue requirement for federal income tax is $T\%$ of <u>investors' committed capital</u>, represented by plant currently in service, for both public utilities and nonregulated enterprises. Formulas 8.1, 8.3, and 8.4 apply equally well to both.

3. Federal income tax on Profit Incentive is $T'\%$ of such Profit Incentive, for both public utilities and nonregulated enterprises. Formula 8.2 applies equally well to both.

4. For public utilities, as for nonregulated enterprises, income tax is paid on contributions of a project to earnings on the <u>company pool</u> of investors' committed capital. All individual projects are financed out of that company pool of capital; none are financed by means of specific issues of debt, equity, or specifically identifiable internally generated funds. Any necessary assumptions with respect to amount of debt, interest rates, or persistence of such data throughout service life are identical whether the firm is a public utility or nonregulated enterprise. There is no difference whatever in assumptions necessary for public utilities.

Other misconceptions, mostly attributable to Annual Cost reasoning, may be listed and disposed of briefly as follows:

5. Arguments arising from the unsound conclusion that because the <u>amount</u> of tax is related to the <u>amount</u> of income, the tax should be regarded as a component of income, or a part of "cost of capital." The most harmful notion in this category is the proposal to use a discount rate, in present worth and levelizing operations, that includes T in some form. Sometimes a rate of MAR $+ T$ is proposed; sometimes MAR $- tbB$; sometimes MAR $+ tbB$. Some even go so far as to define "attractive return" as "attractive return plus tax."

6. The misleading proposition that one dollar of added expense actually costs the company only about 50 cents, because the extra expense reduces income, and thereby reduces income tax. This is a favorite in arguments for fringe benefits "at half their cost," or for increased insurance which is claimed to "cost only half the premium payments." It springs from assuming a fixed amount of <u>revenues,</u> deducting larger expenses results in <u>reduced income</u> and, consequently, reduced <u>tax on income</u>. Can anyone imagine the owners of a business (stockholders) regarding reduced earnings per share as desirable just because it reduces taxes? This is discussed further in Appendix C.

7. The proposal to ignore income taxes in making economic studies because, it is claimed, the effect of the tax on alternative proposals is about the same — a prime example of disrespect for disciplined reasoning. What if one alternative involves large investment plus small maintenance expense, to be compared with another involving large maintenance expense and no investment whatever? <u>The latter has no revenue requirement for income tax at all</u>; the former, a substantial tax.

8. The notion that there is disagreement as to the appropriate tax rate applicable, because tax schedules are graduated, or set up in blocks. This is plain ignorance of tax law. The graduated schedule of <u>personal</u> income tax does not apply to corporations.

9. The unsound proposal (on occasion made by governmental agencies) to estimate income tax for any particular project at the company's average annual tax rate, in percent of capital investment. This overlooks three facts:

   (a) The company's tax rate is made up of $T\%$ plus $T'\%$; and $T'\%$ is not involved in economic comparisons.
   (b) The tax applicable to specific assets depends upon service life, dispersion type, and salvage value for those specific assets.
   (c) The average tax rate depends upon the average age of composite plant at the moment. It differs from a composite made up of different amounts of plant having different service lives, currently of different ages.

10. The curious proposition that income taxes tend to reduce cost of borrowed money, because, it is asserted, interest payments reduce taxable income. True, interest payments do reduce taxable income. But unless the tax payable were reduced to zero, income tax would still add to the revenue requirements for any given output, reduce earnings out of the given sales, and thus tend to <u>increase</u> cost of money, including cost of borrowed funds. (Another error typical of the Annual Cost reasoning.)

Tax Law

The law defines taxable income precisely and stipulates the percentage tax rate to be applied to it to find the tax payable.

Prior to 1964, federal income tax on corporate taxable income in excess of $25,000 per year was 52%. This was formally described as a "normal" tax rate of 30% on all taxable income, with a 22% "surtax" on taxable income over $25,000. The 1964 law revised these rates downward. In effect, a rate of 22% is applied to the first $25,000 and 48% (50% in 1964 only) on the excess. It is unlikely that the 1964 rates will go unchanged forever. The analyst's first task, therefore, is to ascertain the exact provisions of current law.

For purposes of explaining principles herein, we will assume that the statutory tax rate is 48%, unless otherwise stated. We will also, for simplicity and convenience, assume that company earnings are in excess of $25,000 annually, and that the sole purpose of these studies is to discover differences in the tax — differences as between adoption of alternative proposals, or as between adopting or rejecting proposals whose profitability is of concern.

Taxable income, for purposes of the federal income tax, is currently defined by law as revenues less specified "deductibles," which are:

1. Expenses other than depreciation, including all taxes except federal income tax itself, which is not deductible;
2. Interest on debt; and
3. An allowance for depreciation, which may differ from the accountant's charges to depreciation expense. Hence, an important distinction is made between (a) book depreciation and (b) tax-deductible depreciation, or "tax depreciation."

In studies of profitability and economic choice, we are concerned with future taxes throughout the whole service lifetime of physical assets. As noted before, tax law can change. However, retroactive changes in the tax have been substantially less than changes applicable to new investment. Formulas 8.1, 8.2, 8.3, and 8.4 can be readily modified when and if the law is modified in the future.

Derivation of Basic Formula 8.1

Expressed arithmetically, then, the law defines taxable income as:

$$\text{Taxable income} = \text{Revenues less deductibles} \qquad (1)$$

Thus, if revenues are just sufficient to yield a return equal to minimum acceptable return (MAR), "after taxes," they are identified as minimum revenue requirements; for short, as agreed upon earlier, simply revenue requirements.

In such case, the resultant income tax payable is the revenue

<u>requirement for income tax.</u> It will be represented herein by the following symbols:

T = revenue requirement for income tax, <u>in dollars.</u>

$T\%$ = revenue requirement for income tax, <u>in percent.</u>

This makes the symbol t available to represent the statutory tax rate,[6] currently 48% as just mentioned.

The tax is levied annually on taxable income in terms of gross income (Form X, discussed on page 118), as follows:

$$\text{Revenue requirement for income tax} = T = P_x \cdot T\%$$
$$= ti\,(P_{\overline{x}} - R_{\overline{x}}) + d'\,P_{\overline{x}} + eP_{\overline{x}} + T\% \text{ less deductibles} \qquad (2)$$

where

t = statutory rate as a decimal fraction of taxable income.

i = minimum acceptable return (MAR), in percent.

$P_{\overline{x}}$ = average capital investment, in dollars in service in Year x.

$R_{\overline{x}}$ = average depreciation reserve associated with P, in dollars, in Year x.

d' = book depreciation expense, here at the "straight-line" rate $_0d$.

e = expense other than depreciation and income tax, in percent.

The three kinds of deductibles allowed by law are:

1. Expenses $(eP_{\overline{x}})$ other than depreciation and income tax (<u>Income tax itself (T) is not a deductible expense.</u>);
2. Tax-deductible depreciation $(d_t P_{\overline{x}})$, which may differ from book depreciation $(d' P_{\overline{x}})$; and
3. The portion of gross income represented by interest on debt $(\frac{Bb}{i})(P_{\overline{x}} - R_{\overline{x}})$;

where

B = ratio of outstanding debt to total investors' committed capital.

b = average interest rate, in percent, on outstanding debt.

$R_{\overline{x}}$ = depreciation reserve in Year x.

Substituting in (2):

$$P_{\overline{x}}T\% = t\left[i(P_{\overline{x}} - R_{\overline{x}})(1 - \frac{Bb}{i}) + d'P_{\overline{x}} - d_t P_{\overline{x}} + P_{\overline{x}} \cdot T\%\right]$$

Dividing through by P_x:

$$T\% = t\left[\frac{(iP_x - R_x)}{P_x}(1 - \frac{Bb}{i}) + d' - d_t + T\%\right] \qquad (3)$$

Referring back to Tables 6.6 and 6.7 on pages 126 and 127, you will recall that the present worth of service-lifetime gross income can be expressed as:

---

[6]Note that a shortage of symbols convenient for the present purpose exists. In general, capital letters are used to designate capital amounts in dollars, or annual outlays if in dollars per year. Lowercase letters are used to designate quantities expressed in percent, or for constants. $T\%$ is an exception, as is B.

$$\sum_{x=0}^{x=\omega} v^x \cdot i(P_{\overline{x}} - R_{\overline{x}}) = \sum_{x=0}^{x=\omega} v^x(i + \tfrac{\beta}{i}d - {}_0d)P_{\overline{x}}$$

so that

$$\frac{i(P_{\overline{x}} - R_{\overline{x}})}{P_{\overline{x}}} = i + \tfrac{\beta}{i}d - {}_0d$$

If depreciation for book purposes (d') and for tax purposes (d_t) are both "straight-line" $({}_0d)$, then they cancel out, and (3) becomes:

$$T\% = t\,(i + \tfrac{\beta}{i}d - {}_0d)(1 - \frac{Bb}{i}) + tT\%$$

then

$$T\%\,(1 - t) = t\,(i + \tfrac{\beta}{i}d - {}_0d)(1 - \frac{Bb}{i})$$

and

$$T\% = \frac{t}{1-t}(i + \tfrac{\beta}{i}d - {}_0d)(1 - \frac{Bb}{i}) \quad \text{(Basic Formula 8.1)}$$

$T\%$, so calculated, is necessarily a lifetime-levelized quantity, since i (= MAR), $\tfrac{\beta}{i}d$, and Bb, are all lifetime-levelized figures, while ${}_0d$ and t are constants. As noted before, $\tfrac{\beta}{i}d$ and ${}_0d$ must be adjusted for salvage; this too is recognized in the statute. Multipliers $(1 - c)$ have been omitted from the expression for simplicity.

Since all deductibles have been utilized in calculating the revenue requirement for income tax, any margin of earnings above or below MAR is taxed directly at rate $t/(1 - t)$. This is not taxed at $t\%$, since the tax itself is not deductible; in other words, the tax is $t\%$ of taxable income, "before the tax." To clarify this situation, consider the foregoing example where we computed $T\%$ and $T'\%$ as: $T\% = 3.17\%$; and $T'\% = 3.69\%$.

With a capital investment of $10,000, the "before tax" and "after tax" relations for both MAR and the margin of earnings in excess of MAR (= Profit Incentive) may be summarized as follows:

	MAR (The "Floor")	Profit Incentive (Earnings Above the "Floor")	Total Earnings
"After tax" earnings	$600	$400	$1,000
Income tax at $t = 48\%$	317	369	686
"Before tax" earnings	$917	$769	$1,686
Tax in % of "before tax" earnings	34.6%	48.0%	40.7%
Tax in % of "after tax" earnings	52.8%	92.3%	68.6%

This illustrates what is wrong with the proposal to base economic studies on earnings "before tax." That is, there is a single figure for MAR, "after tax," that is statistically estimable and which applies to all projects, in all departments, and for all products or services sold by the company. This is the MAR on the company pool of investors' committed capital, which is the source of capital funds for all projects.

Percentage earnings "before tax" may be different for every project, because they include the tax which depends upon quantities that may differ for every individual project, such as:

1. Average life and type of dispersion;
2. Ultimate net salvage; and
3. Amount of earnings in excess of MAR.

A Reservation

As stated at the beginning of this chapter, the estimator's first duty is to become thoroughly familiar at firsthand with the tax law and details of its administration by the Internal Revenue Service. There is one detail of that administration, not mentioned before, which is very often overlooked, and which demands consideration. That is, it is ordinarily impossible to earmark the particular tax payment that is associated with any particular asset. This is because deductible depreciation for tax purposes is not calculated for each individual property unit. It is calculated by use of an established average life for each account, for each guideline group, or even for the company as a whole. For example, the IRS has in some cases allowed deductible depreciation for a company without change at the same percentage (for example, 3%) over a period of 25 years or more, where justified. This is recognized as a reasonable procedure and will not be criticized here. It does mean, however, that deductible depreciation, d_t, is not based on actual service life of individual items whose life differs from that average. And in such case, d' and d_t do not cancel out in simplifying (3) on page 197.

Note that it is not the departure from actual service life (the basis for $\frac{\beta}{i}d$) that matters. It is the difference between book depreciation (d') and tax depreciation (d_t) that is of concern here. Note also that Basic Formula 8.1 could be modified to allow for this contingency by recognizing that d' and d_t do not cancel out in developing (3). The result would be that the modified Basic Formula becomes identical with (4) (Formula 8.3) on page 184 for $T\%$ with liberalized depreciation.

A more important aspect of this situation is the effect on exact reasoning. We cannot be certain that adopting an alternative having different service life will actually affect tax differentials in the exact manner indicated by Formulas 8.1, 8.3, and 8.4 — or in any calculable manner. This is because the difference in actual service life does not affect deductible depreciation allowances immediately; it might conceivably never affect either d' or d_t. However, deliberately assuming that d' and d_t would assuredly never be affected is indefensible; and that is the only alternative. Adoption of "guidelines" and penalties for substantial departure from reasonable estimates (that is, the "reserve test") emphasize that conclusion. Thus, it is necessary to rely on an inference and hypothesis that taxes identifiable with any particular asset are reasonably estimated by using d' and d_t, associated with the service life of those particular assets.

Quantitatively, the question discussed here is of small moment. It might become significant, though, when large capital investments, whose estimated life differs substantially from those on which d' and d_t are based, are under consideration.

Year-By-Year Taxes

In studies of profitability and economic choice, need almost never arises to discover income tax obligations in any particular year. The lifetime-levelized percentage is all that is needed for most problems. However, there may be some borderline cases. Also, it cannot be said that comprehension of lifetime-levelized values is 100% complete unless their relation to year-by-year behavior is thoroughly understood. Therefore, we must understand this relation between lifetime-levelized income taxes, per Basic Formula 8.1, and their year-by-year equivalent.

Consider the following situations:[7]

Average life = 5 years, Type SC dispersion.
MAR = 6%.
Debt ratio = 60%.
Interest rate on debt = 4.50%.
Ultimate net salvage zero.
"Straight-line" depreciation for books and for taxes.

Table 8.1 shows the calculation of year-by-year revenue requirements for return and depreciation. This follows the procedure described in Chapter 6. Half of each year's retirements are assumed to occur on the first of the year and the other half at the end of the year, thus producing a "step" curve with the year's average survivors in service throughout the entire year.

Table 8.2 shows the calculations of related year-by-year income tax, assuming that tax-deductible depreciation is also "straight-line." (This proviso is important, as will be discussed later.)

The lifetime-levelized value of $T\%$, in this example would be as follows, per Basic Formula 8.1:

$$T\% = \frac{0.48}{0.52}(6.00 + 18.80 - 20.00)(1 - \frac{0.60 \times 4.50}{6.00}) = 2.438\%$$

Suppose we check this result against the data of Table 8.2. This can be done in several ways using the technique of "financial equivalency" developed in Chapter 5. Two obvious methods are:

---

[7]Several of these tables are based, with permission, on those of the paper "Can Changes in Book Depreciation Accrual Affect Income Taxes?" by Bert J. Blewitt, presented at the 1964 Annual Conference of Electric and Gas Utility Accountants. The paper is highly recommended; the principles elucidated apply to regulated or nonregulated industry equally well.

Table 8.1. Year-by-year revenue requirements for return and depreciation.
Single placement of plant, 5-year life, Type SC dispersion, zero net salvage, MAR at 6%, "straight-line" depreciation, initial capital investment $1,000.

1	2	3	4	5	6	7	8
Year	Mean Annual Survivors	Book Depreciation Accruals	Periodic Retirements at Beginning of Year	Mean Annual Depreciation Reserve Balance	Mean Annual "Net Plant" Balance*	Minimal Gross Income at 6% of Col. 6	Revenue Requirements for Return Plus Depreciation (Col.3 +, Col.7)
1	$950	$ 190	$ 50	$(50)	$1,000	$60.00	$250.00
2	850	170	100	40	810	48.60	218.60
3	750	150	100	110	640	38.40	188.40
4	650	130	100	160	490	29.40	159.40
5	550	110	100	190	360	21.60	131.60
6	450	90	100	200	250	15.00	105.00
7	350	70	100	190	160	9.60	79.60
8	250	50	100	160	90	5.40	55.40
9	150	30	100	110	40	2.40	32.40
10	50	10	100	40	10	0.60	10.60
11	...		50	...	...	...	...
Totals		$1,000	$1,000				

*"Net Plant" is the familiar but loose expression for Col. 2 - Col. 5.

200

Table 8.2. Year-by-year revenue requirements for income taxes, return, and depreciation; same plant as Table 8.1. Book depreciation method: "straight-line"; tax depreciation method: "straight-line"; debt ratio = 60%; interest rate on debt = 4.50%; statutory tax rate = 48%.

1	2	3	4	5	6	7
Year	Debt Component of "Net Plant" (1)	Revenue Requirement for Interest On Debt (2)	Revenue Requirement for Total Return (MAR) (3)	Revenue Requirement for Return on Equity (4)	Revenue Requirement for Income Tax (5)	Revenue Requirement for Income Tax, Return, and Depreciation (6)
1	$600	$27.00	$60.00	$33.00	$30.46	$280.46
2	486	21.87	48.60	26.73	24.67	243.27
3	384	17.28	38.40	21.12	19.50	207.90
4	294	13.23	29.40	16.17	14.93	174.33
5	216	9.72	21.60	11.88	10.97	142.57
6	150	6.75	15.00	8.25	7.62	112.62
7	96	4.32	9.60	5.28	4.87	84.47
8	54	2.43	5.40	2.97	2.74	58.14
9	24	1.08	2.40	1.32	1.22	33.62
10	6	0.27	0.60	0.33	0.30	10.90

(1) At 60% of Col. 6, Table 8.1
(2) At 4.50% of Col. 2
(3) Per Col. 7, Table 8.1

(4) Col. 4 - Col. 3
(5) At 48/52 times Col. 5
(6) Col. 6 + Col. 4 + Col. 3, Table 8.1

201

Table 8.3. Part I: Present worth of year-by-year revenue requirements (from Tables 8.1 and 8.2).

1	2	3	4	5	6	7	8	9
						Present Worth of		
Year	Minimal Gross Income	Book Depreciation	Income Tax	Present Worth Factors at 6%	Minimal Gross Income	Depreciation	Tax	Total
1	$60.00	$190.00	$30.46	0.9434	$ 56.60	$179.25	$28.74	$ 264.59
2	48.60	170.00	24.67	.8900	43.25	151.30	21.96	216.51
3	38.40	150.00	19.50	.8396	32.24	125.94	16.37	174.55
4	29.40	130.00	14.93	.7921	23.29	102.97	11.82	138.08
5	21.60	110.00	10.97	.7473	16.14	82.20	8.19	106.53
6	15.00	90.00	7.62	.7050	10.57	63.45	5.37	79.39
7	9.60	70.00	4.87	.6651	6.39	46.55	3.24	56.18
8	5.40	50.00	2.74	.6274	3.39	31.37	1.72	36.48
9	2.40	30.00	1.22	.5919	1.42	17.76	0.72	19.90
10	0.60	10.00	0.30	.5584	0.34	5.58	0.17	6.09
				Totals	$193.63	$806.37	$98.30	$1,098.30

Part II: Present worth of lifetime-levelized tax, at 2.438%, per Formula 5.3a.

10	11	12	13
Year	Plant in Service (P)	Tax at 2.438% of P	Present Worth of Tax
1	$950	$23.16	$21.85
2	850	20.72	18.44
3	750	18.28	15.36
4	650	15.85	12.55
5	550	13.41	10.02
6	450	10.97	7.73
7	350	8.53	5.67
8	250	6.10	3.83
9	150	3.66	2.17
10	50	1.22	0.68
		Total	$98.30 (as in Col.8, Part I)

Part III: Annuity equivalent to present worth of lifetime taxes.

$$98.30 \ (i + \frac{\beta}{i}d) = 98.30 \ (0.0600 + 0.1880) = \$24.38$$
$$= 2.438\%$$

1. Convert the year-by-year taxes of Table 8.2 into their present worth. Then convert that present worth into its equivalent lifetime-levelized annuity, and compare the result with $T\%$ at 2.438%, per Basic Formula 8.2.
2. Convert the year-by-year taxes of Table 8.2 into their present worth, as in the first method above. Then calculate the present worth of lifetime-levelized taxes at 2.438%, as determined by Basic Formula 8.1, and compare the two present worths.

Both checks are carried out in Table 8.3. Present worth of year-by-year return (MAR) and book depreciation $(_0d \cdot P_x)$ are calculated, as well as present worth of taxes, to verify once more the useful fact that the present worth of lifetime capital-recovery costs (return plus depreciation, adjusted for salvage if any) is exactly equal to the initial capital investment, as discussed in Chapter 6.

Note that Table 8.3 does not disclose the tax each year as a percentage of P_x in that year, or the tax each year if renewals were to be made — that is, retirements replaced as they occur in order to maintain plant in service at its original level, P_0.

Liberalized Depreciation

The tax law of 1954 introduced an ingenious and unnecessarily complicated procedure for reducing the amount of taxes payable without reducing the statutory tax rate, by permitting use of some depreciation method other than "straight-line" for purposes of books and/or tax-deductible depreciation.

The favorite methods of "fast" depreciation are:

1. The Double-Rate Declining-Balance Method (DRDB); and
2. The Sum-of-Years'-Digits Method (SYD).

The Double-Rate Declining-Balance Method (DRDB) charges twice the "straight-line" rate in the first year of life. This leaves an undepreciated balance, which is depreciated at the same rate in the following year. Thus, the annual rate of depreciation remains fixed, at double the "straight-line" rate $\overline{(= 2/L}$, or $2 \cdot {_0d})$; but instead of applying the rate to the cost of plant in service — as in "straight-line" procedure — it is applied to the annually declining balance.

That balance declines very rapidly at first; but shortly, the undepreciated residual becomes so small that annual taxes become less than "straight-line" charges would be. Another technicality will also be apparent. That is, always some residual remains; it is impossible to recover 100% of the first cost, in theory. These two complications have been responsible for much confusion and misleading advice of tax "experts," which will be commented upon shortly.

The DRDB method is supposed to establish the outside limit of permissible "fast" depreciation. As might be anticipated, when legislators tinker with technicalities beyond their comprehension, the method does not necessarily work out that way. Under some circumstances, the SYD rate, which is also approved, depreciates faster than DRDB, as was shown in Figures 8.1a, b, and c.

The present law stipulates that if the taxpayer elects to use DRDB, he cannot allow for ultimate net salvage in calculating the resultant annual rate.[8] However, he may revert to the "straight-line" method, based on remaining life, at any future date. Of course, remaining-life allowances differ substantially from the lifetime group-basis figures.

The sum-of-years'-digits method (SYD) is readily explained in application to a single property unit which must be retired all at once on some future date (Type SQ). Actually, this situation never arises. And in application to the usual situation, where dispersed retirements are encountered, the SYD procedure is quite complicated. Also, if the taxpayer adopts SYD, he may be required to use "vintage" accounting, which adds to bookkeeping expense.

Possibly it is this fantastic complication of practical applications that induces so many writers to take the easy way out, to pretend that income tax differentials are of small importance in economic decisions, and to satisfy themselves with crude approximations that are far removed from actual fact. At any rate, practically all published methods of estimating income tax are woefully inaccurate and misleading.

For introductory purposes, it is advantageous to first describe the SYD method (sum-of-years'-digits) as it would be applied after retirement of a unit of plant, when the exact date of retirement is known. This will explain the principle of SYD depreciation most simply. It obviously departs drastically from the practical situation, since the SYD method is actually applied to groups of units which do have retirement dispersion, and whose service life (depending on date of retirement) cannot be known exactly in advance.

The annual SYD depreciation rate decreases each successive year, unlike the "straight-line" rate. It is applied to the capital cost of plant in service, as is the "straight-line" rate. That is, it depreciates gross plant (= initial placements plus replacements), as all methods must. The approved method of practical application is described in Appendix C.

The annual rate is defined as a fraction, the numerator of which is remaining years of life, and the denominator the "sum of years' digits." For example, for 10-year life, the "sum of years' digits" is:

$$1 + 2 + 3 + 4 + 5 + 6 + 7 + 8 + 9 + 10 = 55$$

Then the first year's rate is 10/55; the second is 9/55; the third is 8/55; and on down to 1/55 in Year 10. Obviously, this does not work if there are dispersed retirements, as there always are. The prescribed procedure under such circumstances is also described in Appendix C.

---

[8]When using DRDB it is still necessary to estimate salvage, nevertheless, because the law also states that assets must not be depreciated beyond their depreciable value by this method.

Simple Examples; Liberalized Depreciation

Before developing an arithmetical formula for $T\%$ with liberalized depreciation, suppose we take a look at the year-by-year behavior of the tax.

Table 8.4 assumes the same conditions as Tables 8.1 and 8.2, except that tax-deductible depreciation is DRDB, instead of "straight-line"; "straight-line" is still used for book purposes. As before, we assume that in each year 50% of the year's retirements occur on the first of the year and the other 50% at the end of the year, so that the average plant balance is a level amount throughout the whole year (that is, the equivalent "step" curve). The accrual rate is double the "straight-line" rate, or 40% in this case. (For 5-year life, 1/5 = 20%; doubled, it equals 40%.)

Table 8.4. Liberalized depreciation. Double-rate declining-balance method (DRDB), reverting to "straight-line" after Year 6. (Same plant as in Tables 8.1 and 8.2.)

1	2	3	4	5
Year	Accrual Method	Depreciation Rate	Declining Balance at End of Year	Annual Accrual
1	DRDB	40.0%	$600.00	$400.00
2	DRDB	40.0	360.00	240.00
3	DRDB	40.0	216.00	144.00
4	DRDB	40.0	129.60	86.40
5	DRDB	40.0	77.76	51.84
6	DRDB	40.0	46.66	31.10
7	SL(RL)*	43.7†	26.27	20.39
8	SL(RL)	55.6	11.66	14.61
9	SL(RL)	75.0	2.92	8.74
10	SL(RL)	100.0	0.00	2.92

*Where SL(RL) is the "straight-line" depreciation rate based on remaining life, rather than on total life.

† $\dfrac{\text{Year } n \text{ survivors}}{\sum\limits_{n}^{\omega} \text{Year } x \text{ survivors}} = \dfrac{350}{800} = 43.7\%$

It is further assumed that the accountants would switch to "straight-line" at the end of Year 6, at which point the DRDB accruals would begin to fall below the "straight-line" remaining-life rate.

Remaining life, each year, depends upon the type of dispersion as well as on average life. It is to be calculated each year by measuring the area under the remainder of the survivor curve, and dividing that area (in unit-years) by the number of units surviving at the beginning of the period. For the Type SC survivorship pattern here assumed, remaining life and the resultant depreciation rates applied to the declining balance of net plant each year would be so calculated as follows:

Year	Mean Survivors (Column 2, Table 8.1)	Area Under Survivor Curve*	Remaining Life**	"Straight-Line" Rate in Percent of Declining Balance (= Reciprocal of Remaining Life)
6	$450	1250 dollar-years	2.78 years	36.0%
7	350	800	2.29	43.7
8	250	450	1.80	55.6
9	150	200	1.33	75.0
10	50	50	1.00	100.0

*By cumulative addition of mean survivors backwards from end of Year 10.

**By dividing area under survivor curve by mean survivors in the current year.

Year 7 is the first in which the "straight-line" accrual so calculated (43.7%) exceeds the DRDB rate of 40% (= 2 x 1/5 years); both applied to the same balance of $46.66 (see Column 6 in Year 7, Table 8.4).

In this particular example, the "straight-line" remaining-life accrual happened to be a constant percentage of mean survivors in each year. (To check, divide the annual accrual in Column 5 of Table 8.4 by mean survivors in each year, above, in each year after Year 6.)

The depreciation reserve each year is calculated as:

1. The average reserve throughout the previous year;
2. Less one-half of the previous year's retirements, treated as occurring at the end of the previous year;
3. Plus the depreciation accrual, at the end of the previous year; and
4. Less one-half of the current year's retirements.

The "liberalized" allowance for tax-deductible depreciation, so calculated for one lifetime, is summarized in Table 8.4.

Taxable income, out of the same revenues, will now be less than the amounts in Column 2 of Table 8.3; less by the difference between Column 5 of Table 8.4 versus Column 3 of Table 8.3.

That difference can be converted into its equivalent lifetime annuity, utilizing the procedure described in Chapter 5. The year-by-year calculations appear in Table 8.5, where the increase in deductible depreciation is found to be 1.590%. That is:

$$\text{Tax depreciation } (d_t) = d' + 1.590 = 21.590\%$$
$$\text{Book depreciation } (d') = {}_0d = 1/20 = 20.000$$
$$(d_t - d') = d_t - {}_0d = 1.590\%$$

Referring back to our generalized expression (2) on page 196, we find that we have thus added one more "deductible": $(d_t - d') = 1.590\%$.

Inserting this into Basic Formula 8.1:

Table 8.5. Effects of liberalized depreciation. Double-rate
declining-balance method (DRDB); reverting to "straight-line"
at end of Year 6. (Same plant as in Tables 8.1 - 8.3.)

1	2	3	4
	Increase in Depreciation Accruals	Present Worth Factors	Present Worth
Year	$(d_t - d)$	at 6%	of Col. 2
1	400.00-190.00=$210.00	0.9434	$198.11
2	240.00-170.00= 70.00	.8900	62.30
3	144.00-150.00= (6.00)	.8396	(5.04)
4	86.40-130.00= (43.60)	.7921	(34.54)
5	51.84-110.00= (58.16)	.7473	(43.46)
6	31.10- 90.00= (58.90)	.7050	(41.52)
7	20.39- 70.00= (49.61)	.6651	(33.00)
8	14.61- 50.00= (35.39)	.6274	(22.20)
9	8.74- 30.00= (21.26)	.5919	(12.58)
10	2.92- 10.00= (7.08)	.5584	(3.95)

Present worth of differential = $ 64.12

Equivalent Annuity

$64.12 (i + \frac{\beta}{i}d) = 64.12 \times 24.80\% = \$15.90$ per year.

The increase in deductible depreciation $= \frac{15.90}{1,000} = 1.590\%$.

The year-by-year behavior of the tax is shown in Table 8.6.

$$T\% = \frac{t}{1 - t}\left[(i + \frac{\beta}{i}d - d')(1 - \frac{Bb}{i}) - (d_t - d')\right] \quad \text{(Formula 8.3)}$$
$$(4)$$

$$= \frac{0.48}{0.52}\left[(6.00 + 18.80 - 20.00)(1 - \frac{0.60 \times 4.50}{6.00}) - 1.590\right]$$

$$= \frac{0.48}{0.52}\left[(4.80)(0.55) - 1.590\right] = 0.969\%$$

Thus, "liberalizing" has reduced $T\%$ by: $(2.437 - 0.969)/2.437 = 60.2\%$,
in this case.

The increase in depreciation accruals (taken from Column 2, Table
8.5) results in a decrease in the annual tax at 0.48/0.52 times the increase in accruals. The decrease in the annual tax, so calculated, appears in Column 3, Table 8.6.

The adjusted tax, in dollars per year, is tabulated in Column 4. It
is obtained by subtracting the decrease (Column 3) from the "nonliber-
alized" tax of Column 4, Table 8.3.

The present worth of the adjusted taxes (Column 6) is totalled and
converted into the equivalent annuity by multiplying by $(i + \frac{\beta}{i}d)$, as before. The result is a figure for $T\%$ that duplicates the foregoing calculation of 0.969%.

Comments on Table 8.6

Some of the complexities of income tax behavior with liberalized
depreciation are well illustrated by Table 8.6. Note that annual income

Table 8.6. Year-by-year behavior of income tax with liberalized depreciation. (Same conditions as Table 8.5.)

1	2	3	4	5	6
Year	Increase in Depreciation Accruals (Table 8.5, Col.2)	Resultant Decrease in Tax ($\frac{0.48}{0.52}$ x Col. 2)	Adjusted Tax (Table 8.3, Col.4 - Col.3)	Present Worth Factors at 6%	Present Worth of Col. 5
1	$210.00	$193.85	$30.46 - 193.85 = $(163.39)	0.9434	$(154.14)
2	70.00	64.62	24.67 - 64.62 = (39.95)	.8900	(35.56)
3	(6.00)	(5.54)	19.50 + 5.54 = 25.04	.8396	21.02
4	(43.60)	(40.25)	14.93 + 40.25 = 55.18	.7921	43.71
5	(58.16)	(53.69)	10.97 + 53.69 = 64.66	.7473	48.32
6	(58.90)	(54.37)	7.62 + 54.37 = 61.99	.7050	43.70
7	(49.61)	(45.79)	4.87 + 45.79 = 50.66	.6651	33.69
8	(35.39)	(32.67)	2.74 + 32.67 = 35.41	.6274	22.22
9	(21.26)	(19.62)	1.22 + 19.62 = 20.84	.5919	12.34
10	(7.08)	(6.54)	0.30 + 6.54 = 6.84	.5584	3.82

Present worth of lifetime taxes, "liberalized" $ 39.12

Equivalent Lifetime Annuity:

$$\frac{39.12}{1,000} \ (i + \beta_i d) = \frac{39.12}{1,000} \times 24.80\% = 0.970\%$$

Note that the tax is greater than in Table 8.3 (Col. 4) in every year except for the first two years. In Years 1 and 2, there is a large tax credit, so large that the net result, over total service life, is a substantial tax reduction despite the increased tax in all other years.

taxes in Table 8.6 (with liberalized depreciation) are greater than in Table 8.3 ("straight-line" for books and taxes) in all but the first two years. Substantially all of the tax reduction occurred in the first year, when a tax credit was equal to about five times the Year 1 tax of Table 8.3.

The annual tax, in percent of investment in service, varies from a maximum of 3.21% in Year 1 to 0.60% in Year 10 (see Column 5, Table 8.7). With liberalized depreciation, it varies from 14.47%, in Year 7 to a minimum of minus 17.20 in Year 1.

One may wonder why anyone should be greatly concerned about spreading depreciation expense at a level annual percentage[9], if no objection is raised about spreading lifetime income taxes in this weird manner.

The 10-year average percentage tax (per Table 8.7) is: with "straight-line" depreciation for books and taxes = 1.859%; with liberalized depreciation (DRDB) = 7.167%.

This demonstrates how misleading arithmetical averaging can be; the "liberalized" tax would appear to be four times greater, or an increase of 300%. Actually, the tax is reduced 60.2%, as revealed by comparing their financial equivalencies, the lifetime annuities.

Accountants and commissions have argued at great length whether the increased latter-day taxes of Column 4, Table 8.6 (that is, the "deferred" taxes, with liberalized depreciation) constitute a future liability or not.

If the company were to fall on evil days, so that no taxable income would be realized in those future years, no tax obligation would be imposed. This situation has been touted as one advantage of the

Table 8.7. Year-by-year income taxes in percent of cost of plant in service.

1	2	3	4	5	6
			Annual Income Taxes		
		In Dollars		In Percent	
Year	Cost of Plant in Service	Table 8.3, Col.4	Table 8.6, Col.4	Table 8.3	Table 8.6
1	$950	$ 30.46	$(163.39)	3.21%	(17.20)%
2	850	24.67	(39.95)	2.90	(4.70)
3	750	19.50	25.04	2.60	3.34
4	650	14.93	55.18	2.30	8.49
5	550	10.97	64.66	1.99	11.76
6	450	7.62	61.99	1.69	13.78
7	350	4.87	50.66	1.39	14.47
8	250	2.74	35.41	1.10	14.16
9	150	1.22	20.84	0.81	13.89
10	50	0.30	6.84	0.60	13.68
	Totals =	$117.28	$ 117.28	Avg. = 1.859%	7.167%
Equivalent lifetime annuities				= 2.438%	0.970%

---

[9] "Great argument about it, and about" has raged for decades, particularly among accountants and within public utility regulatory bodies.

liberalized-depreciation scheme. On the other hand, if the company continues to grow and prosper, the new plant will always have a greatly reduced tax in the first years of its service life. Some argue that this means a "permanent" tax reduction, and therefore they conclude that there is no tax liability in later years to affect the initial tax reduction, a "permanent" saving.

The student can now decide for himself whether such debate contributes anything helpful. A saving is always realized by postponement of due-dates, even in those cases where the arithmetic sum of annual taxes is identical, over total life, with or without liberalized depreciation.

Values of d_t for DRDB and SYD

As just demonstrated, the lifetime-levelized value of d_t depends upon:

1. The method of depreciation (DRDB or SYD);
2. Probable life, in years;[10]
3. Type of retirement dispersion;
4. Net salvage (for SYD); and
5. The point of reverting to "straight-line" (for DRDB).

A convenient plot of values of d_t for various service lives may be prepared by recognizing only two extreme types of retirement dispersion (SQ and SC, respectively), ignoring salvage, which can be adjusted for separately by multiplying d_t by quantity $(1 - c)$ as in the case of $_i d$;[11] and by assuming that DRDB will revert to "straight-line" at the first favorable opportunity (as in Table 8.4).

Dispersions having low index numbers (0 or 1) will lie nearer SC; those having high index numbers (5 or 6) will lie nearer SQ. Hence, Figures 8.1a, b, and c (which present values of d_t for SYD and DRDB depreciation for Types SQ and SC dispersion, and for lives of 5 to 55 years) are calculated in this manner for three values of MAR (6%, 7%, 8%). Data from which these curves were plotted appear in Appendix F. If SYD depreciation is used, adjusting d_t for salvage is accomplished by applying the factor $(1 - c)$, as noted before.

The use of DRDB has some features which have puzzled students unnecessarily; the following remarks may contribute helpful clarification.

Theoretically, it is impossible to recover 100% of the initial investment if DRDB is used. Apparently this question worried legislators when they devised the statute; they permitted reversion to "straight-line" depreciation, adjusted for alternate net salvage, at some future date. But this is not an urgent necessity, for two reasons.

---

[10]Note that probable life for tax purposes ("guidelines") may differ from physical life.
[11]See footnote 2, page 184.

First, by that time of reversion to "straight-line," the greater part of the initial installation would have already been retired and salvage already realized. The reversion to "straight-line" was one more imperfect makeshift complication.

Second, since the whole liberalized-depreciation scheme was simply an arbitrary means of reducing taxes, why be concerned over 100% recovery, or any allowance at all for salvage? Why not arbitrarily ignore both? So long as the depreciation procedure for book purposes recovers the initial investment less net salvage, the reason for so complicating the arbitrary tax-deductible depreciation calculation remains obscure.

In any event, so long as dispersed retirements occur, the whole proposal to revert to "straight-line" accomplishes little. The ultimate unrecovered residual is hardly significant.[12]

It seems probable that the senate Committee on Finance, or their advisers, did not inquire thoroughly into important practical problems introduced by reason of retirement dispersion and plant growth. However, no vagueness nor inexactness introduced into economic studies by reason of inexpert tax law can reflect on the rigor of basic financial principles. It simply means that calculations of tax obligations are unnecessarily difficult to make in view of the peculiar nature of tax law.

Accounting Options

In all of this chapter thus far we have assumed that the reduced taxes resulting from adoption of liberalized depreciation would serve to reduce revenue requirements, and that resultant increased earnings out of given sales and revenues would "flow through" to stated income, thus increasing the Profit Incentive or margin of earnings above the MAR floor in each year.

Recognizing the irregular behavior of annual tax obligations, as illustrated by Column 4, Table 8.7, some accountants have recommended a different accounting treatment which tends to average out, or "normalize," the effect of liberalized depreciation on reported income annually. The same treatment may be accorded the investment credit.

Public utilities, in particular, have been impressed with the risk created by passing on the tax savings to customers immediately, in the form of rate reductions, trusting that future offsetting increases in rates may be obtainable should they be needed to cover the greater future taxes. If the law is not changed, and if annual growth rates do not persist, then a fixed "fair rate" of return assuredly would mean increased taxes in the future.

---

[12]For a discussion of this fact of life, apparently overlooked by framers of the law, see Edward D. Greene, "Changing from Declining Balance to Straight-Line Depreciation," Accounting Review, Vol. 38, No. 2 (April, 1963), p. 355.

The usual normalizing procedure is to calculate each year's tax reduction obtained by use of liberalized depreciation rather than "straight-line," charge that amount each year as a revenue deduction (an expense account), and credit accumulations to a special liability account. In years when the "savings" become negative, the accumulations would be drawn upon to supply the deficit. Under ideal conditions (constant percentage earnings, and so forth), the accumulations generated by a given capital investment would be exactly wiped out by the date of final retirement from that initial placement. Adopting the normalizing treatment, in place of flow-through accounting, reduces the lifetime tax reduction slightly, as will be demonstrated.

The normalizing proposal has been considered by nonregulated companies as well; but it has been explored extensively only by regulated public utilities for a reason connected with regulation. That is, the accumulated tax deferrals, or tax "savings," provide a temporary source of capital funds available for corporate use in the same manner as depreciation reserves. Like depreciation reserves, these tax deferrals are no part of investors' committed capital. Some corporations have regarded this last statement as debatable. If an acceptable alternative treatment is to allow the "savings" to flow through to income, are not the same savings, when accumulated in a reserve, of the nature of retained earnings?

It has been generally recognized that these savings are not retained earnings, since the specific reason for their accumulation was for predictable disbursement when the tax "savings" later become negative for the same assets. Accordingly, even those companies which accumulated the deferrals in a surplus account identified them as "restricted" surplus.

In interests of simplicity, we will first introduce the effect of accounting options by calculating depreciation annuities (d_t or d'), ignoring effects of retirement dispersion. Exact determination of d_t prescribed by the tax code (explained in Appendix C), to be used in practical solutions, can be accomplished by use of Figure 8.1, as discussed before.

Formula 8.3, pages 184 and 207, is

$$T\% = \frac{t}{1-t}\left[(i + \tfrac{\beta}{i}d - d')(1 - \frac{Bb}{i}) - (d_t - d')\right]$$

Obviously, then, tax payments depend upon the depreciation accounting methods used for both d_t and d'

In all this chapter thus far, we have assumed that $d' = {}_0d$, that is, "straight-line" depreciation for the company's books of account. This is usually, but not necessarily, true. The company can use any method of book depreciation it chooses (or, being a regulated public utility, any it is permitted). d' may represent sinking-fund, SYD, DRDB, or any other desired accounting method. As noted before, many companies have abandoned use of "straight-line" depreciation for book purposes in favor of DRDB or SYD. In general, the greater the quantity $(d_t - d')$, the smaller is $T\%$. Thus the tax can be reduced by increasing d_t, or by decreasing d', or by both means.[13] This is why the tax benefit is not fully realized if book depreciation charges are increased by adopting DRDB or SYD.

The simplified examples in Table 8.8 illustrate the principles involved, and the modifications of Basic Formula 8.1 that will yield the exact solution for $T\%$. It is once more remarked that for simplicity in demonstrating the principles involved we are ignoring effects of retirement dispersion and net salvage by assuming Type SQ dispersion. In all practical problems, effects of retirement dispersion and salvage must be recognized, which is not difficult.

In all these examples calling for a "fast" depreciation method, we will use the SYD method. Accordingly, the first step is to develop d_t for SYD depreciation. We will also assume:

Capital investment = $1,000.
Ultimate net salvage is zero.
Service life is 10 years; no retirement dispersion (Type SQ).
MAR = 6%.
Percentage debt = 50%.
Interest rate = 3%.

The Investment Credit

Further tax-tinkering legislation introduced one more complexity in 1963, known as the "investment credit." The rules were altered in 1964, and likely will be again when effects of the new law become apparent in practice. Some of the queer situations that will result from the impact of the investment credit will be pointed out here; it seems unlikely that they were foreseen by those who framed the legislation.

The investment credit amounts to a reduction in the income tax on eligible new construction in the first year only of its service life. The allowed tax reduction is 7% of the capital investment in eligible facilities (more than 8-year service life) or 3% for public utilities.

As originally enacted, the law stipulated that this tax reduction constituted a reduction in the capital cost (that is, depreciable cost) of the new installation; but that provision was repealed in 1964.[14] The reason for this curious proviso apparently was purely political. It created the impression that Uncle Sam was contributing part of the initial capital investment in new equipment. Actually, of course, the investment credit has no effect whatever on capital outlays. It simply reduces an annual expense (income tax), with exactly the same effect as a reduction in maintenance expense, fuel cost, or property taxes.

The groundwork for such misconceptions is laid by unwise or

---

[13]Decreasing d' reduces $T\%$ provided there is debt in the capital structure. See the discussion of Two Effects of Deductible Interest, which follows the examples in Table 8.8.

[14]This provision of the law, since repealed, was known as the "Long Amendment."

Table 8.8. Part I: Calculation of d_t for SYD depreciation.
Capital investment = $10,000; 10, SQ; zero salvage; MAR 6%.*

1	2	3	4
Year	Annual Charge for Depreciation Expense	Present Worth Factors at 6%	Present Worth of Col. 2
1	$\frac{10}{55}$ x 1,000 = $ 181.818	0.9434	$171.5264
2	$\frac{9}{55}$ x 1,000 = 163.636	.8900	145.6355
3	$\frac{8}{55}$ x 1,000 = 145.455	.8396	122.1268
4	$\frac{7}{55}$ x 1,000 = 127.273	.7921	100.8121
5	$\frac{6}{55}$ x 1,000 = 109.091	.7473	81.5192
6	$\frac{5}{55}$ x 1,000 = 90.909	.7050	64.0873
7	$\frac{4}{55}$ x 1,000 = 72.727	.6651	48.3676
8	$\frac{3}{55}$ x 1,000 = 54.545	.6274	34.2222
9	$\frac{2}{55}$ x 1,000 = 36.364	.5919	21.5238
10	$\frac{1}{55}$ x 1,000 = 18.182	.5584	10.1527
	$1,000.000	Total present worth = $799.9736

$$d_t = d_{SYD} = \frac{799.9736}{10,000.0000} \left(i + \frac{\beta}{i}d\right) = \frac{799.9736}{10,000.0000} \times 13.5868\% = 10.8691\%$$

---

*See Appendix A for a discussion of significant figures, desirable number of decimal places, and suggested rounding procedure.

Part II: Calculations of Examples A, B, C, D.

Example A

T%; "straight-line" for books and taxes. Capital investment = $10,000; 10, SQ; zero net salvage; MAR = 6%.

B = 50%; b = 3%; t = 48%

The Basic Formula 8.1:

$$T\% = \frac{t}{1-t}\left(i + \frac{\beta}{i}d - d'\right)\left(1 - \frac{Bb}{i}\right); d' = {_0}d$$

$$T\% = \frac{0.48}{0.52}(6.0000 + 7.5868 - 10.0000)\left(1 - \frac{0.50 \times 3}{6}\right) = 2.483\%$$

Example B

T%; SYD for books and taxes.

The Basic Formula 8.1:

$$T\% = \frac{t}{1-t}\left(i + \frac{\beta}{i}d - d'\right)\left(1 - \frac{Bb}{i}\right); d' = d_{SYD}$$

$$T\% = \frac{0.48}{0.52}(6.0000 + 7.5868 - 10.8691)\left(1 - \frac{0.50 \times 3}{6}\right) = 1.881\%$$

Table 8.8 continued.

Example C

$T\%$; "straight-line" for books; SYD for taxes; "flow-through."

Formula 8.3:

$$T\% = \frac{t}{1-t}\left[(i + {}_i^\beta d - {}_o d)(1 - \frac{Bb}{i}) - (d_{\text{SYD}} - {}_o d)\right]$$

$$= \frac{0.48}{0.52}\left[(6.0000 + 7.5868 - 10.0000)(1 - \frac{0.50 \times 3}{6}) - (10.8691 - 10.0000)\right] = 1.681\%$$

Example D

$T\%$; "straight-line" for books; SYD for taxes; "normalized."

The revenue requirement for the tax, per Basic Formula 8.1, is reduced on two counts:

1. The reduction in lifetime taxes, in dollars, amounting to

$$\frac{t}{1-t}\left[t(d_{\text{SYD}} - {}_o d)\right](1 - \frac{Bb}{i}), \text{ plus}$$

2. The reduction resulting from postponement of the due date of taxes payable, amounting to $t(d_{\text{SYD}} - {}_o d)$.

Thus:

$$T\% = \frac{t}{1-t}\left[(i + {}_i d - {}_o d) - t(d_{\text{SYD}} - {}_o d)\right](1 - \frac{Bb}{i}) - t(d_{\text{SYD}} - {}_o d)$$

$$= \frac{0.48}{0.52}\left[(6.0000 + 7.5868 - 10.0000) - 0.48(10.8691 - 10.0000)\right](1 - \frac{0.50 \times 3}{6})$$

$$- 0.48(10.8691 - 10.0000) = 1.777\%$$

Part III: Summary.

		$T\%$	% Reduction
Example A:	"Straight-line" for books and taxes	2.483	0.0
Example B:	SYD for books and taxes	1.881	24.2
Example C:	"Straight-line" for books, SYD for taxes, "flow-through"	1.681	32.3
Example D:	"Straight-line" for books, SYD for taxes, "normalized"	1.777	28.4

Two Effects of Deductible Interest

Note that if there is no debt in the company's capital structure (that is, no deductible interest), quantity d' cancels out in Formulas 8.3 and 8.4. There are two important results:

1. There is then no difference between $T\%$, normalized, and $T\%$, flow-through.
2. $T\%$ is then independent of the method of depreciation used for book purposes.

In general, the larger d_t is, the smaller is $T\%$. And if there is debt in the company's capital structure, the smaller d' is, the smaller is $T\%$, as noted before.

careless phraseology of writers on the subject of taxes. A tendency to refer to the "partnership" of government and business is misleading. The government imposes taxes; the amount of taxes is proportional to taxable income and this is the extent of the "partnership." Any capital investment by government in productive plant reduces the opportunity for investment by individuals in such projects, which is hardly characteristic of a "partnership." The word should be reserved for use where it is appropriate.

Development of Formula 8.4, the revenue requirement for federal income tax adjusted for liberalized depreciation and for investment credit (*IC*), proceeds as follows. Two slightly different variations of the development will be suggested; the student may choose whichever appeals to him most. Both arrive at the same conclusion, and the first six steps are identical:

1. Revenue requirement for federal income tax payable = T
   = $T_{(\text{exclusive of } IC)}$ less investment credit
   = T_{eic} - IC
   ≠ t(taxable income) - IC

2. Total revenue requirements = Minimal gross income + depreciation + expenses + $T = (i + \frac{\beta}{i}d - d') + d' + e + (T_{eic} - IC)$

3. Taxable income = Total revenue requirements less deductibles
   = $(i + \frac{\beta}{i}d - d') + d' + e + T_{eic} - IC$ - deductibles

4. Deductibles = $e + d_t + \frac{Bb}{i}(i + \frac{\beta}{i}d - d')$

5. Therefore, taxable income, per Item 3, equals:

   $(i + \frac{\beta}{i}d - d')(1 - \frac{Bb}{i}) - (d_t - d') + T_{eic} - IC$

6. Hence, tax payable, per Item 1, is:

   $T_{eic} - IC = t\left[(i + \frac{\beta}{i}d - d')(1 - \frac{Bb}{i}) - (d_t - d') + T_{eic} - IC\right] - IC$

7. Canceling IC's, and collecting T_{eic} on the left side of the equation:

   $T_{eic}(1 - t) = t\left[(i + \frac{\beta}{i}d - d')(1 - \frac{Bb}{i}) - (d_t - d') - IC\right]$

8. Solving for T_{eic}:

   $T_{eic} = \frac{t}{1 - t}\left[(i + \frac{\beta}{i}d - d')(1 - \frac{Bb}{i}) - (d_t - d') - IC\right]$

9. Income tax payable, per Item 1:

   $T_{eic} - IC = \frac{t}{1 - t}\left[(i + \frac{\beta}{i}d - d')(1 - \frac{Bb}{i}) - (d_t - d') - IC\right] - IC$

The alternative development after Item 6 is as follows:

7'. Collecting $(T_{eic} - IC)$ on the left side of the equation:

   $(1 - t)(T_{eic} - IC) = t\left[(i + \frac{\beta}{i}d - d')(1 - \frac{Bb}{i}) - (d_t - d')\right] - IC$

8'. Dividing by $(1 - t)$:

   $T_{eic} - IC = \left[\frac{t}{1 - t}(i + \frac{\beta}{i}d - d')(1 - \frac{Bb}{i}) - (d_t - d')\right] - \frac{IC}{1 - t}$

9′. Since $-\dfrac{IC}{1-t} = \dfrac{t}{1-t}(-IC) - IC$

and $T_{eic} - IC = $ tax payable $= T$ (per Item 1)

10′. Therefore:

$$T = \frac{t}{1-t}\left[(i + {}^{\beta}_{i}d - d\,')(1 - \frac{Bb}{i}) - (d_t - d\,') - IC\right] - IC$$

As always, depreciation annuities ${}^{\beta}_{i}d$, $d\,'$, and d_t are to be adjusted for ultimate net salvage, except d_t when DRDB is used.

Observe that $T\%$, per Formula 8.4, is greater than per Formula 8.3 by the amount of $IC\,(\dfrac{t}{1-t} + 1)$, or nearly double the 7% (or 3%) fig-ure commonly concluded to be the effect of investment credit, for a fixed percentage MAR ("after tax"). For a statutory tax rate of 48%, this equals 1.9231 x IC; a tax reduction of 13.46% (= 1.9231 x 7) of the capital cost of eligible new capital investment for a fixed percentage MAR after tax, which is the only meaningful way to express MAR. For public utilities granted a 3% investment credit, the tax reduction for a given MAR is 5.77% (= 1.9231 x 3).

For short-lived plant, around 10-year life, the investment credit ordinarily eliminates the revenue requirement for federal income tax completely -- and then some. It seems unlikely that this result was anticipated in framing the law.

Some Quantitative Results (Investment Credit)

How much is the lifetime-levelized revenue requirement for fed-eral income tax on property having exactly 10-year life (no retirement dispersion), as follows?

Investment credit = 7%;

Service life is 10 years (Type SQ dispersion);

Ultimate net salvage is zero;

MAR = 6%; 50% debt at 4% interest;

"Straight-line" depreciation for books; SYD for taxes; and

"flow through" accounting.

${}^{\beta}_{i}d = 7.59\%$, from Table 6.17, on page 142.

$d\,' = {}_{0}d = 1/\text{Life} = 10.00\%$.

$d_t = 10.87\%$, from Figure 8.1a, on page 186.

Per Formula 8.4:

$$T\% = \frac{0.48}{0.52}\left[(6.00 + 7.59 - 10.00)(1 - \frac{0.50 \times 4.00}{6.00}) - 10.87 - 10.00)\right.$$

$$\left. - IC\right] - IC$$

$$IC = \frac{k(i + {}^{\beta}_{i}d)}{1+i} \cdot P_0,$$

where

P_0 = the new capital investment, and

$k = 7\%$.

$$IC = \frac{7\%(0.06 + 0.0759)}{1.06} \cdot P_0 = 0.90\% \times P_0.$$

Thus:

$$T\% = 0.9231\,[(3.59)(0.67) - 0.87 - 0.90] - 0.90 = -\underline{\underline{0.31}}$$

Liberalized depreciation alone would reduce the tax to 1.42%; investment credit reduces it still further to a minus quantity: 1.42 - 1.9231 x 0.90 = -0.31.

For longer life the effect is less spectacular. But for <u>30-year life</u>, all other assumptions the same as above, the tax reduction is still enormous:

$\beta_i d = 1.26\%$, from Table 6.17, on page 142.

$d' = {}_0d = 1/L = 3.33\%$.

$d_t = 4.25\%$, from Figure 8.1a.

$IC = \dfrac{7\%(0.06 + 0.0126)}{1.06} = 0.48\%$.

Per Formula 8.4:

$$T\% = \frac{0.48}{0.52}\left[(6.00 + 1.26 - 3.33)(1 - \frac{0.50 \times 4}{6}) - (4.23 - 3.33) - 0.48\right]$$
$$-\,0.48 = 0.9231\,[(3.93)(0.67) - 0.90 - 0.48] - 0.48 = \underline{\underline{0.66\%}}$$

Were it not for liberalized depreciation and the investment credit, the revenue requirement for federal income tax in this case would have been (per Basic Formula 8.1):

$$T = \frac{t}{1 - t}\,(i + \beta_i d - {}_0d)(1 - \frac{Bb}{i})$$
$$= 0.9231 \times (3.93)(0.67) = 2.43\%$$

The revenue requirement for income tax has thus been reduced (2.43 - 0.66)/2.43 = 72.8%.

As noted, it is the impact of this phenomenon <u>on economic comparisons</u> that is important, because economic comparisons look at the <u>revenue requirement</u> for income tax ($T\%$), not at total income tax payments ($T\% + T'\%$). To illustrate the force of this statement, suppose the company is earning 10% on its pool of investors' committed capital, or a Profit Incentive of 4% above its MAR of 6%. Then its lifetime-levelized <u>total</u> tax obligation would be $T\% + T'\%$, where $T'\%$ is 48% of 4%, or 1.92%. Thus, the total tax obligation without benefit of liberalized depreciation and investment credit would be:

$$T\% + T'\% = 2.43 + 1.92 = 4.35\%$$

And by virtue of liberalized depreciation and investment credit total income taxes would be:

$$T\% + T'\% = -\,0.45 + 1.92 = 1.47\%$$

Accordingly, the reduction in <u>total</u> tax paid would not be 77.8%, but only: (4.35 - 1.47)/4.35 = 66.2%. This percent still is substantial, but the effect as perceived from the company's financial statements would be less than the effect to be taken into account in the company's studies of economic choice.

Actually, the effect observed per the companies' financial state-

ments would be much less than the foregoing, because liberalized depreciation applies only to plant installed after 1953. In other words,
the effect of recent tax law on economic comparisons is very much
greater than is made apparent by companies' financial statements.

"Guidelines"

Revenue Procedure 62-21, adopted in 1962, provides for computation of deductible depreciation based on lives which reflect actual retirement practice and experience of the taxpayer. It was intended to be
in the nature of a reform in administration of the tax law, designed to
set forth "simpler standards and more objective rules which will facilitate adoption of rapid equipment replacement practices in keeping
with current and prospective economic conditions."

All it amounts to is an attempt to establish common sense in place
of rigorously enforced Bulletin F lives for tax-depreciation purposes.
The taxpayer can select what he believes to be a reasonable life, guided
by suggested figures applicable to broad classes of assets. The reasonableness of such estimates is to be tested by means of observed
reserve-ratio tables or other devices.

The reserve-ratio tests currently proposed are not realistic in
that they assume a sustained rate of growth and ignore retirement dispersion. No doubt substantial revisions will have to be made as the
Treasury Department discovers their shortcomings.[15] As a result, the
exact amount of the effect on taxes is different for each company. It
may increase the tax slightly in some cases. In most cases, however,
it probably will reduce the tax slightly; initially probably less than a
5% reduction in the tax payable without benefit of guidelines. Eventually, we can expect that guidelines will not affect the amount of the tax
at all, and we suggest it be ignored, unless there is good reason to expect a significant effect under specific conditions, in economic studies.

In problems where the increased accuracy of estimate appears to
justify the effort, adjustment for effect of the guideline provision may
be introduced by recalculating the revenue requirement for income tax,
substituting the "reasonable" life (suggested by the guidelines test) for
the estimated probable life that would otherwise be used to estimate d_t.
In the great majority of cases, the effect is too small to be worthwhile.
However, as emphasized frequently throughout this book, the only way
to be sure of that fact is to comprehend the exactly appropriate calculation. When capital investments of competing proposals differ largely,
this adjustment could assume importance. This subject arises again in
connection with the economics of replacement, in Chapter 12.

---

[15]For a first-rate discussion of this situation see:
E. T. Wildfong, "Behavior of Reserve Ratio Under Variable Growth Conditions," Proceedings of the Annual Conference of Electric and Gas Utility Accountants, 1964.

State Income Taxes

Several states levy taxes on corporate income, in addition to the federal income tax. Because provisions of state laws differ, the treatment of the revenue requirement for state income tax will not be discussed here in detail.

The general procedure, in making an appropriate allowance for state income tax, is the same as described herein. The first step is to become thoroughly acquainted with the law and with details of its administration. The second step is to develop the arithmetic that will carry out this exact intent.

Résumé

I. Income tax is a matter of law, and the law is complicated. Nevertheless, it is possible to write exact expressions for the revenue requirement for income tax, in terms of specific variables for a given project.

II. Because tax law is subject to change, the analyst's first step must be to acquaint himself with details of the current tax law.

III. The two components of a company's income tax obligations are: (a) the revenue requirement for income tax (= T), and (b) the income tax on earnings above the level of MAR (= T').

IV. Basic Formula 8.1 for the revenue requirement ($T\%$) assumes (a) that "straight-line" depreciation is used for both books and for taxes, (b) that investment-credit provisions of the law are ignored, and (c) that the company's annual taxable income exceeds \$25,000.

The revenue requirement for income tax is:

$$T\% = \frac{t}{1 - t}\,(i + {}^{\beta}_{i}d - {}_{0}d)(1 - \frac{Bb}{i}) \qquad \text{(Formula 8.1)}$$

where

t = statutory rate as a decimal fraction of taxable income.
i = MAR, in % of capital investment.
${}^{\beta}_{i}d$ = depreciation annuity (to be adjusted for salvage), in %.
${}_{0}d$ = "straight-line" depreciation rate (to be adjusted for salvage), in %.
B = ratio of debt to the company's total capitalization.
b = average interest rate on outstanding debt, in %.

V. Basic Formula 8.2, for the tax on Profit Incentive ($T'\%$), is:

$$T'\% = \frac{t}{1 - t}\,(\text{actual earnings - MAR}) \qquad \text{(Formula 8.2)}$$

VI. Formula 8.3 is a modification of Basic Formula 8.1 to reflect effects of liberalized depreciation, not including effects of investment credit. Since adoption of the investment credit is mandatory, Formula 8.3 is a special case at the moment. However, the investment

credit provision of the 1963-64 statute is so peculiar that drastic
revision seems likely. Accordingly, Formula 8.3 is included for informative purposes, even though it may be of limited usefulness at the
moment:

$$T\% = \frac{t}{1 - t}\left[(i + \tfrac{\beta}{i}d - d')(1 - \frac{Bb}{i}) - (d_t - d')\right] \quad \text{(Formula 8.3)}$$

where all symbols are the same as in Formula 8.1 except:

d' = the book depreciation annuity (= $_0d$ for "straight-line").

d_t = the tax-depreciation annuity (DRDB or SYD) per Figure 8.1.
As before, all depreciation annuities are to be multiplied by $(1 - c)$ if
there is net salvage.

VII. Formula 8.4 is a modification of Formula 8.3 to reflect effects of investment credit, together with effects of liberalized depreciation. The amount of investment credit (1963-64 law) is 7% of eligible new investment (more than 8-year service life), except for certain
public utilities which are allowed only 3%, in the year of installation
only.

The lifetime-levelized annuity corresponding to the Year 1 investment credit is

$$IC = \frac{k \cdot (i + \tfrac{\beta}{i}d)}{(1 + i)}$$

where k = 3%, or 7%, as appropriate. Other symbols are as before.

$$T\% = \frac{t}{1 - t}\left[(i + \tfrac{\beta}{i}d - d')(1 - \frac{Bb}{i}) - (d_t - d') - IC\right] - IC \quad \text{(Formula 8.4)}$$

VIII. A number of serious misconceptions concerning the nature
and behavior of income taxes have gained such currency that it is necessary to call specific attention to them, with a warning not to accept
opinion in such matters, no matter how "authoritative" the source.
These misconceptions require a personal investigation based on meticulous observance of the tax law plus the arithmetic appropriate to
implement provisions of the law.

IX. Formulas 8.1, 8.2, 8.3, and 8.4 are readily developed by
means of year-by-year tabulations of the revenue requirement for
income tax, as stipulated by law, and the arithmetical reduction of such
year-by-year tax obligations to their levelized-lifetime equivalency as
a percentage of capital investment in service.

X. A clear understanding of the relation of (a) the tax, to
(b) the so-called "before-tax earnings," and to (c) the "after-tax earnings" is important. Misunderstandings of this situation are unhappily
common and serious. Actually, the expression "before-tax earnings"
is a self-contradiction in terms, similar to "before-repairs earnings,"
or "before-payroll earnings."

XI. The term "liberalized depreciation" refers to use of an approved method of depreciation, for tax-deductible purposes, which is
"faster" than the "straight-line" method. That is, it depreciates at a
rate greater than $_0d$ in the early years of service life and at a slower

rate in later years. Liberalized depreciation was made permissive by law in 1954 for application to depreciable plant installed since 1953.

XII. The two major "faster" depreciation methods are: (a) double-rate declining-balance (DRDB), and (b) sum-of-years'-digits (SYD).

XIII. Effects of adopting permissive liberalized-depreciation provisions of the law may be evaluated in the manner of Item IX by means of year-by-year analyses of the tax obligations prescribed by law, and their reduction to lifetime-levelized equivalencies.

XIV. The most common accounting disposition of tax credits obtained from adoption of liberalized depreciation is to allow them to "flow through" to reported current income. An alternative treatment, permissive in any industry but most commonly encountered among public utilities, is to "normalize" reported current income by not permitting tax credits to inflate income, but to accumulate early-year credits in a special liability account (reserve) which is later drawn upon to supply the offsetting increased tax obligations of later years. Thus, the reserve so accumulated is a temporary source of capital funds similar to depreciation reserves, not a part of investors' committed capital, and therefore not expected to earn a return for investors.

XV. The 1963 tax law prescribed a further reduction in income taxes in the form of an "investment credit" device. This, too, is readily expressed as a lifetime-levelized percentage of capital investment in service, in the manner of Items IX and XIII. A still further complication (intended simplification) known as "guidelines" has relatively small economic effect and can ordinarily be disregarded. However, if this provision is adopted by the company, careful evaluation in the same general manner is recommended.

XVI. The larger d_t is, the smaller is $T\%$. In addition if debt exists in the company's capital structure (that is, deductible interest), then the smaller d' is, the smaller is $T\%$. Thus, the revenue requirement for income tax may be affected by the selection of depreciation accounting methods for both d' (for books) and d_t (for taxes).

XVII. When there is no debt in the company's capital structure (that is, no deductible interest), then $T\%$ is the same percentage for flow-through or normalized accounting.

XVIII. Attention is called to the material of Appendix C, so segregated because it demands lengthy discussion awkward for inclusion in the main text, and because it discusses technical details of greater interest to advanced students. Of particular importance is the discussion of popular misrepresentations of the factual situation which can be financially disastrous.

XIX. Appendix C contains tables of d_t for DRDB and SYD, for service lives from 1 to 60 years, for all Iowa Types of dispersion, and for several values of MAR (= $i\%$). Appendix C also deals with the behavior of income taxes, year by year, for a "continuing plant." The concept of a continuing plant, which is the subject of Chapter 10, is of importance when it is desired to investigate revenue requirements of a project defined as consisting of an initial placement plus subsequent replacements.

XX. Liberalized depreciation and the investment credit affect economic studies (by way of revenue requirements) much more than is apparent from the company's financial statements, for two reasons:

(a) Neither liberalized depreciation nor investment credit reduces the tax on Profit Incentive; that is, on earnings in excess of MAR.

(b) Most companies own large amounts of property not eligible for liberalized depreciation because it was installed before 1954. The portion of total plant eligible for liberalized depreciation thus increases each year.

XXI. The material of this chapter points out one more reason why MRRD must not be described as "a special case of the Annual Cost Method, with return pegged at MAR." MRRD does not peg return at MAR. Return is recognized as composed of MAR plus Profit Incentive, and Profit Incentive is not pegged at any value.

Formulas 8.1, 8.2, 8.3, and 8.4 apply to public utilities in exactly the same way as for nonregulated enterprises.

Problems

1. Former President Eisenhower had hoped to reduce the statutory tax rate from its then 52% figure to 40%, a reduction of $12/52 = 23.1\%$. What would be the percentage reduction in tax payments?

2. Under what conditions is it necessary to recognize the present lower tax rate on annual taxable income of less than $25,000?

3. Referring to the material of Part II, Table 8.8 on page 215, Example C ("straight-line" for books, SYD for taxes, "flow-through") would reduce the tax 32.3%, as compared with Example A ("straight-line" for both books and taxes). On the other hand, Example D ("straight-line" for books, SYD for taxes, "normalized") accomplishes a reduction of only 28.4%. Yet it might be pointed out that Example C reduces the tax by reason of an absolute reduction in dollars payable, as well as by postponement of payments due, while Example D reduces the tax by reason of the postponement only. Explain the apparent paradox.

4. Calculate d_t for DRDB and for SYD, assuming lives of 8, 10, and 12 years, Type SQ. Discuss results.

5. Determine the date at which to revert from DRDB to "straight-line" depreciation, for purposes of liberalized depreciation, for 10, SC. How is the calculation affected if ultimate net salvage is <u>minus</u> 20%?

6. Explain in layman's terms why an incremental outlay of $1,000 for unexpected repairs resulting from an accident not insured against increases revenue requirements by at least $1,000. Why the proviso "at least"?

7. Some corporations report to their stockholders that their common dividends are wholly or partially exempt from personal income tax. Apparently, then, something is peculiar about their reported earnings. Explain.

8. If it is impossible to make earnings on common equity without paying income tax thereon, why is it not correct to use $(i + T\%)$ as the discounting "interest" rate in calculating present worth of such earnings?

9. Assume a capital investment of $100,000. Probable life 20 years, Type R_1, 10% ultimate net salvage; 10% of investors' committee capital is long-term debt at 4% interest; MAR = 6%.

    a. Assuming "straight-line" depreciation for books and taxes, calculate $T\%$.

    b. Assuming "straight-line" depreciation for books, SYD for taxes (d_{SYD} per Figure 8.1), and ignoring the "investment credit," calculate $T\%$.

    c. Assuming some reasonable percentage for the Year 1 "investment credit," calculate its effect on the tax.

10. An analyst calculated revenue requirements of a project as follows, assuming probable life of 25, R_1, zero net salvage, MAR = 6%, 50% debt at 3% interest deductible, $t = 50\%$, and "straight-line" depreciation for books and taxes:

$$\begin{array}{ll} \text{Return} & 6.00\% \\ \text{Depreciation} & 2.05 \\ \text{Income tax} & \underline{3.04} \\ \text{Total} & \overline{11.09\%} \end{array} = \frac{0.50}{1.00 - 0.50}(6.00 + 2.05 - 4.00)(1 - \frac{0.50 \times 3}{6})$$

It then occurred to him that he should be able to check this calculation of the tax as follows:

Revenues (as above)		11.09%
Less deductibles:		
Depreciation	2.05%	
Interest at 0.50 x 3%	1.50	
Total deductibles		3.55
Taxable income, by difference		7.54%

Income tax at 50% of taxable income: $0.50 \times 7.54 = 3.77\%$

This does not check with the foregoing estimate of 3.04%. What is wrong?

11. In Problems 9 and 10, suppose actual earnings were 7.5%. What would the company's total tax obligation be (= $T\%$ + T' %), for Problems 9(a), 9(b), 9(c), and 10?

12. Repeat Tables 8.1, 8.2, 8.3, 8.4, 8.5, and 8.6, using the same assumptions except that probable life is 10 years, Type SC dispersion.

13. It is sometimes asserted that the appropriate method for estimating income taxes for public utilities differs from that applicable to nonregulated industry. Why is that statement untrue?

14. In general, income tax as a percentage of investment is relatively high for land. Why?

15. Calculate (i + $_id$ + $T\%$) for the following probable lives: 5, 10, 20, 50 years; Type R_1 dispersion. Make any assumptions you wish as to $i\%$, $c\%$, $t\%$, $B\%$, and $b\%$, and as to the methods of depreciation for books and for taxes. Plot the results against L (life, in years), and comment on the results.

16. Calculate lifetime-levelized taxes $P_X \cdot T\%$ and $P_X \cdot T'\%$ for the example of pages 185 and 189, assuming MAR = 7%, and ultimate net salvage is minus 10%.

17. Ben Franklin observed that "A penny saved is a penny earned." How is that conclusion modified by existing tax laws for (a) individuals, and (b) corporations? Does it make a difference just what kind of penny is saved? For example, a penny of capital cost, of maintenance expense, of depreciation expense, of income tax, of dividend payout? Explain.

18. Does the effect of liberalized depreciation depend upon service life of the assets? Does the revenue requirement for investment credit depend upon the service life of the assets? Does the amount of debt in the company's capital structure affect the impact of liberalized depreciation? Does the amount of debt affect the impact of investment credit?

19. If a company decides to rent some property, instead of owning it, the firm will have zero capital investment in the property. Yet there would be no point in renting if the company did not expect to make a profit by the deal; and those earnings assuredly would be subject to income tax. Explain exactly how such taxes are allowed for in the MRRD analysis. Discuss exactly how the corresponding taxes on the same property, if owned, are handled in the MRRD analysis.

20. One engineering economy textbook states that individual income taxes paid by a company's stockholders on their dividends are involved in the company's economy studies. Exactly what is wrong with that notion?

21. Is it possible for a company to make large income tax payments regularly and still have a revenue requirement for income tax of zero? Explain, using a simple numerical example to illustrate.

22. From the standpoint of income taxes, why is it incorrect to describe MRRD as "a special case of the Annual Cost Method with return pegged at MAR"?

23. A manufacturer of alloy steels uses large amounts of power for its electric furnaces. The firm's engineers decide to look into possibilities of savings by building their own power plant and producing their own electricity instead of purchasing it from the local public utility. Extensive studies reveal that the decision hinges on estimated percentage return, together with related income taxes.

Company return averages 10% on its capital investment. Using 10% return together with associated taxes at the current 48% statutory rate (and 7% investment credit), the cost comparison is almost a standoff. Purchased power would cost practically the same as self-generated electricity. But if the company should be prosperous and increase average earnings to 15% as hoped, use of 15% return plus related taxes would make self-generated power too expensive.

On the other hand, if severe competition and rising wage rates should knock down average return to a level below 10%, the resultant low cost of self-generation, figuring return at less than 10% (plus related taxes) would make purchased electricity a costly luxury.

In view of these considerations, the engineers recommend construction of the company-owned power plant. They argue that if company earnings do increase above 10% after its installation, the firm will have demonstrated its ability to afford this apparent error in judgment; and if company earnings fall below 10% after its installation, the firm will know that it has made the best decision in this case — every penny counts when earnings are poor.

a. Discuss in detail the numerous nonsensical aspects of the foregoing reasoning.

b. What should the decision be? Demonstrate by a simple example.

c. What light does this incident cast on the importance of distinguishing between T (the revenue requirement for income tax) and T' (income tax on Profit Incentive), which is an essential feature of MRRD but overlooked by other methods of analysis?

9

· · · · · **Cost Behavior** · ·
and the
Decision Process

<u>Some Fundamentals</u>

P roblems of profitability and economic choice are fundamentally
studies in conservation of resources. Their major objective is to
discover minimized costs, meaning the smallest outlays of capital
and/or expense that will permit minimized pricing (revenues) of desired outputs while producing the desired earnings. Earnings, sometimes inaccurately referred to as "profits," represent the difference
between <u>inputs</u> (revenues from sales) and the related <u>outlays</u> (costs).

Honest differences of opinion may be voiced as to estimated
amounts of future revenues or costs. Sound reasons may also be given
for adopting satisfactory approximations of the exactly correct arithmetic involved in making such estimates or for taking safe shortcuts.
Both of these considerations are <u>quantitative</u>. A disciplined theory,
however, can leave no room for differences of opinion as to correct
basic principles, nor as to the exact measures that are to be approximated, that is, <u>qualitative</u> matters.

It is commonplace defiance of these facts in the practice and literature of this subject that has invited the familiar and often justified accu-
sation of skeptics: "You engineers (or you teachers, or you accountants,
or you economists) can make the figures prove whatever you like."

To equip the analyst to cope with this awkward situation and to enable him to refute such criticism, it is necessary to spell out carefully
several details of cost behavior and the decision process that are widely
overlooked, misunderstood, or misrepresented.

<u>Pitfalls</u>

A few examples may be found helpful in suggesting how to avoid
common pitfalls that await the unwary. All illustrate the alliance of
loose usage with unsound reasoning.

For example, some nonregulated enterprises refer to interest
payments on the firm's debt as "interest <u>expense</u>." Such payments are
of course not <u>expense</u> at all but the direct <u>opposite</u> — a component of
earnings. Some analysts include as an estimated expense an item they

call "interim replacements," apart from their estimates of maintenance expense, and treat it as an addition to depreciation expense. Actually, no such expense exists. Replacements, interim or otherwise, are never chargeable to depreciation expense. They are either: (a) included in maintenance expense, or (b) a separate capital outlay. Adjustment of the depreciation annuity for retirement dispersion is not an allowance for replacement.

It is also wise to be on guard against literal interpretations of mis- leading semantics, as in the following example taken from a recent textbook which condemns as "inexact" an estimate in error by 42%, while approving as "correct" an estimate of the same quantity which is in error by 44%:

Estimates of the Depreciation Annuity
Life 25 Years; Type L_0 Probability; MAR 7%

Intended estimate; actual behavior (Table 6.10, on page 135) = 2.82%.

1/Life, said to be "inexact," = 4.00%.   Error + 42%.

$\dfrac{i}{(1 + i)^n - 1}$, called "correct," = 1.58%.   Error - 44%.

An interesting example of this penchant for misleading usage, badge of the amateur, is the popular term "fixed charges," generally applied to the sum of return, depreciation, and taxes. This quantity is neither fixed nor a charge. What is more variable than income tax rates? Is not profit the direct opposite of a "charge"? Other instances are the curious term "annual costs," used to describe the sum of costs plus profits, and the descriptive term "straight-line" to identify a method of depreciation which does not accumulate depreciation at a "straight-line" rate.

Relation of Expenses to Capital Investment and Age

It is often convenient to express annual expense as a percentage of related capital investment, which is apt to convey the unsound and un- intended impression that the amount of expense varies proportionally with a change in capital investment when that is not the case.

For example, fuel consumption of an engine may be expressed as a percentage of the first cost (capital outlay) of the engine, while actually it depends rather on hours of use and/or the load supplied. A more expensive engine (larger capital cost) might have smaller fuel consump- tion for the same output.

Gasoline consumption of an automobile may be almost directly pro- portional to mileage, under some conditions, rather than to the capital cost of the car. On the other hand, the annual cost of car licenses and insurance may be unrelated to either the capital investment or to the mileage, although they are conveniently expressed as a percentage of capital cost.

At any rate, most kinds of equipment have cost behavior quite unlike that of automobiles. Some kinds of machinery require greater attention early in service life when they are being "broken in" and are used most. As newer and better designs become available, the old units may not be scrapped and replaced but used less, thus needing less attention and maintenance. On the other hand, some kinds of facilities may require more repair work and adjustment as their age increases.

Some kinds of plant are purchased with reserve capacity beyond immediate needs to provide for anticipated future increase in output. Operation and maintenance expenses, together with raw material costs, may be expected to increase regularly for a period of years and then level off or even decrease thereafter.

Occasionally, plant purchased for one particular application initially may be used for other purposes later on, with consequent effect on annual expenses. Buildings are sometimes given more attention and higher-grade maintenance when new; later they may be used for other purposes which do not demand such expensive maintenance and housekeeping.

Effects of price inflation on expenses, with passage of time, introduces problems into both the review of past expenses and the forecast of future outlays.

The point of these observations is that studies of profitability and economic choice call for estimates of expense outlays throughout the whole future service life of projects, not merely an estimate of current rates.

Taxes other than income taxes may not be related to capital investment at all, like the so-called "payroll taxes." Or they may be indirectly related to capital investment, such as the so-called "ad valorem taxes" based on assessed value rather than on actual cost. Or they may be remotely associated with both capital and expense outlays, such as taxes levied on sales or on gross receipts. We will return to this subject of taxes other than income tax.

For all such reasons, even though expense outlays are finally tabulated as a percentage of capital investment, it is often desirable to first estimate them in other terms, such as dollars per year per mile (of highway or pipeline), or per square foot of painted or frozen or otherwise treated surface, or per trench foot (of multi-duct underground conduit line), or per circuit-foot of transmission line, or per cubic foot of space to be heated, and so forth.

Analysis of Outlays

Most projects call for outlays of both kinds: capital and expense. The commonest type of economic problem is that of weighing a reduction in expense outlays against the proposed capital outlay that will accomplish the reduction, or vice versa. This is the way, for example, that automation is justified or that the desirability of an economic replacement is demonstrated. An extra capital outlay may buy reduced lifetime expense outlays in several forms: increased efficiency, longer life, greater output, decreased maintenance, less operating labor, fewer rejects, smaller power bills, less "down time," ability to use cheaper raw materials, more effective supervision, minimized packaging or shipping costs, reduced spare requirements, tax savings, or whatnot.

In order to weigh such benefits against their cost in greater capital outlays, it is of course necessary to identify and estimate the expense differentials just as accurately as the incremental capital outlay is estimated. Accordingly, the first task is to define exactly what constitutes an expense, as distinguished from a capital outlay ("investment"). Sometimes this is easy; sometimes difficult; occasionally very difficult indeed.

Basically, the difference is that capital outlays are disbursements of money that belong to owners of the firm to purchase assets. Such funds are obtained by sale of the company's securities to investors, by borrowing, or by use of retained earnings. Retained earnings come from revenues, after being earmarked as earnings by the subtraction of revenue deductions (expenses) from revenues. Expense outlays, in general, make use of funds obtained from revenues before being earmarked as earnings which belong to owners of the business; they purchase services, materials, and so forth, which are not assets. Thus, the final decision rests with the accountants and their disposition of charges.

Many companies maintain a list of "units of property," to define exactly what items constitute capital outlays. The capital outlay for each asset is a single payment made at the time of purchase. Outlays of expense are commonly more or less continuous in every year of the asset's service life. Accordingly, if one desires to add or compare the two kinds of outlays for the asset, it is necessary to do one of two things:

1. Convert the lifetime annual expense outlays — not including depreciation, which is not an outlay — into their financially equivalent single immediate outlay (their present worth); or
2. Convert the single immediate capital outlay into its financially equivalent service-lifetime annuity (the minimum revenue requirement for MAR plus depreciation).

Preceding chapters have described details of both procedures, which arrive at identical conclusions.

Capitalizing Versus Expensing

Borderline cases are occasionally encountered where certain expenditures might reasonably be treated as either capital or expense outlays. Situations of this kind usually arise with respect to subassemblies (components of a larger property unit or complex — sometimes of interchangeable parts) and may involve costs of removal and reinstallation. Several questions may be asked, as follows:

1. Should the equipment be treated as a property unit (capital) or as an expense?
2. Should associated removal and/or reinstallation costs be capitalized or expensed?
3. If capitalized, should average service life be regarded as: (a) the period from the date of initial installation to the date of final retirement ("womb to tomb"), or (b) the average of the several periods of service, initially installed and reinstalled?

Appendix F suggests some of the considerations of importance that enter into an analysis of such questions. A major factor is the effect on income taxes.

Taxes Other Than Income Tax

Two comments may be found helpful concerning estimates and behavior of taxes other than income tax:

1. Property taxes are commonly calculated by municipalities at a stated percentage of assessed value. Careless estimators sometimes apply that same percentage to the capital investment in taxable property. The appropriate procedure, of course, is first to estimate the tax obligation in dollars, ignoring both the tax rate and assessed value unless they are necessary to making that estimate. Then, if desired, express the dollars as a percentage of the capital cost.
2. State or city taxes are sometimes levied on company sales or gross receipts. Since the amount of the tax is only partially related to capital investment, the revenue requirement for such taxes is calculated as a percentage of total revenue requirements.

To illustrate, suppose minimum revenue requirements, exclusive of the tax on gross receipts, are placed at 26.07% of the capital investment in a project, as follows:

MAR	7.00%
Depreciation	7.25%
Income tax	1.82%
Operation, maintenance	10.00%
Total before the tax on gross receipts	26.07%

Suppose that a state tax of 10% is imposed on current gross receipts. Then:

Total revenue requirements, before state tax   = 26.07%

State tax at 10% of gross receipts = $\dfrac{26.07}{(100-10)}$ = $\underline{\ \ 2.90}$

Total revenue requirements   = 28.97%

Note that 2.90% is the <u>revenue requirement</u> for state tax only. There will also be a state tax, at the same rate, on the excess of revenues above minimum revenue requirements. However, the tax on that excess is no part of revenue requirements and is not involved in economic comparisons. For the parallel situation with respect to income tax, see Chapter 8.

We will observe that this kind of levy is indeed "double taxation." The more a company pays for income tax or property taxes, the more state tax it must pay, all else being the same.

Allowing for taxes on sales or on gross receipts does not change the identity of the superior plan, since it increases all revenue requirements of competing proposals by the same percentage. It does, however, increase the margin of superiority of the superior choice, as the following example illustrates.

<u>Superiority of Plan A, ignoring taxes on gross receipts</u>

Present worth of lifetime revenue requirements:

Plan A:	$1,000,000
Plan B:	1,100,000
Superiority of Plan A	$ 100,000 (incorrect)

<u>Superiority of Plan A, recognizing 10% taxes on gross receipts</u>

Revenue requirements, including tax = revenue requirements before tax, plus tax at 10% of revenue requirements including tax. Thus, 0.90 x revenue requirements, including tax = revenue requirements before tax. And revenue requirements, including tax = revenue requirements before tax, divided by 0.90.

Plan A:	1,000,000/ 0.90	= $1,111,111
Plan B:	1,100,000/ 0.90	= 1,222,222
	Superiority of Plan A	= $ 111,111 (correct)

Allocated Expenses Versus Incremental Cost Behavior

An important source of error, repetitiously encountered, is failure to discriminate between: (a) allocations of expense, and (b) cause-related expense differentials.

For example, certain expense outlays, such as administrative and supervisory expense, accounting and clerical expense, legal expense, engineering and storeroom charges, and so forth, are commonly classified as "overheads." They are apt to be overlooked altogether in making economic studies, perhaps because it is implicitly assumed, lacking evidence to the contrary, that they will not be affected by the immediate decision. Or, sometimes, a portion of overheads is assigned (allocated) to the project under study on some arbitrary but presumed reasonable basis, such as an average percentage of project outlays, capital or expense or both. The customary explanation of such assignments is that they appear to be "fair."

It must be obvious that estimators are never safe in assuming that overheads are "the same unless shown to be otherwise." On the contrary, the safe procedure is to assume that overheads will be affected by the immediate project unless it can be demonstrated that such is not the case. This is of greatest importance in making studies of profitability, which are apt to overstate earnings if overheads are ignored, or if reliance is placed on some presumed "fair" allocation without investigating probable incremental charges.

A homely analogy may be found helpful at this point. Four men ride to work daily in a jointly owned car. Monthly expenditures for gasoline, oil, tolls, and parking are quite regular and readily determinate; so are annual costs of licenses and insurance. These expenses amount to $72 per month, or $18 per passenger. Then one of the riders takes a vacation. If the other three pay the usual $18 per month, they discover that expenses will not be recovered; their costs still amount to the same $72. It is necessary to charge $24 apiece, although that may not seem fair, because the same service is rendered as before. The same problem arises if one rider gets a job nearer home so that he travels only half as far as the others. Since he is rendered only half the service, it may seem fair to cut his charges in half. But if that is done, the others must pay more to make up the deficit; total costs remain $72. However, that increased charge would not be "fair" to the others who are rendered exactly the same service as before.

Similar questions of "fair pricing" always arise when costs do not vary directly with output in goods or services. It is reasonable to attempt allocations on some basis regarded by all parties concerned as "fair"; but there is no absolute basis for measuring fairness, as there is for measuring costs. Every allocation must either: (a) reflect cause-related expense differentials, or (b) reflect some arbitrary but acceptable theory of "fairness," regardless of cost behavior.

There is no room for arbitrary allocations in economic comparisons or profitability studies. Apportionment of indirect costs must reflect actual outlays, however difficult to determine. "Fair allocations" are matters of product pricing, or rate making, which is a distinctly different question.

One purpose of cost studies may be to discover earnings, in terms of Profit Incentive (after taxes) as the difference between:

1. Revenues obtained from existing price schedules or rates for service, perhaps based on allocated costs before addition of proposed new property; and

2. <u>Revenue requirements</u>, including allocated costs after addition of the proposed new property.

This is a legitimate concern of management; but such studies do not reveal the company's incremental earnings from the incremental sales and revenues — except, perhaps, by happy accident. In general, it tends to overstate incremental revenue requirements of new projects and understate incremental earnings. It amounts to arbitrarily transferring to new projects some of the jointly incurred expenses previously assigned to other existing projects, other classes of service, or other departments of the company.

The appropriate procedure depends upon the exact intent of the study. If the purpose is to ascertain the productivity or relative efficiency of the several departments of the company, none of them should be allocated any part of jointly incurred costs beyond the amounts indicated by a multiple-correlation analysis. This means that the study may not account for all of the costs incurred; in such case, it should not. The exact purpose is to examine each department's performance in reducing those costs that are under its control. Including allocations of costs not under its control invalidates results of the study, which was intended to inquire into cost behavior.

On the other hand, if the purpose of the study were to arrive at price schedules desirably ("fairly") charged for the output of each department, such schedules must be sufficient to recover all company costs (plus a profit) regardless of identifiable departmental responsibility for them. This is a pricing problem, not one of profitability or economic choice. Allocations of costs to the department will then depend upon what the traffic will bear, what the competitive situation will permit, what regulatory authorities may allow, or what promotional rates may be deemed advisable.

It is easy to confuse economic analysis of outlays (to which this book is devoted) with analyses of "fair," competitive, or otherwise desirable product pricing or rate making. An interesting example of such confusion appears in Appendix D; it clarifies a situation that has often led to unsound conclusions.

The Decision Process

Table 9.1 outlines the decision process envisioned by MRRD. It starts with the estimate of minimum revenue requirements, whether the problem be one of profitability or economic choice. Minimum revenue requirements (outlays) reveal the <u>financial</u> status of proposals over their service lifetime.

Usually this financial situation is the controlling influence in the final decision to adopt or reject a proposal; but sometimes nonfinancial considerations or second choices are deemed desirable aside from the matter of Profit Incentive. For example, a less profitable alternative may have appeal because it creates a better company "image" sufficient

Table 9.1. The decision process.

I. Diagnosis of the Problem

a. Definition of "the project"

All economic evaluations depend to some extent on the reservation "if all else remains the same." This means that "all else" affected by adopting a course of action must be evaluated as part of the proposal, no matter how indirect or tenuous the connection. Thus, the first task is to define the project exactly.

b. Profitability versus economic choice

The nature of the analysis depends upon whether the problem is one of profitability or economic choice. It is an economic choice only if alternative plans contemplate identical sales and revenues.

c. Continuing plant

Must provision for replacements be considered?

d. Denomination of conclusions

Ultimate objective of the study is to estimate potential effect of proposals on company earnings per share, not to estimate percentage return on investment in the project.

Results may be appropriately stated in terms of annual minimum revenue requirements, their lifetime present worth, present worth of all future revenue requirements, dollars of Profit Incentive, or some "per unit" quantity such as per unit of output, per dollar of sales, and so on.

II. The Profit Analysis

Step 1: Estimate "receipts less outlays" in the manner indicated by the foregoing diagnosis of the problem.

If it is a study of economic choice, revenues need not be estimated, beyond the stipulation that they are identical for all alternative proposals.

III. Irreducibles, Intangibles, Contingencies

Step 2: This item deals only with considerations affecting the firm's "best position," but which are substantially impossible to reduce to meaningful dollar values. All factors that affect estimable receipts or outlays must be evaluated as part of Step 1.

IV. Sensitivity Studies, if Justified

V. The Budgeting Function

The term "budgeting function" is here given a special comprehensive connotation.

Here is made the final decision as to the recommended course of action to be taken in view of foregoing findings as to profitability or economic choice, and intangible factors.

Here, for the first time, enter considerations for capital rationing, financing details, feedback effects of pricing policy, labor relations, public policy, elasticity of demand, payout period, etc.

to justify the penalty in reduced earnings for stockholders; it may be more expedient politically; or it may create less noise, have a more pleasing appearance. All these inducements must be in sufficient amount to make the owners of the business (stockholders) satisfied to accept the sacrifice in their earnings. This situation is recognized by specifying two distinct steps in the initial cost analysis:

Step 1. Estimate the revenue requirement, including evaluation of Profit Incentive in profitability studies.

Step 2. Consider other factors (impossible to reduce to dollars) which have a bearing on desirability of adopting the proposal. Some may be reasons for preferring an alternative other than the economic choice. Some may be borderline cases of contingencies so remote that it is impossible to assign any reasonable degree of probability or cost penalty. Step 2 factors are sometimes described as imponderables, intangibles, or irreducibles.

If an element can affect minimum revenue requirements, it must be financial in nature and therefore part of the Step 1 analysis. Its effect could not be weighed against its penalty in reduced earnings (as is characteristic of Step 2 factors) if the nonfinancial benefit were "quantified," as sometimes recommended. Step 2 considerations must be treated strictly as separate and supplementary data to accompany the financial analysis (Step 1) if they are not to destroy the integrity and usefulness of the whole study.

In the great majority of problems, no Step 2 questions arise; however, considerations of a somewhat similar nature may be encountered in connection with the subsequent budgeting function. In general, Step 2 deals with the query: "How much financial penalty would owners of the business be willing to suffer in order for the company to obtain this claimed advantage over the Number 1 economic choice?"

Sensitivity studies (Item IV of Table 9.1) are sometimes worthwhile making if it is difficult to prepare firm estimates of probable future outlays. These studies are simply inquiries into the effect of possible but unlikely extreme variations (optimistically low or pessimistically high) in future costs that are not estimable with assurance. Because sensitivity studies are not usually necessary, this item appears within dotted lines.

The budgeting function (Item V) is concerned with the final decision to adopt or reject a proposal in the light of conclusions reached in Step 1 and Step 2. That is, the matter of profitability or economic choice is completely disposed of in the first three (or four) items of the process; the budgeting function consists in deciding what to do about it.

It is important to discriminate sharply between the budgeting function and the prerequisite cost and earnings analysis. This sharp distinction is an essential feature of MRRD which calls for further special attention. Traditional decision theory is notably deficient and unhelpful in this respect. By failing to observe the distinction, the theory proceeds to apply criteria which may not carry out the analyst's intent at all, as will be shown.

Nature of the Budgeting Function

Sound decision making must start with agreement on ultimate objectives, followed by agreement on the criteria by which to gauge attainment of those objectives. There is only one exact statement of ultimate financial objectives; that is expressed by the now-familiar MRRD principle: to place the firm in the best position to optimize (hopefully, but not necessarily, maximize) return to its owners while optimizing its competitive position.

Having established the profitability and/or economic superiority of the proposals (Step 1), and having weighed nonfinancial factors and contingencies (Step 2), there remains the question: In view of the findings of Step 1 and Step 2, what action should be taken?

It is at this point and not before that attention should turn to details such as opportunity cost, elasticity of demand, availability of requisite capital (capital rationing), details of financing (alternative sources of funds); availability of materials, time, and personnel; optimized timing of operations and spending; short-term business conditions; payout periods; relative risks and cutoff rates; and so forth. Some of these considerations may also have entered into Step 2, but in a different sense. In Step 2, their bearing on the instant project alone was in question; in the budgeting function, it is their bearing on relative desirability of projects in competition with other proposals that is scrutinized. An illustrative example will follow.

Great care must be taken to use in the budgeting function only those criteria relevant to the budgeting decision; and vice versa, criteria relevant only to the budgeting decision have no place in determinations of economic choice nor profitability. Failure to recognize clearly this essential and distinctive nature of the budgeting function accounts for many of the faulty and wasteful business decisions that show up in reduced company earnings, impaired competitive position of the firm, and injured reputation of its management.

Oddly enough, the dictionary provides a better definition of "budget" than do most textbooks on budgeting. Most dictionaries say something like this (from Funk and Wagnalls College Standard): "A statement of probable revenue and expenditure and financial proposals for the ensuing year as presented to or passed upon by a legislative body." This is its exact meaning as used in this book. Rendering this exact concept in vaguer and more elegant terms is often attempted. The result is unhelpful.

The budget is a statement. It refers to estimates for an ensuing period; a year is a good basis which permits the long-range distinction between budgeting and system planning. The "legislative body" may be the firm's review board, committee on operations, board of directors, or some similar group. Even though there may be no such formal separate body, and the course of action is decided upon by the same individual who makes the estimates, the "legislative" function occupies its own distinctive spot in the process.

Among the criteria, such darlings of traditional decision theory as the minimax, minimax expectation, and Hurwicz criteria — if they perform any useful function — may now be considered. They will not be discussed here, because they are ordinarily of substantially zero value, being simply a listing of imaginable bases for decision, without regard for merit.

In brief, the budgeting function is helpfully regarded as the final step in the task of reviewing a number of proposals for corporate action, each proposal being accompanied by a statement of its estimated profitability (Profit Incentive in dollars per year) or a statement of the economic superiority of the recommended procedure over specified alternatives. The purpose of the final review is to select from among the proposals and to recommend courses of action.

It is possible that other options may be to consider still other alternatives not yet investigated or to suggest modification of objectives, size, timing, and so forth, of specific projects. If modifications are to be made, the alternatives may then be referred back for reprocessing through the same routine analyses, starting with Step 1 again. That reestimating is not part of the budgeting function; it is triggered by the budgeting function.

Good reasons to reject proposals demonstrated to be profitable and relatively desirable in the light of the Step 1-Step 2 analysis may include such considerations as capital rationing, inadvisable timing politically or financially, temporarily excessive cost of new capital, and inability to secure the necessary materials, talent, or labor. Thus, the budgeting function may overrule the Step 1-Step 2 conclusions without disputing their correctness.

Such is the "legislative" function mentioned in the foregoing definition, which sometimes introduces a practical situation endangering effectiveness of the most careful planning. That is, having compiled a budget for the coming fiscal period, there still remains, in some organizations, the matter of "selling" it to the individual or group whose approval puts it into effect. This may involve piecemeal approval of each item as the budget is assembled or approval of the "package" after the total recommended outlay and program has been decided upon.

In the American jury system, the intimate knowledge of jurisprudence necessary to sound decisions seldom resides in the jury that makes ultimate decisions. It is the duty of learned counsel and the bench to see to it that the jury is presented the facts of each case and that the prescribed methods whereby juries reach sound decisions are respected. Incontestable laws and rules of evidence are points which the "experts" (lawyers and judge) must know and must insist that the jury honor.

Similarly, in American business the jury whose function it is to make the ultimate budgeting decision cannot always be expected to possess the intimate knowledge of economic principles necessary to sound decisions; this "jury" must be instructed by the "experts." This remains the case no matter what level of management constitutes the "jury," which may include accountants, engineers, system planners, budget directors, finance officers, boards of directors, or even majority stockholders, commissions, and financial advisers. It would be a serious mistake to defer to contrary opinion from any such sources without protest if that opinion ignores or violates principles of MRRD. It would also be unforgivable to compromise principle in order to gain approval of the "jury" in such cases. To repeat, there is always room for honest difference of opinion as to estimated quantities; no room at all for difference of opinion as to principle.

Skepticism, expressed or not, may be encountered as to validity of the MRRD solution (particularly, validity of the PWAFRR solution) as the only appropriate basis for economic choice, or even as the major consideration. Various other "success indicators," intangibles, or vague and unspecified judgment factors may be advanced as controlling. Short-term financial benefits may be urged, to the exclusion of adverse long-term or feedback effects which can be predicted to affect the firm's future competitive position seriously. To resolve such issues, diligence may be required in winning intelligent appreciation of the practical nature of MRRD. It may be necessary to repeat that Step 1 conclusions reveal the most likely financial developments. These conclusions make no pretense of 100% accuracy, being based on the best possible estimates of future outlays; it may on occasion be necessary to present several possible financial results (several estimates of PWAFRR) having different degrees of probability. However, no dependable substitute for the Step 1 approach has been found.

If some intangible judgment factor is urged in support of any alternative other than the Step 1 choice, it means deliberately advocating a course of action that is not expected to place the firm in the best position to maximize the owners' earnings, nor expected to be best for the company's competitive position. This is a serious matter, to recommend procedures that are admittedly not in the best financial interests of owners of the firm and its creditors. For this reason, if the claimed intangible "judgment" advantages cannot be specifically described and their presumed benefits argued, then it must be concluded that they do not in fact exist. The excuse that they are difficult to evaluate does not make them Step 2 considerations. They are then Step 1 factors whose quantification is difficult and uncertain and which therefore have some smaller degree of probability than other Step 1 estimates. They call for calculation of tentative minimum revenue requirements whose probability of occurrence is small.

Of course, proposing to base decisions on judgment alone, without any attempt to inquire into minimum revenue requirements, is naive, though it is sometimes proposed. Making decisions in this manner is

often described as "acting on a hunch." One might do well to inquire
whether such "hunches" are more accurately described as a natural
reaction of management jealous of its own prerogatives and suspicious
of unexpected conclusions of the MRRD analysis but unable to find any
specific error in it.

Risk and Uncertainty

"Risk" is often regarded as a vague and amorphous threat like
"uncertainty." Statistical means have sometimes been proposed for
dealing with it, without any clear idea of just what the source of the
menace might be. That makes a difference to the appropriate manipulation of the data.

A major source of risk is failure of anticipated markets to develop
as expected; sales and revenues fail to match estimates. As noted before, this contingency ordinarily does not affect estimates of minimum
revenue requirements beyond suggesting tests for sensitivity to shorter
probable service life of assets and possibly a slightly increased MAR.
As a practical matter, it is safe to conclude that considerations of risk
or uncertainty from this source have no place in economic comparisons
(as distinguished from profitability studies).

Since estimates of revenues are an essential part of profitability
studies, risk or uncertainty on that score enters from the beginning in
such problems. It cannot then be left for later sensitivity studies or
the budgeting function. However, the important point is that this has no
bearing on the nature of the criteria to be used in Step 1, in any case.
The appropriate criterion in profitability studies remains the amount
of Profit Incentive — earnings in dollars in excess of MAR — the probability of which must be examined. The budgeting decision — whether
to accept or reject the proposal in the light of probable Profit Incentives — is quite a separate matter.

Another fact is worth thinking about at this point. Sales and revenues are to a large degree controllable. Competent management is not
the helpless prey of the random uncertainty with which classical decision theory is obsessed. Practical applications of probability theory
(not "uncertainty theory"), whether by way of well-established forecasting techniques or more elaborate statistical procedures, commonly
produce reasonably dependable predictions of sales and revenues and
effects thereon of proposed pricing policy, advertising campaigns, and
sales effort.

Note again that a differential in expected revenues has no effect on
identification of the economic choice, which is discovered by applying
the "iffy hypothesis" of identical sales and revenues for competing alternatives, beyond possible minor feedback effect on service lives and
MAR.

Ignoring the phenomenon of "probable departure from certainty"
would mean overlooking the very foundation of realistic estimating. It

is difficult to understand the willingness of so many analysts to ignore clearly foreseeable effects of probable departures from what is regarded as "normal," when these effects are of such great quantitative consequence and so readily allowed for.

This book opened with a comment on change as the predominant feature characteristic of business. At the same time, the assumption "if all other things remain the same" is indispensable if one wishes to examine impact of change in only one of the several variables influencing a decision. That impact is the very heart of most problems. It is sometimes difficult to specify just what details can be reasonably assumed to "stay put" and still arrive at meaningful conclusions. Critics have accused the economist of being totally inconsistent on this score. He first calls attention to the importance of change; then he proceeds to recommend methods of estimate which depend on the "ceteris paribus" principle. "Here are your answers," he says, "provided everything stays the same — which it never does."

Appendix B discusses some of the severely restricted limitations of the ceteris paribus hypothesis and the fact that these limitations are so commonly disregarded in theory and practice.

To illustrate, if ten coins are tossed a large number of times, the one most frequent combination of heads and tails to come up will be five heads and five tails. But betting even money that this will occur each time is a losing game; it occurs much less than half the time. The thoughtful person will question whether or not some sort of parallel can be obtained by basing investment decisions on the single most likely combination of circumstances. Aren't decisions so reached apt to be wrong more than half the time? It is true that conclusions based on the single most likely, most typical, or demonstrably average set of circumstances — disregarding purely arithmetical effects of probability — are apt to be inadequate to produce sound decisions. The MRRD technique provides specific measures for dealing with this situation, from reliance on the relatively stable statistic MAR and utilization of the "iffy hypothesis" to a simple means of allowing for probable retirement dispersion and recognition of the budgeting function as a separate operation in the decision process.

Ranking Proposals; Optimized Budgets

An important consideration in making budget decisions that demands further attention is the concept of cutoff rate of individual projects. The importance of company-average cutoff rate was discussed before; Figures 14.2 and 14.3 of Chapter 14 reproduce Exhibits A and B as a refresher. In the present case, it is a matter of deciding whether earnings of the particular project are expected to exceed company MAR by a sufficient margin to make the proposal inviting, in view of its risks and prospects in competition with other proposals.

No matter how well equipped with traditional decision theory, with

such technical details as LaPlace transforms or indeed with knowledge
of MRRD, the analyst must still face up to that subjective decision.
How much more than MAR must this proposal promise to earn throughout its service life before it can be considered to be worth undertaking?

Such data-manipulating devices as the corporate model (simulation)
or decision trees may be helpful tools, but it is not the function of such
tools to make up the analyst's mind. They simply facilitate the mental
process whereby he makes up his mind. They are contrivances, akin
to the slide rule, used to arrange data in a manner more conveniently
scanned by our limited powers of human observation and deliberation,
in order to facilitate the reaching of a decision by whatever mental
process may be possible. However, it is possible to present an arithmetical example to illustrate how the amount of Profit Incentive and the
level of cutoff rate operate to provide a sound criterion for ranking
proposals and arriving at the optimized budget.

Given a number of attractive proposals for inclusion in the company's capital budget, how then does one go about deciding which are
the most desirable and which the least? This question is most pressing
when the company has limited resources of capital, labor, materials,
talent, time, or other essentials. Probably most important of these is
the limitation on amount of capital available, which must be rationed by
carefully restricting the budget to distinctly superior proposals only.

A general basis for such decisions is obvious: Select the most
promising proposals first and devote available funds to them until the
money is used up. It hurts least to forego the poorer prospects. But
exactly what is the quantitative measure of "most promising"? And if
sufficient funds are at hand to permit considering some of the poorer
prospects, exactly where does one draw the line? When do proposals
become assuredly not worthwhile?

A great deal has been written on this subject that is unhelpful and
unsound. Some popular and recommended procedures almost guarantee
that company finances will be impaired. Yet the principles to be observed are crystal-clear and beautifully simple, as follows:

1. Desirability of a capital budget is gauged by its benefits to owners
   of the business, that is, to pre-project shares. (See the lemonade
   stand analogy of Chapter 2.)
2. Pre-project shares can realize benefits of adopting the budget only
   by way of its effect on their dividends and market price (capital
   gains) per share. (See the discussion of evaluating minimum acceptable return, Chapter 3.)
3. Dividends and market price of the company's shares depend upon
   earnings per share, not necessarily on percentage return, as will
   be shown.
4. Consequently, desirability of budget proposals depend upon their potential effect on the company's earnings per share.

Note that it is necessary to stipulate potential effect on earnings
per share. That, of course, is because earnings of any individual

project can be estimated if its revenues and costs can be foreseen. Future company earnings, however, depend upon the contribution of all other existing projects to the firm's pool of earnings. Behavior of those other earnings or disposition of benefits from those other projects must not affect rating of the immediate proposal under study.

In ranking proposals, great care must be taken to define "the project" exactly to evaluate results of all activities whose costs or revenues will be affected by its adoption, even though these proposals involve no capital outlay in the current budget. Such exact identification of "the project" is the very first thought in the decision process as outlined in Table 9.1.

For example, it may be proposed to continue supplying repair parts for obsolete models of the company's manufacture, even at a loss. Several reasons may provide a basis for that proposal, all describable as placing the firm in the best position. But a question arises. If done at a loss, how does one evaluate seriousness of that loss? Certainly not in percent of the capital investment involved. The percentage loss could be tremendous — 100% or more — and still be unimportant if the capital investment is small; or, conversely, a small percentage could mean damaging losses if the capital investment were large. At the same time, benefits of the proposal could be substantial indeed in terms of customer loyalty retained and profitable new business attributable to the policy of supplying repair parts.

This elementary example illustrates not only the importance of defining "the project" exactly but also the basic fallacy of ranking proposals in the order of their percentage earnings on capital investment. Yet the great majority of ranking decisions are made in that indefensible manner. For a particularly interesting example of this fallacy, see the discussion of the Percentage Return Method, Chapter 11.

In brief, optimized budgets are those that are most effective in placing the firm in the best position. The best position is gauged by potential company earnings per share, post project; more specifically, by potential earnings per share in excess of MAR; and still more specifically, by potential earnings per share in excess of project cutoff rate per share, which cutoff rate is always greater than company MAR.

The appropriate amount of that indispensable margin of cutoff rate above MAR is not demonstrable mathematically; it remains a subjective decision for management. Investors can and do register their opinion of the relation between company earnings per share and company-average risk, by way of market price per share of the firm's stock. Cutoff rate for any individual project, however, may be greater or less than company-average cutoff rate (which lies between MAR and company-pool earnings), since project risk may be greater or less than company-average risk. The point remains that if project earnings do not promise to equal or exceed project cutoff rate, which is greater than MAR by some margin, then by definition of terms the project is not worth adopting, even though its earnings may exceed MAR by some smaller margin.

The classical and oft-repeated error on this score has been mentioned before. This persistent misrepresentation insists that any project earning in excess of "cost of capital" (meaning MAR) is worthwhile because it necessarily adds something to the firm's net worth. This is another good example of that vicious alliance between bad usage and bad reasoning. Cutoff rate is not "cost of capital"; it is always greater than MAR by some margin depending upon the degree of project risk.

Nobody raises money at a cost of $i\%$ in order to reinvest the funds in projects capable of earning only that same $i\%$, not even if there were zero risk. There is nothing in such proposals for owners of the business — for pre-project shares. Existing stockholders would profit nothing and would be obliged to share the risk with "newcomers." This simple principle, obvious even to proprietors of lemonade stands, has been stated repeatedly before in this book. Yet it is contradicted repeatedly in unexpected places. Beware!

Retroactive effect on MAR of adopting successively less desirable proposals is discussed in Chapters 3 and 14. That aspect of the "iffy hypothesis" need only be mentioned here to indicate that it is pertinent.

Ultimate desirability of projects which do not contemplate capital outlays (that is, expense only) may be gauged in this same general manner, by their effect on company earnings per share. Suitability of this criterion is not affected by the nebulous nature of benefits of certain proposals such as outlays for advertising, research, charity, community welfare, and so on. If the ultimate effect is to reduce earnings per share, as compared to the situation if the proposals were rejected, then owners suffer a penalty. Owners may be willing to accept that penalty, which is a matter for the "legislative" function to decide on behalf of the stockholders they represent.

Illustrative Example

Ten projects are proposed for budgeting. Each project has been investigated to establish the economic choice (Step 1) between two alternatives, Plans (a) and (b). Output and revenues for Plans (a) and (b) are identical, for a given project. Also, Plans (a) and (b) are mutually exclusive; only one or the other will be adopted for each project. To minimize calculations and facilitate understanding the arithmetic, the following assumptions apply to all cases:

Minimum acceptable return (MAR) = 6%.
Service life = 20 years. Net salvage is zero. $_6d$ = 2.7185%.
Taxes (income plus other) = 2%.

Plans (a) and (b) differ as to all other expenses, in each case.

For purposes of this example, the alternative demanding the greater investment has the smaller revenue requirements but the greater percentage return. This is done deliberately to illustrate the effect on the budgeting function; that situation is not necessarily typical.

Before adopting any of the proposals, the company's finances are as follows:

Investors' committed capital	$100,000,000
Outstanding common stock (no debt; no preferred stock)	2,500,000 shares
Book value per share	$40 per share
Market price per new share	$50 per share
Annual earnings (7.5% of $100,000,000)	$7,500,000 per year
Pre-project earnings per share	$3.00 per share

A sample worksheet (Table 9.2) shows the nature of calculations made for each of the two plans for each of the ten proposals.

A summary of findings appears in Table 9.3. The underlined figure in Line 6 for each proposal indicates maximum percentage return, as between Plans (a) and (b). Note that this percentage return is not a safe criterion of economic choice; it is the wrong choice in every case, in this example.

Post-project percentage return for the company appears in Line 7; the greater percentage, as between competing Plans (a) and (b), is again underlined.

Line 8 shows project earnings per new share.

Line 9 shows the exactly intended criterion: earnings per share for the company, post project. The larger figure, for Plan (a) versus Plan (b), is underlined for each proposal.

Line 10 presents an alternative statement of the situation of Line 9; it is in terms of Profit Incentive per pre-project share in the company, obtained by adopting the proposal. As before, the superior figure is underlined for each proposal.

Arrows indicate that the alternative having minimum revenue requirements, as between (a) and (b) for each proposal, is the one also producing maximum company earnings per share, post project. It is also the alternative that maximizes Profit Incentive per post-project share in the firm. None of the other criteria (Lines 6, 7, 8) can be trusted to accomplish that.

Table 9.4 summarizes the rankings of the twenty plans and alternatives, listing them in descending order as follows:

Criterion I.   By Percentage Return of Project
Criterion II.   By Earnings per Incremental Share of Project
Criterion III.   By Percentage Return of the Company, Post Project
Criterion IV.   By Earnings per Share of the Company, Post Project.

Observe that the appropriate Criterion IV, by earnings per share of the company, post project, selects only the economic choices established by the Step 1 analysis: Alternatives (b).

Details of this example have been specially selected to provide materials for further study by the student, if desired.

Table 9.2. Rating proposals for budget purposes; work sheet.
(Illustrating calculations underlying Table 9.3.) Applied to Proposal 1, Plans (a) and (b). (Annual Revenues = $1,200,000.)

	Plan (a)	Plan (b)
1. Minimum revenue requirements		
Capital investment (see Table 9.3)	$4,000,000	$5,000,000
MAR at 6% per year	$ 240,000	$ 300,000
Depreciation at 2.7185%	108,740	135,925
Taxes (income and others)	80,000	100,000
All other expenses	350,000	200,000
	$ 778,740	$ 735,925
2. Percentage return of project	$\dfrac{240{,}000 + 0.52(1{,}200{,}000 - 778{,}740)}{4{,}000{,}000} = 11.476\%$	$\dfrac{300{,}000 + 0.52(1{,}200{,}000 - 735{,}925)}{5{,}000{,}000} = 10.826\%$
3. Percentage return of company, post-project	$\dfrac{7{,}500{,}000 + 459{,}055}{100{,}000{,}000 + 4{,}000{,}000} = 7.653\%$	$\dfrac{7{,}500{,}000 + 541{,}319}{100{,}000{,}000 + 5{,}000{,}000} = 7.658\%$
4. Earnings per share, project	$\dfrac{459{,}055}{80{,}000} = \$5.738$	$\dfrac{541{,}319}{100{,}000} = \$5.413$
5. Earnings per share of company, post-project	$\dfrac{7{,}500{,}000 + 459{,}055}{2{,}500{,}000 + 80{,}000} = \$3.085$	$\dfrac{7{,}500{,}000 + 541{,}319}{2{,}500{,}000 + 100{,}000} = \$3.093$
6. Profit Incentive per pre-project share	$\dfrac{459{,}055 - 240{,}000}{2{,}500{,}000} = 8.76¢$	$\dfrac{541{,}319 - 300{,}000}{2{,}500{,}000} = 9.65¢$

Table 9.3. Rating proposals for budget purposes. Details of Alternative Plans (a) and (b) for 10 Proposals.*

	Proposal I		Proposal II		Proposal III		Proposal IV		Proposal V	
	Plan (a)	Plan (b)	Plan (a)	Plan (b)	Plan (a)	Plan (b)	Plan (a)	Plan (b)	Plan (a)	Plan (b)
1. Capital investment	$4,000,000	$5,000,000	$4,000,000	$5,000,000	$1,000,000	$2,000,000	$1,000,000	$2,000,000	$1,000,000	$2,000,000
2. Number of new shares at $50 per share	80,000	100,000	80,000	100,000	20,000	40,000	20,000	40,000	20,000	40,000
3. Annual revenues	$1,200,000	$1,200,000	$1,100,000	$1,100,000	$375,000	$375,000	$325,000	$325,000	$300,000	$300,000
4. "All other expenses"	$350,000	$200,000	$350,000	$200,000	$140,000	$10,000	$140,000	$10,000	$140,000	$10,000
5. Minimum revenue requirements	$778,740	$735,925	$778,740	$735,925	$247,185	$224,370	$247,185	$224,370	$247,185	$224,370
6. Percentage return of project	11.476%	10.826%	10.176%	9.786%	12.646%	9.916%	10.046%	8.616%	8.746%	7.966%
7. Percentage return of company, post project	7.653%	7.658%	7.603%	7.609%	7.551%	7.547%	7.525%	7.522%	7.512%	7.509%
8. Earnings per share of project	$5,738	$5,413	$5,088	$4,893	$6,323	$4,958	$5,023	$4,308	$4,373	$3,983
9. Earnings per share of company, post project	$3,085	$3,093	$3,065	$3,073	$3,026	$3,031	$3.0161	$3.0206	$3,011	$3,015
10. Profit Incentive per pre-project share	8.76¢	9.65¢	6.68¢	7.57¢	2.66¢	3.13¢	1.62¢	2.09¢	1.10¢	1.57¢

	Proposal VI		Proposal VII		Proposal VIII		Proposal IX		Proposal X	
	Plan (a)	Plan (b)	Plan (a)	Plan (b)	Plan (a)	Plan (b)	Plan (a)	Plan (b)	Plan (a)	Plan (b)
1. Capital investment	$1,000,000	$1,500,000	$500,000	$1,000,000	$500,000	$1,000,000	$500,000	$1,000,000	$100,000	$200,000
2. Number of new shares at $50 per share	20,000	30,000	10,000	20,000	10,000	20,000	10,000	20,000	2,000	4,000
3. Annual revenues	$300,000	$300,000	$250,000	$250,000	$200,000	$200,000	$175,000	$175,000	$50,000	$50,000
4. "All other expenses"	$80,000	$20,000	$75,000	$10,000	$75,000	$10,000	$75,000	$10,000	$14,000	$1,000
5. Minimum revenue requirements	$187,185	$180,777	$128,592	$117,185	$128,592	$117,185	$128,592	$117,185	$24,718	$22,437
6. Percentage return of project	11.866%	10.133%	18.626%	12.906%	13.426%	10.306%	10.826%	9.006%	19.147%	13.167%
7. Percentage return of company, post project	7.543%	7.539%	7.555%	7.554%	7.528%	7.528%	7.517%	7.515%	7.5116%	7.5113%
8. Earnings per share of project	$5,933	$5,067	$9,313	$6,453	$6,713	$5,153	$5,413	$4,503	$9,573	$6,583
9. Earnings per share of company, post project	$3,023	$3,025	$3,025	$3,027	$3,015	$3,017	$3.0096	$3.0119	$3.0052	$3.0057
10. Profit Incentive per pre-project share	2.35¢	2.48¢	2.52¢	2.76¢	1.50¢	1.72¢	0.97¢	1.20¢	0.53¢	0.57¢

*Some of the solutions have been carried out to more decimal places than others to indicate a difference in significant figures.

Table 9.4. Ranking of proposals and alternatives.

I. Percentage Return of Projects		II. Earnings per Incremental Share		III. Percentage Return of Company, Post Project		IV. Earnings per Share of Company, Post Project	
1 X(a)	19.147%	1 X(a)	$9.573	1 I(b)	7.658%	1 I(b)	$3.093
2 VII(a)	18.626	2 VII(a)	9.313	~~I(a) 7.653~~		~~I(a) 3.085~~	
3 VIII(a)	13.426	3 VIII(a)	6.713	2 II(b)	7.609	2 II(b)	3.073
~~X(b) 13.167~~ (1)		~~X(b) 6.583~~		~~II(a) 7.603~~		~~II(a) 3.065~~	
~~VII(b) 12.906~~ (2)		~~VII(b) 6.453~~		3 VII(a)	7.555	3 III(b)	3.031
4 III(a)	12.646	4 III(a)	6.323	~~VII(b) 7.554~~		4 VII(b)	3.027
5 VI(a)	11.866	5 VI(a)	5.933	4 III(a)	7.551	~~III(a) 3.026~~	
6 I(a)	11.476	6 I(a)	5.738	~~III(b) 7.547~~		~~VII(a) 3.025~~	
7 IX(a)	10.826	7 IX(a)	5.413	5 VI(a)	7.543	5 VI(b)	3.025
~~I(b) 10.826~~ (3)		~~I(b) 5.413~~		~~VI(b) 7.539~~		~~VI(a) 3.023~~	
~~VIII(b) 10.306~~ (4)		~~VIII(b) 5.153~~		6 VIII(a)	7.529	6 IV(b)	3.021
8 II(a)	10.176	8 II(a)	5.088	~~VIII(b) 7.528~~		7 VIII(b)	3.017
~~VI(b) 10.133~~ (5)		~~VI(b) 5.067~~		7 IV(a)	7.525	~~IV(a) 3.016~~	
9 IV(a)	10.046	9 IV(a)	5.023	~~IV(b) 7.522~~		~~VIII(a) 3.015~~	
~~III(b) 9.916~~ (6)		~~III(b) 4.958~~		8 IX(a)	7.517	8 V(b)	3.015
~~II(b) 9.786~~ (7)		~~II(b) 4.893~~		~~IX(b) 7.515~~		9 IX(b)	3.012
~~IX(b) 9.006~~ (8)		~~IX(b) 4.503~~		9 V(a)	7.512	~~V(a) 3.011~~	
10 V(a)	8.746	10 V(a)	4.373	10 X(a)	7.512	~~IX(a) 3.010~~	
~~IV(b) 8.616~~ (9)		~~IV(b) 4.308~~		~~X(b) 7.511~~		10 X(b)	3.006
~~V(b) 7.966~~ (10)		~~V(b) 3.983~~		~~V(b) 7.509~~		~~X(a) 3.005~~	

Note: Since Alternatives (a) and (b) for any given project are mutually exclusive, either (a) or (b) may be adopted, but not both. Thus, some alternatives must be ruled out, as indicated. For example, in ranking by Percentage Return of Projects (Criterion I), X(a) is assigned No.1 rank; therefore X(b) must be ruled out as a candidate for No. 4 rank.

Note that Criteria I and II select only Alternatives (a); Criterion IV selects only Alternatives (b) on this basis.

Interpreting Results of Table 9.4.

What conclusions, then, can be drawn from Table 9.4? Obviously there are several ways in which the projects may be ranked, all arriving at different orders of preference.

In this example, ranking by percentage return of proposals (Criterion I) would identify X(a) as first choice, with a return of 19.147%. Proposal I does poorly; I(a) is sixth of the (a) alternatives, with a return of only 11.476%. On the other hand, ranking by company earnings per share, post project (Criterion IV) would call I(b) first choice. Proposal X(a) or X(b) is the last of all!

Obviously, it is highly important to decide upon our exact objective in undertaking to "rank" proposals before these results can have any helpful interpretation.

If only one project were to be adopted from among the twenty proposals and alternatives, no question would arise as to which it should be: I(b), per Criterion IV. If a second is then to be added, it should be II(b), also per Criterion IV, and so on. This will unmistakably maximize company earnings per share out of the revenues obtained.

This process should be continued until a point is reached where poorer proposals are unattractive, gauged by their cutoff rate. For example, suppose cutoff rate for all (b) alternatives is 9.5%. As shown under Criterion I, this would mean rejecting Project IX(b) promising only 9.006%, IV(b) promising only 8.616%, and V(b) promising only 7.966%. Since IX(a), IV(a), and V(a) have already been rejected by applying Criterion IV, Projects IX, IV, and V would be abandoned. But now suppose that there are insufficient capital funds available to finance the remaining seven (b) alternatives that are attractive. To adopt all seven would call for $15,700,000. Suppose, for example, that the "legislative body" mentioned in our definition of "budget" is unwilling to provide more than $13,600,000 of capital funds. What is the best use that could be made of that limited outlay? This question introduces the problem of capital rationing.

Capital Rationing

Capital rationing may be defined as the restricting of capital outlays within some stipulated total in deciding which of otherwise desirable and profitable proposals to adopt.

In the present case, the limited outlay of $13,600,000 would be sufficient to finance all ten of the (a) alternatives. It would finance only the four top-rank economic choices or (b) alternatives (I, II, III, VII) with $600,000 left over to finance 40% of VI(b) if that is feasible. Which use of the funds is preferable?

Adopting all ten of the (a) alternatives certainly will maximize the company's percentage return as well as its immediate earnings per post-project share. The arithmetical demonstration of that situation is simple and clear, as Table 9.5 indicates. Applying Criterion I (project percentage return) would mean adopting Schedule A, the ten (a) alternatives, yielding company earnings of 7.95% (against 7.85% for Schedule B) and $3.26 per share (against only $3.22 for Schedule B).

Then what is wrong with the percentage return ranking? Should we not adopt Schedule A? The answer is that a great deal is wrong; every effort should be made to adopt only the economic choices, Alternatives (b), selected by applying Criterion IV.

In the first place, setting a limit on capital funds in this manner is always arbitrary to a degree. There are substantially always alternatives that ought to be explored before bowing to such a dictum, as will be discussed.

Second, accepting Criterion I (project percentage return) and adopting Schedule A means failing to maximize company earnings out of identical revenues. Settling for only 4.4 projects of Schedule B means

Table 9.5. Alternative budgets of $13,600,000.

| | | Schedule A | | |
Plan	Capital	Earnings	Incremental Shares	Revenues
I(a)	$ 4,000,000	$459,055	80,000	$1,200,000
II(a)	4,000,000	407,055	80,000	1,100,000
III(a)	1,000,000	126,464	20,000	375,000
IV(a)	1,000,000	100,464	20,000	325,000
V(a)	1,000,000	87,464	20,000	300,000
VI(a)	1,000,000	118,664	20,000	300,000
VII(a)	500,000	93,132	10,000	250,000
VIII(a)	500,000	67,132	10,000	200,000
IX(a)	500,000	54,132	10,000	175,000
X(a)	100,000	19,147	2,000	50,000
Totals	$13,600,000	$1,532,709	272,000	$4,275,000

Company investment, post project = $113,600,000

Company earnings, post project = $9,032,709

Company shares, post project = 2,772,000

Company percentage return, post project = $\frac{9,032,709}{113,600,000}$ = 7.95%

Company earnings per share, post project = $\frac{9,032,709}{2,772,000}$ = $3.26

		Schedule B		
I(b)	$5,000,000	$541,319	100,000	$1,200,000
II(b)	5,000,000	489,319	100,000	1,100,000
VII(b)	1,000,000	129,064	20,000	250,000
III(b)	2,000,000	198,328	40,000	375,000
40% of VI(b)	600,000	60,798	12,000	120,000
Totals	$13,600,000	$1,418,828	272,000	$3,045,000

Company percentage return, post project = $\frac{8,918,828}{113,600,000}$ = 7.85%

Company earnings per share, post project = $\frac{8,918,828}{2,772,000}$ = $3.22

turning down an attractive opportunity: failing to go out after $1,230,000 of new business (compare revenues of the two schedules, Table 9.5). It is the smaller sales of Schedule B that make that selection look bad in terms of return.

Third, it must not be forgotten that adopting any alternative that is not an economic choice means passing up twenty years (in this case) of better earnings for the sake of one year's budget reduction.

Alternative Financing

Whenever capital rationing threatens to rule out adoption of an economic choice in favor of a noneconomic choice, determined by Step 1, the first move should be to reexamine reasons given for placing the proposed limit on capital outlays, to see if some way is possible to avoid that threat. It is substantially never true that capital funds are unobtainable by a financially sound company; what is really intended is that capital is obtainable at a price regarded as too high.

Sometimes the dictated limit may represent the amount obtainable from internal sources — retained earnings plus depreciation accruals — rather than from new financing. This fear of "equity dilution" is a favorite notion of financial analysts and captains of industry that is unsound and unjustified more often than not. It is discussed at length in Appendix B.

In this connection, note that rankings in earnings per share have been calculated in Table 9.3 by hypothesizing that new common shares would be issued to finance all proposals adopted. But note, too, that exactly the same conclusions would be reached if it were hypothesized that all funds would be raised internally. Ranking by Profit Incentive per company pre-project share assumes internal financing (Line 10 of Table 9.3).

This matter of looking to alternative means of financing is an important part of the budgeting function. If new common shares can be sold at a price above book value of existing common equity, that is apt to be the best way to obtain funds externally. The next best way may be an increase in company debt, particularly if interest rates are favorable. This subject is treated in Chapter 13. A short-term bank loan may be desirable to postpone new issues of the firm's securities, if conditions for the latter are momentarily unfavorable.

Rather than to adopt a noneconomic choice Plan (a), it might be considered whether the economic alternative could be postponed rather than rejected. This is often feasible in the case of proposed economic replacements of equipment capable of continued use if necessary. Temporary postponement then means a short-term penalty that may be less serious than the loss from adoption of a noneconomic replacement. It is even possible that if replacement were postponed, a still more desirable replacement might become available in the interim. This is discussed in Chapter 12.

If it is felt desirable to postpone some of the attractive economic choices — in this example, all Alternatives (b) are attractive except for IX(b), IV(b), and V(b) — those to be adopted first might be identified by ranking in the order of project percentage return as shown in parentheses under Criterion I, Table 9.4. This will maximize immediate earnings per share as compared to any other order of investing the same capital in Alternatives (b). Or, as a further nicety, rank in terms of percentage project return above project cutoff rate, as mentioned before, takes relative risk into account as well.

Although leasing the same equipment is seldom as profitable as owning it, a small penalty by reason of leasing temporarily may be worthy of consideration as preferable to making a lifetime commitment in a noneconomic choice.

One phenomenon commonly overlooked deserves mention. Inability to raise new capital at favorable cost is ordinarily associated with a firm's inability to report attractive earnings per share. Poor earnings mean capital scarcity which means poor earnings. This vicious circle is aggravated if the capital scarcity leads to adopting noneconomic alternatives that depress earnings. Capital scarcity thus connotes a <u>high</u> MAR; and this higher MAR may change the identity of economic <u>choices</u>. In the present example, if MAR were 10% instead of the assumed 6%, several of the alternatives herein classified as second choice (noneconomic) would become the economic choice. In brief, <u>the popular conclusion that proposals can be safely ranked simply by listing in order of percentage return ignores realities and does not carry out exact intent.</u>

Public-Utility Viewpoint

Tables 9.4 and 9.5 suggest why the earnings-per-share criterion is apt to be better understood and appreciated by public utilities than by nonregulated industry. The four major reasons are:

1. Earnings of public utilities are restricted by regulation to some maximum <u>percentage</u> return on investors' committed capital (expressed in terms of "rate base"). Ranking proposals by <u>earnings per share</u> maximizes owners' yield for any given percentage return.

   To illustrate, in the example of Table 9.5, suppose company earnings were restricted to 7.85%. Schedule B installations would all qualify; company earnings per share would be $3.22. But if Schedule A earnings were to duplicate that $3.22 per share (by omitting the last three projects: VIIIa, IXa, and Xa), the company's percentage return would be 7.88%. A rate reduction would be in order to bring down the percentage to 7.85% and earnings per share to less than $3.22.

2. Public utilities are ordinarily obliged to accept increased customer demands for service. They are not at liberty to ration capital arbitrarily by rejecting proposals necessary to supply such demands just because they are less attractive financially.

3. For a number of reasons (rapid growth, stability of earnings, and so on) public utilities are usually able to obtain capital funds, in some form, at reasonable cost. In general, they are less hesitant to do new financing.

4. When utility earnings rise above the permitted maximum percentage return, revenues must be reduced. Reducing revenues (rates) does not affect identity of economic choices; the economic choice remains that same alternative which has minimum <u>outlays</u> (= minimum revenue requirements) for the newly stipulated revenues.

"Exact" Models

In order to grasp essential details of a complicated system, it is often convenient and sometimes essential to make use of a model. In the literature of this subject, the term "model" has been applied to a number of devices, all the way from diagrams and algebraic expressions to matrices and computer programs.

On occasion, traditional decision theory has been described as the assembly of cost data in the form of a model, the "profit function," which is then to be solved for optimal values of its component variables by whatever mathematical techniques may be deemed appropriate. Much more attention has been given to the mathematical means of solution than to the question of the model's reliability as a representation of the facts at issue. Quite commonly, sophisticated techniques of solution serve to conceal the naively unsound nature of proposed models. Frequently such advanced technology as regression theory, gaming techniques, the calculus of variations, and so forth, are employed to solve models of plain nonsense.

Typical of this situation is the position taken by some that there is no need for models to be particularly realistic, and that several different models can be developed to represent a single given situation. Such a state of affairs is naturally to be expected when analysts are unable to define their own exact intent, entertaining the notion that no single finite criterion is applicable in any event. If the whole basis for decisions is in doubt, as so many have been led to suppose, why bother with exact models? This familiar attitude and its unhappy consequences are discussed in Chapter 1 and Appendix A.

The two contributing factors for exactness of a model are: (a) conformity of the model to the analyst's exact intent; and (b) validity of that intent.

To illustrate dubious validity of intent, consider the following statement, more or less typical of some popular writings: "Interest on debt is a function of debt ratio and percentage interest rate. It is usually assumed to diminish along with the diminishing book value of the asset."

A model can be set up to reproduce that behavior exactly; but it remains an example of the "baby duck" approach. The sex of the pet duck is to be established by majority vote! The analyst has proposed a hypothesis to which the "exact" model is to conform. Whether that hypothesis represents a "usual assumption" or not is immaterial to exactness of the model. Whether proceeding on that basis constitutes a logical procedure or merely demonstrates the analyst's incompetence is another matter.

One way to avoid difficulties that can originate in foggy reasoning of this sort is to make a sharp mental distinction between:

1. Assumptions as to events believed likely to occur; and
2. Working hypotheses, which are to be tested or which are to serve as a tentative basis for examining consequences if the hypothesized conditions were to prevail; reasonableness of the

hypothesized conditions is a separate matter for separate consideration as a logical assumption.

For example, in this instance one might hypothesize a constant
debt ratio of 30% and observe consequences. A model constructed on
that basis can provide conclusions that are trustworthy, even though
the assumption of a 30% figure may turn out to be a bad guess at future
events. Ordinarily, there is room for a difference of opinion as to
probable future debt ratios, which might lie within a range of zero to
60%; but there is no room for difference of opinion as to predictable
effects of any particular hypothesized percentage.

The term "exact model" is not intended as a synonym for "comprehensive model." An interesting example of a simple but exact model
which reproduces an abbreviated income statement appears in Exhibits
A and B, Table 9.6. A related Exhibit C is left for the student to complete as Problem 1 at the end of this chapter. This model was suggested by Robert H. Sarikas, of Illinois Power Company, to illustrate
behavior of the minimum revenue requirement for income tax, particularly behavior (unexpected by many) of the investment credit. The
general form of this model will suggest other useful applications. For
a related graphical model, see Figure C.1, on page 501.

The Corporate Model

A unique and, if desired, comprehensive application of the simulation process is the corporate model, designed to reproduce all essential
financial and accounting transactions of the firm. One application of the
corporate model is to reconcile individual studies of profitability or
economic choice with the associated overall performance of the company
as reported by the accountant's routine annual financial statements.
Several different situations arise where this device may perform a
valuable function.

The first such situation is that disclosed by the state of mind which
has for generations raised imagined objections to present worth techniques in supplying criteria for business decisions. It can be said that
current near-unanimity on validity of present worth criteria is of fairly
recent birth; a mature understanding of all its implications is still
rarely encountered. One expression of this attitude sometimes occurs
in the form of the peremptory challenge: "Show me where compound
interest calculations appear on the company's books of account." Inability to show any mention or use of compound interest in the company's financial statements is then construed as prima facie evidence
of basic error in the analyst's utilization of the present worth concept.
Of course, a complete answer can be given to that challenge; readers
of this book should now be able to produce it on their own. But the sort
of person who makes such defiant charges is apt to lack the will or patience to listen to the orderly reasoning — unless, perhaps, it is presented in the form of a corporate model.

Table 9.6. Effect of an incremental expense on revenue requirements (if statutory federal income tax rate is 50%).

Exhibit A

Expense Increased From $100 to $110

Assumption 1; Constant Revenue

	Before			After	
$200	Revenue		$200	Revenue	
(100)	Expense		(110)	Expense	
100	"Before-tax" income		90	"Before-tax" income	
(50)	Federal income tax		(45)	Federal income tax	
$ 50	"After-tax" income		$ 45	"After-tax" income	

Conclusion: An increase in expense of $10 reduces after-tax income only $5, out of fixed revenues.

Assumption 2: Constant Income (= MAR)

$200	Revenue requirement		$210	Revenue requirement	
(100)	Expense		(110)	Expense	
100	"Before-tax" income		100	"Before-tax" income	
(50)	Federal income tax		(50)	Federal income tax	
$ 50	"After-tax" income (= MAR)		$ 50	"After-tax" income (MAR)	

Conclusion: An increase in expense of $10 increases revenue requirements by $10, since income (= MAR) is to be unaffected.

Exhibit B

Investment Credit of $10

Case 1: Constant Revenue

	Before			After	
$200	Revenue		$200	Revenue	
(100)	Expense		(100)	Expense	
100	"Before-tax" income		100	"Before-tax" income	
(50)	Federal income tax		(40)	Federal income tax (50-10)	
$ 50	"After-tax" income		$ 60	"After-tax" income	

Conclusion: The tax credit of $10 increases after-tax income by $10, with fixed revenues.

Case 2: Constant Income (= MAR)

$200	Revenue requirement		$180	Revenue requirement	
(100)	Expense		(100)	Expense	
100	"Before-tax" income		80	"Before-tax" income	
(50)	Federal income tax		(30)	Federal income tax (40-10)	
$ 50	"After-tax" income (= MAR)		$ 50	"After-tax" income (MAR)	

Conclusion: The tax credit of $10 reduces revenue requirements by $20, since after-tax income (= MAR) is to be unaffected.

This fact does not seem to be generally recognized. Compare Formula 8.4, Chapter 8.

255

A second situation where the corporate model may be useful is in connection with decisions as to Step 2 considerations, in studies of profitability and economic choice. Step 2 analyses deal mainly with two kinds of considerations: (a) those which cannot and must not be quantified, being irreducible to dollars by nature and definition; and (b) considerations described as "contingencies," which are deviations from normally expected orderly behavior, occurrence of which cannot be predicted beyond the fact that it is not impossible.

That "normally expected orderly behavior" includes ups and downs of daily and annual experience whose exact variations cannot be foreseen but which are reasonably certain to be encountered. The "contingencies" envisioned are more in the nature of the "cult of equity," which affected price/earnings ratios so drastically in the 1950's. The effects are quite calculable; but who could have foreseen that the situation might arise? Who can guess how much a firm's inventory of steel sheets ought to be increased as a hedge against strikes in the steel industry not now on the horizon? The corporate model permits reviewing past experience and facilitates anticipating future possibilities that can be hypothesized, though not defensibly assumed as a firm forecast.

Third, corporate models are invaluable for managerial purposes other than in connection with formal studies of profitability or economic choice. The models are helpful in observing and anticipating cash flow, in judging when new issues of company securities may be desirable or necessary, and what nature and amount of new financing is in order. Also, they are useful for anticipating when and how much price lists or tariff schedules should be modified, for what lines of product or classes of service, and in what detail.

Fourth, the corporate model may be particularly helpful in explaining managerial strategy to boards of directors, financial analysts, or even stockholders. Powerful financial interests are not always well informed in fundamental principles of economic business decisions. Witness the indorsement of leasing, instead of owning identical equipment, described by some such authorities as "astute management" when the facts were manifestly otherwise — "manifestly" to those more familiar with the economic principles involved. Management sometimes needs persuasive argument beyond the dependable comparison of PWAFRR's to comprehend policies dictated by such criteria. The corporate model presents the same facts in less efficient form but in more understandable language.

Finally, the corporate model may be helpful to the analyst in clarifying his own exact intent, upon which the "correctness" of his model and its solution depend, as just discussed. It may serve to confirm his reliance on the concept of minimized revenue requirements when he is under all sorts of pressure to adopt other criteria. It is sometimes a forceful way to demonstrate the financial losses that can result from depending on unsound methodology such as the Annual Cost Method, the Discounted Cash Flow Method, the Percentage Return Method, the Payback Period Method, and others. For such reasons, the corporate model, in simplified but rigorous form, is a valuable teaching aid. It supports the view that exact models are indispensable, by demonstrating the chaos that can result from unsound pedagogical opinion to the contrary.

The most desirable type of corporate model incorporates three special features from which a number of desirable characteristics flow:

1. It permits introduction of either discrete (noncontinuous) series of data or smoothed continuous functions as most desirable at any time. This facilitates use of algebraic expressions to simulate current and projected behavior of pertinent data as appropriate.
2. It provides for a "build-up" period, separate and distinct from but inextricably associated with the separate "forecast" period. Every past commitment which reflects actual history must proceed to its ultimate fate. It is impossible to assume taking any action without recognizing its contribution to all future events.
3. It simulates the actual periodic double entry accounting procedure and the regular periodic reports produced by such bookkeeping, without reliance on analytical expressions nor on convenient financial equivalencies.

In brief, outputs of the corporate model supply an independent means for demonstrating validity and importance of the dual objective of MRRD: optimized return on pre-project capital investment, together with optimized ability to minimize selling price of output consistent with any specified level of Profit Incentive.

Application to Project Proposals

The corporate model is not an efficient means for solving problems in profitability or economic choice.

In this application, the decision process via corporate model consists in a comparison of the primary outputs:

1. The series of financial statements if a proposal is adopted, versus
2. The series of financial statements if the proposal is not adopted, all else remaining the same.

Each of these two outputs results from a single set of inputs, each set of inputs representing the complicated build-up period to date, plus the stipulated current changes constituting the transition to the forecast period. In the one case, the current changes will include the proposal under investigation; in the other, they will not.

This provides an answer based on the single most likely, most typical, or average behavior, not only of the new inputs but also of the inherited "existing conglomeration" from the build-up period. Thus, the critic's aspersion of economic studies made on this basis, mentioned before, cannot be evaded by adopting the simulation process in place of the infinitely simpler and more efficient analysis of the project's revenue requirements. Also, the ultimate criterion remains a comparison of present worths, and it is not easy to extract them from a series of financial statements extending over an indefinite period. It is difficult enough to prepare simulated data for twenty years in advance; and that span is commonly quite inadequate for a dependable survey of service-lifetime financial results.

Such considerations make the corporate model not particularly useful as the primary means for reaching decisions in studies of profitability and economic choice. Its most useful function, as just discussed, is as a reassuring complement to the usual studies of lifetime-levelized annual revenue requirements, or their present worth over an appropriate period, or PWAFRR's, or in situations where Step 2 considerations — particularly "contingencies" — are of special importance. Its most helpful contribution is then to a better understanding of conclusions reached by the simpler process. It places in sharp relief the total reliance of rational estimates on exact concepts of objectives, exact models to simulate those objectives, and exact arithmetic to evaluate the model.

It is quickly discovered, if anyone ever doubted or overlooked it, that accuracy of results is no better than that of the information fed into the program.[1] However, experience has demonstrated that it is possible and feasible to realize a rather surprising conformance to results as they later transpire. The degree of reliability of financial outputs of the corporate model can equal that attained in other more familiar ways of forecasting company sales, revenues, and earnings.

Decision Trees

The "decision tree" is a flow chart adapted to placing alternative courses of action and their consequences in convenient perspective for purposes of performing the budgeting function. It resembles the flow chart representing programming of the corporate model in that it proceeds logically to a point at which more than one possibility or more than one set of circumstances call for consideration. However, instead of reverting at that point to a new input (new consideration) based on the new set of assumptions or introducing a subroutine before proceeding further, it branches off into the several courses of action to be explored.

It is a valuable tool when used for this function of enabling the budgeter to "collect his thoughts." Any attempt to apply it beyond this use invites the confusion of data manipulation with principle manipulation that is deplored throughout this chapter. The decision tree does not rely on traditional decision theory, as has sometimes been implied.

---

[1]The principle is well described as GIGO: "Garbage in, garbage out."

It stands on its own merits as a helpful device.[2] Nor does the decision
tree have any bearing on the appropriateness of Step 1-Step 2 criteria
or procedures. It sheds no light whatever, for instance, on the suitability or otherwise of present worth versus discounted-cash-flow methodology, although it has been presumed to do so. Nor does it provide any
special basis for taking risk into account. It simply displays an array
of facts in a convenient pattern for taking risk or alternative methodology into account by whatever mental process the analyst may have at
his command or prefer to use; it supplies no philosophy by which to do
the deciding.

It may help to avoid wasting time on unlikely eventualities, in minimizing duplications and contradictions in sorting out and rating the
likelihood of events, and in discovering interrelations between individual
projects.

Matrices

Among the ingenious devices that have been proposed to help in the
final decision process is the matrix. The commonest form of matrix
for this purpose resembles, in form, the determinants of advanced algebra. Rows of the matrix represent possible courses of action; columns represent the several situations or "states of nature" assumed to
prevail or to have a bearing on selection of the most prudent choice.
The purpose is to present in minimum space a summary of all possible
combinations of alternatives and contexts that ought to be examined.

This subject will not be pursued herein because it is seldom of
great practical value outside of certain kinds of problems in operations
research. It is used more often as a teaching device, to illustrate a
theoretical analysis of hypothetical combinations of circumstances.
Most of these hypothetical combinations are introduced unnecessarily
in the process, by failing to make a sharp distinction between the budgeting function and Step 1 determinations of profitability and economic
choice.

Résumé

I. Before discussing the decision process, it is necessary to have
a clear conception, qualitative and quantitative, of factors that affect
Profit Incentive.

II. There is room for difference of opinion as to future costs
(quantitative); no room for difference of opinion as to exact principles
(qualitative).

---

[2]John F. Magee, The Decision Tree: A Guide for Analyzing Capital Investment Risk
Opportunities (Arthur D. Little, New York), 1964.

III. A deplorable viewpoint, to be condemned, entertains the notion that oversimplified and inexact models of cost behavior are not to be avoided but encouraged. This view has actually been indorsed by some schools of business.

IV. Two aspects of statistical probability are of major importance in estimating revenue requirements:

1. Tests for significance of past and present experience as an index to future expectations, based on studies of averages and variance therefrom; and
2. Recognition of the correct arithmetical treatment of effects of probable average occurrence and probable departure therefrom. Statistical theory suggests appropriate allowance for probabilities. Attempting to evade that situation by indefensible assumption of 100% certainty (unfortunately, the usual procedure) can introduce flagrant and costly errors.

V. A case in point is estimating the depreciation annuity at $\frac{i}{(1 + i)^n - 1}$, recommended by many textbooks, and even called by most authors the "exact calculation." It is always an underestimate of the actually intended percentage (where n = average service life).

VI. The significance of Item V is not just that the depreciation annuity is incorrectly estimated, but also incorrectly estimated are income taxes and taxes on sales or gross receipts. Rate of replacements and amount of depreciation reserves are misrepresented; present worths are miscalculated. Its most serious aspect is ignoring the penalty in earnings of owners of the business, all for the sake of "simplifying" the analyst's task. Yet many engineering economists disparage its importance.

VII. Expenses are identified by the accountant's disposition of charges, not reliably by general nature or purpose of the job.

VIII. It is often convenient to express expenses as a percentage of related capital investment. Great care must be taken, though, to avoid concluding that expenses are therefore necessarily directly proportional to capital investment.

IX. Three items of minimum revenue requirements are directly proportional to related capital investment: (a) minimum acceptable return; (b) the depreciation annuity; and (c) income taxes. These items are sometimes known as "fixed charges," but that misnomer is well avoided and discouraged.

X. Annual expense does not necessarily increase as equipment ages. Quite often the reverse is discovered.

XI. A tax of t% levied on sales or on gross receipts has the effect of multiplying each component of revenue requirements by the factor $1/(1 - t)$, where t = tax rate, decimally expressed. This does not affect identity of the economic choice, but it does affect its margin of superiority.

XII. A sharp distinction must be made between (a) incremental, and (b) allocated costs. Careful analysis of the exact purpose of the study will reveal whether incremental, allocated, or average quantities are appropriate to its exact intent.

XIII. This chapter provides a number of illustrations of the need to differentiate exactly between concepts that appear superficially to be identical or nearly alike, such as:

1. Interest on debt as a component of earnings versus "interest expense" deductible from earnings to determine return on equity;
2. "Interim replacements" as a charge to capital investment versus a charge to expense (as part of maintenance expense; never a charge to depreciation, and not represented by adjustment of the depreciation annuity for retirement dispersion);
3. Studies of profitability versus studies of economic choice;
4. Annual revenue requirements versus (a) annual revenues, (b) annual costs, or (c) "fixed charges";
5. Allocated versus incremental costs;
6. The economic analysis versus the pricing problem (rate making);
7. Probability versus "uncertainty"; and
8. Lifetime-levelized data versus (a) lifetime-averaged data, or (b) year-by-year equivalencies.

XIV. The fact that costs may be difficult to establish or even impossible to anticipate in advance does not mean that principles of economic studies are vague or uncertain.

XV. Step 1 in every profitability study or economic choice is concerned with the estimate of revenue requirements, based on: (a) estimated annual revenues and sales, in studies of profitability; (b) hypothesized identical annual revenues and sales for competing proposals, in studies of economic choice; and (c) hypothesized identical percentage MAR, in all cases.

XVI. Subsequent disposition of benefits from selecting the economic choice, whether channelled 100% to investors via improved earnings, or 100% to customers via reduced price of product, or partly to both, must not affect Step 1 identification of the economic choice. Feedback effects of any disposition of benefits can be expected to reinforce the advantage of the plan identified as superior on the basis of minimum revenue requirements.

XVII. Step 2 in every investment decision is the weighing of Step 1 advantages against other possible nonfinancial advantages. Such other advantages are often, though inexactly, described as intangible or imponderable; they are better described as "irreducible," though they may include certain "contingencies." Strictly speaking, nonfinancial advantages are not properly included in revenue requirements because they are to be weighed against the added cost required to obtain them. The question to be answered is whether a Step 1 cost penalty is worth incurring in order to obtain the "intangible" Step 2 claimed advantage.

XVIII. Revenue requirements for expenses, other than depreciation and income taxes, include only identifiable outlays which are chargeable to specific expense accounts and which are contingent upon adoption of the project. They must not include quantified allowances for "intangibles," "irreducibles," "imponderables," and so forth, which are not evidenced as actual book charges attributable to adoption of the project.

XIX. The decision process envisioned by MRRD calls attention to an unhelpful body of literature often referred to as "traditional decision theory," which may be recognized by its peculiar phraseology and academic viewpoint. It is not only impracticable but contributes positive and serious misunderstanding, which may be largely avoided by observing the essential distinctions between: (a) objectives and criteria appropriate for evaluation of profitability and economic choice; and (b) objectives and criteria appropriate for carrying out the subsequent budgeting function.

XX. The term "budget" as used in this book is well described by the dictionary definition: "A statement of probable revenue and expenditure and financial proposals for the ensuing year as presented to or passed upon by a legislative body." Budgeting is concerned with determining the course of action best taken in view of the profitability and economic choice of proposals which have been separately and previously evaluated by Step 1-Step 2 criteria. Thus, such considerations as capital rationing enter at the budgeting level and not before.

XXI. A major decision to be made as part of the budgeting function is whether the project promises to earn enough more than MAR to make the opportunity attractive. This means inquiry into the project's cutoff rate, which percentage is purely a matter for expert business judgment.

XXII. "Ranking" projects in the order of their relative profitability means listing according to the company's earnings per share, out of stipulated revenues, resulting from their adoption. Or to obtain the same ranking, the listing can be done according to the amount of price reduction possible while realizing any stipulated company earnings per common share.

XXIII. Ranking projects by percentage return, the most widely used and generally approved basis, is a naive and unsound procedure that casts doubt on the competency of the company's management. Stockholders would do well to inquire about the management's policy.

XXIV. Since economic comparisons are made by stipulating that competing alternatives have identical sales and revenues, the element of risk on that score does not enter into economic comparisons. Consideration for risk remains a part of the budgeting function. Controllable aspects of sales and revenues (that is, the pricing function) is no part of economic comparisons except to the extent that they may enter into initial definition of "the project."

XXV. The simulation technique, performed with the help of electronic data processing is a powerful tool. However, it manifestly defeats its own purpose if the simulation does not reproduce factual behavior with fidelity, since the essential criterion applied is "goodness of fit."

XXVI. The fact and significance of change must be recognized.

Analytical techniques based on the single most likely set of circumstances leading to a single conclusion are apt to be grossly unsound.
To illustrate, if ten coins are tossed a large number of times, the one
most frequent combination to turn up will be five heads and five tails.
Betting even money on this result, however, is a losing proposition; it
happens only about one-fourth of the time. In view of the presumed difficulty of testing solutions for all possible circumstances, many writers
recommend accepting an unsound solution that ignores this aspect of
probability.

   XXVII. The more logical mechanics of prediction, making use of
the elementary arithmetic of probability, is no more difficult than the
foregoing unsound procedure. It is an essential part of MRRD.

   XXVIII. Change is best regarded in terms of probability rather
than "uncertainty"; as a largely controllable phenomenon rather than
an ominous unpredictable threat; as presenting an opportunity rather
than an obstacle. This is the temper of free enterprise, not well simulated by "traditional decision theory."

   XXIX. The rationale of simulation is well illustrated by the simulated plant record method of analyzing mortality experience, described
in Chapter 7. Hypotheses with respect to probable occurrences are
first formulated, then tested. It is a process of inquiring into "likely
departures from certainty." Ignoring departures from average experience is a statistical absurdity bordering on intellectual dishonesty.

   XXX. The corporate model is a convenient device for:

1. Demonstrating the relationships between individual project behavior and overall experience of the company as revealed by
   subsequent income statements and balance sheets;
2. Observing short-term contingencies given consideration in
   Step 2 of the MRRD decision process;
3. Displaying the true purpose and exact nature of the ceteris
   paribus principle;
4. Explaining managerial strategy by observing and anticipating
   behavior of cash flow; and
5. As a teaching aid and means for crystallizing the analyst's own
   exact intent, on which MRRD depends.

   XXXI. A comprehensive corporate model provides for a build-up
period as well as a forecast period. Inputs during the build-up period
re-create past events, whose future effects cannot be ignored. Inputs
during the forecast period may be in the form of discrete or continuous
series of data based on forecasts of pertinent plant additions plus other
items rationally generated from such basic data. Major outputs are the
items normally reported in periodic financial statements. Other information relevant to economic or financial studies can be obtained if
desired.

   XXXII. Although technically possible to make economic studies by
means of the corporate model, that is an inefficient procedure. It means
setting up a "base case," producing outputs over a lengthy period of

years, then repeating the process using inputs which include proposed projects. Outputs are then compared. Reduction of data to present worth form is difficult.

XXXIII. The most helpful contribution of the corporate model is its persuasive demonstration of the importance of exact models, the degree of acceptability of approximations and shortcuts, and the dangers of permitting data manipulation to confuse or misstate principles.

XXXIV. The "decision tree" is a helpful device for organizing one's thinking in performing the budgeting function. It is not concerned with determinations of economic choice (Step 1 of the MRRD decision process). It does not supply criteria for any purpose; it presents the results of applying criteria. It suggests a neat pattern for arraying alternative courses of action and their consequences in order to pass upon them by other means. Great care must be taken in using such devices to manipulate data only, not to manipulate principles.

Problems

1. Complete the entries in Exhibit C, below, associated with Exhibits A and B of Table 9.6.

Exhibit C

Suppose someone said, "Here is $10 to help pay your income tax."

Case 1. Assume that the $10 gift (credit) is added to revenues.

Before		After	
$	Revenue requirement	$	Revenue (___ + 10)
-_____	Expense	-_____	Expense
	"Before tax" income		"Before tax" income
-_____	Federal income tax	-_____	Federal income tax
$_____		$_____	"After tax" income

Case 2. Assume that the $10 gift (credit) may be deducted directly from the tax.

Before		After	
$	Revenue requirement	$	Revenue requirement
-_____	Expense	-_____	Expense
	"Before tax" income		"Before tax" income
-_____	Federal income tax	-_____	Federal income tax
$_____	"After tax" income	$_____	"After tax" income

Note: The $10 credit in Case 2 increases "After tax" income by $____, whereas the increase in Case 1 was only $____. The change in Case 2 is therefore equivalent to an increase in revenue of $____, as shown below:

Before		After	
$	Revenue requirement	$	Revenue (___ + ___)
-_____	Expense	-_____	Expense
	"Before tax" income		"Before tax" income
-_____	Federal income tax	-_____	Federal income tax
$_____	"After tax" income	$_____	"After tax" income

2. The following statement was attributed to a United States senator in an article devoted to Social Security: "I'm against any program that's based on payroll taxes. Payroll taxes boost business costs and prices.... That is not true of profit or income taxes."

    a. Is it true that profit or income taxes do not boost business costs and prices? What do you think creates that impression?

    b. Would you say that the difficulty here arises from: (1) inexact definition of terms or intent; (2) both; (3) politics? Explain all answers. What do you think was the senator's exact intent? Do you agree? Explain your own position.

    (Hint: Total income tax obligation = $T + T'$; see Chapter 8.)

3. In 1966, President Lyndon Johnson proposed two measures to help combat price inflation: repeal of the investment credit provision of the federal income tax law; and repeal of accelerated depreciation provisions applicable to certain classifications of plant.

Explain:

    a. How such measures might be expected to help curb price inflation.

    b. How such measures might be expected to aggravate price inflation.

    c. Why they might be expected to affect public utilities less than non-regulated enterprises.

    4. Discuss the minimax criterion and explain why it is of substantially zero value in making business decisions.

    (Note: Minimax is mentioned but not explained in the text.)

    5. Suggest a simple example to illustrate the important distinction between (a) a hypothesis, and (b) an assumption.

    (Hint: Prescriptive versus predictive models.)

    6. Several popular and widely taught procedures other than MRRD for evaluating projects convey the impression that their users and advocates cannot be well acquainted with fundamentals of the American free enterprise system. Explain.

    7. MRRD recognizes that one major objective of economic studies is to place the firm in the best position to minimize prices charged for its products. It is also claimed in the Preface to this book that MRRD is unique in that it introduces no self-contradictions into the reasoning.

    How, then, can you reconcile approval of "company earnings per share, post project" as the appropriate criterion for budgeting purposes, as in Table 9.1c?

    8. In preparing Tables 9.2, 9.3, and 9.4, suppose MAR were 10%, instead of 6%. Prepare revised tables to show how that would affect ranking of the ten proposals and ten alternatives.

    9. Two projects, X and Y, promise identical earnings of 10% of their respective capital investments. They are believed to involve identical risk. Yet one is adopted enthusiastically while the other is promptly rejected. Explain the probable reason.

    10. Present in your own words some reasons why it is important to discriminate between (a) determinations of profitability or economic choice, and (b) the budgeting function.

    11. Is it possible for a company to earn a level annual percentage return on its capital investment (that is, its investors' committed capital) and pay a regularly increasing dividend rate in dollars per share without increasing its payout ratio? Explain in detail.

    12. Construction estimates often include allowances for "contingencies." Is this a capital item or an expense? To what account is it charged? If expenditures are actually made for this reason, do they affect minimum revenue requirements?

    13. Several ways are possible to average data in order to estimate future annual expenses. One way is to calculate annual charges to expense as a percentage of average capital investment each year and average the percentages so obtained over a period of years. Another way is to add annual dollars of expense over a period of years, add up average capital investments in each year over the same period, and divide the former by the latter. Still another way is to calculate present worth of year-by-year annual expenses in dollars per year over a period, calculate present worth of annual average capital investments for each year over the same period, and divide the first by the latter.

    What is the difference in significance of results? How do you draw conclusions as to future trends in each case? What conditions tend to magnify the differences between the three results? Illustrate by means of a simple table.

    14. Select a company whose annual earnings per share have been fairly regular. Plot ten years of such earnings. Fit a straight line to the plot, using the "method of least squares," and write the expression for the resultant straight line.

(Note: This is a standard and fairly elementary method of statistical "levelizing" which is worth knowing about. The procedure is not explained in this book.)

15. What is a power series? What is the significance of the expression: $Y = a + bx$?

16. List the several different kinds of taxes paid by an industrial corporation.

Some kinds of manufacturers have to pay exceptionally large taxes, as a fraction of their revenues. List as many as possible.

17. Automation often offers advantages aside from the reduction in payrolls. List as many as you can think of and indicate whether each serves to reduce or increase revenue requirements.

18. The owner of a large diesel engine discovers several reasons why he had to shut up shop during the past year while the unit was down for repairs: Which of these jobs would be charged to capital; which to expense? How do you decide?

    a. Scheduled routine maintenance during normal vacation period for production workers.

    b. Vibration. Cause unknown until the engine was dismantled. Found to be a worn bearing; required a whole new bearing. The old one could have been repaired, but that would have taken too long a time.

    c. Fire in an adjacent building. The diesel itself was not harmed, but some piping had to be replaced.

    d. Injection pump failure. Replaced; partly on overtime. Manufacturer allows substantial salvage value on the faulty unit.

19. The company needs a construction shanty for a few engineers, draftsmen, clerks, and tool storage for a job expected to last two years. It can erect its own building on its own temporarily available property, at a cost of $S. Or it can rent a nearby vacant building, larger but not quite as convenient, for a monthly rental of $r.

Assume reasonable values for all outlays involved, and show how a decision should be reached.

20. It could happen that one alternative might require considerable use of storeroom space and services, while a competing plan could rely on a vendor's facilities and services and require none.

How would such costs enter into the economic comparison? Should you include revenue requirements on the capital investment in company storeroom buildings and equipment, as well as storeroom expense itself? Should you use average or incremental or allocated costs? Explain.

21. Most thermometers use either the Fahrenheit or centigrade scales. The essential difference between them is simply illustrated as follows:

	Degrees Fahrenheit	Degrees Centigrade
Water freezes at	32	0
Water boils at	212	100

Using the Fahrenheit scale, one might say that the boiling temperature of water is about 6.6 times as hot as its freezing temperature. Using the centigrade scale seems to contradict that observation.

Exactly what is wrong here? Does it have any bearing on the Percentage Return Method of ranking projects? Explain.

22. Some popular engineering economy textbooks point out that the present worth analysis has a serious shortcoming which is illustrated by the following example.

A present worth study is made using an interest rate of 20%. It shows the present worth of lifetime earnings to be $100,000, while the present worth of outlays is $90,000. Thus, it would be concluded that the project yields more than the stipulated minimum attractive rate of 20%. But, it goes on to say, this is not a sound conclusion unless the analyst can be sure that cash flow from the project could be reinvested at that same 20%.

Something is wrong here. Exactly what is it?

23. On occasion, it has been charged that the difference between pre-project investors and "newcomers," which is depended upon in Chapter 3 to estimate MAR, is imaginary and a misconception of fact. That is, both pre-project investors and newcomers enjoy exactly the same yield from their investments: identical annual cash dividends, identical capital gains. Their decisions to buy or to sell are based on exactly the same observations of probable earnings, probable dividends, and market price.

The fact that pre-project investors may have paid, in the past, some price per share different from today's market price is held to be irrelevant. Present value per share is the same: today's market price. Therefore, it is argued, their respective percentage returns are identical. Consequently, it is alleged, the whole approach described in Chapter 3 is unsound.

What is the major fact, quite simple and obvious, that is overlooked in this reasoning, which demolishes the argument? How does that oversight reveal a gross misconception of the motivating principle of the free enterprise system?

24. It has been asserted that in all economy studies, whether of investor-financed or tax-financed proposals, any minimum attractive return assumed (the term "minimum acceptable return" was not used) should include, as a safety factor, some allowance for the fact that the best of cost estimates are subject to some degree of error.

Is this a good idea? Or does the suggestion reveal a gross failure to grasp the purpose of economic studies? Explain.

25. An assertion somewhat as follows can be found in several textbooks on engineering economy:

"Often the project will be financed by borrowed capital only or by equity capital only. In such case, the corresponding cost of capital should be used in the economy study. Or, if general funds of the corporation are to be used, part borrowed and part equity, then an average rate should be used."

Exactly what is wrong here? How does this notion betray ignorance of elementary principles of economic studies?

26. Some economists and others feel that the "straight-line" method of depreciation, based on service life of assets, is not rapid enough, aside from income tax aspects of the situation. Three reasons have been advanced in support of that notion:

a. Economic factors that ultimately are responsible for retirement of the assets account for a loss of competitive value, in early years, at a rate faster than "straight-line."
b. Economic lives are much shorter than service lives.
c. Decisions involving consideration for depreciation are made on a sounder basis if book depreciation is faster in early life.

Point out:

a. A glaring self-contradiction in the argument.
b. How the fallacious reasoning results from acceptance of inexact definitions of terms.
c. Why such arguments have no bearing on determinations of economic choice.

27. A public utility supplies manufactured gas to its customers. For many years it has charged for depreciation at 5 cents per thousand cubic feet delivered. When the possibility of obtaining natural gas arose, the company engaged a firm of consulting engineers to inquire into the economics of the situation. In their studies, the consultants also estimated depreciation at 5 cents per thousand cubic feet.

    a. What was wrong here?

    b. In Chapter 6 it is demonstrated that the revenue requirement for depreciation is independent of the company's method of accounting for depreciation. How, then, do you reconcile your answer to (a) with this fact?

    28. In 1966, when the investment credit provision of federal income tax was 7%, financial analysts asserted that the credit was equivalent to a 7% reduction in the cost of new equipment. Suspension of the credit would therefore mean an increase in capital cost from 93% to 100% of purchase price, or 7.5% of the sale price.

    By means of a simple tabulation of minimum revenue requirements point out the error in this conclusion.

    (Hint: Chapter 8 contains some convenient calculations of the revenue requirement for federal income tax with and without the investment credit.)

    29. Consult any other textbook on the subject of appropriate percentage return for use in making economic studies for public utilities, and discuss what is wrong with such conclusions. Comment on the seriousness of this situation.

    30. All of the proposals examined in Tables 9.2-9.5 were estimated to have the same 20-year service life. That assumption was made to simplify explanation of the principles involved in performing the budgeting function. But suppose anticipated service lives differed for several proposals. For the present purpose, assuming no difference between Plans (a) and (b) for any one proposal, for which lives and revenues remain the same as before.

    For example, suppose Proposal I were expected to have only ten year life, while estimated life for Proposal II remained at twenty years. Recalculate data for Proposal I, and revise the comparison (Tables 9.3 and 9.4) with Proposal II. Comment on the new questions encountered in making this change, particularly that of reinvesting Proposal I's capital recoveries throughout the second decade, and probable earnings on such reinvested funds.

    (Hint: By the end of the first ten years, isn't the capital recovered in Proposal I already fully reinvested in other projects? What assumptions did you make on that score, in estimating earnings for the first ten years?)

10

· · · · · **The Continuing** ·
Plant

Nature of the Problem

It is the exception rather than the rule when an economic decision can be made just by inquiring into costs of the immediate installations, without regard for their future replacements. This has become apparent on several occasions in earlier chapters, and in connection with problems which did <u>not</u> deal with economic replacement.

The need to consider replacements came up in discussing how to handle problems where alternative installations have different service lives. It became apparent also in Chapter 8, in connection with income taxes, where expressions were derived for the revenue requirements for income tax in percent (= $T\%$). The question arose, "Percent of what?" The capital investment, to which $T\%$ is to be applied may or may not include replacements, depending upon the analyst's exact intent.

In Chapter 9 we discovered that the very first task in the decision process (diagnosis of the problem) is to decide whether it is necessary to give consideration to costs of future replacements (that is, the continuing plant). Appropriate procedures for evaluating revenue requirements of the continuing plant are substantially as simple as for an initial installation exclusive of replacements. However, they are grossly misunderstood by the majority of analysts.

The concept of present worth is a powerful tool. It is almost impossible to make long-range decisions competently without it. But used in the way it is by most system planners, it is worse than useless. Critics can be excused for claiming that present worth calculations are usually encountered when they produce a solution the estimator likes; if he doesn't like that answer, he conveniently omits the present worth calculations. The reason for this unhappy situation is not the familiar excuse that it is impossible to peer far into the future with assurance. The real reason is that so few understand how to go about making the study, even if future costs and prices were known with assurance.

Definition of "The Project"

The first task in making studies of profitability or economic choice is to define exactly what the analyst himself means by "the project," whose economy or profitability is to be investigated.

There are three major classifications of projects and one subclassification, depending on the nature and timing of capital investment:

1. The single placement ("decaying plant"), consisting of an initial property unit or group of units, to be analyzed throughout its service life without regard for replacements;
2. The static plant (nongrowing), consisting of an initial placement of a property unit or group of units, together with replacements just sufficient to maintain the initial placement intact indefinitely;
3. The growing plant, consisting of an initial placement of a property unit or group of units, together with subsequent replacements and net additions thereto; and
4. The subclassification of the shrinking plant, following a period when the project was either static or growing, when replacements are discontinued and the plant is gradually reduced by reason of retirements.

It is essential that every project be classified in this manner before attempting to calculate its minimum revenue requirements (or even its annual costs), though this fact is commonly overlooked by all methods other than MRRD. To repeat the reason why this is necessary:

1. The first act in the decision process (Table 9.1, on page 235) is to define "the project" exactly. That definition identifies capital investment in the project in each year (= $P_{\overline{X}}$), which depends upon this classification.
2. Annual revenue requirements (like annual costs) are customarily calculated as a percentage of $P_{\overline{X}}$ in each year. Thus, annual revenue requirements (like annual costs) of every project depend upon this classification of the project as a single placement, a static plant, a growing plant, or a shrinking plant.

If the project constitutes a single placement (or, of course, a shrinking plant), then $P_{\overline{X}}$ and annual revenue requirements in dollars decrease regularly each successive year. Methods other than MRRD treat the single placement as though it were the usual case, but they proceed to overlook this regular decrease in annual revenue requirements (or in annual costs) that results from two effects:

1. The reduction in net capital investment as depreciation reserves accumulate; and
2. The additional gradual loss of capital investment as piecemeal retirements occur (retirement dispersion).

Only if the project constitutes a static plant (replacements made in kind at the same unit cost as retirements occur) does <u>gross</u> capital investment in the project remain constant each successive year. Methods other than MRRD treat annual costs as constant in each year but forget to allow for the extra cost of renewals then necessary.

If the project constitutes a <u>growing plant</u> ($P_{\overline{x}}$ increases as time passes), then Form Y revenue requirements <u>of each successive placement in the project</u> remain constant in dollars each year. That is, revenue requirements for the project as a whole increase as time passes; however, their calculation can be vastly simplified by regarding that total as a summation, in each year, of level amounts for successive net additions, one more net addition being made each year.

For a shrinking plant, an initially "static" or "growing" phase is stipulated for a period of years, followed by a period of decline when no further additions or replacements are made. The situation is ordinarily contemplated as a manipulative device rather than as a firm forecast that events will actually behave in this manner. It provides a satisfactory basis for estimating costs expected to continue indefinitely, as for static or growing plants.

The alternative basis is to assume some finite coterminate date, when all property units comprising the project magically reach the end of their probable lives simultaneously. Stipulating a finite end point to an indefinite period is actually a contradiction in terms, which demands more thoughtful consideration than assumption of an arbitrary terminal date, if it is to be quantitatively adequate!

Analyses of Single Placements (No Replacements)

To review the situation, a desirable solution to problems in profitability and economic choice is the estimate of revenue requirements for the contemplated <u>single placement</u>, when that technique is appropriate. For problems in <u>economic choice</u> it is appropriate only if two conditions are met:

1. Annual sales and revenues are identical for competing proposals; and
2. Estimated service lives of the competing assets are identical.

When the first condition is not satisfied, meaning that annual sales and/or revenues are not expected to be identical for competing proposals, then the problem becomes one of <u>profitability</u>, not of economic choice. Usually values must then be assigned to revenues, and the decision cannot be made by a simple direct comparison of revenue requirements of the projects.

When estimated <u>service lives</u> of competing assets are not identical, then it is impossible to use the technique of the single placement. Provided annual sales and revenues are identical in all cases, it remains possible to reach decisions by direct comparison of the revenue requirements of proposals; it is not then necessary to assign values to the identical revenues. It does become necessary, however, to adopt the technique of the "continuing plant," either static or growing, or possibly terminating by shrinking. That technique is the subject of this chapter.

There is one situation where it may be possible to reach a decision without estimating annual revenues in such cases. It arises when relative economy of competing proposals may be gauged by comparing revenue requirements per unit of output. For example:

$$\frac{\text{Revenue requirements, in dollars per year}}{\text{Number of gadgets produced per year}} = \text{Cost per gadget}$$

Of course, a knowledge of cost per unit produced may not supply the whole answer sought. If there is a limited market (say for only 1,000 gadgets salable annually), or if the timing of output is of consequence, it still may not be apparent which proposal would be best capable of maximizing percentage yield to pre-project investors in the company, which remains the criterion.

To summarize the situation, when replacements are ignored (the single placement):

1. Form X revenue requirements (= book depreciation at other than the annuity, plus return at MAR% of net capital investment, $P_{\overline{x}} - R_{\overline{x}}$) decrease each successive year, whether retirements are dispersed or not. (See pages 117-20.)
2. Both Form X revenue requirements and their levelized Form Y equivalent (= depreciation at the annuity, plus return at MAR% of gross capital investment, $P_{\overline{x}}$) decrease each successive year if retirements are dispersed.

Said another way, if revenue requirements (or, indeed, annual costs) for the single placement are stated at a level annual figure in dollars, as they ordinarily are, then it must be concluded that:

1. The estimate is in Form Y, and retirements are not dispersed (that is, the unlikely "one hoss shay" phenomenon has been assumed), or else
2. The analyst has unwittingly assumed replacements to be made "in kind" but has failed to include them in his costs. Such is the usual situation when using methods other than MRRD.

Should the reader feel that this point has been stressed ad nauseam, let him recall that overlooking it almost always results in underestimates of costs (revenue requirements) and overestimates of profitability, both of which can be fatal. Here is a problem that cannot be evaded, yet most estimators and most authors apparently do not even perceive that this is a problem. They do not attempt to describe it, nor make any attempt to deal with it.

No doubt it is unnecessary to point out that all these phenomena are encountered regardless of the source of the capital funds: from depreciation charges against other projects, from retained earnings, from borrowings, or from new issues of the company's securities.

It might be said that the appropriate calculations of minimum revenue requirements are simple in the same sense that operation of the family car's automatic transmission is simple. That is, merely placing the transmission lever in position "D" causes the car to move ahead as desired — maybe! It is essential that the highly complicated mechanism be in working order, and that the engine be running.

Similarly, the simple MRRD calculations of Table 10.10, Summary, on page 293, accomplish the analyst's exact intent — maybe! It is essential that cost behavior of the project be represented by an "exact model," as discussed in Chapter 9. The model must conform to the analyst's exact intent, and that intent must be valid. Unless the complicated cost behavior is adequately represented, actual desirability of the project may be far removed from calculated conclusions. That unhappy result occurs more often than not when using procedures other than MRRD, as will be discussed in Chapter 11.

With that introduction, let us proceed to examine the actually intended model of cost behavior that makes possible the simple calculations of Table 10.10, Summary. It takes more explaining than might be anticipated by the uninitiated.

Illustrative Example (Replacements Ignored)

Suppose we illustrate the problem by analyzing lifetime revenue requirements of a single unit of property which costs $10,000 initially. It has a probable life of 10 years, with its chance of retirement at each age represented by the Iowa Type R_1 survivor curve, as discussed in Chapter 7. Ultimate net salvage is expected to be 10%.

Income taxes, at 48% statutory rate, are based on "straight-line" depreciation for books, SYD for taxes, and investment credit of 7%. A 35% debt is in the firm's capital structure, with interest at 5%. Operation and maintenance expense are estimated at 10% per year. There are no other expenses. Two questions are asked:

1. If the company's MAR is 7%, how much are annual revenue requirements of the unit?
2. What is the present worth of its lifetime revenue requirements?

Annual Revenue Requirements of a Single Placement (Form Y)

Annual revenue requirements for return, depreciation, and income taxes are readily estimated in the manner described in previous chapters (Form Y), in percent of $P_{\overline{x}}$.

Return	7.00%	
Depreciation	7.25	(0.90 x 8.05%; from Table 6.18, on page 143)
Income tax	.62	(Formula 8.4, on page 184)
Operation & maintenance	10.00	
Total =	24.87%	

As emphasized before, whenever quantities are stated as a percentage, it is important to ask: "Percentage of what?" In this case, the above revenue requirements are not 24.87% of $10,000, or $2,487 in each year, as will be seen. Nevertheless, it is commonly and incorrectly assumed that revenue requirements are thereby estimated at $2,487 per year. That is not the intent of the calculation; it is not the arithmetical result. This illustrates the error that is generally committed by reason of failure to recognize the problem.

Column 7, Table 10.1, shows the year-by-year minimum revenue requirements as estimated in the above manner. Observe that they do indeed decrease in each successive year, as repetitiously stated. The explanation is that their lifetime-levelized amount is expressed as a percentage of probable surviving investment $P_{\overline{X}}$ in service each year. The probable surviving investment is not $10,000 (= P_0) in every year, 1 to 10 inclusive. The statement of the problem carefully stipulates otherwise.

Only about a 50/50 chance is given that the unit will serve exactly 10 years. To base the calculation on this "half-a-chance" situation would ignore an equal number of other possibilities of service life. The most likely requirement for depreciation, for example, is 11% greater than for a 10-year life "certain," as follows (from Table 6.16):

Service Life	Annuity (10% Salvage)	Difference (Ratio)
10 years, "certain" (Type SQ)	0.90 x 7.24 = 6.516%	
10, R_1	0.90 x 8.05 = 7.245%	7.245/6.516 = 1.11

In Table 10.1, return (Column 3) is calculated as $i \cdot P_{\overline{X}}$, which is Form Y. This means that depreciation (Column 4) must be tabulated on the same Form Y basis, as explained on page 118. It is calculated as $_i^{\beta}d \cdot P_{\overline{X}}$ in each year, meaning that the lifetime-levelized annuity ($_i^{\beta}d$) is applied to the regularly decreasing investment in plant in service ($P_{\overline{X}}$) each year. Income tax is calculated in the same manner, as $T\% \cdot P_{\overline{X}}$.

As discussed before, all these components of revenue requirements could, if desired, be calculated on the Form X basis. Depreciation would then be shown in each year as the book accrual. If "straight-line" depreciation were used by the company for book purposes, the annual accrual would be $_0d \cdot P_{\overline{X}}$, adjusted for net salvage, or $_0d(1 - c)P_{\overline{X}}$ in each year. Return must then be tabulated as the corresponding Form X gross income, $i(P_{\overline{X}} - R_{\overline{X}})$, and income tax in each year must be based on taxable gross income in each year. These expenses are

Table 10.1. Lifetime-levelized revenue requirements (Form Y). Probable life = 10, R_i; 7% MAR; 35% debt at 5% interest; zero net salvage. "Straight-line" for books; SYD for taxes. Operation and maintenance expense at 10%.

1	2	3	4	5	6	7
Year (x)	Probable Investment in Service (P_{-x})	MAR at 7% of $P_{\bar{x}}$	Depreciation at 7.25% of $P_{\bar{x}}$	Income Tax at 0.62% of $P_{\bar{x}}$	Operation & Maintenance 10% of $P_{\bar{x}}$	All Annual Revenue Requirements (Cols. 3 + 4 + 5 + 6)
1	$9,860	$690.20	$714.85	$61.13	$986.00	$2,452.18
2	9,570	669.90	693.82	59.33	957.00	2,380.05
3	9,240	646.80	669.90	57.29	924.00	2,297.99
4	8,880	621.60	643.80	55.06	888.00	2,208.46
5	8,480	593.60	614.80	52.58	848.00	2,108.98
6	8,030	562.10	582.18	49.79	803.00	1,997.07
7	7,520	526.40	545.20	46.62	752.00	1,870.22
8	6,960	487.20	504.60	43.15	696.00	1,730.95
9	6,340	443.80	459.65	39.31	634.00	1,576.76
10	5,650	395.50	409.62	35.03	565.00	1,405.15
11	4,910	343.70	355.98	30.44	491.00	1,221.12
12	4,140	289.80	300.15	25.67	414.00	1,029.62
13	3,360	235.20	243.60	20.83	336.00	835.63
14	2,600	182.00	188.50	16.12	260.00	646.62
15	1,890	132.30	137.02	11.72	189.00	470.04
16	1,270	88.90	92.08	7.87	127.00	315.85
17	750	52.50	54.38	4.65	75.00	186.53
18	380	26.60	27.55	2.36	38.00	94.51
19	140	9.80	10.15	0.87	14.00	34.82
20	30	2.10	2.18	0.19	3.00	7.47

276

10% of $P_{\overline{x}}$ in every year. That is, since we are dealing with a single unit of property, one might expect Column 6 to be 10% of $10,000, or $1,000, in every year that the unit is in service.

Since the unit is expected to have a 10-year life, why does not Column 6 show $1,000 in each year from 1 to 10, and zero thereafter? The explanation is that the probable capital investment in service is not $10,000 in each year for 10 years. The probable surviving invest-ment in each year is shown in Column 2. This was stipulated in the statement of the problem. A 10-year life is not certain. In fact, if in-stead of a single unit the problem dealt with a larger group of similar units, the average experience of all units would be expressed by Col-umn 2. Only a few units would be expected to be retired in Year 1; only a few in Year 20. The largest number of annual retirements would occur in Year 13, although probable average life is only 10 years.

Since we cannot tell in advance exactly which units out of a large group will be the ones retired at any particular date, the only rational procedure is to treat each individual unit as probably conforming to the average behavior of all units. This is the exact intent of Table 10.1. This is ordinarily the analyst's exact intent when making analyses of single placements or of "decaying plant." It may be well to review Chapter 6 on this point; particularly the discussion of Tables 6.20 and 6.21.

It is not an acceptable simplification to predict constant annual revenue requirements in every year for 10 years, as is common prac-tice in such problems. That is an incompetent estimate which does not represent the estimator's actual intent, whether he recognizes it or not. If the estimator did intend to calculate revenue requirements at a constant amount in each year for 10 years, then he could not have in-tended to analyze costs of the single placement. He must have meant to analyze costs of a "continuing plant," with retirements replaced as they occur, so that $P_{\overline{x}} = P_0$ = the initial capital investment at all times.

Then what was his intent after Year 10? At the end of Year 10 he would then have a group of units some 10 years old, some 9, some 8, down to those that are nearly new (recent replacements). These re-placements cost money; they have useful life left in them. How does the estimator propose to account for that? Commonly, that question is evaded, not simplified. The estimator takes the position, perhaps sub-conciously and without serious consideration, that the level annual rate of revenue requirements will go on "indefinitely." Such is the basis for many decisions reached by estimating "annual costs." In some cases, it results in wrong and unintended decisions.

On the other hand, many situations arise where respectable and intended decisions can be reached in this manner, as will be explained. One initial requirement is that the estimator must answer the question "How many years is indefinitely?" The importance of this question will be discussed in the following section, which will introduce the more comprehensive treatment of the continuing plant.

Present Worth of Lifetime Revenue Requirements; Single Placement

The second question asked about the single placement is still to be answered: What is the present worth of its lifetime revenue requirements?

This quantity provides the comprehensive answer in problems of economic choice between competing projects consisting of a single initial placement, provided the competing projects have the same probable life. Otherwise, it is not reasonable to expect that all could produce the same annual sales and revenues, which is the major premise essential to this approach. The exact intent of the foregoing estimate of annual revenue requirements may be expressed as follows:

Return	7.00% of $10,000 x $Y_{\bar{x}}$ (or x $P_{\bar{x}}$)
Depreciation	7.25% of $10,000 x $Y_{\bar{x}}$ (or x $P_{\bar{x}}$)
Income tax	0.62% of $10,000 x $Y_{\bar{x}}$ (or x $P_{\bar{x}}$)
Operation & maintenance	10.00% of $10,000 x $Y_{\bar{x}}$ (or x $P_{\bar{x}}$
Total	24.87% of $10,000 x $Y_{\bar{x}}$ (or x $P_{\bar{x}}$)

where

$Y_{\bar{x}}$ = average percentage survivors of the initial placement, in each year.

$P_{\bar{x}}$ = capital investment represented by $Y_{\bar{x}}$.

As discussed in Chapter 5, the present worth of a lifetime annuity is readily calculated simply by dividing it by $(i + {}^{\beta}_{i}d)$, where ${}^{\beta}_{i}d$ is not adjusted for salvage. In this case, $(i + {}^{\beta}_{i}d)$ amounts to 15.05%, and the present worth of lifetime revenue requirements is as follows, as at the date of initial placement:

Return	$\dfrac{7.00\% \text{ of } \$10,000}{0.1505}$	= $ 4,651.16
Depreciation	$\dfrac{7.25\% \text{ of } \$10,000}{0.1505}$	= 4,817.28
Income tax	$\dfrac{0.62\% \text{ of } \$10,000}{0.1505}$	= 411.96
Operation and maintenance	$\dfrac{10.00\% \text{ of } \$10,000}{0.1505}$	= 6,644.52
Total present worth	$\dfrac{24.87\% \text{ of } \$10,000}{0.1505}$	= $16,524.92

This result prompts two pertinent questions:

1. The present worth of return + depreciation is:

$$\begin{array}{r} \$4,651.16 \\ 4,817.28 \\ \hline \$9,468.44 \end{array}$$

Why is it not $10,000, the initial capital investment?

The explanation is that $9,468.44 is the present worth of revenue requirements, which are less than $10,000, by the present worth of net

salvage credits obtained from the junkman, not from revenues. The
reconciliation is as follows:

> Present worth of revenue requirements
>   for return and depreciation   = $ 9,468.44
> Present worth of credit from piecemeal
>   net salvage   =   531.56
>   Initial capital investment   = $10,000.00

These quick and easy evaluations of present worth will be found to
be identical with the present worth of the year-by-year items of Table
10.1. That demonstration will be left to the reader.

2. Had the Type R_1 probability of service life been ignored and calculations been made on the basis of 10-year life certain, no more and
no less (no retirements before or after Age 10), how much different
would the estimate of lifetime worth be?
    The answer is as follows:

> ### Annual Revenue Requirements; Type SQ Dispersion
> #### (Form Y)

Return	7.00%	
Depreciation	6.52	(0.90 x 7.24%, per Table 6.18 on page 143)
Income tax	0.50	(Formula 8.4, on page 184)
Operation & maintenance	10.00	
Total	24.02%	

The present worth of ten years' revenue requirements would then
be:

Return $\dfrac{7.00\% \text{ of } \$10,000}{0.142378} = \$ 4,916.49$

Depreciation $\dfrac{6.514\% \text{ of } \$10,000}{0.142378} = 4,575.16$

Income tax $\dfrac{0.50\% \text{ of } \$10,000}{0.142378} = 351.18$

Operation and maintenance $\dfrac{10.00\% \text{ of } \$10,000}{0.142378} = 7,023.58$

Total present worth $\dfrac{24.02\% \text{ of } \$10,000}{0.142378} = \$16,866.41$

Reconciliation of capital-recovery cost with initial capital investment:

> Present worth of return plus depreciation   = $ 9,491.65
> Present worth of credits for piecemeal net salvage = 508.35
>   Initial capital investment   = $10,000.00

These quantitative results must not be regarded as a generalized
evaluation of the importance of recognizing retirement dispersion or

probability of life in any particular problem. Their purpose is to explain methods of analysis. The exactly intended procedure is relatively
simple, and there is little excuse for being satisfied with inexact
methods. In some practical problems, this error from use of "slightly"
inexact models could be disastrous.

The "Renewal Function"; Static Plant

The rate of replacement necessary to maintain a project at its
initial level as retirements occur is known as the "renewal function."
Assuming that replacements have the same probable average life as
the units they replace, it is not too difficult to calculate the renewal
function for any project. This is described as replacement "in kind."

If it can further be assumed that replacements will be made at the
same cost per unit as those replaced, then the capital investment in the
project also is maintained at a constant level equal to the initial investment. Otherwise, an adjustment for price levels must be made, as
mentioned before, to establish the capital investment with passage of
time. Since revenue requirements are ordinarily expressed as a percentage of capital investment currently in service, current revenue
requirements are readily calculated.

For purposes of this explanation, short service lives will be assumed to minimize the number of calculations and thus simplify the
explanations. For the lengthier calculations, the simplest dispersion
type (SC) will be assumed. No doubt it will be obvious that net salvage
is not involved in the renewal function. Another simplifying convention
used before will be employed to make the arithmetic more readily understandable. That is, 50% of annual retirements (and replacements
thereof) will be assumed to occur on the first day of each year and 50%
on the last day. This results in an average figure for $P_{\bar{x}}$ effective
throughout the whole year.

Applied to a single property unit, which must be retired and replaced "all at once, and nothing first," the renewal function represents
the probability of that occurrence at any date. Applied to a group of
similar units initially installed at the same time, the renewal function
represents the probable rate of retirement and renewal at any date.

To grasp the physical situation, it may be helpful to think of a
group of 1,000 glass tumblers, bought on opening day of a restaurant.
A reasonably predictable number can be expected to be chipped,
cracked, or broken every day, and replaced immediately by identical
new ones. This is kept up as long as the restaurant is in business,
which may be much longer than the life of any of its dishes. When the
restaurant finally does close for the last time, some of its glasses will
be nearly new (recent replacements); some older; and a few will be of
age ω (omega is the age of the oldest survivor of a group) but not as
old as the business.

It may be that the reason for winding up the business was a gradual
loss of customers. In such case, a day may have come when broken

Table 10.2. Retirements from a group of 1,000 units.
5-Year average life; Type SC dispersion (single placement).

Annual Retirements

Year (x)	First of Year x	First of Year (x + 1)	First-of-Year Retirements, Total
1	50	--	50
2	50	50	100
3	50	50	100
4	50	50	100
5	50	50	100
6	50	50	100
7	50	50	100
8	50	50	100
9	50	50	100
10	50	50	100
11	--	50	50
Totals	500	500	1,000

glasses were no longer replaced; the gradually decreasing number
were made to serve, by speeding up the dishwashing. At the closing
date an insignificant number may have been serviceable; all were of an
age approximating average life (of glasses, not of the restaurant itself).
This is an example of the shrinking plant. The renewal function no
longer applies, once renewals are discontinued.

Calculation of the Renewal Function (Static Plant)

Appendix E describes calculation of the renewal function for Iowa
Type Curve R_1, 10 years average life, by developing (a) a general expression; (b) a diagram that is helpful in its application; (c) a tabular
form for listing results of the calculation; and (d) a plot of the final result. That final result is a damped oscillatory curve which settles
down, after several generations of replacements, to an asymptotic
value of 1/life.

Consider a group of 1,000 units having an average life of 5 years,
Type SC dispersion. This means that the last unit will be retired at
Age 10. In each of the 10 years, 100 units will be retired, so that at
Age 5 (= average life), 500 units will still be in service. Thus, if retirements were not to be replaced, they would occur on the first of
each year per Table 10.2 (treating "end of Year x" as equivalent to
"first of Year $x + 1$"). However, if the total number in service is to be
kept at 1,000, replacement of 50 units on the first of Year 1 will not be
sufficient, because some of those 50 will be retired during Year 1. How
many must be installed?

The answer is enough so that 95% of the "initial placement plus
one-half of Year 1 retirement" will equal 1,000:

0.95 x first of Year 1 "placement + replacement" = 1,000.

Thus: First of Year 1 "placement + replacement" = $\dfrac{1,000}{0.95}$ = 1,052.63.

Hence: First of Year 1 replacement = 1,052.63 - 1,000 = 52.63 units.

Average annual survivors will then be, per the SC curve:

Year (x)	Survivors of 1,000 Placements	Survivors of 52.63 Replacements	Total Survivors
0.5	950.000	50.00	1,000.00
1.5	850.000	44.74	894.74
2.5	750.000	39.48	789.48
3.5	650.000	34.21	684.21
4.5	550.000	29.95	579.95
5.5	450.000	24.69	474.69
6.5	350.000	19.42	369.12
7.5	250.000	14.16	264.16
8.5	150.000	8.90	158.90
9.5	50.000	2.63	52.63

At the beginning of Year 2, enough replacements must be made to bring the total back to 1,000 from 894.74 above; or 1,000 - 894.74 = 105.26 after retirements from the Year 2 replacement. In order to have 105.26, survivors of the replacement, we must install 105.26/0.95 = 110.80 units.

Survivors thereafter can then be summarized as follows:

Year (x)	Survivors of 1,000 Placements	Survivors of 52.63 Replacements	Survivors of 110.80 Replacements	Total Survivors
0.5	950.00	50.00	—	1,000.00
1.5	850.00	44.74	105.26	1,000.00
2.5	750.00	39.48	94.18	883.66
3.5	650.00	34.21	83.10	767.31
4.5	550.00	29.95	72.02	651.97
5.5	450.00	24.69	60.94	535.63
6.5	350.00	19.42	49.86	419.28
7.5	250.00	14.16	38.78	302.94
8.5	150.00	8.90	27.70	186.60
9.5	50.00	2.63	16.62	69.25
10.5	—	—	5.54	5.54

At the beginning of Year 3, enough replacements must be made to bring the total back to 1,000 from 883.66, above; or 1,000 - 883.66 = 116.34 after retirements from the Year 3 replacement. In order to have 116.34 survivors of the replacement, we must install 116.34/0.95 = 122.47 units.

If this same sort of calculation is repeated for 30 years, annual replacements will be found as summarized in Table 10.3, which represents the "replacement function" we have been seeking.

Table 10.3. Replacement function for 5, SC. Annual replacements necessary to keep intact a placement of 1,000 units, replaced "in kind" as retirements occur.

Year	Replacements	Year	Replacements	Year	Replacements
1	52.63	11	217.34	21	197.39
2	110.80	12	178.98	22	197.31
3	122.47	13	185.54	23	198.89
4	135.36	14	191.50	24	199.98
5	149.61	15	196.66	25	200.60
6	165.35	16	200.79	26	200.80
7	182.76	17	203.60	27	200.65
8	202.00	18	204.78	28	200.28
9	223.26	19	203.96	29	199.85
10	246.76	20	200.69	30	199.59

Notice that replacements get under way slowly; it is Year 8 (= 160% of average life) before annual replacements equal or exceed the "straight-line" rate of 1/life = 20%.

The cost of replacements, so calculated, and their revenue requirements constitute the difference between (a) the single placement, and (b) the continuing plant. These are the extra costs incurred if annual revenue requirements are to be estimated at a constant annual rate in dollars, instead of a regularly decreasing annual rate. These costs are commonly overlooked.

The Shrinking Plant

Referring to Table 10.3, suppose no more replacements are made after Year 30. What happens to the 1,000 units then in service?

This situation is illustrated by Table 10.4. Retirements of each vintage of replacements (all of the initial placements are gone after Year 10) proceed at the SC rate, leaving a balance in service as shown in Column 2.

As a matter of interest, the "straight-line" reserves and resultant "net plant" are also tabulated in Table 10.4. Note how reserves had stabilized at about 23% of the 1,000 in service, by Year 30 — not at 50%, as is commonly assumed.

A most important conclusion worth remembering is that the replacement rate does settle down at a figure equal to 1/life, but the reserve does not stabilize at 50%.

Table 10.4 suggests an important practical application of the "shrinking plant" concept. That is, consider a problem which is not adapted to solution by comparing revenue requirements for single placements because lives of competing assets are different. We then must look at revenue requirements for the static plant for the competing proposals, that is, at revenue requirements each year, indefinitely. The question then arises; "How long is indefinitely?"

Referring to Table 10.4, in that case one could evaluate revenue

Table 10.4. The shrinking plant. Mean annual depreciation reserve
and net plant computations. 5-year life, Type SC dispersion,
no replacements after Year 30.

1	2	3	4	5	6
Year	Mean Annual Gross Plant Balance	Accumulated Annual Depreciation Accrual	Accumulated Retirements Between Equivalent Mean Annual Balances	Mean Annual Depreciation Reserve	Mean Annual Net Plant Balance
1	$1,000.00	$ ---	$ 52.63	$(52.63)	$1,052.63
2	1,000.00	200.00	163.43	36.57	963.43
3	1,000.00	400.00	285.90	114.10	885.90
4	1,000.00	600.00	421.26	178.74	821.26
5	1,000.00	800.00	570.87	229.13	770.87
6	1,000.00	1,000.00	736.22	263.78	736.22
7	1,000.00	1,200.00	918.98	281.02	718.98
8	1,000.00	1,400.00	1,120.98	279.02	720.98
9	1,000.00	1,600.00	1,344.24	255.76	744.24
10	1,000.00	1,800.00	1,591.00	209.00	791.00
. . . . . .	. . . . . .	. . . . . .	. . . . . .	. . . . . .	. . . . . .
26	1,000.00	5,000.00	4,769.80	230.20	769.80
27	1,000.00	5,200.00	4,970.45	229.55	770.45
28	1,000.00	5,400.00	5,170.72	229.28	770.72
29	1,000.00	5,600.00	5,370.57	229.43	770.57
30	1,000.00	5,800.00	5,570.16	229.84	770.16
31	810.34	6,000.00	5,759.82	240.18	570.16
32	640.41	6,162.07	5,929.75	232.32	408.09
33	490.29	6,290.15	6,079.87	210.28	280.01
34	360.11	6,388.21	6,210.05	178.16	181.95
35	249.97	6,460.23	6,320.19	140.04	109.93
36	159.80	6,510.22	6,410.27	99.95	59.94
37	89.89	6,542.20	6,480.27	61.93	27.96
38	39.93	6,560.18	6,530.23	29.95	9.98
39	9.98	6,568.17	6,560.18	7.99	1.99
40	---	6,570.16	6,570.16	---	---

requirements for the static plant over 30 years and assume a "shrinking plant" thereafter for both projects. Ending the study at Year 30
and ignoring the differences thereafter would introduce an error; differentials during the "shrinking" period must be considered. However,
two reassuring things may be said about them:

1. The quantities are smaller than during the "static plant" period.
   Differentials between competing proposals are therefore less important.
2. Because these smaller differentials are more remote, their present
   worth (as at the beginning of Year 1) is still less significant.

    For plant having an average life around 30 years, the last survivor
of the initial placement will serve around 60 years ($\omega = 60$ years).

Thus, a study of single placements must extend over 60 years or thereabouts.

At usual rates of MAR, the present worth of differentials more than 60 years in the future approaches insignificance, as will be shown. Thus, a study of the static plant, no more extended than a study of single placements (60 years for either one, for an average life near 30), can ignore differentials thereafter with small effect on accuracy of results; hence the usefulness of the continuing-plant concept. It becomes unnecessary to rely on such unsatisfactory devices as the "coterminous date" fiction. It is not necessary to adopt the "static plant, forever" fiction. It is not necessary to violate common sense by comparing alternative single placements having different lives. The arithmetical effect of the present worth principle makes it possible to make a finite evaluation of costs that persist over infinite (indefinite) periods.

The Growing Plant

In long-range planning, or "systems engineering," the project ordinarily consists of a program for capital placement over an extended period of years. Attempting to reach decisions by direct comparison of annual revenue requirements or by comparison of their present worths over a finite period of years is quite impracticable. The special conditions which apply to the continuing (static) plant do not apply, and there is no rational basis for assuming a shrinking plant in the foreseeable future.

As mentioned before, the concept of PWAFRR (present worth of all future revenue requirements) is then a useful tool. In fact, it is the only dependable means for evaluating such situations. The principles involved in this concept and appropriate ways of manipulating the cost data will be described in Tables 10.5-10.9.

As before, for purposes of simplicity and easy comprehension, a very short life (4 years) and simple type of dispersion (SC) will be assumed. Net salvage will be ignored for the same reason. Revenue requirements other than return and depreciation will also be ignored; their treatment should be obvious.

This presentation is comprised of five major tables, together with several supplementary tables which will be found in Appendix E.[1] The five major tables are as follows:

Table 10.5. Gross Additions and Mean Survivors

An initial placement of 1,000; growth (= net additions) 10% annually. Four-year life, type SC retirement dispersion.

---

[1]Substantial portions of Chapter 10 and the related Appendix E are adapted from unpublished papers prepared by L. Van Nimwegen of Public Service Electric and Gas Company, Newark, N.J., and Paul H. Jeynes.

Table 10.6. Revenue Requirements for Each Vintage of Gross Addi-
    tions (Form X)
Revenue requirements for return (MAR = 6%) and depreciation
only, for 15 years. "Straight-line" depreciation; this requires calculation of depreciation reserves each year.

Table 10.7. Levelized Revenue Requirements for Each Vintage of
    Gross Additions (Form Y)
For any given placement, the lifetime-levelized Form Y data of
Table 10.7 are financially equivalent to the Form X nonlevelized-
lifetime revenue requirements of Table 10.6. These Form Y equivalencies have a special feature revealed by Table 10.8. It is not necessary to calculate depreciation reserves.

Table 10.8. Levelized Revenue Requirements for Each Vintage of Net
    Additions (Form Y)
Each annual net addition is treated as an independent "continuing
plant." Revenue requirements for the growing plant (the whole project)
are obtained by their summation. Note that the totals, in each year,
are identical with the totals each year in Table 10.7. It is this special
circumstance which permits the simple calculation, in Table 10.9, of
PWAFRR (that is, present worth of all future revenue requirements) of
the specific placements which constitute the particular project exactly
described in Table 10.5.

Table 10.9. Present Worth to Eternity of Revenue Requirements of the
    Specific Placements of Table 10.5
This special calculation of PWAFRR has all the advantages of
heavily discounted significance of remote differences. It has none of
the faults of short-term (20 years, or so) comparisons of revenue requirements, which cover only about one-third of the life span of the
last survivor of a single placement having a probable life of 30 years.
    This calculation of PWAFRR does not assume that replacements
will be made forever. It simply observes that omitting all differences
between competing projects more remote than 60 years (or so) in the
future affects conclusions so little that the calculation "to eternity" is
adequate for any end point to the study beyond Year 60.
    No internal self-contradiction is made here, as in the "cotermi-
nous date" assumption, between the lives assumed in calculating revenue requirements and the lives that must result from retirement at any
finite "coterminous" date.[2]
    These five tables are needed to explain the recommended proce-
dure. In application to actual problems, though, the only tabulations
necessary are:

---

[2]"Coterminous" (with quotation marks) refers to a theoretical date on which all units
simultaneously serve out their predicted service life. But there can be no such single date
unless predicted life recognizes that differences in date of placement for each vintage then
result in a different life and type of dispersion for each such vintage.

Table 10.5. Gross additions and mean survivors.

End of Year	Gross Additions	1	2	3	4	5	6	7	8	9	10	11	12	13	14	15
0	1,066.67	1,000.00	866.67	733.33	600.00	466.67	333.33	200.00	66.67							
1	1,315.55		1,233.33	1,068.89	904.44	740.00	575.56	411.11	246.67	82.22						
2	1,608.30			1,507.78	1,306.74	1,105.71	904.67	703.63	502.59	301.56	100.52					
3	1,951.81				1,829.82	1,585.85	1,341.87	1,097.89	853.92	609.94	365.96	121.99				
4	2,353.99					2,206.87	1,912.62	1,618.37	1,324.12	1,029.87	735.62	441.37	147.12			
5	2,824.06						2,647.56	2,294.55	1,941.54	1,588.53	1,235.53	882.52	529.51	176.50		
6	3,372.39							3,161.62	2,740.07	2,318.52	1,896.97	1,475.42	1,053.87	632.32	210.77	
7	4,011.00								3,760.31	3,258.94	2,757.56	2,256.19	1,754.81	1,253.44	752.06	250.69
8	4,682.56									4,389.90	3,804.58	3,219.26	2,633.94	2,048.62	1,463.30	877.98
9	5,376.73										5,040.68	4,368.59	3,696.50	3,024.41	2,352.32	1,680.23
10	6,150.22											5,765.83	4,997.05	4,228.28	3,459.50	2,690.72
11	7,009.58												6,571.48	5,695.28	4,819.09	3,942.89
12	7,961.45													7,463.86	6,468.68	5,473.50
13	9,012.54														8,449.26	7,322.69
14	10,169.37															9,533.78
Gross Plant		1,000.00	2,100.00	3,310.00	4,641.00	6,105.10	7,715.61	9,487.17	11,435.89	13,579.48	15,937.42	18,531.17	21,384.28	24,522.71	27,974.98	31,772.48

2,100.00 = 1,000.00 +1,100.00

3,310.00 = 1,000.00 +1,100.00 +1,210.00, etc.

Initial placement 1,000. Net additions increase 10% annually.
4-year life, Type SC dispersion, zero net salvage. 6% return.

Table 10.6. Revenue requirements for each vintage of gross additions (Form X).

End of Year	Years														
	1	2	3	4	5	6	7	8	9	10	11	12	13	14	15
0	314.00	265.67	219.33	175.00	132.67	92.33	54.00	17.67							
1		387.26	327.66	270.51	215.83	163.63	113.87	66.60	21.79						
2			473.44	400.57	330.70	263.86	200.04	139.21	81.42	26.64					
3				574.56	486.13	401.33	320.22	242.76	168.95	98.81	32.33				
4					692.96	586.30	484.03	386.20	292.79	203.76	119.17	39.00			
5						831.33	703.38	580.69	463.32	351.25	244.45	142.97	46.78		
6							992.75	839.95	693.44	553.28	419.45	291.91	170.73	55.87	
7								1,180.74	999.00	824.75	658.05	498.88	347.19	203.06	66.44
8									1,378.43	1,166.26	962.84	768.23	582.41	405.32	237.05
9										1,582.77	1,339.16	1,105.57	882.12	668.75	465.41
10											1,810.47	1,531.81	1,264.62	1,009.02	764.95
11												2,063.44	1,745.85	1,441.32	1,150.01
12													2,343.65	1,982.92	1,637.05
13														2,653.07	2,244.71
14															2,993.61
System Revenue Requirements	314.00	652.93	1,020.43	1,420.64	1,858.29	2,338.78	2,868.31	3,453.82	4,099.14	4,807.52	5,585.92	6,441.81	7,383.35	8,419.33	9,559.23

Revenue requirements for capital recovery (return + depreciation) only.

Return at 6% of (mean plant in service - reserve) each year.

"Straight-line" depreciation at one-fourth of mean plant in service each year.

Table 10.7. Levelized revenue requirements for each vintage of gross additions (Form Y).

End of Year	Years														
	1	2	3	4	5	6	7	8	9	10	11	12	13	14	15
0	299.27	259.37	219.46	179.56	139.66	99.76	59.85	19.95							
1		369.10	319.88	270.67	221.46	172.25	123.03	73.82	24.61						
2			451.23	391.07	330.90	270.74	210.57	150.41	90.25	30.08					
3				547.61	474.59	401.58	328.56	255.55	182.54	109.52	36.51				
4					660.45	572.39	484.33	396.27	308.21	220.15	132.09	44.03			
5						792.33	686.69	581.04	475.40	369.75	264.11	158.47	52.82		
6							946.17	820.02	693.86	567.70	441.55	315.39	189.23	63.08	
7								1,125.34	975.30	825.25	675.21	525.16	375.11	225.07	75.02
8									1,313.76	1,138.59	963.42	788.25	613.09	437.92	262.75
9										1,508.52	1,307.38	1,106.24	905.11	703.97	502.84
10											1,725.53	1,495.46	1,265.39	1,035.32	805.25
11												1,966.64	1,704.42	1,442.20	1,179.98
12													2,233.70	1,935.87	1,638.04
13														2,528.59	2,191.45
14															2,853.16
System Revenue Requirements	299.27	628.47	990.57	1,388.91	1,827.06	2,309.05	2,839.20	3,422.40	4,063.93	4,769.56	5,545.80	6,399.64	7,338.87	8,372.02	9,508.49

Revenue requirements for capital recovery (return + depreciation) only.

Return at 6% of mean plant in service.

"Sinking-fund" depreciation at 23.927% (more exactly, 23.926 821 91%) ($= \beta_i^d$) of mean plant in service.

System revenue requirements here tabulated do not represent actual revenues reported per annual income statements. This remains the case even if actual return were 6%.

289

Table 10.8. Levelized revenue requirements for each vintage of net additions.

End of Year	Net Additions	Years														
		1	2	3	4	5	6	7	8	9	10	11	12	13	14	15
0	1,000.00	299.27	299.27	299.27	299.27	299.27	299.27	299.27	299.27							
1	1,100.00		329.20	329.20	329.20	329.20	329.20	329.20	329.20	329.20						
2	1,210.00			362.11	362.11	362.11	362.11	362.11	362.11	362.11	362.11					
3	1,331.00				398.33	398.33	398.33	398.33	398.33	398.33	398.33	398.33				
4	1,464.10					438.16	438.16	438.16	438.16	438.16	438.16	438.16	438.16			
5	1,610.51						481.97	481.97	481.97	481.97	481.97	481.97	481.97	481.97		
6	1,771.56							530.17	530.17	530.17	530.17	530.17	530.17	530.17	530.17	
7	1,948.72								583.19	583.19	583.19	583.19	583.19	583.19	583.19	583.19
8	2,143.59									641.51	641.51	641.51	641.51	641.51	641.51	641.51
9	2,357.95										705.66	705.66	705.66	705.66	705.66	705.66
10	2,593.74											776.22	776.22	776.22	776.22	776.22
11	2,853.12												853.85	853.85	853.85	853.85
12	3,138.43													939.23	939.23	939.23
13	3,452.27														1,033.15	1,033.15
14	3,797.50															1,136.47
Total	31,772.49	299.27	628.47	990.58	1,388.91	1,827.07	2,309.04	2,839.21	3,422.40	3,764.64	4,141.10	4,555.21	5,010.73	5,511.80	6,062.98	6,669.28

(Omitted after 8th year of service to show that such omission results in under-statement of system total.)

(Compare with system revenue requirements of Table 10.7.)

Revenue requirements at 29.926 821 91% of mean plant in service. (See footnote, Table 10.7.)

System revenue requirements here tabulated do not represent actual revenues reported per annual income statements. This remains the case even if actual return were 6%.

Table 10.9. Present worth, "to eternity," of revenue requirements for net additions over a 15-year period.

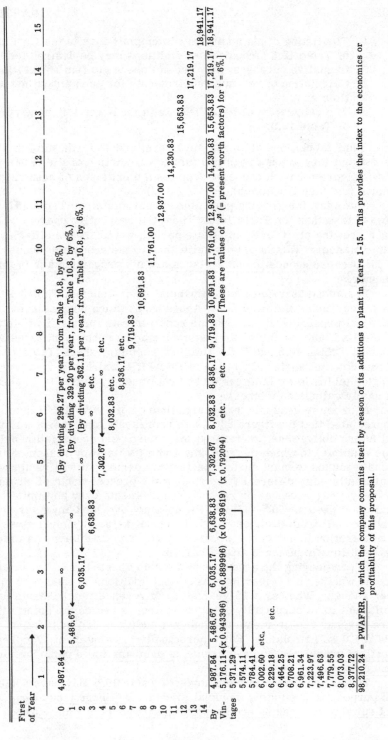

First of Year: 1 2 3 4 5 6 7 8 9 10 11 12 13 14 15

0 4,987.84 (By dividing 299.27 per year, from Table 10.8, by 6%.)

1 5,486.67 (By dividing 329.20 per year, from Table 10.8, by 6%.)

2 6,035.17 (By dividing 362.11 per year, from Table 10.8, by 6%.)

3 6,638.83 ∞ etc.

4 7,302.67 ∞ etc.

5 8,032.83 etc.

6 8,836.17 etc.

7 9,719.83

8 10,691.83

9 11,761.00

10 12,937.00

11 14,230.83

12 15,653.83

13 17,219.17

14 18,941.17

By Vin-tages

4,987.84 | 5,486.67 | 6,035.17 | 6,638.83 | 7,302.67 | 8,032.83 | 8,836.17 | 9,719.83 | 10,691.83 | 11,761.00 | 12,937.00 | 14,230.83 | 15,653.83 | 17,219.17 | 18,941.17

5,176.11 (x 0.943396) | (x 0.889996) | (x 0.839619) | (x 0.792094)

[These are values of v^n (= present worth factors) for i = 6%.]

5,371.29
5,574.11
5,784.41
6,002.60   etc.
6,229.18
6,464.25
6,708.21
6,961.34
7,223.97
7,496.63
7,779.55
8,073.03
8,377.72

98,210.24 = PWAFRR, to which the company commits itself by reason of its additions to plant in Years 1-15. This provides the index to the economics or profitability of this proposal.

291

1. The listing of net additions contemplated, as in the first column of Table 10.8 (annual gross additions may be desired for informative purposes; they are not needed to find PWAFRR);
2. Calculation of revenue requirements for each annual net addition; and
3. The calculation of PWAFRR, as in the lower left-hand corner of Table 10.9.

Other tabulations of annual survivors, and so forth, may be of interest, but they are not required for the calculation of PWAFRR, which single figure for each proposal supplies the criterion of economic choice (the Step 1 decision).

Note that, for growing plant, the annual totals per Table 10.7 are always less than for Table 10.6. Thus, the respective present worths for a growing plant, over any finite period, would always differ in that same manner. This is of no significance to the economic comparison at all because economic comparisons are not properly made in this manner.

For added assurance as to financial equivalencies, Tables 10.6 and 10.7, see Tables E.13 and E.14, Appendix E, which demonstrate the identical present worth of revenue requirements for the first vintage, Table 10.5, and for the whole history including subsequently "decaying" plant of Tables 10.5 and E.5. The final summary sheet (Table 10.10) shows how the whole calculation of PWAFRR, which required five lengthy tables to explain, can be accomplished by listing two columns of easily calculated figures.

In order to grasp the exact significance of PWAFRR, it must be appreciated that the figure 98,210.24 represents the present worth of all future obligations (to eternity; for return plus depreciation only, in this example) to which the company commits itself by reason of additions it makes to plant during the 15-year period. It will be agreed that this is quite different from finding the present worth of summated year-by-year revenues or revenue requirements over any finite installation period. Such a PWAFRR does not overlook any future costs which result from decisions made in Years 1-15. It simply gives no consideration to any costs incurred by reason of decisions as to further net additions to be made after Year 15.

In considering the adequacy of the study period, it is necessary to decide whether a 15-year forecast of net additions is enough or more than enough. Whether a 15-year study of revenue requirements may be sufficient for a perpetually growing system is beside the point; all future revenue requirements of those net additions are included in PWAFRR so calculated. For a perpetually growing plant, the present worth of annual revenue requirements over any finite period would be unacceptable, as observed before.

Tabulations made in the manner of Table 10.6 may have some useful purpose in predicting financial effects. But these tabulations are not suitable for making economic comparisons or for anticipating

Table 10.10. Summary of Table 10.9 calculations of PWAFRR.

Year n	Annual Revenue Requirement for Net Addition per Table 10.8	v^n times Annual Revenue Requirement Divided by MAR (here 6%)
0	299.27	4,987.84
1	329.20	5,176.11
2	362.11	5,371.29
3	398.33	5,574.11
4	438.16	5,784.41
5	481.97	6,002.60
6	530.17	6,229.18
7	583.19	6,464.25
8	641.51	6,708.21
9	705.66	6,961.34
10	776.22	7,223.97
11	853.85	7,496.63
12	939.23	7,779.55
13	1,033.15	8,073.03
14	1,136.47	8,377.72
		PWAFRR = 98,210.24

This summary sheet, then, describes the recommended procedure in making economic comparisons of alternative proposals which give consideration to replacements of the initial installations (that is, the continuing plant).

In making actual studies, these two columns of figures are the only calculations necessary to a complete solution. All the other tables, 10.5-10.9 and those of Appendix E, are here included merely to explain why this simple solution accomplishes the analyst's exact intent and to introduce further discussion of the reasons why other procedures are not recommended.

relative profitability of alternative proposals. This cannot be stressed too emphatically.

The student may satisfy his curiosity as to the comparative nature of Tables 10.6 and 10.7 versus Tables 10.8 and 10.9 by inquiring into conditions at stabilization or for a decaying plant. Tables E.5 and E.6 are included for that purpose (Appendix E).

In conclusion, when analyzing growing systems, it is essential that the exact nature of these revenue requirement estimates be recognized. They are not, as often misinterpreted, attempts to foresee the effect of proposals on future annual income statements. Two major reasons are:

1. Annual income statements report actual (that is, reported) costs and actual earnings in each year. Revenue requirements do not include actual earnings. They include only the smaller incentive-lacking, minimum-acceptable floor of earnings and associated fraction of actual taxes.

2. For a growing plant the present worth of annual revenues per income statements is not the same as, nor involved in, calculation of PWAFRR. This is purely a matter of arithmetic, as demonstrated here. It remains the case even though actual return were to exactly equal minimum acceptable return in every year.

An Example of Long-Term Planning

The following example presents a problem of a kind familiar to system planners. Several ways of assembling revenue requirements will be described and the advantages of the PWAFRR solution indicated.

Three mutually exclusive proposals are under consideration; all will produce identical sales and revenues. Some of the plant involved will have a relatively long life; it consists of heavy machinery, foundations, buildings, electrical wiring, and so forth. The life of the project is indefinite but certainly long enough to justify installation of this long-lived plant.

A program of installations for each proposal has been prepared for the next 5 years. No doubt such installations will continue thereafter, but their nature cannot be foreseen at this time. Accordingly, the problem is to pass upon the relative economy of these 5-year programs.[3]

Owing to a difference in the "mix" of component plant, percentage revenue requirements are not identical for all three proposals:

Plan A	20%
Plan B	15%
Plan C	20%

Table 10.11 shows the proposed annual installations, and resultant cumulative gross plant over the next 5 years. For simplicity, it is assumed that no retirements would occur during this 5-year period, so that net additions are identical with gross additions.

This is a common assumption, often made without giving it serious thought. For short-lived plant, it could introduce serious error; for example, note the differences between gross additions of Table 10.5 and corresponding net additions of Table 10.8. By Year 5, they are

Table 10.11. Annual and cumulative capital investments.

1	2	3	4	5	6	7
	Plan A		Plan B		Plan C	
Year	Annual Installations	Cumulative Capital Investment	Annual Installations	Cumulative Capital Investment	Annual Installations	Cumulative Capital Investment
1	$ 50,000	$ 50,000	$500,000	$500,000	$250,000	$250,000
2	50,000	100,000	...	500,000	...	250,000
3	200,000	300,000	...	500,000	...	250,000
4	200,000	500,000	...	500,000	200,000	450,000
5	100,000	600,000	100,000	600,000	100,000	550,000

[3]Cumulative capital investment at the end of Year 5 is not the same for all three proposals (see Table 10.11). If a program for installations beyond Year 5 could be foreseen, it is possible that Plan B would require somewhat smaller installations, and thus have some small advantage not revealed by this analysis. This problem of differences in capability at the end point of the installation schedule will be discussed later.

2353.99 versus 1464.10; by Year 15, they are 10,169.37 versus
3,797.50.

In problems of this kind, several methods of solution are encountered in practice, most of them quite incompetent. This discussion will compare three proposals for assembling revenue requirements (from Table 10.12), plus a fourth "desperation" proposal
sometimes made, as follows:[4]

1. Present worth of 5 years of revenue requirements, that is, revenue requirements during the period when placements are predictable (Table 10.13).
2. Present worth of one lifetime of revenue requirements, for all
   placements made in the 5-year period (Tables 10.14 and 10.15).
3. PWAFRR, or present worth to eternity of revenue requirements for
   plant installed in the 5-year period (Table 10.16).
4. Since the estimate of future revenue requirements into the dim and
   distant future is so uncertain, and the appropriate period of survey
   so vague, and the appropriate present worth calculation so controversial, is the effort worthwhile? Why not simply prefer the plan
   requiring minimum capital investment?

The pessimistic view of 4 reflects the attitude that it is impossible
to estimate present worth of future revenue requirements for capital
investments that cannot be estimated. Revenue requirements for operation, maintenance, and taxes are almost certain to change with passage of time; even MAR is apt to change, though perhaps to a smaller
extent. If installations cannot be predicted beyond 5 years ahead, does
not that apply as well to revenue requirements? It makes a difference
whether replacements are considered or not; how does one decide? If
replaced, will it be "in kind"? At the same unit cost?

Also, if "one lifetime" of revenue requirements is contemplated,
and plant of various service lives is involved, just what lifetime is intended? And is it not unrealistic to assume eternal life for the project,
or indeed for the enterprise itself?

Such questions are not unreasonable. They must be answered, because the decision depends upon the method of analysis selected, as
follows:

1. The present worth of 5 years of revenue requirements (that is, revenue requirements during the period when placements are predictable) would favor Plan A, by a significant margin. From Table
   10.13:

   Plan A $246,496
   Plan B $327,140 = 133% of A
   Plan C $287,142 = 116% of A

2. The present worth of "one lifetime" of revenue requirements would

---

[4]Techniques which do not look to revenue requirements for a solution are discussed in
Chapter 11.

Table 10.12. Annual revenue requirements for Table 10.11.

1	2	3	4	5	6	7
	Plan A		Plan B		Plan C	
Year	At 20% of Annual Installations	At 20% of Cumulative Capital Investment	At 15% of Annual Installations	At 15% of Cumulative Capital Investment	At 20% of Annual Installations	At 20% of Cumulative Capital Investment
1	$10,000	$ 10,000	$75,000	$ 75,000	$50,000	$ 50,000
2	10,000	20,000	...	75,000	...	50,000
3	40,000	60,000	...	75,000	...	50,000
4	40,000	100,000	...	75,000	40,000	90,000
5	20,000	120,000	15,000	90,000	20,000	110,000
		$310,000		$390,000		$350,000

Table 10.13. Present worth of 5-years' revenue requirements per Table 10.12.

1	2	3	4	5
Year (n)	Present Worth Factors at 6%*	Plan A	Plan B	Plan C
1	0.9434	$ 9,434	$ 70,755	$ 47,170
2	0.8900	17,800	66,750	44,500
3	0.8396	50,376	62,970	41,980
4	0.7921	79,210	59,408	71,289
5	0.7473	89,676	67,257	82,203
	5-Years' present worth	$246,496	$327,140	$287,142

*Present worth factors v^n, applicable to annual payments made at end of each year, per Columns 3, 5, and 7 of Table 10.12.

Table 10.14. Present worth of "lifetime" revenue requirements per Table 10.12.

1	2	3	4	5	6	7
	Present Worth Factors at 6%*					
Year (n)	$a\overline{\omega + 5 - n}$	v^{n-1}	Col. 2 x Col. 3	Plan A	Plan B	Plan C
1	16.2665	1.0000	16.2665	$ 162,665	$1,219,988	$ 813,325
2	16.2425	0.9434	15.3232	153,232	...	...
3	16.2170	0.8900	14.4331	577,324	...	...
4	16.1900	0.8396	13.5931	543,724	...	543,724
5	16.1614	0.7921	12.8014	256,028	192,021	256,028
	Present worth for "one lifetime"			$1,692,973	$1,412,009	$1,613,077

*"One lifetime" here means the period from initial date of the project (beginning of Year 1) to the date of retirement of the last survivor from installations made during the 5-year period of firm estimate. Accordingly, $\omega + 5 - n$ (in Column 2) indicates the common terminal date of study for all plans so as to include the final survivor of any installation made during the 5-year period of firm estimate. For purposes of this table, ω is placed at 60 years, corresponding to an average life near 30. Revenue requirements per Table 10.12 (Columns 2, 4, and 6) represent year-end payments. Present worths obtained by applying Column 2 factors represent their equivalent as of the first of the year of installation. To find the present worth as of the initial date of the project (first of Year 1), it is necessary to apply Column 3 factors, v^{n-1} rather than v^n.

Table 10.15. Present worth of lifetime revenue requirements; no replacements.

1	2	3	4	5	6	7	8
Year (n)	Formula 10.1, page 299, applied to Table 10.11*			Present Worth Factors at 6%	Present Worth of Cols. 2, 3, and 4		
	Plan A	Plan B	Plan C		Plan A	Plan B	Plan C
1	$125,000	$937,500	$625,000	1.0000	$ 125,000	$ 937,500	$ 625,000
2	125,000	...	...	0.9434	117,925	...	...
3	500,000	...	...	0.8900	445,000	...	...
4	500,000	...	500,000	0.8396	419,800	...	419,800
5	250,000	187,500	250,000	0.7921	198,025	148,519	198,025
			Present worth, one lifetime		$1,305,750	$1,086,019	$1,242,825

*The quantity $(i + \frac{\beta}{i}d)$ assumed at 8%; e (other expense) at 12% for Plans A and C; 7% for Plan B.

Table 10.16. Present worth "to eternity" of revenue requirements per Table 10.12.

1	2	3	4	5	6	7
Year (n)	Present Worth Factors at 6%*					
	$a_{\overline{\infty}|}$	v^{n-1}	Col. 3 x Col. 2	Plan A	Plan B	Plan C
1	16.6667	1.0000	16.6667	$ 166,667	$1,250,002	$ 833,335
2	16.6667	0.9434	15.7234	157,234	...	...
3	16.6667	0.8900	14.8334	593,336	...	...
4	16.6667	0.8396	13.9934	559,736	...	559,736
5	16.6667	0.7921	13.2017	264,034	198,026	264,034
		Present worth "to eternity"		$1,741,007	$1,448,028	$1,657,105

*Present worth per Column 2 factors represent payments made at the beginning of each year. Hence, the factors per Column 3 applicable to such payments must be v^{n-1}. The multipliers of Column 4 are applied to revenue requirements per Columns 2, 4, and 6, of Table 10.12.

favor Plan B by a somewhat smaller margin, whether replacements are considered or not:

	With Replacements (Table 10.14)	No Replacements (Table 10.15)
Plan A	$1,692,973 = 120% of B	$1,305,750 = 120% of B
Plan B	$1,412,009	$1,086,019
Plan C	$1,613,077 = 114% of B	$1,242,825 = 114% of B

3. PWAFRR, or the present worth "to eternity" of revenue requirements, would also favor Plan B (Table 10.16), by about the same margin:

Plan A $1,741,007 = 121% of B
Plan B $1,448,028
Plan C $1,657,105 = 114% of B

4. The comparison of capital investments, ignoring present worth, would select Plan C (Table 10.11):

$$\begin{aligned} \text{Plan A } \$600,000 &= 109\% \text{ of C} \\ \text{Plan B } \$600,000 &= 109\% \text{ of C} \\ \text{Plan C } \underline{\$550,000} \end{aligned}$$

What should be concluded? Surely, simple comparison of capital investments (4) must be ruled out. It ignores all outlays for operation, maintenance, and taxes, which amount to more than return plus depreciation (whose lifetime present worth equals capital investment).

If simplicity of estimate is a factor, 3 is preferred. It is as simple as 1 or 4, and simpler than 2, whether replacements are taken into account in 2 or not. And note that the proposed calculations involved in 2 are greatly simplified in this example. The usual practical problem, attacked in the manner of 2, will be more difficult.

Proposal 1 is clearly indefensible. The plant installed is expected to have a long life; yet 1 examines revenue requirements for only 5 years. It arrives at a conclusion different from 2 (based on lifetime revenue requirements), and it fails to answer the question whether replacements will be made or not, and if so whether they will be made in kind and at the same unit price. It assumes that there will be no difference in revenue requirements of the three proposals after Year 5, which is plain nonsense. Thus, it must be concluded that studies of this kind must extend over at least one lifetime of all placements (2) and preferably "to eternity" (3 = PWAFRR).

PWAFRR (3), with its implication of revenue requirements "to eternity" may be regarded as an overestimate; certainly an end point will occur short of eternity. PWRR (2), with its implication of no replacements, may be regarded as an underestimate. It may be less of an underestimate if replacements are allowed for during that one lifetime; but it still ignores outlays beyond one lifetime but short of eternity, which are probable even though indefinite.

For this reason, it would be helpful to employ 2 (PWRR), allowing for replacements, as a test of minimum differentials; and 3 (PWAFRR) as a test of maximum differentials between competing proposals. If both favor the same plan, as they do here (Plan B), it is reasonably certain that the economic choice has been identified with assurance. That conclusion is further supported if the differentials are quantitatively about the same, arrived at either way (that is, by comparison of PWRR's or PWAFRR's, for competing plans). That, too, is the case in this example.

Plan B is the economic choice, and the margin of superiority is fairly definite:

	Per Proposal 2	Per Proposal 3
	PWRR (including replacements)	PWAFRR (including replacements)
Advantage of B over A	1,692,973 - 1,412,009 = $280,964	1,741,007 - 1,448,028 = $292,979
Advantage of B over C	1,613,077 - 1,412,009 = $201,068	1,657,105 - 1,448,028 = $209,097

The advantage of Plan B over Plan C, second best, is about $205,000. That is, a difference equivalent to $205,000 in hard cash, at the beginning of Year 1, available to:

1. Increase earnings and pay income tax thereon (increase earnings reported for Year 0 by 52% of $205,000, or $106,600);
2. Reduce the price tag on Year 1 sales by $205,000 without affecting earnings; or
3. Increase earnings some smaller amount while reducing the price of Year 1 output, say $70,000 (= approximately 52% of $135,000) while reducing the price of output by approximately the same amount, as compared to the situation if Plan C were adopted.

PWRR and PWAFRR

Estimates must cover at least one lifetime of contemplated installations, because the initial cost, P_0, commits the company to revenue requirements having a present worth of:

$$P_0 + \frac{P_0 \cdot e}{i + \frac{\beta}{i}d} \qquad \text{(Formula 10.1)}$$

regardless of their future life, and not allowing for replacements, where

P_0 = initial capital investment.
e = annual revenue requirements for expense, other than depreciation.
i = MAR.
$\frac{\beta}{i}d$ = depreciation annuity.
Net salvage is zero.

This fact was introduced in Chapter 5 and discussed at several other points.

A logical definition of "one lifetime" for this purpose is $\omega + t$, where

ω = age of longest-lived survivor, at retirement.
t = number of years in the period of placements.

If replacements are assumed to be made in kind, and at the same unit cost as for P_0, the present worth of resultant level annual revenue requirements for ω years is:

$$a_{\overline{\omega}|} P_0 (i + \frac{\beta}{i}d + e) \qquad \text{(Formula 10.2)}$$

$a_{\overline{\omega}|}$ is the standard symbol for present worth of an annuity of ω years.

For long average lives, ω (which may approximate double average life; see the Iowa Type Curve, Chapter 6) approaches $1/i$, per Table 10.17.

In such case Formula 10.2 approaches:

$$\frac{P_0}{i} (i + \frac{\beta}{i}d + e) = P_0 + \frac{P_0(\frac{\beta}{i}d + e)}{i} \qquad \text{(Formula 10.3)}$$

Table 10.17

Present Worth of an Annuity ($a_{\overline{n}|}$)

Period in Years	Present Worth, for MAR (i) at		
(n)	5%	6%	7%
10	7.72	7.36	7.02
20	12.46	11.47	10.59
30	15.37	13.76	12.41
40	17.16	15.05	13.33
50	18.26	15.76	13.80
60	18.93	16.16	14.04
70	19.34	16.38	14.16
Eternity ($a_{\overline{\infty}|} = 1/i$)	20.00	16.67	14.29

which is the present worth of revenue requirements "to eternity." Accordingly, if it is probable that replacements will be made, the most likely solution lies between Formulas 10.2 and 10.3, as in the preceding example. If there is a possibility that replacements may not be made (usually an unlikely assumption, representing "decaying plant"), the solution is Formula 10.1.

These three expressions, together with intelligent classification of proposals as single placements, static plant, or growing plant (possibly in combination with decaying plant) permit making quick and dependable calculations of reasonable upper and lower limits of a reasonable estimate.

Adjustment for ultimate net salvage has been discussed before. For a single placement, annual revenue requirements for return + depreciation are $P_{\bar{x}}[i + \frac{\beta}{i}d(1 - c)]$. If net salvage is zero, their lifetime present worth is simply P_0. For finite salvage, it is $P_0\left[\frac{i + \frac{\beta}{i}d(1 - c)}{(i + \frac{\beta}{i}d)}\right]$. For static plant, the denominator becomes $a_{\overline{n}|}$, instead of $(i + \frac{\beta}{i}d)$, the limit being $a_{\overline{\infty}|} = i$. For growing plant, the present worth calculation is best made in the manner of Table 10.9; the adjustment for salvage is made in the calculation of revenue requirements for each annual net addition rather than in the present worth factors.

Terminal Inequalities

At the end of the period of predicted placements, it may be that the capabilities of alternative proposals are not identical. That is, one or more may have greater potential ability to produce output, sales, or revenues.

For example, in Table 10.11, at the end of Year 5, Plan C represents a capital investment of only $550,000, or $50,000 less than for Plans A and B. This is not disturbing in Year 5, for which identical sales and revenues were stipulated. But in Year 6, it may be that greater sales and revenues are probable, and that they could be obtained with a smaller incremental capital investment in Year 6 had Plans A or B been adopted instead of C. Thus, it might be said that use of 5-year data may be unfair to Plans A and B. This is not because of any error in the calculation of PWAFRR for the three proposals, but because in effect "the project" consists of more than these three proposals. That is, resting the decision on costs of this 5-year installation program implicitly assumes that revenue requirements for unpredictable installations made after Year 5 will not affect the decision. In other words, it assumes that revenue requirements of those unpredictable future placements will be the same whether A, B, or C is now adopted. The latter may be an indefensible assumption whenever one or more alternatives have greater capability (= potentiality of output, sales, or revenues) at the end of the installation period.

The rational procedure is to extend the estimated program of installations one year, or a few years — even if it must be done arbitrarily, to a degree — "forcing" a plan to identical capability at the end of the period of installations. This can be done by use of reasonable unit costs (dollars per unit of output, or per dollar of sales, or per capacity in kva, therms, passenger-miles, or whatnot). It may be advisable to try several methods of projecting the estimate to test for sensitivity. Although the methods are arbitrary, one will usually find that the uncertainty so introduced will be less serious than the demonstrable error otherwise incurred.

Income Tax, Continuing Plant

In Chapter 8, reference was made to the calculation of income taxes as a percentage of P_0, the initial capital investment which, for a continuing plant, is maintained at that level continuously by making immediate replacement of retirements as they occur.

Just as the revenue requirements for capital recovery (return plus depreciation) are greater for a continuing plant (= $[i + \frac{\beta}{i}d] \times P_0$) than for a single initial placement (= $[i + \frac{\beta}{i}d] \times P_{\overline{x}}$), so is the revenue requirement for income tax for a continuing plant (= $T\% \times P_0$) greater than for a single initial placement (= $T\% \times P_{\overline{x}}$). This fact is commonly overlooked, with the result that income taxes are usually estimated incorrectly in studies of profitability and economic choice. Income tax in each year for a continuing plant is a composite of the independent year-by-year taxes for each vintage of initial placements which make up the total installation currently in service.

The total amount of income tax payable in each year of the continuing plant can be discovered by summation of these tax obligations for all the survivors of the several vintages, at their respective ages, for the particular year. This summation process is so laborious that it is best performed (as a practical matter, necessarily performed) by electronic data processing. An abbreviated example appears in Appendix C to illustrate the procedure.

Table 10.18. Annual revenue requirements for income tax; continuing plant.
30-year life, Type R₁ dispersion. Zero net salvage. MAR 6%;
50% debt at 4% interest. Statutory tax 48%. "Straight-line" depreciation
for books, SYD for taxes. "Flow-through" accounting.

Year	$T\%$	Year	$T\%$	Year	$T\%$
1	8.2983	21	22.3180	41	21.3645
2	9.3500	22	22.5076	42	21.4081
3	10.3716	23	22.6267	43	21.4674
4	11.3580	24	22.6998	44	21.5416
5	12.3459	25	22.7439	45	21.6301
6	13.2922	26	22.7351	46	21.7320
7	14.1905	27	22.6824	47	21.8728
8	15.0839	28	22.5959	48	22.0186
9	15.9230	29	22.4843	49	22.1681
10	16.7161	30	22.3554	50	22.3198
11	17.4859	31	22.2173	51	22.4729
12	18.1848	32	22.0766	52	22.6250
13	18.8668	33	21.9389	53	22.7745
14	19.4767	34	21.8091	54	22.9194
15	20.0532	35	21.6912	55	23.0571
16	20.5616	36	21.5881	56	23.1849
17	21.0328	37	21.5019	57	23.3005
18	21.4250	38	21.4343	58	23.4002
19	21.7927	39	21.3861	59	23.4838
20	22.0758	40	21.3578	60	23.5514

The important fact to be noted here is the year-by-year behavior of the tax for the continuing plant. It varies, as might be expected, in somewhat the same way as the renewal function, discussed before and illustrated in Appendix E. Eventually, the tax in each year settles down to a stabilized rate; the long-term-levelized equivalency is exactly the same as $T\%$ for a single initial placement calculated per the formulas of Chapter 8.

To illustrate the quantitative effect, Table 10.18 shows the annual revenue requirement for income tax for a continuing plant under the following conditions:

Average life = 30 years, Iowa Type R₁ dispersion.
Ultimate net salvage is zero.
MAR = 6%; 50% debt at 4% interest.
Statutory tax rate = 48%.
"Straight-line" depreciation is used for books, SYD for taxes.
"Flow-through" accounting is used.

$T\%$, per the formulas of Chapter 8, checked by this approach, equals 1.727%, before allowance for investment credit.

The year-by-year rate eventually stabilizes at 2.3087% after about 210 years (7 average-life cycles). Table 10.18 shows its behavior in the first 60 years (2 average-life cycles). This situation cannot be evaded by making the usual unrealistic assumption that service life of the replacement can be foreseen with 100% certainty and that no retirements will occur before or after that precise date (= Type SQ). Income tax still increases each successive year for a few initial years, in the general manner of Column 4, Table 8.6 (for 5-year life, Type SC), as the student can demonstrate to his own satisfaction by making a few test calculations.

Résumé

I. It is essential that the analyst start by delineating exactly "the project" whose profitability or economics are to be investigated.

II. Projects are desirably classified as:

1. A single placement ("decaying plant"), without consideration for replacements;
2. A static plant, including replacements as needed to just maintain the initial placement intact indefinitely;
3. A growing plant, including subsequent replacements plus further net additions; and
4. A shrinking plant, consisting of an initially static or growing plant, followed by a period of decay.

III. A major reason for such classification is the fact that life of the project is ordinarily greater than the service life of some or all of its components. This affects the nature of appropriate analyses of revenue requirements.

IV. The most desirable solution to problems in profitability and economic choice is the estimate of revenue requirements for contemplated single placements, throughout their lifetime, without consideration for replacements, when that technique is appropriate. This, however, is not the general case. For problems in economic choice, it is appropriate only: (a) when annual sales and revenues are identical for competing proposals; and (b) estimated service lives of competing assets are identical.

V. When sales and revenues are not identical for competing proposals, the problem becomes one of profitability rather than economic choice. In general, this problem demands estimates of sales and revenues in each year. A special case is sometimes encountered where decisions can be reached on the basis of cost per unit of output (where "cost" is in terms of revenue requirements).

VI. Estimated annual revenue requirements in dollars per year, representing probable annual quantities, decrease with passage of time for the single placement, whether that placement is one property unit (which must be retired at a single date) or a group of units subject to retirement dispersion. That is because probable surviving plant, $P_{\bar{x}}$, decreases with passage of time.

VII. When annual revenue requirements are estimated as a level amount, in dollars per year, the analyst must have envisioned a continuing plant, with probable retirements replaced "in kind" and at the same unit cost as the initial placement, indefinitely.

VIII. It is possible to calculate annual revenue requirements as a level amount, in dollars per year, for a single placement, in retrospect, when actual service life is known (= 100% probability) without envisioning a continuing plant. No replacements are then involved.

IX. When the life of a project exceeds the service life of its components, revenue requirements of the project would be underestimated if they did not allow for two separate and distinct factors: (a) the increase in the depreciation annuity resulting from dispersed retirements (not a function of replacements); and (b) the increase in capital investment and in related revenue requirements reflecting replacements.

X. Price inflation affects the capital investment necessary for replacements, even though they are "in kind."

XI. The "continuing plant" concept is a helpful device (often, the only possible means) for dealing with several awkward problems, such as:

1. Economic comparisons of plant which differ in service life;
2. Determination of the appropriate period of study;
3. Evaluation of the effects of possible price inflation;
4. Studies of economic replacement; and
5. Estimates of depreciated cost, rationally acceptable as representing "depreciated value."

XII. The expression for annual replacement rate necessary to maintain an initial placement intact as retirements occur is known as the "renewal function." It is readily calculated for any anticipated average life and type of dispersion, though the calculation may be regarded as "tricky" by those unfamiliar with it. A plant so maintained at its initial level is known as a "static plant."

XIII. A continuing plant, either static or growing at a regular rate, gradually stabilizes as to: (a) the renewal rate, and (b) the depreciation reserve, in percent of gross plant.

XIV. The renewal rate for static plant is a damped oscillatory curve which eventually settles down at an asymptote equal to 1/life. The corresponding depreciation reserve settles down at a percentage dependent upon the type of dispersion; not at 50%, as commonly assumed.

XV. Analyses of growing systems are commonly incompetent. The appropriate analysis consists in estimating PWAFRR, the present worth of all future revenue requirements of stipulated placements; that is, revenue requirements to eternity, not for any finite short period of years. Any analysis covering less than the total expectancy of life for estimated placements (to Year ω for the last placement) is manifestly an underestimate of the obligations (future revenue requirements) undertaken by the company in making the initial investment.

XVI. Because present worth of outlays more remote than 60 years (or so) are of relatively small significance, the nature of the project beyond the sixtieth year (single placement, static plant, growing plant, shrinking plant) is of small importance. This is the basic justification for use of PWAFRR as the criterion. It does not apply to short-term estimates of revenue requirements.

XVII. The calculation of PWAFRR is vastly simplified by using a special technique, treating each net addition as a separate static plant, whose revenue requirements are easily reduced to an aggregate present worth.

XVIII. Use of PWAFRR as the criterion of economic choice does not assume that replacements will in fact continue forever. It simply recognizes that present worth so calculated is a close approximation of the present worth (a) of the initial placements, throughout their service life, without replacement; (b) plus replacements as necessary to maintain each net addition as a static plant for a period of years equal to $\omega + t$ (that is, up to the date of the last retirement from the initial placements); plus (c) any reasonably anticipated behavior thereafter, whether decaying or static.

XIX. In order to acquire a "feel" for the behavior of revenue requirements of the several kinds of continuing plant, it is desirable to explore alternative manipulations of the data (gross plant versus net plant, gross additions versus net additions, Form X versus Form Y, alternative calculations of reserves, and so on). Material to facilitate such studies is included in Appendix E.

XX. For relatively long-lived plant PWRR (present worth of one generation of revenue requirements, including replacements through year ω) approaches PWAFRR (present worth "to eternity" of an infinite number of successive generations at the same unit cost). This fact provides a convenient index to minimum and maximum estimates of the obligation undertaken by a company when it makes a capital investment. Expressions for PWRR and PWAFRR, for convenient comparison are:

$$\text{PWRR (no replacements)} = P_0 + \frac{P_0 \cdot e}{i + \beta d} \qquad (1)$$

$$\text{PWRR (including replacements)} = a_{\overline{\omega}|} \cdot P_0 \cdot (i + \tfrac{\beta}{i} d + e) \qquad (2)$$

$$\text{PWAFRR ("to eternity")} = \frac{P_0}{i} \cdot (i + \tfrac{\beta}{i} d + e) \qquad (3)$$

XXI. Consideration must be given to adjustment for terminal inequalities; that is, for any inequality in capabilities (for potential output, sales, revenues) at the end of the period of predicted placements.

This chapter substantially completes our outline of the exact terms, exact intent, and arithmetic appropriate to implement both, which constitutes the Minimum Revenue Requirements Discipline. The analyst familiar with this organized course of reasoning now has a sound basis for reaching conclusions of his own. He will promptly discover that his conclusions so reached are frequently at odds with those reached by other routes. Accordingly, it may be helpful to consider exactly why that is so, and how serious the discrepancies and self-contradictions of other popular methods are apt to be. This will be a subject treated in Chapter 11.

Problems

1. Derive the renewal function, for 10 years, for 30, R_1.
2. How is the renewal function affected by:
   a. Net salvage
   b. Average life
   c. MAR
   d. Method of depreciation accounting ("straight-line," sinking-fund, SYD, DRDB)
   e. Type of retirement dispersion
   f. Price inflation
   g. Statutory income tax rate
   h. Amount of debt in the company's capital structure
3. Is the present worth of lifetime revenue requirements for capital recovery (return plus depreciation) always equal to the initial capital investment? Explain.
4. What are the exact differences among:
   a. Decaying plant
   b. Static plant
   c. Continuing plant
   d. Single placement
   e. Shrinking plant
Is this a matter of any practical importance, or is it purely academic? Explain.
5. It has been stated repeatedly that economic comparisons can be made by direct reference to revenue requirements if sales and revenues of competing proposals are identical. Explain exactly what is meant by:
   a. Competing proposals;
   b. Sales, as distinguished from revenues; and
   c. "Identical."
Suggest simple examples to illustrate misconceptions with respect to these terms which could result in wrong answers.
6. For plant having mortality characteristics of 30, R_1, when is net salvage realized, at age 30, or ω? Explain.
7. Sketch the renewal function, for four life cycles, for a single property unit having 10-year life: (a) in prospect, and (b) in retrospect. Discuss.
8. Describe several kinds of problems whose solution is facilitated by use of the "continuing plant" concept.
9. Revise Table 10.4 to allow for 10% negative net salvage.
10. Suggest a simple example (not from the text) to illustrate the difference between net additions and gross additions. Explain why this is of importance in the calculation of PWAFRR.
11. Why and when is PWAFRR little different from PWRR. What are the advantages, under such conditions, of accepting PWAFRR as the criterion of economic choice?
12. Exactly what is meant by "economic choice"?
13. Tables 10.6, 10.7, and 10.8 all present year-by-year system revenue requirements for the same system. Tables 10.7 and 10.8 agree on system totals each year but not on the components thereof. Table 10.6 differs as to annual totals and components thereof. Which version may be regarded as "actual" costs, and which as "financial equivalencies"? Explain.
14. Since Table 10.6 totals are greater in every year, present worth over any period whatever must be greater than for Tables 10.7 and 10.8. Yet the two approaches are said to be financially equivalent. How can that be? Explain fully.
15. A company maintains a large fleet of passenger automobiles of various

makes. It has collected information as to initial cost, operating and maintenance expense, and turn-in allowances. Its needs increase about 10% annually. It wishes to determine whether it should purchase only one make; if so, which one. How should the study be made:

    a. By comparing single placements over probable life of the average car:
       1. For a single typical car?
       2. For one year's net additions?
       3. For one year's gross additions?
    b. By comparing revenue requirements for:
       1. A static plant, the size of the present fleet?
       2. A plant starting at the present size of the fleet and growing 10% annually indefinitely?
    c. By investigating:
       1. Annual revenue requirements?
       2. Present worth of future revenue requirements?

    16. a. Since specifications of new models of automobiles change appreciably from year to year, to what extent is information collected concerning operation and maintenance expense of any value for estimating future expense? Especially if replacements are envisioned "to eternity"?

    b. Since it is future experience with repair costs, turn-in value, and so on, together with company policy that affects service life of cars, how useful is information collected with respect to service life in the past as an index to future revenue requirements for depreciation and income tax?

    c. In recent years, the company's salesmen have made greater use of rent-a-car service, instead of using company cars on long trips. That practice might increase, and if so, it would affect the company's need for a fleet of its own. Should not that be considered?

    d. On occasion, the company has considered leasing its fleet of passenger cars, instead of renting them. Is not that also a factor to be considered in this study?

    e. In view of all these uncertainties, is there not some truth in the assertion that principles of economic studies are necessarily loose and indefinite?

    17. The difference between (a) PWAFRR of Plan A, and (b) PWAFRR of competing Plan B is an amount of hard cash, in hand today, which is equivalent to exactly what?

    18. a. Exactly what is the difference between PWAFRR of a project, and the present worth of all its future revenues?

    b. What is the important difference between PWAFRR and PWRR of the same project? Explain how that difference affects one's choice of the preferred method of solution.

    19. In the text of this chapter, the revenue requirements tabulated in Table 10.1 were reduced to their present worth at the date of initial placement, by dividing lifetime-levelized quantities by $(i + {}_{i}^{\beta}d)$.

    Demonstrate that exactly the same present worth is obtained by multiplying year-by-year quantities by present worth factor v^n and totalizing.

    20. Columns 3, 4, and 5 of Table 10.1 were calculated in the manner of Form Y, where return = $iP_{\overline{x}}$, and depreciation is the associated annuity.

    a. Recalculate these data in the manner of Form X, where depreciation is the "straight-line" book charge for depreciation expense $(= P_{\overline{x}} \cdot {}_{0}d(1 - c)$ and return is the associated gross income.

    b. Demonstrate that the present worth of the recalculated data remains identical with that calculated in Problem 19.

    21. One of the classical problems which plague those who are not familiar with MRRD is the matter of "reinvestment rate." This problem arises from the

supposition that evaluation of a project depends upon future earnings on the reinvested depreciation reserves accumulated by the project. A few typical references appear below.[5]

In the numerous examples that have been advanced to support such reasoning, not one has recognized nor attempted to deal with two practical considerations which would contribute enormous complications:

    a. The fact that each periodic depreciation accrual would be reinvested in a different "other" project.

    b. The fact that each periodic depreciation accrual of each such "other" project would in turn be reinvested in still "other" projects, ad infinitum.

Discuss the following aspects of the situation in the light of what you have learned from the discussion of the continuing plant, in this chapter:

    a. For longer-lived plant, the complication is even more serious than apparent from the tables in this chapter. Explain.

    b. Each "other" project could be expected to differ in at least three important respects from the initial project, adding further complications which cannot be ignored. Explain.

    c. MRRD reveals that the whole "reinvestment rate" problem is actually nonexistent, being a misconception of fact arising from failure to respect two basic phenomena: the company-pool source of capital funds; and the exact nature of financial equivalency at "interest" rate MAR. Explain.

    d. But the tables of this chapter deal only with a special case never actually encountered in practical experience. Namely, each successive generation of placements has the same average life, type of dispersion, and net salvage as the initial placement. Explain why this has no bearing on the question at issue.

22. One might say that the "reinvestment-rate" fallacy (Problem 21) is a product of inexact definition of terms; that is, failure to define "the project" precisely, which is the first item in the decision process, Table 9.1.

Discuss that proposition, noting its relation to:

    a. The several definitions of "investment," to be carefully distinguished from each other, Chapter 1.

    b. Form X versus Form Y treatment of annual capital recovery costs, Chapter 3.

    c. Evaluation of a single initial placement versus a continuing plant, Chapter 10.

23. It is common practice to estimate annual revenue requirements of a project (or its "annual costs," which is not the same thing) at a level annual figure in dollars per year, representing a constant percentage applied to a fixed capital investment. It might be said that this implies that one of two assumptions has been made by the analyst: (a) Type SQ retirement dispersion, or (b) a continuing plant, with renewals "in kind."

But several important differences must be recognized between these two assumptions, which affect evaluation of the project. Explain.

---

[5] Eugene L. Grant and W. Grant Ireson, Principles of Engineering Economy, 4th ed. (The Ronald Press Co., New York, 1960), p. 514.

David V. Heebink, "Rate of Return, Reinvestment, and the Evaluation of Capital Expenditures," Journal of Industrial Engineering, Vol. XIII, No. 1 (January-February, 1962), p. 48.

John R. Canada, "A Comparison Between the Discounted Cash Flow Model and a Model Which Assumes an Explicit Reinvestment Rate for the Nonuniform Income Flow Case," The Engineering Economist, Vol. 9, No. 3 (April-May, 1964), p. 1.

Paul H. Jeynes, "The Significance of Reinvestment Rate," The Engineering Economist, Vol. 11, No. 1 (October-November, 1965), p. 1.

Eugene L. Grant, "Reinvestment of Cash Flow Controversy," The Engineering Economist, Vol. 11, No. 3 (April-May, 1966), p. 23.

11

. . . . . Methods Other . .
Than MRRD

A Grievous Condition[1]

At least eight "methods" of analysis other than MRRD are in general use.[2] Not one of them can be depended upon to accomplish their user's end purpose, which is to identify proposals expected to improve profit margins, maximize earnings per common share, and put the firm in the best competitive position by minimizing outlays of capital and expense to produce given sales and revenues. Our vaunted American know-how is not in evidence here.

These several methods, when applied to the same problem, yield as many different answers. They are apt to disagree as to which proposal is best; if by chance they do agree on the identity of the "best" proposal, they differ as to the amount of its superiority.

On the other hand, given reasonable estimates of the variables involved (no method of analysis can produce good answers from bad estimates), MRRD will unfailingly identify the proposal that accomplishes the analyst's exact intent, and MRRD also reveals that project's degree of superiority. Already demonstrated, this will be illustrated by further numerical examples.

It might be added that MRRD is neither new nor untested. It has for many years been in use, extensively though not always expertly, in the public utility and some associated industries. There are several reasons for its appeal to the public utility industry. Public utilities are keenly aware of the cost of new capital and its important bearing on their welfare. Their ratio of capital investment per dollar of sales is greater than for most other industries. Their growth has been rapid

---

[1] "It is a condition that confronts us — not a theory." Grover Cleveland, in his Annual Message of 1887.

[2] Among the methods other than MRRD, in common use, are:
1. Percentage Return, or "Investors'" Method
2. Payout (or Payback, or Payoff) Period Method
3. Annual Cost Method
4. Discounted Cash Flow (Profitability Index) Method
5. Capitalized Cost Method
6. MAPI Formula
7. Avoided Cost Method
8. The Test Year

and sustained. More capital has been sought from external sources by frequent new issues of stocks and bonds. Rate regulation forces attention on careful determinations of "cost of capital." Plant is typically long-lived; long-range planning is highly developed. Intercompany agreements related to gas, oil, and electric transmission lines and communication lines encourage agreement on all details of economic behavior. All these facts serve to call attention to the exact nature and behavior of MAR and its influence on rates, earnings, and budgeting decisions. As a result, the merits of MRRD are accentuated, and the faults of other methods are embarrassingly apparent.

MRRD is not just one more good method of analysis. It is the only procedure that can dependably accomplish the company's end objectives. A prevailing opinion that the principles involved in economic comparisons, unlike the principles of other technologies, are vague, loose, and uncertain is completely indefensible.[3] That disparaging comment is actually an appraisal of methods other than MRRD, not of basic principle. It is only MRRD that insists upon respect for basic principles that are not in dispute.

Nevertheless, there is urgent reason to study these methods other than MRRD, at least briefly, for the same purpose that Boy Scouts learn about the granny; that is, in order to be sure they will never mistake it for the dependable square knot they intend to tie. The granny looks something like a square knot, but it is a worthless device that does not accomplish its intended purpose. It lets go. Accordingly, we will look into some methods other than MRRD so that the student will be able to recognize and avoid their faults. Wrong methods would not be so widely accepted if their faults were readily apparent. In fact, some students may be reluctant (and properly so) to condemn them until satisfied that they are indeed mischief-makers, as described here for the first time. The Annual Cost Method will be given first attention, because it is most easily confused with MRRD.

Annual Cost Method

What can possibly be wrong with the Annual Cost Method? If the company selects proposals which minimize its annual costs, does not that accomplish its exact intent of maximizing profit margin, maximizing earnings per share, and placing the firm in the best competitive position?

The answer is that it does not. The principal reason why it does not ought to be readily apparent. A major component of "annual costs"

---

[3]For expressions of the opinion that principles of economic studies are vague, loose, and uncertain, see:

"Engineering Economy," Journal of Engineering Education (September, 1963), pp. 27, 28.

Also:

Patrick S. Kemp, "Controversies on the Construction of Financial Statements," Accounting Review (January, 1963).

is return. You cannot maximize earnings by adopting the proposals
that minimize return! A good deal more than this is wrong with the
Annual Cost Method, as will be shown. But this is the source of most
of the reasons why the Annual Cost Method cannot accomplish the company's end purpose. It does not minimize outlays of capital and expense, as MRRD does. It is not really an estimate of "costs" at all; it
is an estimate of revenues. Its name is misleading.

By definition, the Annual Cost Method includes as one "cost" a
stipulated attractive rate of return. A few advocates of this method
say "a stipulated minimum attractive rate of return." Whichever is
regarded as the exact intent, it remains an obvious fact that you cannot
accomplish your purpose by picking proposals that expect to make the
smallest attractive earnings. MRRD does not proceed in that way at
all. MRRD picks the proposals that make the largest earnings in excess of a base MAR. MAR is not an attractive rate of return; it is the
minimum acceptable return, less than the smallest attractive return by
the margin of Profit Incentive. MAR is truly a "cost"; "attractive return" is not. MAR is desirably minimized; "attractive return" is not.

The Annual Cost Philosophy

Those familiar with the Minimum Revenue Requirements Discipline (MRRD) will observe that if return is estimated at MAR, it cannot
be the Annual Cost Method. This, in turn, might prompt others to say
that MRRD, then, is just a special case of the Annual Cost Method, with
the estimate of "return" pegged at MAR instead of at an attractive return.

But the essential nature of that course of reasoning underlying the
Annual Cost Method, together with well-established attitudes associated
with it for many years, all well described as the Annual Cost Philosophy, provides compelling grounds for concluding otherwise.

To illustrate the difficulty, certain surgeons claim that girls can
now be transformed into boys if subjected to a drastic operation that
changes their essential characteristics. This suggests that a new addition be made to dictionary definitions of the word "boy": "A girl
whose essential characteristics have been radically changed by a drastic operation." Similarly, one might propose that MRRD be defined as:
"The Annual Cost Method after its essential characteristics have been
radically changed by a drastic operation." But neither proposal seems
necessary nor desirable.

Essential characteristics of the Annual Cost Method have become
associated with a number of harmful misunderstandings, both quantitative and qualitative. Some of the most obvious (but still commonly
overlooked) are as follows:

1. A quantitative error arises from the unsound definition and evaluation of "return," said to be an "attractive" rate. It is overlooked

that the attractive rate of earnings should not be minimized but should be maximized. It is overlooked that attractive rates of return depend upon earnings possibilities and risks of each separate project. It is not agreed which of the several percentages listed at the end of Chapter 3 is appropriate. The significance of "cost of capital" (Table 11.1) is ignored.

It is overlooked that benefits of adopting the superior plan may accrue variously to consumers (via reduced price of output), to investors (via increased earnings per share, and probable related increase in market price of securities), or partly to both; all without influencing identity of the economic choice from among the competing alternatives.

2. Qualitative errors are associated with the concept of "attractive rate." An attractive rate necessarily includes an attractive margin of Profit Incentive in excess of MAR. It is this Profit Incentive that measures profitability of a project in dollars; that is the only part of return subject to regulation in public utility practice; that makes the free enterprise system work. No one raises capital at a cost of $i\%$ in order to reinvest it at that same $i\%$. It is this Profit Incentive which the Annual Cost Method ignores; indeed, it insists that profit incentive does not exist.

3. Errors in estimates of income taxes flow out of the foregoing fallacies. Because income is improperly designated, income tax is improperly calculated. It is overlooked that of the two components of income tax payable ($T\%$ and $T'\%$), only one ($T\%$) is involved in economic comparisons. It is incorrectly concluded that public utility taxes must be calculated on a basis different from that appropriate for nonregulated industries. It is incorrectly concluded that income tax reduces interest costs of debt.

4. All compounding, discounting, and annuitizing operations yield incorrect answers, because an improper "interest" rate is used. (See Chapter 5.) Every individual levelized "annual cost" is incorrect for this reason, particularly depreciation, income tax, and taxes levied on sales or on gross receipts.

5. A number of fallacious conclusions flow from the unsound concept of financial equivalency (Item 4) that is inherent in the Annual Cost Method. Among them are the notions that reinvestment opportunities must be assumed always available at the same rate of earnings as for the project under study; that present worth of lifetime earnings plus depreciation must equal initial capital investment for a project; and that "capitalized cost" comparisons assume perpetual lives.

All these faults and others are illustrated by numerical problems in this chapter or elsewhere. One of the most striking examples of the mischief attributable to the Annual Cost Philosophy appears in Chapter 14 which deals with public utility economics.

Table 11.1. The significance of cost of capital.

The company's pool of investors' committed capital = $400,000. 10,000 shares of common stock outstanding, issued at $40 per share. Current earnings are $4 per share = $40,000 per year = 10% return. A new project is proposed; capital investment $100,000.

Part I. The new project will earn $9,000 per year. This is 9% return, or less than the company is already earning. Should the proposal therefore be rejected?

The new capital is raised by issuing 2,000 new common shares at $50 per share (that is, above book value of $40).

Company Earnings

Before adopting the project:

$$\frac{40,000}{400,000} = 10.0\%$$
$$\frac{40,000}{10,000} = \$4.00 \text{ per share}$$

After adopting the project:

$$\frac{49,000}{500,000} = 9.8\% \text{ (Down)}$$
$$\frac{49,000}{12,000} = \$4.08 \text{ per share (Up)}$$

"Newcomers'" Earnings

$4.08 per share

$$\frac{4.08}{50} = 8.16\%$$

Pre-Project Owners' Earnings

Before adopting the project:

$4.00 per share

$$\frac{4.00}{40} = 10.00\%$$

After adopting the project:

$4.08 per share

$$\frac{4.08}{40} = 10.20\% \text{ (Up)}$$

Conclusion: In the stockholders' best interests, the project should be adopted, even though it reduces the company's percentage return from 10.0% to 9.8%.

Part II. The new project will earn $11,000 per year. This is 11% return, or more than the company is already earning. Should the project therefore be adopted?

The new capital is raised by issuing 3,000 new common shares at $33.33 per share (that is, below book value of $40).

Company Earnings

Before adopting the project:

$$\frac{40,000}{400,000} = 10.0\%$$
$$\frac{40,000}{10,000} = \$4.00 \text{ per share}$$

After adopting the project:

$$\frac{51,000}{500,000} = 10.2 \text{ (Up)}$$
$$\frac{51,000}{13,000} = \$3.92 \text{ per share (Down)}$$

Newcomers' Earnings

$3.92 per share

$$\frac{3.92}{33.33} = 11.76\%$$

Pre-Project Owners' Earnings

Before adopting the project:

$4.00 per share

$$\frac{4.00}{40} = 10.0\%$$

After adopting the project:

$3.92 per share

$$\frac{3.92}{40} = 9.80\% \text{ (Down)}$$

Conclusion: In the stockholders' best interests, the project should not be adopted, even though it increases the company's percentage return from 10.0% to 10.2%.

The Moral: Prospective percentage return of a project is not a safe test of the profitability or economic choice of projects. It is not a safe test to compare the prospective percentage return with any "bench mark" percentage other than the long-term cost of financing, that is, minimum acceptable return (MAR) as exactly defined herein.

A Numerical Example of Annual Costs

A motor freight trucking company is considering purchase of an electronic computer to handle economic load dispatching, otherwise the assignment of a large scattered group of employees.

The major difference between the two alternatives is the large investment in the computer, which requires a small number of technicians, versus the large outlay for salaries and fringe benefits for the alternative plan, which involves a relatively small investment in furniture and desk calculators. Building space is substantially the same in either case.

Probable life of the computer is placed at 15 years. Less than 8 years or more than 20 is regarded as most unlikely; Iowa Type R_3 dispersion best reflects this situation. Because of certain special features of design, zero net salvage is anticipated. The alternative smaller investment in desk calculators and furniture has a longer potential life than 15 years, but growth of the business suggests that within that period conversion to Electronic Data Processing will be a necessity. Accordingly, the same life characteristics are assigned to both groups of assets. However, ultimate net salvage of the calculators and furniture is expected to be 20%.

Over many years, earnings of the company have averaged 10% of investors' committed capital, and they are tending to increase. A target return of 12% over the next 15 years is conservatively anticipated. MAR has been quite steady at near 7% and is expected to decrease slightly in the future as earnings per share rise.

The company has outstanding debt amounting to 20% of its capitalization, on which it pays 5% interest. This policy is expected to continue in the foreseeable future. It practices double-rate declining-balance depreciation (DRDB) for taxes, "straight-line" for books, and "flow-through." For simplicity, ignore investment credit. Statutory income tax rate is 48%, which is expected to continue. No taxes are levied on sales nor gross receipts.

The Annual Cost analysis based on this information appears in Table 11.2. A footnote explains the estimates of depreciation and income tax. As indicated in the footnote, it is not entirely certain that advocates of the Annual Cost technique would estimate depreciation and income tax in this manner, since they substantially always overlook effects of retirement dispersion. Furthermore, textbooks dealing with the Annual Cost Method fail to treat income tax properly. However, they will be given the benefit of the doubt; our main purpose here is to focus attention on the unsound general approach rather than on such details.[4]

Compare the Annual Cost estimate of Table 11.2 with the estimate of annual revenue requirements, Table 11.3. The estimate of annual

---

[4] Investment credit is ignored "for simplicity," because it is uncertain how it would be treated by users of the Annual Cost Method.

Table 11.2. The annual cost analysis (an incorrect solution).

	Plan A (Computer)		Plan B (Manual)
Capital Investment	$1,000,000		$100,000
"Annual Costs"			
Return at 12%	$120,000 per year		$ 12,000 per year
Depreciation ($^\beta_{12}d = 3.13\%$)*	31,300	(x 0.80)	2,500
Federal income tax†	59,300		6,800
Operation and maintenance	30,000		170,000
Total "Annual Costs"	$240,600 per year		$191,300 per year

Conclusion: Plan B (Manual) appears to be superior by a substantial margin.

---

*Since Annual Cost advocates customarily overlook effects of retirement probability (dispersion), it is more likely that they would underestimate depreciation as:

Plan A: 2.68%
Plan B: 0.80 x 2.68% = 2.14%

This would also affect their estimate of income tax. However, to focus attention on the main issue we will assume that the depreciation annuity is estimated as above.

†It is impossible to guess exactly what estimates of income tax would be made by users of the Annual Cost Method, since they do not agree among themselves and no published procedures can be justified. As in the case of depreciation, to focus attention on the main issue, we will assume that Formula 8.3, Chapter 8, is used. This still leaves in doubt the value that would be assigned to d_t, since no tables of d_t for return at 12% are available.

Since the estimate of taxes is not critical (the Annual Cost analysis would select Plan B in any event) we will assign d_t the rounded value of 8.00% (compare with 7.52% in Table 11.3), and assume that the tax would be estimated as follows:

Plan A: $\frac{0.48}{0.52} \left[(12.00 + 3.13 - 6.67) (1 - \frac{0.20 \times 5}{12}) - (8.00 - 6.67) \right] = 5.93\%$

Plan B: $\frac{0.48}{0.52} \left[(12.00 + 0.80 \times 3.13 - 0.80 \times 6.67) (1 - \frac{.20 \times 5}{12}) - 0.80 (8.00 - 6.67) \right] = 6.79\%$

revenue requirements does not quite satisfy the analyst's exact intent in this case. It was specifically assumed that the probability of P_0 (initial capital investment) remaining in service each year would diminish gradually, per the Type R_3 survivor curve. Accordingly, the intended criterion, if replacements are not to be considered, is a comparison of present worths of lifetime revenue requirements for the single placement, as shown in Table 11.4.

This quantitatively correct analysis confirms the qualitative conclusion reached by comparing annual revenue requirements; Plan A (computer) is preferred by a wide margin. The Annual Cost selection (Table 11.2) is not correct.

We might say that this confirmation of Table 11.3 conclusions was to be expected. That is, if no partial retirements were made before the date when the whole installation is retired all at once, then the capital investment in service each year would remain constant at initial cost P_0 (= $1,000,000 for Plan A; $100,000 for Plan B). The unknown factor is the date of final retirement.

In such case, annual revenue requirements would favor Plan A (computer) by:

Table 11.3. Annual revenue requirements
(same problem as Table 11.2).

	Plan A (Computer)	Plan B (Manual)
MAR at 7%	$ 70,000 per year	$ 7,000 per year
Depreciation ($\frac{\beta}{i}d$ at 4.25%; Table 6.18)	42,500	3,400
Federal income tax*	28,400	3,400
Operation and maintenance	30,000	170,000
Total annual revenue requirements	$170,900 per year	$183,800 per year

*Federal income tax, per Formula 8.3 of Chapter 8:

Plan A
$$\frac{0.48}{0.52}\left[(7.00 + 4.25 - 6.67)(1 - \frac{0.20 \times 5}{7}) - (7.52 - 6.67)\right] = 2.84\%$$

Plan B
$$\frac{0.48}{0.52}\left[(7.00 + 0.80 \times 4.25 - 0.80 \times 6.67)(1 - \frac{0.20 \times 5}{7}) - (0.80 \times 7.52 - 0.80 \times 6.67)\right] = 3.38\%$$

Conclusion: Contrary to the Annual Cost solution, Plan A (Computer) is superior.

$$183,800 - 170,900 = \$12,900 \text{ per year (Table 11.3)}$$

This represents lifetime-levelized equivalent, in every year of service life. The exact number of years is indefinite, but it is probably not less than 8 nor more than 20, as expressed by the 15, Type R_3 assumption.

The difference in present worths of that lifetime annual differential is a perfectly definite figure, per Table 11.4:

$$1,633,800 - 1,519,100 = \$114,700$$

It may be calculated by dividing the annual differential ($12,900) by the capital-recovery factor for 15, Type R_3, with MAR at 7%:

Table 11.4. Present worth of lifetime revenue requirements of Table 11.3.

Plan A

Present worth of return + depreciation (= initial investment) =	$1,000,000
Present worth of other revenue requirements	
$= \dfrac{28,400 + 30,000}{i + \beta_7 d} = \dfrac{58,400}{11.25\%} =$	519,100
Total present worth, Plan A	$1,519,100

Plan B

Present worth of return + depreciation	
$= \dfrac{7,000 + 3,400}{i + \beta_7 d} = \dfrac{10,400}{11.25\%} =$	$ 92,500*
Present worth of other revenue requirements	
$= \dfrac{3,400 + 170,000}{i + \beta_7 d} = \dfrac{173,400}{11.25\%} =$	1,541,300
Total present worth, Plan B	$1,633,800

*Note that present worth of "return + depreciation" is less than initial capital investment (= $100,000) by an amount equal to present worth of ultimate net salvage.

$$i + \frac{\beta}{7}d = 7.00 + 4.25 = 11.25\%$$

$$12,900/11.25\% = \$114,700$$

Clearly, the Annual Cost estimate of Table 11.2 was incompetent; it selected the wrong proposal as superior.

To illustrate further, assume <u>any</u> annual revenues whatever. The only stipulation is that they be the <u>same</u> for Plan A as for Plan B. Let's say revenues are $240,600 in each year. This represents the Annual Cost figure for Plan A, in Table 11.2. Then adoption of the computer would result in a Profit Incentive of $36,244 annually, as follows:

Annual revenues	
(arbitrarily from Plan A, Table 11.2)	$240,600 per year
Annual revenue requirements	
(Plan A, Table 11.3)	170,900
Difference (= Profit Incentive + tax thereon)	$ 69,700
Income tax on Profit Incentive at 48%	33,456
Profit Incentive, by difference	$ 36,244 per year

On the other hand, if Plan B (manual) were adopted, then out of those same revenues Profit Incentive would be only $29,536 annually:

Annual revenues	
(= "annual costs" of Plan A, Table 11.2)	$240,600 per year
Annual revenue requirements	
(Plan B, Table 11.3)	183,800
Difference (= Profit Incentive + tax thereon)	56,800
Income tax on Profit Incentive at 48%	27,264
Profit Incentive, by difference	$ 29,536 per year

This means that existing (pre-project) owners of the business, before adoption of the proposal, would have their earnings increased by $36,244 per year, in every year of service life, if Plan A (computer) is adopted.

If Plan B (manual) were adopted, as recommended by the Annual Cost analysis, existing owners would have their earnings increased by only $29,536 per year. In both cases, this is assuming revenues at $240,600 a year.

That <u>differential</u> in favor of Plan A (computer) of $6,708 per year (= 36,244 - 29,536) remains the same <u>whatever the amount of identical revenues may be</u>. Existing owners need not contribute one cent of the new capital investment, if they do not care to. This is the way to decide whether a solution is "correct" or not.

A few helpful comments:

1. Selecting Plan A (computer) will result in greater improvement in earnings per share than Plan B (manual). That might result in an increased market price of company stock sufficient to <u>decrease</u> MAR slightly. Such a result would tend to accentuate the advantage of Plan A (computer).

2. The analysis of annual revenue requirements in this particular
   problem may be regarded as an acceptable shortcut in place of the
   present worth analysis, which in turn is an acceptable shortcut solution in place of the Profit Incentive evaluation which is the exact
   intent of the study.
3. In most cases, the Annual Cost Method favors alternatives calling
   for smaller capital investment, because most percentage return and
   taxes are overstated. Thus, it tends to discourage automation or
   other proposals for improving efficiency by increasing capital investment. The Annual Cost Method makes leasing equipment look
   more attractive than owning the same facilities, because it usually
   overstates costs of ownership. Even when it picks the right alternative, it fails to evaluate its degree of superiority with accuracy.
4. In brief, the Annual Cost Method is a dangerously incompetent procedure. Furthermore, it is no simpler than the MRRD analysis.[5]

The Percentage Return or "Investors'" Method

The term "Investors'" Method is misleading semantics, because
investors do not look to percentage return on incremental capital investment to gauge the desirability of investing in a company. They
look at earnings per share for the firm as a whole. And that is not at
all the same thing, as demonstrated in Table 2.1 on page 19 and Table
11.1.

Although the basic error in the Percentage Return approach is
amply demonstrated by Tables 2.1 and 11.1, it may be of interest to
consider a practical example of the unwise and unintended decisions
that are engendered by relying on percentage return as a criterion.[6]
There is little doubt but that the Percentage Return Method is responsible for millions of dollars of losses each year from illogical decisions; only the Payoff Period Method has a worse record.

Dozens of books on budgeting, systems engineering, electronic
date processing, and advanced analytical techniques in business management have been published which treat their subject with great competence — down to the final topic which is the ultimate purpose of the
whole undertaking: the investment decision. That is made by the Percentage Return Method; all the elegant technique has been wasted on a
wrong and unintended conclusion.

Following is a simplified example illustrating one kind of error in
reasoning invited by relying on the Percentage Return philosophy. It

---

[5] Arbitrary omission of items considered difficult to estimate is not simplification. It
amounts to making the firm and unjustified assumption that such items are costs which will
be incurred in any event, whichever project is adopted or rejected. An even more impres-
sive example of wrong conclusions reached by the Annual Cost Method appears in Chapter 14.
  [6] For a scholarly confirmation of the faults of the Percentage Return Method, see:
  William Beranek, "A Note on the Equivalence of Certain Capital Budgeting Criteria,"
Accounting Review (October, 1964), p. 914.

should be stated in advance that the cost estimates in this example are deliberately fictitious, in order to avoid any suspicion of ulterior motive in suggesting this comparison of electricity versus gas for space heating.

A combination (electric and gas) public utility offers its customers both electricity and gas for residential space heating. Revenue requirements for either service to a given house are identical. Total revenue requirements, if all of the company's sales were supplied by one department (electric or gas), would be as in Table 11.5. The capital investment for electric supply is substantially greater because the company generates its own power. The capital investment for gas supply is relatively small; the company purchases natural gas from an outside supplier, so production plant is unnecessary. MAR is 6%, and the company's tariff schedules provide a satisfactory Profit Incentive.

An abbreviated version of annual revenue requirements for the continuing plant appears in Table 11.5.

Identical revenue requirements indicate that there is no economic choice between the two alternatives. Existing rate schedules would mean revenues of the same $60,000,000 per year in either case; hence, Profit Incentive is identical in either case. Percentage return, though, is substantially greater for gas service, as shown in Table 11.6.

The gas department, jubilant at this result, claims that existing tariff schedules for gas could be reduced substantially, the company could still make the same 7.30% return as for electric supply, and more new business would be acquired from customers now heating with oil or coal who would be attracted by the bargain rate for gas. To illustrate, suppose rates are lowered to bring in revenues of $56,250,000 (instead of $60,000,000) for the same output as Tables 11.5 and 11.6, as shown in Table 11.7.

Is anything wrong in the resultant decision to forget about electric heating, to adopt a reduced promotional rate for gas service, and to authorize spending some money for the "hard sell" to maximize new business of this class? As an added inducement, it would be necessary to obtain only $50,000,000 of new capital, as compared to $200,000,000 for electric service. A great deal is wrong with the proposal, as will be seen.

Problems of this kind occur frequently in the experience of

Table 11.5. Annual revenue requirements.

Electric Service (Capital investment $200,000,000)	
MAR at 6%	$12,000,000 per year
Expenses	43,000,000
Revenue requirements	$55,000,000 per year
Gas Service (Capital investment $50,000,000)	
MAR at 6%	$ 3,000,000 per year
Expenses (largely fuel)	52,000,000
Revenue requirements	$55,000,000 per year

Table 11.6. Percentage return analysis (a misleading criterion).

Electric or Gas Service	
Revenues	$60,000,000 per year
Revenue requirements (Table 11.5)	55,000,000
Available for Profit Incentive plus tax thereon	5,000,000
Less income tax at 48% of $5,000,000	2,400,000
Profit Incentive, by difference	$ 2,600,000 per year
Percentage Return, Electric	
Profit Incentive, as above	$ 2,600,000 per year
MAR at 6% of $200,000,000	12,000,000
Total annual earnings, electric supply	$14,600,000 per year

$$\text{Percentage return, electric} = \frac{14,600,000}{200,000,000} = \underline{\underline{7.30\%}}$$

Percentage Return, Gas	
Profit Incentive, as above	$ 2,600,000 per year
MAR at 6% of $50,000,000	3,000,000
Total annual earnings, gas service	$ 5,600,000 per year

$$\text{Percentage return, gas} = \frac{5,600,000}{50,000,000} = \underline{\underline{11.20\%}}$$

Conclusion: Gas heating appears to be superior, contrary to the MRRD conclusion of Table 11.5.

companies which sell mutually competing products, such as cigarettes and cigars, nylon and rayon, oleomargarine and "the high-priced spread," Chevromobiles and Pontuicks, liquid detergents and soap powder, and other similar combinations.

Whatever number of common shares may be outstanding before adoption of this project, MAR included in revenue requirements satisfies return on the new shares; Profit Incentive flows to the pre-project shares. (See Tables 2.1 and 11.1.) Thus, if there were 12,000,000 common shares, pre-project, Table 11.6 indicates that earnings per share would increase by 2,600,000/12,000,000 = 21.7 cents per share, whether electric or gas supply is adopted.

Table 11.7 proposes to reduce that Profit Incentive to $650,000 per year, which is one-fourth of $2,600,000. Instead of 21.7 cents, the increase in per-share earnings would be only 5.4 cents, a 75% reduction in Profit Incentive. In addition, the reduced earnings per share would

Table 11.7. Percentage return analysis; gas service at reduced rate
(same output as Tables 11.5 and 11.6).

Adjusted revenues	$56,250,000 per year
Revenue requirements (Table 11.5)	55,000,000
Available for Profit Incentive plus tax thereon	1,250,000
Less income tax at 48% of $1,250,000	600,000
Profit Incentive, by difference	650,000
Plus MAR at 6% of $50,000,000	3,000,000
Total annual earnings, at adjusted rate	$ 3,650,000 per year

$$\text{Adjusted percentage return, gas} = \frac{3,650,000}{50,000,000} = 7.30\%, \underline{\text{the same as electric.}}$$

certainly affect market price per share; if **MAR** is 6% under conditions of Tables 11.5 and 11.6, it must increase if the proposal of Table 11.7 were adopted. New financing will cost more. Revenue requirements, Table 11.7, would not be $55,000,000, but appreciably more. Revenue requirements of all the company's assets would increase, not just those of this particular project. All the company's classes of service would suffer a decrease in profitability!

A glance at Profit Incentive, Table 11.7 versus Table 11.6, tells the story. Profit Incentive in Table 11.6 is $2,600,000 per year, for either electric or gas. This is the amount that flows to existing owners of the business to increase earnings per pre-project share of stock. These pre-project owners need not contribute one cent of the new capital if the financing is done externally.

As for claimed advantages of the smaller capital investment in gas facilities in the standoff situation of Table 11.5, review the discussion of Appendix B. Ordinarily the larger investment (in electric facilities) could be expected to have some small advantage.

Table 11.8 illustrates the foregoing general problem graphically, in the manner of the Diagram of Intent.

In brief, the profitability or economic superiority of projects cannot be safely gauged by looking at their percentage return, whether that percentage is determined correctly or not. This comment applies not only to the Percentage Return Method ("Investors'" Method), but to the Discounted Cash Flow Method or any other that depends upon this unsafe criterion.

Table 11.8. The "percentage return" fallacy.

Plan A and Plan B have identical Profit Incentive (in dollars/per year) out of identical revenues from identical sales. Therefore, they are equally profitable; there is no choice between them. But earnings of Plan A are a larger % of the smaller investment. Plan A appears to be superior; actually it is not.

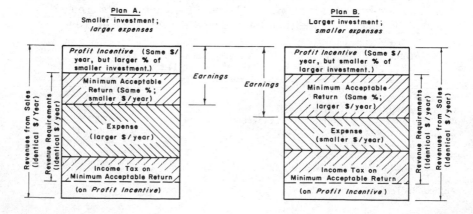

The "Test Year"

The "Test Year" is a crude method of analysis still encountered occasionally, though in recent times its shortcomings have been fairly generally appreciated, and it is falling into disuse. It attempts to determine the merits of proposals by setting up financial statements (income statements and/or balance sheets) for one or a few test years. Almost always the first year of operation of a proposed project is selected for examination, though sometimes an arbitrary choice is made of several later years.

More sophisticated businessmen realize that the buyer of new equipment commits himself to revenue requirements for at least the whole service lifetime of the facilities, so that any worthwhile analysis must cover at least that life span. Future replacements and possible growth may make an even longer term of study necessary. It is this situation that demands either year-by-year analyses or their more efficient lifetime-levelized equivalencies or the present worth treatment.

The Discounted Cash Flow Method

The Discounted Cash Flow Method is one device developed to deal with the relation of lifetime-levelized quantities to a single initial capital outlay.

As ordinarily employed, it starts with an estimate of annual revenues, either year-by-year or lifetime-levelized. All expenses are subtracted except for return and depreciation, which are thus represented by the difference and identified as "cash flow." This quantity (amounts available for return plus depreciation) is reduced to an annuity, $1/a_{\overline{n}|}$, which will be recognized as equal to $(i + {}_id)$.[7] That is, $1/a_{\overline{n}|}$ is the annuity, at some "interest" rate to be discovered, which will just recover the initial capital investment (less ultimate net salvage) in service life of n years.

By setting n equal to service life and consulting a table of values for $1/a_{\overline{n}|}$ (or of $a_{\overline{n}|}$), it is possible to discover the rate $i\%$ at which lifetime annual "cash flows" must be discounted to yield a present worth equal to initial capital investment; hence the name of the method. The value of $i\%$ so determined is then interpreted as in the Percentage Return or "Investors'" Method. The two methods share the same shortcomings in this respect.

The Discounted Cash Flow Method has other shortcomings. Like the Annual Cost Method, it ignores the difference between MAR and actual return (that is, it overlooks Profit Incentive). As a result it discounts at the wrong "interest" rate; it is incorrect in principle. Like the Annual Cost Method, it customarily ignores effects of retirement dispersion. It is extremely difficult, though technically not absolutely

---

[7]See Chapter 5.

impossible, to make correct allowance for retirement dispersion in estimating depreciation as well as income tax in this method. In practice, neither is ever attempted. The Discounted Cash Flow Method assumes a single service life for all assets involved in the project; it is difficult, if not impossible, to apply to projects made up of components having various service lives.

Because practical application is so difficult, correct solutions rarely are made in this manner. For example, in actual experience, net salvage is commonly treated improperly.

Both the economic usage and the financial usage suffer from inexact definitions of terms and of intent. The popularity of both seems to spring more from the impressively "technical" appearance of the technique than from any completely understood actual merits. In brief, the Discounted Cash Flow Method is not an appropriate procedure for making studies in profitability and economic choice. Its use has been responsible for many reduced profit margins.

A Numerical Example, Discounted Cash Flow

In order to simplify this illustration, we will assume that it is a post-audit, made after the event. All revenues and outlays for Plan X are known. The question asked is whether Plan Y, originally considered but rejected in favor of Plan X, would have been superior, had it been looked at with benefit of hindsight.

This makes it possible to eliminate from this illustrative example several awkward features of the Discounted Cash Flow approach, such as forecasts of revenues (which presumably are known or discoverable, after the event) and failure to consider retirement probability (not necessary after the event, because actual life is then known). It also permits using a simplified estimate of income taxes. In further interests of simplicity, it will be assumed that there is no debt in the company's capital structure, zero net salvage, "straight-line" depreciation for books and for taxes, a 50% statutory tax rate, and that all facilities involved in either project would have had exactly the same life (20 years).[8]

All these simplifying assumptions, which ordinarily would be impossible in any practical application of the method, are made in order to make details of the example easy to comprehend and check. Thus, it is easy to concentrate attention on basic faults of the Discounted Cash Flow Method rather than on these awkward but less important features of its practical application.

The problem is described in Table 11.9, which presents the simple

---

[8]To observe the complications introduced in this method, by giving proper regard to retirement dispersion probabilities (including their effect on income taxes), the student will be asked to repeat the solution, making such allowances, in Problem 2 at the end of the chapter. It can be done, with the help of the tables of $_i^\beta d$ in Chapter 6, and the tax formulas of Chapter 8. But it is rarely done in actual practice, which adds to the undesirability of this method.

MRRD solution. It will be seen that there was no choice between Plans X and Y; either one would have been equally profitable. Table 11.9 also explains the simplified tax calculation, which would have represented the exact figure under the circumstances assumed.

The conclusion remains the case whatever the revenues may have been, so long as they were the same for both X and Y; Profit Incentive for Plan X would have been the same as for Plan Y, out of any given revenues.

Now let's look at the Discounted Cash Flow solution, which starts with an estimate of revenues. We will investigate the situation for three different amounts of annual revenues:

Table 11.10. Revenues for either project just equal to the revenue requirements of Table 11.7, at $286,600 per year.

Table 11.11. Revenues for either project at $366,600 per year, or $80,000 more than revenue requirements.

Table 11.12. Revenues for either project at $246,600 per year, or $40,000 less than revenue requirements.

Table 11.10 (revenues just equal to revenue requirements) appears to confirm the MRRD conclusion of Table 11.9; Plans X and Y are a standoff. In other words, if revenues, by happy accident, are such that

Table 11.9. The revenue requirement analysis.

	Plan X	Plan Y
Capital investment	$1,000,000	$1,500,000
MAR at 6%	$ 60,000 per year	$ 90,000 per year
Depreciation (20-year life, Type SQ, no salvage)*	27,200	40,800
Federal income tax †	37,200	55,800
All other expenses	162,200	100,000
	$286,600 per year	$286,600 per year

Conclusion: There was no choice between the two proposals. They would have been equally economic and would have produced identical Profit Incentives out of the same revenues.

There is no need for a present worth calculation in this instance; but here it is, if of interest:

Present worth of return plus depreciation	$1,000,000	$1,500,000
Present worth of all other expenses	2,286,697	1,786,697
Total present worth	$3,286,697	$3,286,697

*See Table 6.17, Chapter 6. Type SQ signifies no dispersion of retirements.
†Per Basic Formula 8.1, Chapter 8:

$$T\% = \frac{t}{1 - t} (i + {}_i d - {}_o d) (1 - \frac{Bb}{i})$$

$$= \frac{.50}{1 - .50} (6.00 + 2.72 - \frac{1}{20}) (1 - \frac{0 \times 0}{6}) = 3.72\%,$$

which is also minimal gross income ($= i + {}_i d - {}_o d$). Hence the simplification of Tables 10.10, 10.11, and 10.12. See footnote, Table 11.10.

the rate of return turns out to be MAR, no more and no less, then the Discounted Cash Flow Method yields the correct solution.[9] This is provided, of course, that all the appropriate allowances for retirement dispersion, net salvage, liberalized depreciation, investment credit, deductible interest, and so on, are correctly made — awkward in the Discounted Cash Flow Method, easy in the MRRD approach. But in such case (return discovered to be just equal to MAR), projects are not worth undertaking; they produce no Profit Incentive. In other words, <u>if</u>

Table 11.10. Discounted cash flow solution 1 for the problem of Table 11.9. Annual revenues $286,600, just equal to revenue requirements. <u>No Profit Incentive.</u>

	Plan X	Plan Y
Annual revenues	$286,600	$286,600
Less taxes* and all expenses except		
depreciation	199,400	155,800
Annual "cash flow"	$ 87,200	$130,800
Present worth of a 20-year annuity, per		
interest tables, at trial interest		
rate (6%): $a_{\overline{20}|}$ =	11.4699	11.4699
Present worth of "cash flow"	87,200 x 11.4699	130,800 x 11.4699
	= $1,000,000	= $1,500,000

Since the trial calculation of present worth of each flow, at 6% discount rate, equals initial capital investment, the apparent rate of return is:

$$6.00\% \qquad\qquad 6.00\%$$

<u>Conclusion:</u> The same as in Table 11.9; there is no choice between the two plans.

---

*How could the amount of taxes be discovered, were it not available in Table 11.9, the revenue requirements analysis? By expressing the tax in relation to gross income, always possible. Under our simplified assumption, tax at 50% = lifetime-levelized Form X gross income = $i + {}^{\beta}_{i}d - {}_{0}d$.

To illustrate, for Plan X above:

Revenues - income tax - all other expenses = Form Y return and depreciation.

$286,600 - (i + {}^{\beta}_{i}d - {}_{0}d) P_{0} - 162,200 = (i + {}^{\beta}_{i}d) P_{0}$, where gross income (Form X) is $(i + {}^{\beta}_{i}d - {}_{0}d) P_{0}$, and "cash flow" is $(i + {}^{\beta}_{i}d) P_{0}$.

For the trial value of i at 6%:

$$iP_{0} = \$60,000$$
$$\text{plus } {}^{\beta}_{6}dP_{0} = \underline{\ 27,200}$$
$$\text{"Cash flow"} = \$87,200$$

$$\text{less } {}_{0}dP_{0} \text{ at } \underline{\ 50,000} \ (= \frac{1,000,000}{20})$$

Gross income = tax = $37,200 per year, per simplified assumptions

Under present tax schedules, allowing for liberalized depreciation, the investment credit and a 48% tax rate, the tax would be approximately 54.3% of gross income (see Formula 8.4, Chapter 8), or about $20,200 per year, instead of 100%.

---

[9]The same thing might be said of the Annual Cost Method; if the "attractive" percentage return selected happens to coincide with MAR, the Annual Cost Method would yield the correct solution. But an awkward self-contradiction still arises. The rate of return which yields the correct solution cannot possibly be described as "attractive," since it is <u>less</u> than the minimal attractive percentage (= cutoff rate), which exceeds MAR by the amount of minimal Profit Incentive. Nobody raises capital at a cost of MAR% in order to reinvest it "attractively" at the same MAR%.

a project is worth adopting, the Discounted Cash Flow Method can be counted on to give a wrong answer. This is demonstrated by Table 11.11.

In Table 11.11, revenues are $366,600 annually, or $80,000 greater than revenue requirements. This means that, with an income tax of 50%, there would be a Profit Incentive of $40,000 per year whichever plan is adopted:

$$\text{Revenue requirements less revenues} = \$80,000 \text{ per year}$$
$$\text{Income tax } (T'\%) \text{ at } 50\% = \underline{\quad 40,000}$$
$$\text{Profit Incentive, by difference} = \$40,000 \text{ per year}$$

But the Discounted Cash Flow solution of Table 11.11 does not agree. It seems to show that Plan X is superior; return appears to be 11.20%, against 9.55% for Plan Y. A similar difficulty arises if revenues are less than revenue requirements. This is illustrated by Table 11.12. In this case, however, it is Plan Y that appears to be superior (4.04% against 3.00% for Plan X), although it really is not. It is still a standoff.

In brief, the Discounted Cash Flow (Profitability Index) Method might be cynically described as a complicated way to obtain incorrect answers. It is apt to pick the wrong alternative. If, by happy accident,

Table 11.11. Discounted cash flow solution 2 for the problem of Table 11.9. Annual revenues $366,600, equal to revenue requirements plus $80,000. Here there is a Profit Incentive.

	Plan X	Plan Y
Annual revenues	$366,600	$366,600
Less taxes* and all expenses except		
depreciation	239,400	195,800
Annual "cash flow"	$127,200	$170,800
Present worth of a 20-year annuity,	For trial i	For trial i
per interest tables, at trial interest	at 11.20%	at 9.55%
rate (as indicated for each plan), $a_{\overline{20}|}$ †	= 7.86	= 8.78
Present worth of "cash flow"	127,200 x 7.86	170,800 x 8.78
	= $1,000,000	= $1,500,000
Apparent rate of return is	11.20%	9.55%

Conclusion: Plan X appears to be superior, contradicting Tables 11.9 and 11.10.

$$\quad * \qquad\qquad iP_0 = \$112,000 \text{ for Plan X, at the trial value of } i = 11.2\%$$
$$_{11.2}^{\beta}dP_0 \text{ at } \underline{\quad 15,200}$$
$$\text{"Cash flow"} = \$127,200$$
$$\text{less }_0 dP_0 \text{ at } \underline{\quad 50,000}$$
Gross income = tax = $ 77,200, which may require several trials to discover. See also footnote to Table 11.10.

† Since $1/a_{\overline{20}|}$ x $127,200 is to equal initial investment (= $1,000,000 for Plan X),
$1/a_{\overline{20}|} = \dfrac{1,000,000}{127,200} = 7.86$. It is then necessary to find by reference to interest tables, the "interest rate" for which $1/a_{\overline{20}|} = 7.86$. This is the "trial interest rate."

The Profitability Index Method is a graphical procedure for facilitating this interpolation.

it identifies the superior plan correctly, it will almost assuredly estimate its degree of superiority incorrectly. There is no good reason for using it.

Like all methods which look to percentage return for a solution, the Discounted Cash Flow Method disregards the interests of stockholders. It ignores costs of financing, Profit Incentive, income taxes on earnings in excess of MAR, and earnings per share of common stock. It suffers from a by now familiar complaint: it ignores exact definitions of terms and of intent. It does not dependably select proposals that will maximize earnings per share or place the company in the best position to meet competition. Used by public utilities, it does not put the company in the best position to minimize rates for service.

Payout (or Payback, or Payoff) Period Method

Studies of causes of bankruptcy have repeatedly demonstrated that the two outstanding reasons for business failures are (a) insufficient capital, and (b) inadequate knowledge of business. Use of the Payout (or Payback, or Payoff) Period Method by management to gauge the profitability, economic choice, or financial desirability of proposals contributes to business failures on both counts.

First, it encourages wasteful use of limited funds. That is, it discourages adoption of profitable projects which promise a small but certain Profit Incentive, and encourages the risky ventures of the

Table 11.12. Discounted cash flow solution 3 for the problem of Table 11.9. Annual revenues of $246,600; less than revenue requirements by $40,000. Here there is negative Profit Incentive.

	Plan X	Plan Y
Annual revenues	$246,600	$246,600
Less taxes* and all expenses except depreciation	179,400	135,800
Annual "cash flow"	$ 67,200	$110,800
Present worth of a 20-year annuity, per interest tables, at trial interest rate (as indicated for each plan), $a_{\overline{20}}$	For trial i at 3.00% = 14.88	For trial i at 4.04% = 13.54
Present worth of "cash flow"	67,200 x 14.88 = $1,000,000	100,800 x 13.54 = $1,500,000
Apparent rate of return is	3.00%	4.04%

Conclusion: Plan Y now appears superior, contradicting Tables 11.9, 11.10, and 11.11.

*

$iP_0 = $30,000$ for Plan X, at the trial value of $i = 3.00\%$

$_\beta^\beta dP_0$ at 37,200

"Cash flow" = $67,200
less $_0 dP_0$ at 50,000
Gross income = tax = $17,200, which may require several trials to discover.

"boom or bust" type. This feature of the method is even put forward as one of its "advantages"![10]

Second, its use is prima facie evidence of the user's ignorance of financial principles. This method cannot be depended upon to select proposals best capable of maximizing earnings per share. It makes use of crude and unsound reasoning to accomplish its misdirected purpose. For this reason, its use strongly suggests that managements which depend upon it may be equally incompetent in other matters under their jurisdiction, to an extent that invites "bust" rather than "boom."

In brief, as a device for making Step 1 calculations of profitability or economic choice, the Payout Period Method is worse than worthless. It can almost be said that if the decision is close, this method will always back the loser.

A few writers have long recognized this fact. George Terborgh, of Machinery and Allied Products Institute, has been pointing it out forcefully for about two decades.[11] Meanwhile, in the field of business management and engineering economics, numerous textbooks continued to describe the Payout Period Method as though it were respectable. Business magazines speak approvingly of its use by prominent corporations as an indication of good management. Probably more decisions are reached by use of the Payout Period criterion every day than in all other ways combined. Certainly more unsound decisions are made in this manner. The Payout Period Method seems to appeal to businessmen in the way that bloodletting appealed to doctors before the medical profession came of age. Just what accounts for its fatal fascination?

The usual Payout Period calculation consists in first estimating annual revenues, from which are subtracted all annual expenses (including an allowance for return on the capital investment) except for depreciation expense.[12] Thus, the amount available for depreciation (the amount available to "pay back" the original capital investment) is found by difference.

Dividing this available figure into the capital investment reveals the "payout period," or the number of years to complete the payback. The shorter this period is found to be, the higher the project is rated. On the other hand, if the calculated period is deemed too long, the project is rejected. A survey of American practice indicates that a

---

[10]Perhaps reminiscent of the annoyed gentleman trying unsuccessfully to extract a toothbrush bristle from between his front teeth. Said he, "They told me they won't come out. But I never thought of that as an advantage."

[11]See Dynamic Equipment Policy, McGraw-Hill, 1949; MAPI Replacement Manual, Machinery and Allied Products Institute, 1950; and Business Investment Policy, Machinery and Allied Products Institute, 1958; all by George Terborgh.

[12]Not all users of the Payout Period Method do it exactly the same way, which testifies to lack of a discipline. The procedure described is reasonably typical of actual practice. This particular percentage return to be included in deductibles varies from one user to the next; MAR is never stipulated. Since percentage return is arbitrary, the amount of income tax to be deducted is also uncertain. No distinction is made between book depreciation (usually "straight-line," $_0d$) and the depreciation annuity, $_i^rd$. The allowance for net salvage is not specified. The whole approach is so naive as to deserve its description as "childish."

maximum allowable payout period is commonly set at three to five years; rarely as much as ten years.

This is one reason why <u>Bulletin F</u> was blamed for discouraging economic replacements of equipment. It was claimed that the payout period, interpreted as proposed service life for tax purposes, was too long; hence the large percentage of unduly obsolescent equipment purportedly serving American industry today. This claim has its ludicrous aspects, as mentioned in Chapter 8. That, however, is aside from our present topic of discussion.

Four major reasons for the great appeal of this method to the half-informed are:

1. It is simple;
2. It satisfies a misleading definition of "conservative" policy, since it favors "getting while the getting is good";
3. It appears to make estimates of depreciation unnecessary; and
4. By recovering capital sooner, the superior plan (as judged by this criterion) permits earlier reinvestment of capital funds in other profitable projects.

Let's consider each one of these claims in turn.

First, the claim for simplicity might have merit if the payout period solution itself had any merit. But if it is simplicity that is the major consideration, tossing a coin is even simpler. Furthermore, if the decision is at all close, close enough to justify making a calculation, tossing a coin is a somewhat more dependable way to make decisions than the payout period calculation. In the long run, it has a 50-50 chance of being right. When the decision is close, the payout period solution is wrong more often than not.

Second, it is argued that the payout period criterion is "conservative" just because it rejects proposals (particularly proposals for replacement of existing assets) unless it is certain <u>by a wide margin</u> that the project will be worthwhile.

It does not seem to be realized that this has another meaning. It means that <u>all worthwhile proposals are turned down</u> unless they are so overwhelmingly superior that careful calculations are not necessary to demonstrate their superiority. Since the great majority of profitable proposals worth adopting do not have this tremendous superiority, a large percentage of desirable projects are rejected by depending on this method.

It should be noted that the argument for "getting while the getting is good" has another slightly different connotation. It implies that the estimate of future revenues is less and less certain the more remote their future date of receipt. The project which gets the capital investment back sooner, out of the relatively certain revenues, is therefore said to be preferred, other things being the same.

Sometimes that argument may have merit; sometimes not. Quite often a new project "catches on" slowly after an initial period of uncertainty. In any event, the Payout Period Method is not the way to

implement that thought. It may be most desirable to attract business
by accepting smaller profits in early years, by underselling competition. We will return to this subject. In effect, this reasoning injects
budgeting and pricing problems into the economic comparison, where
they do not belong.

Third, it is impossible to determine profitability or economic
choice if depreciation is to be ignored. The Payout Period Method
does not really ignore depreciation. It determines a quantity said to
be available to cover costs of capital recovery and proceeds to pass
upon its adequacy. The only way, though, to pass upon its adequacy is
to compare amounts so available with the revenue requirement for depreciation. This the Payout Period Method fails to do. Instead, it
compares the amounts available with some arbitrary "maximum allowable payout period" — in someone's subjective opinion. This third
claim is completely false and misleading.

The fourth claim has the one greatest appeal to businessmen. If
Projects A and B have the same investment cost, and earn the same
lifetime-levelized dollars of profits, but A recovers the initial investment in half the time required by B, is not A superior? A's recovered
capital could be reinvested and earn the same profits a second time
while B is doing it once. The Payout Period Method is favored because
it recognizes this great advantage of fast turnover of capital investment. What is wrong with that? The answer is that nothing at all is
wrong with that theory. But a good deal is wrong with the notion that
the Payout Period Method is the only one that recognizes it. Two comments are in order.

First, the arithmetic of MRRD makes this an essential part of Step
1 in all profitability studies. It is impossible to determine profitability
without recognizing the advantage of fast turnover of capital. And it is
automatically introduced into Step 1 of identifying the economic choice,
which hypothesizes identical sales and revenues for alternative proposals. Out of given sales and revenues, the superior alternative
(= minimum revenue requirements) necessarily maximizes Profit Incentive (which is the source of funds, in addition to depreciation accruals) to "pay back" the investment. It simply avoids confusing the
economic choice with the separate and distinct pricing problem. In a
great many problems, the matter of payback period is of no importance
in making the investment decision. In no problem is it of sufficient importance to justify losing sight of the service-lifetime profitability of
the project, which is what happens if the payout period is accepted as
the sole criterion.

Second, there is no difference between funds made available for
reinvestment, or for dividends, or for reduction in price of product
while maintaining the same reinvestment schedules and dividends. The
financial advantage of one dollar made available one year sooner for
any of these purposes is the same. MRRD treats that "dollar made
available sooner" as either earnings or a price reduction, and weights
the time element properly. The Payout Period Method treats the same

quantity as available for reinvestment and does not weight the time element properly. Nor does it determine accurately that the amount is exactly one dollar.

To sum up, the Payout Period Method appeals mostly to the naive. It is not a test of lifetime profitability of a project. It is not a dependable way to discover economic choice; in fact, when that decision is close, the Payout Period decision is almost always wrong.

It may have some merit, in special cases, in connection with the budgeting function but never in Step 1 nor Step 2 calculations. That is, having determined by other means that a proposal would be profitable over its lifetime or that it is the economic choice among several alternatives, the budgeting decision may still be to turn it down because the profits are felt to be too long postponed. Present worth calculations discount the effect of postponement perfectly, but they make no allowance for increasing uncertainty that may accompany postponement; that must be done as a separate operation.

For some kinds of products, there may be a real probability of loss of market within a few years. This applies to such products as toys and novelties, clothing (particularly sportswear), phonograph records, "best-seller" books, movies, costume jewelry, cosmetics, household appliances, and similar faddish items.

The present worth calculation makes no allowance for decreasing probability with lapse of time; it treats each annual expenditure or receipt as equally certain. If it is desired to adjust future revenues for relative degree of probability, that must be done as a separate operation. The trouble with the Payout Period approach in this respect is that it recognizes only one aspect of probability. It looks at estimates of early profits, not average figures. Probability recognizes that the facts, as they transpire, may be worse or better than foreseen. The Payout Period Method assumes that they can only be worse. It always favors the risky "fast buck" over the slow but sure larger profits and regards this policy as "conservative"!

The notion that intelligent use of probability theory can be replaced by such a crude device as the Payout Period Method is one more comment on the unimpressive arguments sometimes advanced in support of this procedure.

The Capitalized Cost Method

The Capitalized Cost Method is a misunderstanding growing out of the Annual Cost Method. It is discussed here to illustrate how disrespect for a discipline invites a multiplication of errors. "Oh what a tangled web we weave ... !"[13]

It is frequently stated that the Capitalized Cost Method contemplates

---

[13]The quotation is from Scott's "Marmion."

annual costs in perpetuity.[14] This, however, is not at all the viewpoint of those who use the method. Their concept is simpler, more realistic, and applied to a single installation without replacement, as follows.

As just remarked, the Capitalized Cost Method is derived from the Annual Cost Method. It is observed that:

$$\text{Annual costs} = P_0 \text{ x \% carrying charges} \qquad (1)$$

where

P_0 = initial capital investment, or capital cost.

Therefore it is concluded that:

$$P_0 = \frac{\text{annual costs}}{\text{\% carrying charges}} \qquad (2)$$

where

P_0 = capital cost; here, "capitalized" cost.

When used in this way, the denominator of (2), "% carrying charges," is commonly referred to as the capitalizing percentage, or capitalizing factor. A favorite percentage appears to be 15%, for reasons never explained.

Assuming that the correct percentage is selected for the "capitalizing factor," what is wrong with this method? It might be said that nothing would be wrong with (2) if the Annual Cost Method itself were dependable, and if the right percentage were selected for the denominator. But the Annual Cost Method is not a dependable procedure, and selection of the proper percentage is not so simple. In fact, a completely correct solution reached by the Capitalized Cost Method is a true rarity, substantially never encountered in actual practice or even in textbook examples.

In the first place, (1) is not correct. The exactly intended version is:

$$\begin{aligned}\text{Annual revenue requirements, in dollars} \\ = P_{\bar{x}} \cdot \text{(revenue requirements, in percent)} \qquad (3)\end{aligned}$$

This expression applies to a single placement, without replacements, as is usually contemplated.

It can be rearranged to provide an expression for $P_{\bar{x}}$, but:

$P_{\bar{x}}$ = initial cost of surviving plant in service in Year x.[15]

$P_{\bar{x}}$ is always less than initial capital cost P_0.[16] Consequently, if the numerator and denominator of (2) are correctly estimated, their ratio

---

[14]For example, see Eugene L. Grant and W. Grant Ireson, Principles of Engineering Economy, 4th ed. (Ronald Press, New York, 1960), p. 100, and E. Paul De Garmo, Engineering Economy, 3rd ed. (Macmillan, New York, 1960), p. 84.

[15]The bar over subscript x indicates the average amount, in Year x.

[16]Unless the exact date of retirement can be foreseen, which is substantially never possible, as discussed in previous chapters.

is an underestimate of capital cost for a single placement. This, presumably, is why textbooks regard the method as contemplating annual costs in perpetuity; that is, including replacements. But let's look into that.

If the annual revenue requirements include costs of replacements, they may be expressed as a percentage of P_0, the initial cost. $P_{\bar{x}}$ is then maintained at a constant level, $= P_0$, by making replacements "in kind" and at the original unit cost, as retirements occur. But in such case, the capital cost of the project is not just the cost of the initial placement, P_0. It is P_0 plus the present worth of subsequent replacements, to eternity! This was thoroughly explained in Chapter 10, which dealt with the concept of a "continuing plant."

In brief, if the numerator and denominator of (2) are correctly evaluated, the Capitalized Cost Method will provide an underestimate of the intended "capitalized cost" whether applied to a single placement (as it usually is in actual practice) or to a hypothetical plant maintained in perpetuity (as conceived in the usual textbook version).

This is only a part of the story; the method has other serious faults. The following simplified example will illustrate some of the incorrect solutions and confused reasoning that is characteristic of this method.

Numerical Example, Capitalized Cost Method

A factory buys its electric power from a public utility at high voltage, and utilizes some of it at that voltage. However, a large part of the total supply is reduced to a lower voltage for distribution to individual small motors, shop lighting, and so on, by means of a large transformer. Two types of transformers are available for the purpose; they differ in capital cost, in the provisions for cooling, and in efficiency (that is, internal losses, mostly as heat). It is desired to select the economic choice.

Costs and estimated "annual costs" are shown in Table 11.13. Capacity and estimated life of the two units are identical; probable life is 30 years, Iowa Type R_1 dispersion, 10% ultimate net salvage. The company's minimum acceptable return is 6%. Capacity and space requirements of the competing units are identical; they differ only in capital cost and cost of losses; the less efficient unit would result in slightly higher bills for power.

Dividing the loss differential ($41 per year) by "% carrying charges," whether at 16.24% for A or 15.24% for B, would suggest that the extra capital cost of Unit B is not justified, by a wide margin:

"Capitalized" Costs

Unit A		Unit B	
$\dfrac{41.00}{0.1624}$	$= \quad \$253.00$	$\dfrac{41.00}{0.1524}$	$= \quad \$269.00$

Table 11.13. An illustration of capitalized-cost confusion.

Transformers A and B are identical <u>except for their first cost and cost of losses</u>, as below. Probable life = 30 R_1; ultimate net salvage at 10%:

Alternative Proposal	Capital Investment	MAR	Deprec.	Taxes	Operation & Maintenance	Cost of Losses
A	$2,000	6.00%	1.74%	2.50%	$120/yr.	$150/yr.
B	$2,400	6.00%	1.74%	2.50%	$120/yr.	$109/yr.

The usual estimate of "annual costs" would estimate return at some figure greater than MAR, would ignore effects of probability, and place annual depreciation at 0.90 x 1.26% = 1.16%. As a result, it would also estimate taxes incorrectly. However, we will assume an enlightened estimator here, to focus attention on the main issue, and for another reason which will appear later.

Ignoring errors of that kind, "annual costs" might be estimated as follows:

	Unit A		Unit B	
	%	$	%	$
Return	6.00%	$120.00	6.00%	$144.00
Depreciation	1.74	34.80	1.74	41.80
Taxes	2.50	50.00	2.50	60.00
Operation and maintenance	6.00	120.00	5.00	120.00
"Carrying charges"	16.24%	$324.80	15.24%	$365.80
Losses	7.50	150.00	4.54	109.00
Total "annual costs"	23.74%	$474.80	19.78%	$474.80

It would be concluded that the two units are economically a standoff; there is no choice between them.

Now consider the capitalized-cost solution.

The two units are identical <u>except for first cost and cost of losses</u>. Is the extra capital cost of Unit B (= $400) justified by its smaller losses (150 - 109 = $41 per year)?

To answer that question, the Capitalized-Cost Method divides $41 (the difference in cost of losses) by the appropriate "capitalizing percentage."

This is the 64-dollar question: What is the appropriate percentage?

If the "annual cost" solution is correct, the extra cost of Unit B is exactly justified by its lower losses. Then the appropriate "capitalizing percentage" <u>ought</u> to be: 41/400 = 10.25%.

Try to find any such "% carrying charges" in the above data.

It will be discovered that the sum of so-called "fixed charges" amounts to 10.24%, as follows:

Return	6.00%
Depreciation	1.74
Taxes	2.50
Total "fixed charges" =	10.24%

Does this signify that the appropriate "capitalizing percentage" is the so-called "fixed charge" percentage, which omits expenses other than depreciation and taxes? Some have so concluded; see discussions of <u>The Criteria of Economic Choice</u>, by Jeynes and Van Nimwegen, Transactions of the American Institute of Electrical Engineers, Volume 77, part III, 1958, page 606; particularly the comment by Robert H. Sarikas and the author's closure.

That is not the solution, as any student can verify for himself by repeating the example and assuming operation and maintenance to be 6% in each case, instead of $120 per year.

And what if service life for the two projects differed, giving two sets of "fixed charges" to choose from?

Yet the "annual cost" analysis seems to prove that the extra cost is justified.

The correct and intended MRRD solution is quickly found by calculating the present worth of lifetime <u>revenue requirements</u>, as in Table 11.14.

Just why was the "annual cost" conclusion correct in this special case? Two parts to the explanation are:

1. This particular "annual cost" estimate was unusual in that it reproduced the <u>revenue requirements</u> for a continuing plant. It estimated return at $\overline{MAR}$; it figured depreciation at $\frac{\beta}{i}d$, also based on MAR; and it calculated income tax correctly (by special dispensation noted in the example).

2. Although the problem did not relate to a continuing plant, an arithmetical quirk makes possible a convenient device. For a continuing plant, $P_{\bar{x}}$ is maintained equal to P_0, by reason of replacements. Annual revenue requirements for a <u>continuing</u> plant are $P_{\bar{x}}$ $(i + \frac{\beta}{i}d$ + other expenses, in %) $= P_0 (i + \frac{\beta}{i}d$ + other expenses, in %). If the quantity in parentheses is described as "% carrying charges," then dividing these annual revenue requirements by "% carrying charges" does happen to produce the correct solution:

$$\frac{P_0 \ (i + \frac{\beta}{i}d + \text{other expenses, in \%})}{(i + \frac{\beta}{i}d + \text{other expenses, in \%})} = P_0 = \frac{\text{"capitalized cost" of}}{\text{the single placement}}$$

It is this quirk of arithmetic, described before, which has misled writers into believing that the Capitalized Cost Method contemplates "annual costs" in perpetuity. It does not. This is one more example of the fuzzy thinking that results from inexact definitions of terms and of intent.

Table 11.14. The MRRD solution.

$$i + \frac{\beta}{i}d = 6.00 + 1.94 = 7.94\%$$
$$i + \frac{\beta}{i}d \ (1 - c) = 6.00 + 1.94 \times 0.90 = 7.74\%$$

The comparison of present worths of one lifetime of annual revenue requirements:

	Unit A	Unit B
Present worth of return + depreciation	$\frac{120.00 + 34.80}{0.0794} = \$1,949.62$	$\frac{144.00 + 41.80}{0.0794} = \$2,340.05$
Present worth of taxes, operation, and maintenance	$\frac{170.00}{0.0794} = 2,141.06$	$\frac{180.00}{0.0794} = 2,267.00$
Subtotals	$4,090.68	$4,607.05
Present worth of losses	$\frac{150.00}{0.0794} = 1,889.17$	$\frac{109.00}{0.0794} = 1,372.80$
Total present worths	$5,979.85	$5,979.85

The difference in present worths of losses offsets, exactly, the differences in present worths of revenue-requirements subtotals. Actually, then, the two units are a standoff.

The example of Table 11.14 is a simplified problem, as noted. Applied to practical situations in which a single project may be made up of components having different lives, different types of dispersion, different salvage values, and necessarily different percentage income tax, correct and actually intended application of the Capitalized Cost Method is hopelessly difficult.

The MAPI Formula

The MAPI Formula may be characterized as a brilliant solution to the problem that the author, George Terborgh, posed for himself. That was to develop a solution obtainable by at most a quick reference to simple charts or tables. A major premise in that development was the belief that, no matter how carefully contrived and "scientific" an investment formula may be, it will fail of acceptance unless it is "gadgeted" for easy application.

It can be said that if it is essential that investment decisions be made in this manner — by reliance on a simple formula — then use of the MAPI Formula is distinctly safer than reliance on any other of the "standard" methods listed before. It applies only to the simplest kind of problems, and gives only a roughly approximate answer. However, it is not apt to be disastrously wrong within those limitations.

One note of caution is important: If the MAPI Formula is to be used, go to the original source for instructions; do not rely on any secondhand version of the method. The authoritative source is:

George Terborgh, Business Investment Policy, A MAPI Study and Manual (Machinery and Allied Products Institute and Council for Technological Advancement, Washington, D.C., 1958).

To sum up the situation, the MAPI Formula is suggestive of the barbecuer's safety code: "Never put kerosene on a fire. But when you do, toss it on from a cup; do not pour or squirt from a can." Never rely on a formula. But if you must, the MAPI Formula is the safest expedient.

Résumé

I. The Minimum Revenue Requirements Discipline (MRRD) does not introduce any new departures from established financial and accounting principles. It differs from other methods of analyzing the merits of financial proposals by its superior organization of well-established principles.

II. Several analytical procedures are in such general use that they have become regarded as "standard" methods. Some of them account for so many unsound decisions that their faults deserve a clear exposition.

III. The major fault of all techniques other than MRRD is that

their use cannot be relied upon to accomplish the intended objective of economic studies, which is to select proposals best capable of:
(a) maximizing percentage return on already committed capital investment in the company; and (b) optimizing the company's competitive position, by permitting the greatest reduction in price of its products while returning an acceptable (to owners of the business) margin of Profit Incentive.

    IV. The decision process envisioned by MRRD is briefly as follows:

A. Diagnosis of the problem. Is it a study of profitability or economic choice? Can it be solved by examining a single initial installation, or must replacements be considered? Must allocated costs be considered in the analysis (ordinarily necessary in a profitability study)? Can expenses common to competing proposals be disregarded?

    Exactly what conditions and expenditures can be or must be treated as "the same in any event"? What period of study is appropriate? Should results be presented in terms of dollars of Profit Incentive, annual revenue requirements, PWAFRR, PWRR for some finite period, dollars per unit of output, break-even point, or some other basis?

B. The Step 1 estimate of revenue requirements. Together with the estimate of Profit Incentives, if it is a profitability study.

C. The Step 2 review of irreducibles, intangibles, imponderables, contingencies, and so on.

D. The budgeting decision. Sensitivity studies, if necessary. Effects of capital rationing, if a factor. Rating of budget proposals. Details of financing and the pricing problem, as separate and distinct propositions from the economic survey.

    V. The Annual Cost Method most nearly resembles Step 1 of MRRD, though it differs in philosophy and in quantification. Its shortcomings have been extremely harmful to economic reasoning and most damaging financially to the public utility industry.

    VI. Major faults of the Annual Cost Method spring from its dependence on an incorrect subjective definition of the percentage return deemed appropriate. It stipulates an "attractive rate," which is not the exact intent, and which is capable of at least ten different interpretations. Values ranging from 4.5% to 15% or more have been suggested. Other specific shortcomings of the Annual Cost Method deserve scrutiny.

    VII. Usually the Annual Cost Method favors projects requiring the smaller capital investment. Thus, it tends to discourage capital investment to increase efficiency or labor costs. It is biased in favor of leasing rather than owning the same equipment. It is apt to select the wrong alternative as superior, and it never estimates the degree of superiority correctly. All these shortcomings are detrimental to interests of stockholders.

VIII. The Percentage Return Method, sometimes misleadingly
called the "Investors'" Method, is apt to select the wrong plan as superior, and it never gauges profitability (Profit Incentive) correctly.
Its use may lead to promoting wrong lines of products. It cannot be
depended upon to optimize earnings per share. In general, its use is
adverse to interests of a company's stockholders.

IX. Like all methods which depend upon percentage return as a
criterion, the Discounted Cash Flow Method shares the shortcomings
of the Percentage Return Method. It cannot be depended upon to select
the most profitable alternative; it is quantitatively unsound. It may be
described as a relatively complicated and awkward way to make dubious decisions. It has a misleading superficial appearance of pro-
fundity.

X. The Payout (or Payback, or Payoff) Method is condemned by
most thoughtful writers. Despite the fact that most decisions are made
in this manner, it is worse than useless as a method for evaluating investment proposals. Its widespread popularity is a denial and contradiction of claimed American business know-how. The reasons for its
appeal to the half-informed are of interest. They reveal convincingly
the urgent need for a discipline in matters of this kind.

XI. The two main reasons for the appeal of the Payout Period
Method are its simplicity and the belief that it recognizes the advantages of a fast turnover of capital in a manner ignored by other methods of analysis. The fact is that MRRD recognizes exactly that same
phenomenon, but does it in a manner which does not distort the economic comparison. In brief, the Payout Period Method does not accomplish its avowed purposes. If great simplicity is the controlling
basis for selection of a method, making decisions by tossing a coin is
preferable to the Payout Period Method. Coin tossing is simpler and
actually superior when decisions are close.

XII. The Capitalized Cost Method is a misleading product of the
Annual Cost philosophy, coupled with a misconception of the present
worth principle. It substantially never results in sound conclusions,
and it should be avoided. As is true of all unsound procedures, resultant financial losses are borne mostly by stockholders, partly by consumers who pay too much for goods and services.

XIII. All the foregoing disparagement of techniques other than
MRRD is readily supported by simple quantitative examples which the
student can verify and elaborate himself, if desired.

XIV. The great variety of "standard" methods in common use,
when applied to the same problem, ordinarily yields as many different
answers. This has caused some to conclude that the diversity of practice allowed makes alternative techniques essential. A more cynical
comment based on observation of the same phenomenon is that, "The
estimator can prove almost anything he likes." Even teachers of engineering economy have concluded that principles involved in economic
studies are loose, vague, and uncertain. This fantastic situation is
curable by adoption of a discipline founded on exact definition of terms

and of intent, together with use of the arithmetic appropriate to carry out that intent. Such is the nature of MRRD, and its raison d'être.

Replacement of existing assets, in order to maintain the earning capacity of the owners' capital investment in the firm, is a major concern of management on behalf of stockholders. Few subjects are so thoroughly misunderstood as the economics of replacement, which is the subject of Chapter 12.

Here is a place where a disciplined approach is essential, if owners' capital is not to be squandered.

Problems

1. Revenue requirements of two proposed projects have been estimated as follows, assuming identical probable life for both. The company's MAR is 7%: Plan A, $1,000,000 per year; Plan B, $1,500,000 per year.

Although Plan A has the smaller revenue requirements beyond question, it was immediately rejected, while Plan B was adopted. What is the most likely explanation?

2. Recalculate Tables 11.9, 11.10, 11.11, and 11.12, repeating all assumptions except as follows:

Service life is 25 years (Iowa Type R_1 dispersion). Ultimate net salvage = 10%; 20% debt in capitalization at 5% interest; and double-rate declining-balance depreciation for both books and taxes.

(Note that this example calls for an <u>exact</u> understanding as to "all other things remaining the same." It is not intended that the same revenues, in dollars per year, be used as in Tables 11.10, 11.11, 11.12. It is intended that the same formula for revenues be used. That is, (a) revenues equal revenue requirements in revising Table 11.10; (b) revenues exceed revenue requirements by $80,000 per year in revising Table 11.11; (c) revenues are less than revenue requirements by $40,000 per year in Table 11.12.)

3. Calculate Profit Incentive for each of the revised tables of Problem 2. Interpret in terms of earnings per share.

4. A company needs a new general office building. Two proposals are under consideration. One calls for a conservative design; present worth of lifetime revenue requirements = $226,780,000. The other is a striking modern design, externally, although it is substantially identical internally. Present worth of lifetime revenue requirements = $300,000,000. The board of directors feels that the advertising value of the modern design justifies its extra cost.

Calculate the dollars per year that could be spent for equally effective advertising in newspapers, magazines, or other media, to permit adopting the conservative design and break even. Make reasonable assumptions of probable life, MAR, ultimate salvage, and all other essential factors.

5. What is the meaning of the expression "capital rationing." If you were a member of a company's board of directors, and the economic choice as between two mutually exclusive proposals was being rejected because of "capital rationing," what information would you demand to have for your consideration before you could agree?

6. In considering the electric-versus-gas supply of Table 11.6, the estimator pointed out that: (a) although revenue requirements of the two proposals are identical, electric supply meant more headaches for the operating department during ice storms, hurricanes, and heat waves; and (b) since commission regulation deprives the utility of its profits above a fixed regulated level in any event, why make the extra effort necessary in adopting the more economic plan?

How would you reply to such questions; or are they unanswerable?

7. The following statement has been made concerning alternative sources of capital: "Utilities traditionally are more willing to seek additional new capital by floating new security issues, rather than limiting expansion to that financed internally. They are less often misled by the false argument of 'dilution.'"

    a. Produce evidence in support of the first statement.

    b. Explain by a simple numerical example exactly what is meant by "the false argument of 'dilution.'"

    c. Why do these policies "promote greater capital gains," as stated?

8. Recalculate Table 11.3, repeating all assumptions except that the company has 20% debt at 4% interest in its capital structure, plus 10% preferred stock at 5% dividend rate.

a. Is it necessary to assume incremental debt and preferred stock in the examples? Discuss pro and con.

b. Is selection of the economic choice of any concern to holders of bonds and/or preferred stock? Explain.

9. Out of the same total earnings, in dollars per year, it is possible to have greater earnings per common share if there is a larger amount of debt in the company's capitalization, because in such case there are fewer common shares outstanding for the same total capitalization.

Illustrate by a simple example, and explain why the increased earnings per share do not necessarily identify the "economic choice" in such case. Or do they?

10. The following observation has been made about the "cash flow" criterion: "There is much merit in this device for comparing the financial performance of different companies, when considering the advisability of investment in their securities. But there is a serious weakness, too. It is possible to 'cash flow' a company into bankruptcy."

a. Explain, and discuss fully.

b. What are some of the practical limitations of the Discounted Cash Flow Method as applied to problems in profitability and economic choice.

11. In describing the nature and behavior of minimum acceptable return (MAR) in Chapter 3, an understanding of the cutoff rate was essential. Yet no means for establishing percentage cutoff rate has been proposed, and little mention of its use in making decisions has been discussed.

a. Explain how it happens that such an important factor need not be quantified in explaining and evaluating MAR.

b. If you were writing this book, what more might you have said about cutoff rate and its part in the decision process as discussed early in this chapter.

12. Two competing proposals, Plan M and Plan N, have identical present worths of revenue requirements as of their starting dates, as estimated in advance. But Plan M, as expected, is somewhat more profitable than Plan N.

If you compared present worths of revenue requirements as at the end of their service lives, would you expect them to be identical? Does it make a difference whether that calculation is (a) an estimate prepared at the starting date, or (b) a post-audit prepared after the fact?

Discuss fully and carefully, in a way that would be helpful to anyone less familiar with MRRD than yourself.

13. Consider the following problem:

Alternative Proposals	Capital Investment	MAR at 6%	Operation and Maintenance Expense
Plan A	$1,500	$90	$100
Plan B	$1,000	$60	$150

a. Calculate revenue requirements if probable life is 20 years. Which plan is the economic choice?

b. Apply the Payout Period technique. Assuming a maximum allowable payout period of 4 years, which plan would be selected?

c. If you were teaching this course: What would your comments be on answers to (a) and (b)? What additional data would you supply in proposing this problem, in order to make it more realistic, and your comments more forceful?

14. Aside from the financial loss and waste of resources which may result from use of techniques other than MRRD, their use also invites the cynical observation: "You can make the figures prove whatever you like."

In order to demonstrate the force of that comment to your own satisfaction,

prepare the following example of solutions to six different proposals, all to produce the same output and revenue; that is, a problem in economic choice. In this
case, successively larger capital investments in automation result in successively smaller operation expense.

Assume full agreement as to costs of each alternative, as given, and to the
common revenues. Several standard methods of analysis are then to be applied
to determine the economic choice.

Agreed-On Costs

A. Capital Investment:

   Plan 1: $ 50,000   Plan 4: $125,000
   Plan 2:   75,000   Plan 5: 150,000
   Plan 3: 100,000   Plan 6: 175,000

B. Operation Expense:

   Plan 1: $24,500 per year   Plan 4: $8,500
   Plan 2: 17,000   Plan 5: 5,000
   Plan 3: 12,500   Plan 6: 1,500

C. Other Expenses:

   a. Maintenance at 2% of capital investment, per year;
   b. Federal income tax based on 48% statutory rate; 50% debt at 4% in-
       terest; ignore liberalized depreciation and investment credit, for
       simplicity; "straight-line" book depreciation.

D. So-called "Fixed Charges":

   Return

   MAR at 6%.
   Minimum attractive return (cutoff rate) at 8%.
   Company average return at 15%.
   Hoped-for project return at 20%.
   Maximum payoff period 5 years (for use in the method of that name).

   Depreciation

   Based on 20-year service life.
   Ignore salvage and retirement dispersion, for simplicity.

   Taxes

   Federal income tax only, for simplicity, per C.

Solutions

The economic choice is Plan 6, as demonstrated by the following comparison
of minimum revenue requirements. Adopting Plan 6 will put the firm in the best
position; it will maximize earnings per share out of the given sales and revenues,
or permit minimized pricing of that output for any other stipulated earnings per
share.

Now compare solutions by other methods.

Minimum Revenue Requirements

	Plan 1	2	3	4	5	6
MAR (6%)	$ 3,000	$ 4,500	$ 6,000	$ 7,500	$ 9,000	$10,500
Depreciation	1,360	2,040	2,718	3,395	4,075	4,750
Federal income tax	1,150	1,725	2,300	2,875	3,450	4,020
Operation	24,500	17,000	12,500	8,500	5,000	1,500
Maintenance	1,000	1,500	2,000	2,500	3,000	3,500
Total	$31,010	$26,765	$25,518	$24,770	$24,525	$24,270

"Annual Cost" Method

The "annual cost" solution must be made for several values of return; see page 30 for ten different percentages regarded as appropriate by advocates of this method.

For the present purpose, try three percentages, as follows:

a. For return at the cutoff rate (8%), show that the apparent economic choice would be Plan 4.

b. For return at company-average earnings (15%), show that the apparent economic choice would be Plan 2.

c. For return at hoped-for project return of 20%, show that the apparent economic choice would be Plan 1.

All these solutions are incompetent; only Plan 6 puts the firm in the best position, as just noted.

"Capitalized Cost" Method

The "capitalized" reduction in operation expense between any two plans is to be compared with the corresponding increase in capital investment. To "capitalize" expense, divide by the appropriate "capitalizing percentage." Among the percentages suggested for this purpose by users of this method are: (a) percentage "fixed charges"; (b) "fixed charge" percentage plus (in this case) 2% for maintenance; and (c) total "carrying charges" of the better alternative.

Derive the several percentages. Demonstrate that almost any one of the plans could be selected as the apparent economic choice (in this case, by chance, Plan 4 would never be selected).

Discounted Cash Flow

This method, with minor variations, is also known as the Profitability Index Method and occasionally as the Percentage Return Method. It calls for an estimate of annual revenues.

Annual revenue less expenses (not including depreciation) equals "cash flow." Cash flow divided by capital investment equals a percentage which is the annuity available for return plus depreciation; that is, the capital-recovery factor for some percentage return, 20-year period (in this case), to be found by reference to compound interest tables. See the text for a method of handling federal income tax.

Try it for revenues of (a) $40,000, (b) $35,000, (c) $28,000, and (d) $25,000 per year.

Demonstrate that the apparent economic choice would be Plans 1, 2, 5, or 6, depending upon the assumed revenues.

"Investors'" Method

This method is also sometimes known as the Percentage Return Method. The usual procedure is to subtract expenses, including depreciation, from revenues to find annual earnings; earnings are then divided by capital investment to find percentage return.

Most advocates of this method estimate depreciation at the "straight-line" percentage, for this purpose. Others use the depreciation annuity, with "interest" at various rates such as: (a) project rate of return before taxes; (b) project rate of return after taxes; (c) project cutoff rate; and (d) company-average return.

For simplicity, it is suggested that you use the "straight-line" rate; but for complete conviction as to the incompetence of this method, you may wish to try other popular estimates as well.

Try it for revenues of (a) $40,000, (b) $35,000, (c) $28,000, and (d) $25,000 per year. Comment on results.

Payout Period Method

Several versions of this procedure, also known as the Payback or Payoff Period Method, all give different answers. One of the simplest is as follows:

		Plan A	Plan B
a.	Capital investment	$6,000	$8,000
b.	Annual revenues less expenses	1,500	1,750
c.	Payout period (= a/b)	4.0 years	4.57 years

Plan A would be preferred, having the shorter payout period.

Another version sometimes used in replacement problems:

Annual expenses:

Existing project	$10,000 per year
Proposed replacement	5,000 per year
"Saving" by replacement	$ 5,000 per year
Capital investment, replacement	$15,000

$$\text{Payout period} = \frac{15,000}{(10,000 - 5,000)} = 3 \text{ years.}$$

The proposed replacement is rejected if the payoff period exceeds some arbitrary figure, usually 3 to 5 years, rarely as much as 10.

Try this method, estimating cash flow as in previous examples, with revenues at (a) $40,000, (b) $35,000, (c) $28,000, and (d) $25,000 per year. To illustrate:

Plan 1

Revenues $40,000	Capital $50,000
	Cash flow $13,705
	a/b 3.65 years

By consulting other textbooks, you can find numerous variations of these methods, as well as other approaches deemed respectable by many writers and businessmen. By acquainting yourself with all of them, you may indeed be able, under all circumstances, to "make the figures prove whatever you like"!

15. Explain in your own words the confused reasoning that is involved in dividing "annual costs" by "% carrying charges" and expecting to discover "capitalized cost."

(Try doing it in terms that would be understood by anyone not familiar with MRRD. Can it be done?)

16. The note at the bottom of Table 11.13 says that the appropriate "% carrying charges" to be used in the Capitalized Cost Method are not necessarily "% fixed charges," and that anyone can demonstrate that fact by repeating the calculations of Table 11.13, assuming operation and maintenance to be 6% in each case instead of $120 per year.

Make the calculation, and discuss results.

17. Explain why it is doubly important for small businesses, with limited capital resources, to avoid use of the Payout Period Method.

12

• • • • • Economic • • •
Replacement

Introduction

Studies of economic replacement have exactly the same financial
objective as studies of initial installations, that is, to discover the
course of action of greatest benefit to already committed owners of the
business — the "pre-project shares." Accordingly, the first task in
such studies is to investigate the minimum revenue requirements of
proposals. The nature of the investigation may be an evaluation of
profitability or of economic choice, depending upon circumstances.

If the decision can be made by reasonably hypothesizing identical
sales and revenues (that is, whether the replacement is made or not),
then an economic comparison is appropriate. If a major objective of
the replacement is to change (ordinarily, to increase) sales and revenues, then a profitability study may be called for. Thus, it is necessary to ascertain whether the replacement is simply a substitute for
the assets it supersedes, or whether it is an improvement which not
only supersedes them but also increases output.

On occasion, the economic comparison may be disposed of by
means of a simple yes-or-no answer as to the advisability of replacement; for budget purposes, though, a quantitative estimate of advantages of the superior plan is ordinarily required. In other cases, even
though immediate replacement is found not to be justified, it may be
asked how long before replacement will be worthwhile. Two other inquiries are sometimes made, as follows:

1. What is optimal service life? That is, what service life will minimize revenue requirements per unit of output or for the lifetime of
   given assets, as a continuing policy?
2. What is the maximum outlay for unusual repairs, at advanced ages
   of equipment, that can be justified as an alternative to replacement?

Revenue requirements of new assets are not affected by the fact
that the installation happens to be a replacement. The only unusual
features of replacement studies relate to revenue requirements of the
old existing assets and to the appropriate period of study. A major
question to be answered is what revenue requirements of the old existing assets will amount to throughout remaining service life, whatever
that residual life might be if retirement were not immediate.

There is no special reason to inquire whether the replacement is necessary because purchase of the old assets was an "error in judgment." Procedure is exactly the same, in any event.

As usual, we encounter a number of popular misconceptions and common errors, both of commission and omission, which require special attention. A phenomenon which has escaped the attention of almost all writers on this subject is the estimator's dependence on group data as his only guide to the probable behavior of a particular single installation of new property.

One would think that the importance of allowing for costs of inevitable future replacements (the continuing plant concept, discussed in Chapter 10) would be uppermost in the mind of the estimator when making studies of economic replacement. It seems incredible that substantially all popular procedures other than MRRD should blandly ignore obligations for future replacements to which the company is committed by its immediate decision. The usual effects of this queer oversight are (a) to underestimate future revenue requirements (that is, overestimate future profits), and (b) to select periods of study which do not reveal the intended economic comparison.

The illustrative examples which follow have been devised not only to indicate how the analyst can carry out his exact intent but also to suggest means for readily recognizing the incompetency of other procedures which do not carry out that intent.

Initial Diagnosis of the Problem

A number of procedures have been proposed for tackling problems in economic replacement. A few are quite unsound and need to be mentioned only to help the analysts recognize their faults and avoid them. Of some others it can be said that if the proposed arithmetic is correctly carried out, they will all give the same yes-or-no answer to the replacement decision, though they may differ as to the amount of superiority of the right decision. The explanation for that quantitative difference deserves attention. And, finally, if there is a choice of ways to arrive at the same answer, the simplest route is to be preferred.

For all these reasons, some rather simple problems will be discussed in considerable detail. This should provide the reader with sufficient depth of understanding so that he can rely on his own judgment in connection with each practical problem he is called upon to handle.

Problems in replacement differ from choosing between alternative new installations in one important respect. That is, if the decision is to replace, then a new capital outlay is necessary (unless, of course, the new replacement is to be rented or leased); if the decision is not to replace, that capital outlay is postponed or avoided.

Exact intent of problems in economic replacement can be clarified by emphasizing one phrase of the familiar statement of intent. It is to

make the decision (replace versus not replace) which will minimize
revenue requirements from now on.

That prompts the question, "From now on until when?" Should we
consider only costs during:

1. Remaining life of the old existing assets if not replaced im-
    mediately, assuming that thereafter annual revenue require-
    ments will be those of new replacements whatever the decision?
2. Or during service life of the proposed immediate replacement?
3. Or over some longer period that will include revenue require-
    ments of the whole chain of future replacements of the immedi-
    ate replacement, whose dates of installation will be affected by
    the immediate decision to replace or not?

Another question that has troubled many economists is concerned
with effects of obsolescence resulting from advances in the art, which
produce continually improved replacements. For instance, suppose it
is agreed that an existing asset A can be economically replaced today
by asset B, though the margin is small. If we postpone replacement
just a few years, may not a still better replacement C become available, which is a still greater improvement that would be worth waiting
for? If we adopt B today, we will be unable to afford replacement by C
so soon thereafter. Therefore, should not today's "economic" replacement B be postponed in favor of C in a year or two?

Ordinary mortals cannot expect to be omniscient; we cannot expect
to foresee the future perfectly. But we can give heed to indications of
strong probability; and we can make allowances for likely deviations
from probable average occurrence of events. Most of the procedures
advocated by other textbooks fail to make such allowances; results of
that failure can be disastrous, as will be shown. The remedy is simple.

It will also be shown that numerous different approaches advocated
by various writers can all be made to indicate a single correct solution,
provided:

1. The proposed procedure is a defensible expression of exact in-
    tent; and
2. The calculations are performed in the manner dictated by that
    exact intent.

In other words the same solution to a given problem can be obtained by comparing annual revenue requirements or by comparing
their present worths; by looking at the immediate replacement without
renewals or by considering the chain of future replacements; by evaluating PWAFRR (revenue requirements "to eternity") or evaluating
costs of the "shrinking plant"; all provided there is agreement on the
exactly intended basis for decision, and provided the calculations carry
out that exact intent.

In brief, the most important step is the analyst's initial diagnosis
of the problem, in which he determines the exact nature of the problem
that he is to solve, and selects the arithmetic that will carry out his
exact intent most simply.

Example 1. A Special Case

Some of the complications of replacement studies can be minimized by first considering a special type of replacement problem. In
this example, the old existing property is not owned but rented. This
stipulation immediately eliminates awkward questions about certain
revenue requirements throughout remaining life, if the existing property were not to be retired immediately. That is, since the user does
not own the property, he has no depreciable assets to be retired. Payments of rent simply stop when the property is no longer used. Its
remaining life is then of no consequence, and there are no calculations
of income tax on facilities to be retired.[1] This permits us to concentrate on the matter of the appropriate period of study.

The company currently rents warehouse space; annual rental is
$23,000. Together with operation expense of $30,000 annually, revenue
requirements, if rented, are $53,000 per year. Facilities are adequate;
the location is convenient. So far as can be foreseen, the arrangement
can be continued indefinitely.

However, the company feels obliged to consider erecting a warehouse of its own, as an alternative to continuing the rental. An equally
convenient site is available, with ample space for future expansion if
necessary. A major reason for inquiring into the replacement is that
the new building could be designed and equipped with special laborsaving features which would reduce the number of employees needed, and
thus minimize operation expenses.

Should the rental be replaced by a company-owned warehouse?
Direct comparison of alternative revenue requirements, per Table
12.1, shows that continued rental is favored by a margin of $625 per
year. Assuming that benefits are realized at year end, this margin
might be expressed as a present worth (first of year) difference of
$590, in favor of continued rental.

An important point, commonly overlooked and sometimes chal-
lenged in analyses of this kind, is as follows: The foregoing solution
rests on the primary assumption of a continuing plant. It is implicitly

---

[1]When property is rented, the user has no revenue requirement for income tax ($= T$).
He does have to pay income tax on earnings in excess of MAR ($= T'$); but tax T' is no part of
the revenue requirements which determine the economic choice. See Chapter 8.

Observe how this unique feature of MRRD avoids an awkward self-contradiction that is
inherent in all other approaches, in examples like this. Owning the property would produce
earnings and taxes thereon. Renting would not be defensible unless it produced equal or
greater earnings (plus taxes thereon), out of identical sales and revenues. But earnings, if
rented, cannot very well be expressed as a percentage of the nonexistent investment.

Obviously, it is Profit Incentive, or earnings in excess of MAR in dollars, that is to be
compared, per the MRRD statement of exact intent. It is Profit Incentive, in dollars out of
identical sales and revenues, that supplies the criterion and which must therefore be omitted
from the estimate of revenue requirements along with the income tax (T') thereon. Such
procedures as the Annual Cost Method, the Discounted Cash Flow Method, the Percentage
Return Method, and other methods can deal with such situations only by abandoning without
explanation their percentage return criteria, which would yield no finite solution. They assume an "attractive" return if owned, no return at all if rented!

hypothesized that a continuing need for the facilities will extend beyond the service life of the initial installation or parts thereof.

Let's consider some implications of this fact, and the misunderstandings and wrong answers that can result if the analyst is not insistent on respecting exact intent.

Alternative Solution A; Retirement Dispersion Ignored

In the foregoing analysis, probable service life was placed at 40 years. It was recognized that actual life might turn out to be more or less than exactly 40 years; effects of that probability were allowed for in the estimates of annual depreciation and income tax and in the nature of the economic comparison.

The conclusion, per Table 12.1, is that continued rental is superior by a margin of $625 per year. One might ask, "$625 per year for how many years?"

Table 12.1. The comparison of annual revenue requirements. Example 1.

Costs and revenue requirements are estimated as follows:
 Capital investment in new facilities $250,000.*
 Estimated service life 40, R_1. 10% ultimate net salvage.
 MAR 6%; 55% debt at 4% interest; no preferred stock.
 DRDB depreciation for books and taxes; 7% investment credit.[†]
 Operation and maintenance expenses, local taxes, insurance; $32,500 per
  year total.

Lifetime-Levelized Annual Revenue Requirements If Owned

Minimum acceptable return		6.00%
Depreciation 0.90 x 1.27% (Table 6.17 on page 142)		1.14

$$\text{Federal income tax } \frac{48}{52}\left[(6.00 + 1.14 - 3.32)(1 - \frac{0.55 \times 4}{6}) - \frac{.07 \times 7.27\%}{1.06}\right]$$

$$- \frac{.07 \times 7.27\%}{1.06} \qquad\qquad 1.31$$

Operation	20,000/250,000	8.00
Maintenance	5,000/250,000	2.00
Local taxes	5,000/250,000	2.00
Insurance	2,500/250,000	1.00
Total		21.45%

Thus, annual revenue requirements of the continuing plant would be:

21.45% of 250,000 = $53,625 per year

Alternative revenue requirements (rented space) would be:

Annual Revenue Requirements, If Rented

Annual rental	$23,000 per year
Operation expense	30,000
Total	$53,000 per year

---

*For simplicity, to focus attention on the main issues, we will treat land, building, and equipment as a single entity.

†For purposes of this illustration it is assumed that the whole new investment is eligible for the investment credit. Actually, land and most kinds of buildings are not eligible under current law.

Table 12.2. A common and unsound solution to Example 1.
Alternative A: Retirement dispersion ignored.

Return (= MAR) at 6%	6.00%
Depreciation (90% of 0.65, per Table 6.17, on page 142)	0.58
Federal income tax (Per Formula 8.4, on page 184)*	1.19
Other expenses at $32,000 per year, as before	13.00
Total "annual costs" †	20.77%

Apparent "annual costs" in dollars:

$$20.77\% \text{ of } 250,000 = \$51,925 \text{ per year}$$

By direct comparison with "annual costs" if rented:

"Annual costs" if rented	$53,000 per year
"Annual costs" of ownership	51,925
Apparent advantage of <u>owning</u>	$ 1,075 per year

$$\frac{*.48}{.52} \left[(6.00 + 0.58 - 3.11)(1 - \frac{4 \times .55}{6}) - \frac{.07 \times 6.58}{1.06} \right] - \frac{.07 \times 6.58}{1.06} = 1.19\%$$

† Since MRRD insists upon recognition of effects of retirement dispersion and the
Annual Cost Method does not, estimated figures in this table are arbitrarily called
"annual costs."

The answer to that question does not affect the yes-or-no decision.
For any specified number of years, simply multiply the annual revenue
requirements (for each alternative separately and subtract, or multiply
the differential of $625 annually) by the appropriate value of $a_{\overline{n}|}$, where
n = specified number of years.[2]

For example, with MAR = 6%, present worth of the differential for
a 40-year period (= probable life of the new warehouse) would be:

If owned 15.046297 x 53,625 = $806,858
<u>If rented</u> 15.046297 x 53,000 =   797,454
Present worth of difference = $ 9,404 in favor of <u>rental</u>

Compare this solution with that of Table 12.2, which is calculated from
the same specifications and in the same manner, <u>but ignoring the effects of retirement dispersion.</u> This means firmly assuming that there
is no possibility of retirement at any age other than exactly 40.0 years.[3]

As the result of insisting on that most unlikely coincidence (and
this is what one does by ignoring the probability of retirement sooner
or later than at 40.0 years), it would be concluded that the <u>company-
owned replacement</u> should be preferred. It is preferred by a sizable
margin, too; the apparent present worth of the difference is $16,175:

$$15.046297 \times 1,075 = \$16,175 \text{ in favor of owning!}$$

The difference in conclusions (9,404 + 16,551 = $25,955) is about
10% of the capital investment involved — a sizable error. The error is
introduced by neglecting one detail of the analyst's exact intent: by

---

[2]For values of $a_{\overline{n}|}$ see Chapter 5.
[3]Most textbooks assume (or "demonstrate") that it is not necessary to consider the
probability of mortality dispersion. A major purpose of this example is to enable the student to apply his own judgment to that issue.

ignoring his specific intent to recognize the possibility of retirement at ages other than exactly 40.0 years.[4] The remedy is obvious.

Alternative Solution B; Future Chain of Replacements Ignored

As pointed out in Chapter 10, it is the exception rather than the rule when a decision can be reached by inquiring into costs of immediate installations only, without regard for their future chain of replacements. A major disturbing factor is a difference in anticipated service lives of alternative proposals, commonly encountered.

In Example 1, however, that awkward detail does not arise, by reason of the nature of the alternative to ownership (that is, rental). The rental contract has no stipulated "mortality characteristics." Accordingly, we would be able to confirm the Table 12.1 revenue requirement solution (= renting preferred) by looking at costs throughout the life of the first generation replacement only, without regard for its future chain of replacements. Of course, so long as replacements of the company-owned alternative are of the same nature as the initial installation and have the same unit cost, annual revenue requirements of the project continue indefinitely at the same lifetime-levelized amount. The effect of the replacement decision is simply to change the timing of the initial placement and subsequent chain of replacements.

The PWAFRR solution (Formula 10.3 on page 299) takes advantage of this situation. It contemplates continuation of the level annual revenue requirements of each alternative indefinitely and proposes to compare their amount in perpetuity, for the rental proposal versus the ownership proposal, as a close approximation of their present worth to any indefinite but remote date. In such case, present worth of the advantage of continued rental would be: $625/6\% = \$10,417$ in favor of rental. Thus, extending the period of comparison from 40 years to eternity increases the estimated present worth from \$9,404 to \$10,417.

This prompts a question. What if we delimit the period of comparison to service life of the first-generation replacement only?

On first thought, it may appear that we have already made this calculation, by computing present worth of the annual differential for 40 years. But this is not so. It is probable average service life that is 40 years. To find present worth of the differential for a probable average life of 40 years, giving weight to the possibilities of longer or shorter life as described by Iowa Type R_1 probability (as specified in our starting assumptions and based on experience), we use Formula 10.1 on page 299, as follows:

$$\text{Present worth} = P_0 + \frac{P_0 \cdot e}{i + \beta_i d} \qquad \text{(Formula 10.1)}$$

which may be restated as $\dfrac{P_0\left[(i + \beta_i d) + e\right]}{i + \beta_i d}.$

---

[4]Other shortcomings of the Annual Cost Method, discussed in Chapter 11, are deliberately eliminated from the suggested solution to emphasize this particular source of error.

In this form, the numerator represents annual revenue requirements. Thus, present worth may be found by dividing annual revenue requirements by $(i + \frac{\beta}{i}d)$. In this case, the numerator becomes the difference in annual revenue requirements, $625:

$$\text{Present worth} = \frac{625}{7.27\%} = \$8,597 \text{ in favor of } \underline{\text{rental}}$$

This differs quantitatively from the previous solutions only by reason of the different period of comparison. The yes-or-no conclusion remains the same in all cases (except for the incompetent Annual Cost solution).

A similar conclusion may be reached by other methods which are respectful of <u>exact</u> intent. Two such alternatives mentioned before, and found useful on occasion, are:

1. Present worth of annual revenue requirements for the continuing plant <u>to age omega</u>, the age at retirement of the oldest surviving part, is the basis for Formula 10.2 on page 299. For a service life probability of 40, R_1, omega is about 80 years.
2. Present worth of annual revenue requirements for the continuing plant for some "reasonable" period, followed by a shrinking plant (renewals of retirements discontinued) until the last survivor is retired, was also discussed in Chapter 10. It is sometimes a more logical device than the unrealistic assumption of a coterminous date at which all components are retired simultaneously, all having magically attained anticipated service life at that particular moment.

Still another helpful way of viewing the problem to be solved is to regard the quantity at issue as the amount of <u>benefit</u> (by way of postponing a proposed replacement project) that can be purchased at a <u>price</u> (the outlay for one year's continued rental in this case).

It is possible to describe the exactly intended arithmetic in several ways, as often happens in expressing financial equivalencies (see Chapter 5); different individuals find some versions of the same thing more readily comprehensible than others. To illustrate, here are two ways of expressing the same idea in Example 1:

"The project" contemplated by **PWAFRR** for a company-owned warehouse is equivalent to an immediate outlay of $53,625/6\% = \$893,750$ (per Formula 10.3 on page 299). Postponing such an outlay one year means a "benefit" of $(1.000000 - 0.943396) \times 893,750 = \$50,590$.

This benefit is obtainable at a price; the price is an alternative immediate outlay; the present worth is equivalent to $53,000 paid at the end of the year for one more year's rental: $0.943396 \times 53,000 = \$50,000$.

The net advantage gained is the excess of the benefit above its price: $50,590 - 50,000 = \$590$ net advantage, which confirms the conclusion of Table 12.1: $0.943396 (53,625 - 53,000) = \$590$ in favor of <u>rental</u>.

A second approach leading to that same conclusion is as follows.

The "ownership project," if adopted one year from today, would have an equivalent present worth (PWAFRR) of (16.666667 - 0.943396) x 53,625 = $843,160. This would mean continuing rental throughout the coming year, adding an outlay having a present worth of 0.943396 x 53,000 = $50,000.

The total present worth of the proposition (PWAFRR) would be: 50,000 + 843,160 = $893,160.

The alternative is to adopt the "ownership project" immediately, which has a present worth (PWAFRR) of: 16.666667 x 53,625 = $893,750. The difference, in favor of the first proposition (renting for one more year) is 893,750 - 893,160 = $590.

Take your choice. All this variety of answers, except for the unsound Annual Cost analysis of Table 12.2, confirm the Step 1 conclusion that continued rental for one more year is desirable. A study made next year will reproduce that conclusion, unless conditions change in the meantime. Present worth of a succession of similar annual studies depends upon the number of successive annual studies to be made before conditions change; that may vary from $8,597 (per Formula 10.1, a period of one probable service life of the initial replacement) to a maximum of $10,417 (per Formula 10.3, no foreseeable change in conditions ever).

Once the yes-or-no decision is established, there is sometimes little reason to inquire into this present worth figure. In any event, the variety of quantitative answers results from the analyst's deliberate and reasoned selection of the most appropriate basis for comparison, not from any defect in the method of analysis.

These analyses do not take into account effects of possible price inflation. Should that adjustment be desired, it becomes necessary to proceed as described in Chapter 10: tabulate year-by-year renewals and price them at the inflated level, while deducting simultaneous retirements at original cost, to establish each year's new value of P_x^-. The previous percentage revenue requirements may then be applied to this capital investment; or, if it reflects exact intent more accurately, adjusted expenses may be separately estimated at the inflated level, as discussed in Chapter 9.

While probably not worth the effort in problems like Example 1, recognition of possible price inflation may be the factor of primary importance in problems like Example 5.

In dealing with the possibility, mentioned before, that by postponing immediate replacement B for a short period, a better deal in the form of replacement C may be available shortly, the analyst must be realistic.

If there is any predictable probability of that kind, then a supplementary calculation may be made, based on a specific prediction of the nature of opportunity C. In general, however, past and present experience with respect to probable service life takes care of such possibilities, unless it can be said that company practice in the past has demonstrably failed to realize most economic potential service lives.

If such a fact is demonstrable, then it must be possible to approximate the probable service life if management had been more proficient.

Added to this is the phenomenon, mentioned before, that whatever the effect of this consideration in the future on one alternative, it is difficult to justify assumption of a markedly different effect if the other decision were made (to replace versus not to replace). The question is usually of minor significance.

A final comment on Example 1 relates to a possible Step 2 conclusion which is also in favor of continued rental. The extra employees currently on the payroll to operate the rented facility might have to be "absorbed" by the replacement project, so that the potential reduction in operating expense might not be realized immediately if the rental were discontinued.

Some truly horrible examples of incompetent planning are provided by the technical literature, illustrating the consequences of overlooking such details as have been described here. They are perhaps most common and most serious in problems that involve replacement of relatively short-lived assets by long-lived plant. Probability of price inflation and its effect on future outlays for replacements of the shorter-lived alternatives aggravate the error. The difficulty of stipulating an end point for the study, when installations are made up of component parts having different probable lives, and the need for a terminal adjustment have been described before as introducing unnecessary complications into studies made by methods other than those recommended here.

In introducing Example 1, it was remarked that this matter of replacing rented facilities by new company-owned property presented a special and unusually simple problem. Example 2 deals with another enlightening special and unusually simple case: replacement of a company-owned property by rented facilities.

Example 2. Another Special Case

In this case, the company owns the warehouse of Example 1, which is now 20 years old. However, having been built before 1954, it is not eligible for liberalized depreciation or for the investment credit provision of current income tax law.

As before, we will treat it first as though land and buildings were a single property unit, with probable life originally estimated as 40, R_1. The facilities would be suitable for continued use were it not for changes in the traffic situation in the neighborhood, as in Example 1. An annual penalty of $10,000 is being incurred in the form of extra time for trucks to reach the building, load and unload, and park.

Suitable space could be rented at a more accessible location at a cost of $53,000 per year, as in Example 1 (rental $23,000; operation expense $30,000). No equally convenient site is currently available for construction of a new company-owned replacement at a reasonable cost.

Should some site later become available, the company would have freedom of choice to build at that time. That is, the proposed rental is on
a year-to-year basis, cancellable by the company on short notice without penalty.[5]

Impact of the decision to retire immediately, on revenue requirements of the existing assets, may be analyzed as follows:

1. Return and depreciation

No effect. Since we are concerned with the difference in revenue requirements, impact of the decision on revenue requirements
for return and depreciation is nil. This is because these annual
revenue requirements represent the lifetime-levelized equivalency
of the initial capital outlay of $250,000. That outlay, already made
20 years ago, is not affected by the present retirement decision at
all. Residual requirements for its recovery are the same figure,
retired immediately or not, whatever portion may have been recovered to date.

2. Salvage

Originally anticipated ultimate net salvage (10%) may be a different figure today for the proposed premature retirement. This is
found to be the case here. It is estimated that the property could be
sold today for $50,000 (= 20%). In addition, that $50,000 would be
realized immediately rather than at some future date, as would be
the case if retirement were not immediate.

3. Income taxes

Taxes on income cease when income ceases at retirement.
Future income taxes (if retirement is not immediate) can be estimated with considerable assurance for a continuing plant. Year-
by-year taxes for a particular unit of property can be estimated
with somewhat less assurance, as explained in Chapter 8.

4. Operation and maintenance expense; local taxes; insurance

We will assume that all such expenses will cease at retirement,
including the transportation penalty. As noted in Chapter 9, this is
not necessarily true, as a generality; sometimes retirement releases a temporary excess of personnel which is absorbed elsewhere without effecting a saving for the company as a whole.

The fundamental basis for decision is the same here as in all
cases; that is, replacement is justified at such date as produces minimized revenue requirements from then on.[6] This means a comparison
of:

A. Revenue requirements from now on, if replacement is immediate, versus

B. Revenue requirements from now on, if replacement is not immediate.

---

[5]For the essential distinction between renting and leasing, see Chapter 13.

[6]This statement of intent assumes that an economic comparison is to be made, that is,
hypothesizing identical sales and revenues in any event. Otherwise, the criterion would be
maximized potential Profit Incentive from then on, out of stipulated sales and revenues.

Since replacement of existing assets is ordinarily inevitable at some future date, if not immediately, evaluation of Alternative B calls for an estimate of remaining life of present old assets, if not retired immediately. This is the major detail in which Example 2 differs from Example 1.

It is possible to imagine circumstances when replacement can never be justified economically. But because depreciable assets do not have eternal life, a time finally comes when replacement must be made, economic or not, for physical reasons.[7] This may at first seem to present a discouraging prospect; Alternative B would involve a large number of possibilities, depending upon probable remaining life of existing assets.

There are two ways to resolve that difficulty. One is to assume that past and present experience with similar plant suggests a "normally expected" remaining life, depending upon present age of existing assets.

The other approach is to assume that year-by-year outlays for expenses, after the initial capital outlay, tend to remain constant each year or to increase with age. One could then look at next year's lifetime-levelized revenue requirements of the proposed replacement (which would not be incurred if the old assets were retained) and compare them with next year's outlays, if the old assets were retained. The presumption is that if next year's situation favors the replacement, then every later year would favor it still more; replacement would be desirable immediately.

Some awkward details are involved in this presumption. One is the matter of salvage credits at retirement of the old assets, which affect the first year's net outlays, and which may be positive or negative. Another is that dubious assumption that expenses increase with age, as discussed in Chapter 9; such an impression is quite often at odds with the facts. Certainly income tax outlays do not always increase with age; see Chapter 8. The year-by-year behavior of taxes is peculiar, and it is different for the old assets and the new. The investment credit is strictly a first-year phenomenon.

All these difficulties are avoided by inquiring, instead, into the effect of one year's postponement of the proposed replacement, as done in Example 1, which is not quite the same thing.[8]

The PWAFRR's of the new replacement and successors are readily calculated, as is present worth of outlays to retain the old assets one more year. The comparison then lies between:

---

[7] It is a common mistake to conclude that "modernization" (= replacement of obsolete equipment) is always financially justified. Often, discontinuance of an unprofitable line of products is preferable to modernization of its production facilities. The mere fact that equipment is obsolete does not necessarily justify replacement; effects of that obsolescence must be severe enough to give new equipment advantages sufficient to offset its cost, before the new outlay is worthwhile. Modernization is sometimes a policy of despair, the lesser of two evils. It may be a temporary unprofitable alternative to severer losses or bankruptcy.

[8] Among the common errors and unnecessary difficulties avoided by the recommended procedure are: (a) incorrect estimates of remaining life; (b) avoidance of need to estimate "deterioration and obsolescence gradients"; and (c) improper handling of salvage credits.

A. Committing the company to PWAFRR of the new assets and future replacements, while accepting immediate salvage credits
for retirement of existing old assets, versus

B. Committing the company to one more year of outlays to retain
the old assets, and then accepting the salvage credits plus
PWAFRR of the new assets and their future replacements.

This PWAFRR analysis has several advantages.[9] In the first place,
future replacements of the immediate new replacements are hypothesized as identical, in A and B; they simply start one year later in B.
Thus, whether they are large or zero, estimable with assurance or not,
the difference in their effect on A versus B is almost negligible. This
advantage is particularly appealing in Example 2, where no problem of
future replacements is encountered; the new replacement is a rental.

The estimate of one more year's outlays for the old existing assets
is not appreciably more difficult than in Example 1, where the existing
facilities were rented property. In Example 2 the only important problems are estimating next year's income tax and the amount of credits
from salvage of old assets; both are readily answered.

The PWAFRR solution, which again involves the continuing plant
concept, is so simple and straightforward that it seems hardly worth
attempting a solution by making the unlikely hypothesis of a noncontin-
uing plant.

Example 2. The Preferred Solution

Example 2 is a special case in that the "replacement" is a rental.
Then we have no need to be concerned about its interim replacements,
nor income tax, nor salvage, nor service life. We can proceed to make
the direct comparison between:

A. One year's rental plus associated operation expense, together

---

[9]For other advantages of the PWAFRR comparison, see Chapter 10.

It is worth repeating here that PWAFRR comparisons do not have the shortcomings
sometimes ascribed to them. They do not assume perpetual life for the facilities; they do
not assume perpetual need for replacements of the initial installation; they do not assume
perpetual need for the services rendered by the facilities.

The PWAFRR comparison is based on these common-sense observations:

First, retirement of the initial installation may occur before or after reaching estimated service life. This is recognized by making the usual allowance for retirement dispersion.

Second, it is almost certain that partial retirements occurring before reaching estimated life will be replaced.

Third, it is less certain, but highly probable, that retirements (partial or total) made
after reaching estimated life will be replaced, at least for some indefinite period thereafter.
To assume that these replacements are certain would definitely overestimate probable outlays. To ignore the possibility would definitely underestimate probable outlays. Accordingly, the PWAFRR procedure assigns a rapidly decreasing probability to that eventuality
after passing the date corresponding to estimated life, approaching zero probability near
Year 60.

B. with immediate realization of net salvage from old existing assets, versus
B. One year of continued outlays for the old existing assets, ending with realization of net salvage at the end of the year.

Beyond that one year, annual revenue requirements would be those of A, whatever the immediate decision; thus, future years may be ignored.

The solution of Table 12.3 presents an opportunity to comment on one common source of error that ought to be obvious but apparently is not always so. That is, problems in replacement economics cannot ordinarily be handled as though they were simply a matter of comparing revenue requirements of alternative new capital placements. In replacement problems, as noted before, the service life of already installed assets will be affected by the decision to replace them or not. Accordingly, their lifetime-levelized revenue requirements in percent and in dollars depend upon that decision.

To illustrate, in this Example 2, lifetime-levelized revenue requirements of the existing warehouse would be estimated as follows, assuming the normally expected probable average service life of 40 years, Type R_1 dispersion:

Minimum acceptable return	6.00%
Depreciation	1.14
Federal income tax, per Table 12.3	2.84
Operation, maintenance, local taxes, insurance	13.00
Trucking penalty	4.00
Total	26.98%

For an original capital investment of $250,000: 26.98% of 250,000 = $67,450 per year. This would appear to justify renting by a margin of 67,450 - 53,000 = $14,450 annually.

Yet the solution of Table 12.3 shows that actually renting is not quite justified. Obviously, problems in economic replacement demand special treatment other than the simple comparison of lifetime-levelized revenue requirements for each of the proposed alternatives — as though such problems start with simultaneous initial installation of each. Beware!

Many of the amateurish pleas for earlier replacement of claimed "obsolete" American machine tools and similar equipment of industry appear to overlook this fact.

As noted in Chapter 8, it is ordinarily impossible to calculate with 100% assurance the exact effect of a specific retirement on company-total income tax obligations, because the latter are not computed for individual assets but for groups thereof. Unit behavior of the tax can only be inferred from the group behavior. Fortunately, this fact is of relatively small importance in many replacement problems; it may sometimes be desirable, though, to inquire into various possibilities in order to be assured of that fact.

In the present example, for instance, it is assumed that early

Table 12.3.   Effect on PWAFRR* of postponing replacement one year.   Example 2.

A. PWRR* if rented (= Immediate replacement)
    One year's rental   = \$23,000
    One year's operation expense, if rented   =   30,000
       Subtotal   = \$53,000
    Present worth at 0.9434 x 53,000   = \$50,000
    Less immediate salvage, old assets   =   50,000
       PWRR, net   =   Zero

B. PWRR* if retirement and replacement are postponed
    Federal income tax, continuing plant: †

$$\frac{48}{52} (6.00 + 1.14 - 2.25) (1 - \frac{0.55 \times 4}{6}) \times 250,000 \qquad = \$\ 7,100$$

    Operation, maintenance, local taxes, insurance   =   32,500
    Transportation penalty   =   10,000
    Less salvage credit, at end of year   = (50,000)
       Subtotal   = \$ (400)
    PWRR at 0.9434 x (400); excluding return and depreciation   = \$ (377)

Comment: Immediate retirement, with replacement by rental, is not quite justified. The margin is \$377 in favor of postponement. But the decision might be to re-
place (the "budgeting function"), swayed by such considerations as discussed in Chapter
9, including the possibility of an increase in the trucking penalty or smaller salvage
value if postponed.

---

    *In this case, the difference in PWAFRR's equals the difference in PWRR's for
the stipulated period, beyond which the differential is zero.
    †"Straight-line" depreciation for books and taxes; no investment credit. Assets
were installed before liberalized depreciation was available. Note that the original
capital investment (\$250,000) must be known to compute income tax, a fact frequently
overlooked.

retirement would not affect <u>percentage</u> income tax at all. This is not
an evasive tactic but a reasoned possibility that is probably the most
likely situation. The result, in Year 21 of service life, may be compared with two other situations, discussed in Chapter 8, as follows:

1. The lifetime-levelized rate of 2.84%, applied to a capital in-
    vestment of \$250,000 (the continuing plant), as in Table 12.4
    = \$7,100 in every year.
2. The same lifetime-levelized rate (2.84%) if applied to survivors
    in Year 21 of an initial placement of \$250,000 reduced by in-
    terim retirements not replaced (the shrinking plant) = \$5,830 in
    Year 21.
3. The Year 21 tax obtained by the year-by-year calculation for a
    shrinking plant (initial capital investment \$250,000), calculated
    in the manner of Table 8.6, on page 208, for 40, R_1 mortality
    and 10% net salvage at 6% MAR = \$4,980 in Year 21.

    Calculation 1 is by far the simplest, being accomplished by appli-
cation of Formula 8.1, on page 182. However, that is not the reason it
was employed here. That calculation <u>for the continuing plant</u> is the
analyst's exact intent in this example. The other calculations, although

Table 12.4. Effect on **PWAFRR** of postponing replacement one year. Example 3.

A. Proposed Benefit (Avoiding One Year's Revenue Requirements of Old Assets)
    Per Part B of Table 12.3:

Federal income tax	$ 7,100
Operation, maintenance, local taxes, insurance	32,500
Transportation penalty	10,000
Less salvage credit, at end of year	(50,000)
One year's revenue requirements	= $ (400)
Present worth, at 0.9434 x (400)	= $ (377)

B. Price to Obtain Benefit (Immediate Replacement)
    One year's outlays for the new replacement, otherwise postponed. Annual
      revenue requirements, lifetime-levelized, per Table 12.1 = $53,625.

$$\text{PWAFRR} = \frac{53,625}{6\%} = \$893,750$$

    Present worth of one year's postponement of an outlay of $893,750:

        (1.000 000 - 0.943 396) x 893,750 = $50,590
            Less immediate salvage credit   = (50,000)
               Price to obtain benefit   = $ 590*

    The benefit (less than nothing) is less than the price of obtaining it. Replacement
is not justified, by a margin of 590 - (377) = $967.†

---

    *Note that this same "price" may be found by taking the present worth of one
year's revenue requirements, lifetime-levelized (= $53,625), and deducting the
salvage credit:

        0.943 396 x 53,625   = $50,590
        Less salvage credit   = (50,000)
        Present worth of "price" = $ 590

    †It is not unusual to find negative present worths, as in this example, when net
salvage is a substantial positive amount. If the handling of negative figures is at first
confusing, try finding the difference exclusive of salvage; then adjust for salvage
separately.

perfectly correct for the special conditions stipulated, are not the
analyst's intent in this case.

Example 3. Replacement of Existing Old Assets (Owned) by New Assets (Owned)

    Example 3 illustrates the situation most commonly encountered.
Rental is not contemplated as an alternative; the choice lies between:

1. Replacing currently owned old assets, which are capable of
    continued use if desired, by a new and more efficient company-
    owned facility; or
2. Rejecting that replacement proposal.

Examples 1 and 2 serve as readily digested separate steps to the solution of such problems.

    The company presently owns the warehouse of Example 2, now 20
years old. Replacement by the new warehouse described in Example 1

is now to be considered for the same reasons as in Example 2; the modern building at a more accessible location will reduce trucking costs $10,000 annually. Net salvage of present assets is $50,000, which is regarded as something of a windfall; ultimate net salvage of only $25,000 was originally anticipated for the old installation and is predicted for the new replacement.

The preferred method of analysis, for reasons discussed in Examples 1 and 2, is to discover the benefits (by avoiding one more year's use of the old warehouse) that could be bought for an immediate outlay equivalent to the price of the alternative: immediate replacement by the more efficient new facilities. If the benefit exceeds its price, the replacement should be made. Table 12.4 shows one way to make the comparison. As in Table 12.3, the effect on PWAFRR's is discovered by comparing alternative present worths for one year's postponement; after Year 1 annual revenue requirements would be identical in any event and, being common to both alternatives, would produce zero differential.

As discussed in Example 1, some individuals may prefer a slightly different version of the same situation; they perform the arithmetic as in Table 12.5 to obtain the same result. Being thoroughly familiar with exact intent suggests helpful ways of checking reasoning and calculations in this manner.

It is pure coincidence that all of the solutions in these examples should be near-standoffs. However, if management is alert, it would be expected that economic replacement should never be <u>overdue</u>. The normal expectation in inquiries of this kind is that replacement should be discovered to be barely or not justifiable economically at the moment, unless the problem is precipitated by some event that could not be foreseen, such as accidental damage of the old assets.

Table 12.5. Effect on PWAFRR of postponing replacement one year (alternative arithmetic; same solution as Table 12.4). Example 3.

A. The new replacement, if adopted today, would have an equivalent present worth (PWAFRR) of:

16.666 667 x 53,625	=	$893,750
Less immediate salvage credit	=	(50,000)
Net PWAFRR, immediate replacement	=	$843,750

B. This would avoid continuing use of the existing old warehouse for one year, followed by replacement at the end of the year.

Use of the existing old warehouse means outlays having a PWRR of
0.9434 x (400) = $(377) (Credit)

Followed by PWAFRR of the proposed replacement having a present worth today of: (16.666 667 - 0.943 396) x 53,625 = 843,160

Net PWAFRR, replacement postponed one year = $842,783

Difference in favor of postponing replacement:

843,750 - 842,783 = $967

Example 4. Optimal Life of Automobiles, Introduction

Exact intent in problems of this kind (optimal life) is a little off-beat. Instead of estimating probable average life in order to predict the depreciation annuity and income taxes, we will assign specific values of life and observe the resultant annual revenue requirements.

Diagnosis of this problem reveals an awkward situation. Economic comparisons are made by setting up the "iffy hypothesis" of identical sales and revenues for all alternatives. That hypothesis is adopted in this case; the decision will rest upon comparative revenue requirements, without stipulating the amount of annual revenues. This means that annual usage, or availability for use, must be the same in all cases (that is, for any assigned life). This requisite introduces two difficulties.

First, the decisive comparison lies between doing maintenance on the old car versus buying a new replacement. Can it be reasonably assumed that the old car, with time out for repairs, can be available for the same annual use as a new one?

Second, is it reasonable to assume identical use per year, old car versus new, even if both are available for identical periods each year? The newest machines in a car pool are apt to have the greatest use, if the driver has his choice, aside from being available more often because of relative freedom from repairs.

What this means is that the analyst may have to adjust actual cost data for any apparent decline in usefulness (or use) with advancing age. In some cases, no such effect may be demonstrable. In others, it may be possible to conclude that identical service rendered means identical annual mileage, and it may be possible to adjust costs that vary with declining mileage (if observed) in later years.

In this presentation of the principles involved, we will assume that annual service rendered is the same, regardless of age. Components of revenue requirements to be evaluated are:

1. MAR on the capital investment

Note that capital investment is gross purchase price, not reduced for turn-in allowance on the old car.

2. Depreciation

Here we have the unusual situation where there is no retirement dispersion. An assigned figure represents actual service life, treated as 100% certain. We will also assume that salvage is treated in the usual way, as an adjustment of the depreciation annuity, not as a capital gain for tax purposes.

3. Federal income tax

The range of assigned service lives affects eligibility for liberalized depreciation (3 years or more) as well as the investment credit (full credit for lives of 8 years or more; two-thirds credit for 6- or 7-year life; one-third credit for 4- or 5-year life). We will assume:

7% credit; "straight-line" depreciation for books, SYD for taxes, "flow-through"; and 50% debt at 4% interest.

4. Maintenance

Two categories of maintenance are desirably recognized: (a) Routine maintenance includes charges for work that can be done without laying up the car for repairs. Such costs are those of changing tires, spark plugs, lamp bulbs, and batteries; washing, cleaning, lubricating, flushing radiators, adding antifreeze, attaching and removing chains; and minor adjustments to carburetor, timer, brakes, windshield wipers, and window mechanisms.

(b) Major repairs include charges for work done "in the shop," which means laying up the car for any period from several hours to a week or more. Work of this nature ranges all the way from renewing brake or clutch linings to repainting and repairing collision damage; from replacement of transmissions and broken springs or axles to engine overhauls.

The reason for distinguishing between (a) routine maintenance and (b) major repairs is that the former ordinarily varies little if at all with age or from one car to another. Major repairs can be expected to vary from one machine to another and with some degree of predictability from year to year. Average experience, with respect to major repairs, is made up of some bad records of performance and some remarkably good ones. This fact has a bearing on the cost analysis.

Outlays not listed above, such as gasoline, oil, garaging, licenses, insurance, taxes other than federal income tax, highway tolls, supervision, and accounting, are assumed to be the same in all cases and are therefore omitted from the economic comparison. It may be discovered in individual cases that this hypothesized "ceteris paribus" situation is not justified and that differentials in such outlays must be recognized.

Example 4. Cost Estimates

Specific values assigned to the foregoing variables in this example are as follows:

Capital investment = $2,000 per car.
MAR = 6%.
Debt = 20%.
Interest = 4%.

"Straight-line" depreciation is used for books, DRDB for taxes; Type SQ dispersion, as explained. Ultimate net salvage (= turn-in allowance) and resultant annuities appear in Table 12.6.

Federal income tax is calculated in Table 12.12. Recognizing that liberalized depreciation is not available for lives of less than 3 years, and that the full investment credit applies only for lives of 8 years or more, the tax would be as follows (7% investment credit) in Table 12.7.

Table 12.6. Depreciation annuities. Example 4.

| Life | Salvage Allowance | | Depreciation Annuities | | |
(years)	$ (= C)	% (= c)	$\frac{\beta}{i}d(1-c)$	$d'(1-c)$	$d_t(=$ DRDB$)^*$
1	$1,500	75%	25.00%	25.00%	-
2	1,200	60	19.42	20.00	-
3	1,000	50	15.70	16.67	18.71%
4	800	40	13.72	15.00	16 78
5	640	32	12.06	13.60	15.17
6	500	25	10.76	12.50	13.87
7	400	20	9.53	11.43	12.66
8	360	18	8.28	10.25	11.41
9	300	15	7.40	9.44	1).51
10	240	12	6.68	8.80	9.79

*In view of the exceptionally large percentage salvage and the unusually short lives in this problem, the exact adjustment of d_t for net salvage is desirable (see footnote, page 184).

The exact calculation for a service life of four years, Type SQ dispersion, per $1,000 capital investment, is as follows:

Year	Annual Deductible Depreciation	Present Worth Factors	Present Worth of Annual Deductible Depreciation
1	$500	0.9434	$471.70
2	250	.8900	222.50
3	125	.8396	104.95
4	125	.7921	99.01
		Total Present Worth	$898.16

Lifetime-levelized annuity = d_t
= (ΣPW of Ann. Deductible Depreciation)/(ΣPW Mean Survivors)
= $898.16/$3,465.11 = 25.92% per year

For Type SQ dispersion, all salvage is realized at end of final year. Present worth of net salvage, at 40%:

$$400 \times 0.7921 = \$316.84$$

Thus, the salvage-adjusted depreciation annuity has a present worth of 898.16 - 316.84 = $581.32. And the lifetime-levelized annuity is $581.32/$3,465.11 = 16.78% per year.

Compare with the ordinarily recommended approximation:

$$(1 - c) d_t = 0.60 \times 25.92 = 15.55\%$$

Maintenance costs are predicted as follows in Table 12.8 for identical annual mileage.

These "ideal" savings of $917 (bottom of Table 12.9) would not quite be realized, because it is probable that a few cars may be wrecked beyond repair before reaching Age 6. Or they may need unusual repairs which are justified at an early age but bring up lifetime cost above the average.

This problem introduces Example 5, which is the question of maximum justifiable repairs, as an alternative to early replacement.

Table 12.7. Federal income tax. Example 4.

Life (Years)	Federal Income Tax in Percent	
1	$\frac{48}{52} \left[(6.00 + 25.00 - 25.00)(1 - \frac{.20 \times 4}{6}) \right]$	= 4.80%
2	$\frac{48}{52} \left[(6.00 + 19.42 - 20.00)(1 - \frac{.20 \times 4}{6}) \right]$	= 4.34%
3	$\frac{48}{52} \left[(6.00 + 15.70 - 16.67)(1 - \frac{.20 \times 4}{6}) - (18.71 - 16.67) \right]$	= 2.30%
4	$\frac{48}{52} \left[(6.00 + 13.72 - 15.00)(1 - \frac{.20 \times 4}{6}) - (16.78 - 15.00) - .64 \right] - .64$	= 0.90%
5	$\frac{48}{52} \left[(6.00 + 12.06 - 13.60)(1 - \frac{.20 \times 4}{6}) - (15.17 - 13.60) - .52 \right] - .52$	= 1.12%
6	$\frac{48}{52} \left[(6.00 + 10.76 - 12.50)(1 - \frac{.20 \times 4}{6}) - (13.87 - 12.50) - .90 \right] - .90$	= 0.41%
7	$\frac{48}{52} \left[(6.00 + 9.53 - 11.43)(1 - \frac{.20 \times 4}{6}) - (12.66 - 11.43) - .79 \right] - .79$	= 0.62%
8	$\frac{48}{52} \left[(6.00 + 8.28 - 10.25)(1 - \frac{.20 \times 4}{6}) - (11.41 - 10.25) - 1.06 \right] - 1.06$	= 0.11%
9	$\frac{48}{52} \left[(6.00 + 7.40 - 9.44)(1 - \frac{.20 \times 4}{6}) - (10.51 - 9.44) - .97 \right] - .97$	= 0.31%
10	$\frac{48}{52} \left[(6.00 + 6.68 - 8.80)(1 - \frac{.20 \times 4}{6}) - (9.79 - 8.80) - .90 \right] - .90$	= 0.46%

The investment credit, above, is calculated as follows:

Year 4 $\qquad \frac{1/3 \times 7\% \times 28.86\%}{1.06} = 0.64\%$

5 $\qquad \frac{1/3 \times 7\% \times 23.74\%}{1.06} = 0.52\%$

6 $\qquad \frac{2/3 \times 7\% \times 20.34\%}{1.06} = 0.90\%$

7 $\qquad \frac{2/3 \times 7\% \times 17.91\%}{1.06} = 0.79\%$

8 $\qquad \frac{7\% \times 16.10\%}{1.06} = 1.06\%$

9 $\qquad \frac{7\% \times 14.70\%}{1.06} = 0.97\%$

10 $\qquad \frac{7\% \times 13.59\%}{1.06} = 0.90\%$

Table 12.8. Maintenance costs. Example 4.

Age (Years)	Routine ($)	Major ($)	Total ($)	Cumulative ($)	Average per Year	Equivalent Annuity
1	$50	$ 50	$100	$ 100	$100	$100
2	50	100	150	250	125	124
3	50	155	205	455	152	150
4	50	215	265	720	180	176
5	50	280	330	1,050	210	203
6	50	350	400	1,450	242	232
7	50	425	475	1,925	275	261
8	50	495	545	2,470	309	289
9	50	560	610	3,080	342	317
10	50	620	670	3,750	375	345

To illustrate calculation of the equivalent annuity, in Year 3:

$$
\begin{aligned}
0.9434 \times 100 &= \$ 94 \\
.8900 \times 150 &= 134 \\
.8396 \times 205 &= 172 \\
\text{Present worth} &= \$400
\end{aligned}
$$

$$
\div \; a_{\overline{3|}} = \frac{400}{2.6730} = \$150
$$

For such short lives, this refinement is hardly worth the effort! But how can one be sure, not knowing <u>exact</u> intent?

Revenue requirements <u>per year</u> may then be summarized as follows for the several different lives (Table 12.9):

Table 12.9. Summary of revenue requirements. Example 4.

Service Life, in Years	1	2	3	4	5
MAR	$120	$120	$120	$120	$120
Depreciation	500	388	314	274	241
Income Tax	96	87	46	18	22
Maintenance	100	124	150	176	203
Totals	$816	$719	$630	$588	$586

Service Life, in Years	6	7	8	9	10
MAR	$120	$120	$120	$120	$120
Depreciation	215	191	166	148	134
Income Tax	8	12	2	6	9
Maintenance	232	261	289	317	345
Totals	$575	$584	$577	$591	$608

In this case optimal life is six years, although the exact service life has relatively small effect on lifetime revenue requirements per year so long as the car serves for more than three years.

Probably the owner would adopt the rule to turn in cars at the first need for a major repair after reaching Age 6. The advantage of such a policy, as compared with keeping cars for three years, for example, might be estimated as follows:

$$
\begin{aligned}
\text{PWAFRR for 3-year life} &= 630/6\% = \$10,500 \\
\text{PWAFRR for 6-year life} &= 575/6\% = \$ 9,583 \\
\text{Advantage of 6-year life} & = \$ 917 \text{ per car}
\end{aligned}
$$

Example 5. Justified Repairs, Nontypical Case

Assuming that the company has adopted the policy of turning in cars at Age 6, based on the foregoing study, suppose a 2-year-old car needs unusual repairs — the result of a collision not covered by insurance — amounting to $200. This would just about double its normal expectation of major repairs for Year 3 (the average is $155).

Were the car 6 years old, the job would not be worth doing; the car is about to be retired. But at Age 2, the cost of the job per year of remaining life is only $50. Would it pay? Three major estimations that must be made are: What will remaining life be, if repaired? What will annual maintenance be, after repairing? What will the cost of the replacement be? If all that is requested is a yes-or-no decision, we can proceed as in the previous examples and inquire into the effect of postponing replacement one year, as in Table 12.10.

Example 5. Postponement for More Than One Year

In the foregoing example, one year's postponement of a replacement was seen to justify an unusual repair job costing not more than $91. This prompts a question: What larger outlay for an unusual repair would be justified at Age 2 if it would postpone replacement two years? It is the normal policy to retire cars at Age 6, in this company.

Table 12.10. Effect on PWRR of postponing replacement one year. Example 5.

A. PWRR, if replaced		
One year's revenue requirements, new car = $575		
Present worth at 0.9434 x 575		= $ 542*
Less immediate salvage credit (Example 4)		= (1,200)
	PWRR	= $ (658)
B. PWRR, if repaired		
One year's outlays, old car:		
Income tax (lifetime-levelized; 3-year life)		= $ 46
Normal maintenance (Example 4)		= 205
Less salvage credit (at end of year)		= (1,000)
Subtotal		= (749)
Present worth of subtotal at 0.9434 x (749)		= $ (707)
Plus abnormal immediate repair		= 200
	PWRR	= $ (507) †

Conclusion: Repair is not justified, by a margin of $151. The maximum justifiable outlay for the unusual repair job would be 200 - 151 = $49.

---

*Note that this is the same figure as obtained by postponing PWAFRR (at 575/6% = $9,583) for one year:

$$(1.0000 - 0.9434) \times 9,583 = \$542$$

†It is not unusual to find negative present worths, as in this example, when net salvage is a substantial positive amount. If the interpretation of differences in negative figures is at first confusing, try finding the difference exclusive of salvage; then adjust for salvage separately.

This may be answered by means of a break-even analysis, as follows (Table 12.11). Solving for $M (= the amount spent for the unusual
repair to make replacement versus repairing a standoff), to break
even:

$$M - 223 = (146)$$
$$M = \underline{\underline{\$77}}$$

This result is not necessarily typical. Here we have a case of rapidly
increasing maintenance with age, together with rapidly decreasing salvage value. The income tax situation, particularly the impact of investment credit, is also unusual in this case of short-lived assets.

Justified Repairs, Long-Lived Plant

Maximum justifiable outlays for unusual repairs are handled in the
manner of Example 5 for long-lived plant. A study is first made to see
whether the cost of the repair would be justified by postponing replacement one year. If so, and if that decision is all that is asked, no need
exists to determine the larger outlay that would be justified by a greater
postponement.

However, often the facts of the case are otherwise; the cost of the
repair would not be justified by postponing replacement just one year,
but it is reasonable to expect that the repaired equipment would serve
for many years.

Table 12.11. Break-even analysis; effect on PWRR of
postponing replacement two years.

A. PWRR, if Replaced

Present worth of two years' revenue requirements for a new car,
  at $575 per year = 1.8334 x 575   = $1,054*
  Less immediate salvage, old car at age 2   = (1,200)
                                        PWRR, if replaced   = $ (146)

B. PWRR, if Repaired

Year 3 outlays, old car:
  Immediate repair, to break even   = $ M
  Income tax, (lifetime-levelized)   = $ 46
  Normal maintenance (Example 4)   =   205
  Subtotal   = $ 251
  Present worth of subtotal at 0.9434 x 251   = $ 237
Year 4 outlays, old car:
  Income tax (lifetime-levelized)   = $ 18
  Normal maintenance (Example 4)   =   265
  Less salvage, end of year (Example 4)   = (800)
  Subtotal   = $(517)
  Present worth of subtotal at 0.8900 x 517   = $ (460)
                                 PWRR, if repaired = $M - 223

---

*Again note that this is the same figure as would be obtained by postponing
PWAFRR (at 575/6% = $9,583) for two years:
                        (1.0000 - 0.8900) x 9,583 = $1,054

Several ways can be used to tackle such problems. One approach is to set up the problem in the manner of Example 5, Postponement for More Than One Year, except that the period of postponement is treated as the unknown, to be found by the break-even process. The procedure is fairly simple for a single property unit not subject to piecemeal replacements of component parts throughout its remaining life.

The model would be as follows:

1. PWRR if Replaced

Present worth of n years' revenue requirements of a new replacement, at $a_{\overline{n}|}$ times the estimated $/year, less immediate salvage credit, old assets, at C.

2. PWRR if Repaired

Levelized annual outlays, old assets:
Income tax	T
Normal operation, maintenance, local taxes, insurance, and so on	E
Subtotal	$T + E$

Present worth of subtotal at $a_{\overline{n}|} \cdot (T + E)$
Less present worth of salvage credits, at
the end of n years $= v^n \cdot C$.

$$\text{Total PWRR, if repaired} = a_{\overline{n}|} \cdot (T + E) - v^n \cdot C.$$

The break-even equation, to be solved for n: $a_{\overline{n}|}$ ($/year for replacement) $= a_{\overline{n}|} \cdot (T + E) - v^n \cdot C$.

This expression may be solved analytically, or more simply by selecting values of n and substituting simultaneous quantities $a_{\overline{n}|}$ and v^n. If probable remaining life, after repairing, equals or exceeds years, so determined, the unusual repair is justified.

Another approach is to estimate remaining life (if repaired) as the first step, basing the prediction on past and current experience as discussed in Chapter 7. This establishes a probable value for $a_{\overline{n}|}$ in the foregoing model. Or, strictly speaking, it establishes a probable value for $\dfrac{1}{i + \frac{\beta}{i}d}$, where $\frac{\beta}{i}d$ is a function of the probable occurrence of partial or total retirements over remaining life, dependent upon the shape of the survivor curve (or retirement-frequency curve) indicated by the survey of actual experience.

$\dfrac{1}{i + \frac{\beta}{i}d}$ may be calculated from these findings and substituted for $a_{\overline{n}|}$ in the preceding model. The treatment of probable or piecemeal salvage credits is a little more complicated, and the following procedure may be found helpful in cases where net salvage (plus or minus) is of sufficient magnitude to warrant the effort.

Present Worth of Probable Salvage Credits

To perceive the problem involved in calculating present worth of future salvage credits realized not at a single predictable date but at dates of various degrees of probability, consider three possibilities for 10-year probable total life. They assume two rather extreme type curves and one intermediate form: (1) L_5, (2) R_1, and (3) SC.

Suppose the equipment is now 10 years old. That is, it has reached an age equal to originally estimated probable life.

Probable remaining life is not zero but some figure that can be estimated by: (a) finding the area under the survivor curve (unit-years) beyond Age 10; and (b) dividing that area by the number of survivors (units) in service at Age 10.

Probable remaining life so calculated in this case is as follows:[10]

1. For Type L_5 = 1.34 years;
2. For Type R_1 = 7.68 years; and
3. For Type SC = 5.00 years.

This does not mean that we expect salvage credits to be realized in one lump sum at:

1. Age 11.34 years (= 10 + 1.34) for Type L_5;
2. Age 17.68 years (= 10 + 7.68) for Type R_1; and
3. Age 15.00 years (= 10 + 5.00) for Type SC.

What it means is that we can stipulate the probability of realizing the salvage credit in each and every year of remaining life, as illustrated by Table 12.12. The survivor curve selected for this illustration is Type SC, mainly because calculations for Type SC are easier to follow. Another reason for that choice will be explained later.

The retirement-frequency curve for Type SC portrays a level expectation of salvage receipts at every age. The weighted probability of retirements occurring at each age is tabulated in Column 3; it represents the year-end retirements per the appropriate "step" curve discussed in Chapter 7. Present worth of the "probable occurrences" of salvage credits are summed up in Column 5. MAR is assumed to be 6%.

Calculation of the penalty for postponement of retirement (from immediate retirement to retirement at the normally expected date) is shown at the bottom of Table 12.12. It amounts to $241.90.

This evaluation might be compared with the more usual estimate, making the firm assumption of retirement 5 years later, as follows:

---

[10]See Iowa Engineering Experiment Station Bulletin 156, pp. 17 and 19, for Types L_5 and R_1, respectively. The calculation for Type SC will be obvious. For graphs of percentage survivors, see Figures 6.1, 6.2, and 6.3, Chapter 6. For more convenient tabular forms, see: Anson Marston *et al.*, Engineering Valuation and Depreciation (Iowa State University Press, Ames, 1953).

Table 12.12. Present worth of deferred salvage credits.

Assume a single property unit, or a group of like-age units having a total life expectancy at installation of 10 years, Type SC. Ultimate net salvage is $1,000, whenever retired.

Survivors at Age 10 have a remaining life of 5 years,

$$\frac{\begin{array}{c}\dot{x} = 10 \\ \sum \quad \text{Survivors, Years } x \\ x = 0\end{array}}{\text{Survivors at Age 10}}$$, with equal possibility of retirement at any age from 10 to

20 years (that is, Type SC).

How much is the present worth of salvage credits reduced by postponing retirement?

1	2	3	4	5
		Probability of Retirement	Present Worth Factors	Present Worth of Probable Salvage
Age (years)	Year No. (x)	1st of Year x Per Type Curve SC	at MAR = 6% (v^x)	Credits (Col. 3 x Col. 4)
10	0	5.0 % (x $1,000)	1.0000	$ 50.00
11	1	10.0 % (x $1,000)	0.9434	94.34
12	2	10.0 % (x $1,000)	.8900	89.00
13	3	10.0 % (x $1,000)	.8396	83.96
14	4	10.0 % (x $1,000)	.7921	79.21
15	5	10.0 % (x $1,000)	.7473	74.73
16	6	10.0 % (x $1,000)	.7050	70.50
17	7	10.00% (x $1,000)	.6651	66.51
18	8	10.00% (x $1,000)	.6274	62.74
19	9	10.00% (x $1,000)	.5919	59.19
20	10	5.0 % (x $1,000)	.5584	27.92

| | | | Present worth of | |
| Totals | | 100.0 % (x $1,000) | deferred credits = | $758.10 |

Reduction in present worth of net salvage credits by postponing retirement
= 1,000.00 - 758.10 = $241.90

The shortcut calculation (see text) is $C\left(\dfrac{i}{i + {}^{\beta}_{i}d}\right)$,

where:

C = ultimate net salvage; here, $1,000.

i = MAR in percent; here 6%.

${}^{\beta}_{i}d$ = the depreciation annuity; here, for 5-year life and Type SC probability = 18.80% (see text).

$$1,000 - \frac{1,000}{(1 + 0.06)^5} = 1,000 - \frac{1,000}{1.338226}$$

$$= 1,000 - 747.26 = \$252.74$$

A better shortcut, described at the bottom of Table 12.12, is a close approximation, whatever the type of dispersion, and is a rigorous calculation if the probability of retirement is a constant at all ages (that is, Type SQ). This recommended method of estimate may be described as follows:

1. Make the best possible estimate of remaining life.
2. Assume Type SQ dispersion, and select ${}_{i}d$ from the appropriate table of Chapter 6 (Tables 6.16-6.19).

3. Calculate the reduction in present worth of salvage credits as $\dfrac{C(i)}{i + {}_id}$

    where C = ultimate net salvage in dollars. In this example:

    $$1,000 \left(\frac{6.00}{6.00 + 18.80}\right) = \$241.92$$

In explanation of this abbreviated expression:

$$a_{\overline{n}|} = \frac{i}{i + {}_id} = \frac{1 - v^n}{i} \qquad\qquad \text{(See Chapter 5)}$$

Thus: $\qquad\qquad\qquad v^n = 1 - i \cdot a_{\overline{n}|}$

Accordingly, dividing by v^n is equivalent to dividing by $\left(1 - \dfrac{i}{i + {}_id}\right)$

Thus, the reduction in present worth of the salvage credit is:

$$C - \left(\frac{C}{1 - \dfrac{i}{i + {}_id}}\right) = C\left(\frac{i}{i + {}_id}\right)$$

For "dispersed retirements" (that is, recognizing the weighted probability of retirement at various future dates), substitute ${}^{\beta}_{i}d$ for ${}_id$, as discussed before.

The major advantage of the preferred calculation is qualitative, though it is much more superior quantitatively. It is just as simple; it involves looking up the value of ${}^{\beta}_{i}d$ in a table, while the less desirable treatment involves looking up the value of v^n in a table. In problems where great accuracy is desirable, the calculation indicated by Table 12.12 (using the appropriate Iowa Type Curve and adjusting for changes in C with change in date if appropriate) may be programmed for computer solution.

In some problems where salvage value is small, this whole matter may be properly regarded as a rather finical nicety of small importance. On the other hand, if salvage is substantial, its treatment may be the controlling influence in management's choice between alternative courses of action. This is particularly true when disposition of land is involved. Even though not treated as a depreciable asset, the selling price of land affects the decision in the same manner as ultimate net salvage.

Note that the assumed probability over remaining life (Type SC) conforms to the initially estimated pattern of retirement (also Type SC) in Table 12.12. This conformity does not apply to ather types of dispersion. That is, if the whole-life dispersion types were R_1 and L_0, the probability over remaining life would not be R_1 or L_0. (A discussion of this point is left to the reader; see Problem 1, at the end of this chapter.) As a general rule, assumption of Type SC probability over remaining life is suggested. However, where the evaluation is important enough to justify more careful consideration, the meticulous calculation of Table 12.12 may be worthwhile, making whatever different assumption may be suitable in Column 3, as said before.

If salvage value, C, is not a constant for all dates of possible retirement, then the expected net salvage in each future year, $C_{\bar{x}}$, is to be inserted in Column 3, Table 12.12, in place of the $1,000 shown there.

Having estimated present worth of salvage credits, or the reduction in salvage credits resulting from postponement of retirement, that present worth is readily converted into its equivalent annuity over remaining life in the usual manner: by multiplying by $(i + {}^{\beta}_{i}d)$, where $i =$ MAR% and ${}^{\beta}_{i}d$ is the appropriate annuity. In this example:

$$241.92 \ (6.00\% + 18.80\%) = \$60.00 \text{ per year}$$

Income Tax Comment

Use of **PWAFRR** analysis justifies estimating income taxes for the new replacement at the lifetime-levelized rate. That is also a convenient assumption for the old existing assets, but it is not entirely consistent with the estimator's exact intent in that case.

Whether it is a satisfactory approximation may be estimated by comparing it with a trial calculation of the year-by-year tax, as suggested on page 360. However, one cannot be absolutely certain about the validity of inferences regarding tax on individual units of property drawn from group data, as was discussed in Chapter 8.

Fortunately, this uncertainty seldom affects replacement decisions significantly. It involves only the question of appropriate allowances for tax-deductible depreciation, d_t, in the years of remaining life of the old assets. It does not affect the impact of investment credit, which is not uncertain.

When the assets to be retired are capable of continued use by their second owner (and they are not to be junked), particularly for exchanges of real estate, a positive or negative tax may be imposed on capital gains at retirement, aside from the normal 48% tax on income. When such possibility exists, it is safer to discuss the particular case at hand with the company's income tax accountant rather than to attempt a solution by scrutinizing apparently applicable tax regulations, as was mentioned in Chapter 8.

Facilities Salvaged for Reuse

Sometimes new assets "displace" old facilities rather than replace them. That is, the old assets are not retired but are "demoted" to some other use within the company. This may not necessarily be an inferior use; possibly it will be the same kind of service at another location.

This reuse of old assets is always economic if their value for such purpose is greater than their net scrap value at the moment. Here we encounter one of the rare instances where it is necessary to ascertain "value," which we have repeatedly warned against.

The term "value" is used here in an exactly defined sense. We refer to the dollars that the company can avoid spending by reusing the old equipment rather than retiring it.

For example, a grinder which must be replaced because it has insufficient capacity for use on the production line may be suitable for occasional use in the toolroom, and thus postpone purchase of a new machine for toolroom use.

The major difference between the old and new machines is usually their age, and therefore their probable remaining life. The old machine is just as useful in each year, but it is expected to render that service for fewer years. There may also be differences in income tax, maintenance cost, efficiency, ultimate net salvage, and so forth. Quite often costs of removing and reinstalling are involved $(= R + L)$. Even though the labor of reinstallation (L) is the same for a new or old unit, the outlay for an old unit must be recovered within its shorter remaining life, thus increasing the revenue requirements per year.

It will be apparent that the "depreciated cost" of old assets established on this basis is not the same thing as "original cost less book depreciation accruals to date," commonly known as "depreciated book cost." Two other problems which make use of this same special concept of "value" are:

1. Determination of adequate reimbursement for useful property damaged, destroyed, or confiscated; and
2. Establishment of appropriate prices for purchase or sale of useful secondhand equipment.

In the first problem, the objective is to obtain reimbursement such that customers and stockholders of the company shall be "saved harmless" as a result of the transaction. That is, revenue requirements for the services rendered, involving outlays for the premature retirement and replacement, are to be the same (in terms of PWAFRR) as though no premature retirement and replacement had been made.

As for the second problem, the company may be willing to sell used equipment at a price below its "depreciated value," determined as described, in the interest of good public relations. Nevertheless, the amount of deliberately accepted penalty is a matter of managerial concern.

A shortcut is available for calculations of this kind. This shortcut is a reasonably good approximation when it can be assumed that the only important difference between new and old assets is their respective ages, and therefore their respective remaining service lives. This amounts to assuming that operation and maintenance expense, taxes (including income tax), insurance, and so on, are identical per year for new or old assets, and that both are equally serviceable.

In such case, the "present worth" of the remaining life of old assets is measured by a factor known as percent condition. Cost of

renewal and reinstallation of the old assets can be deducted directly to
find its corresponding present worth "in place."

Percent Condition

If annual depreciation charges did in fact reflect loss in value,
then depreciation reserve at any time would represent accumulated
loss in value, to date, of equipment currently in service. The factor
percent condition is based on this concept; it is defined as:

$$v_x = \frac{\text{Investment in plant in service - reserve}}{\text{Investment in plant in service}}$$

v_x is the complement of u_x, which is percent depreciation: $u_x = 1 - v_x$.
Thus, if initial capital investment of plant in service is $P = \$1,000$, and
percent condition is 65%, then its so-called "depreciated value" is \$750.
Percent depreciation is 75%.

v_x and u_x were originally defined in terms of human life expectancy;
therefore, they contemplate zero salvage. In applying them to physical
assets, it is customary to use the Greek letter rho (ρ) instead, which is
defined as "the ratio of computed reserve at Age h for a single radix to
the survivors of that radix." That definition automatically allows for
effects of net salvage. Thus, "depreciated value" (or preferably depreciated cost) of survivors P_x in Year x, is:

$$(1 - \rho) \cdot P_x = C_x + v_x (P_x - C_x)$$

where C_x is net salvage in Year x, not depreciable.

Practical Applications of ρ

Annual revenue requirements (lifetime-levelized) of the new and
old assets consist of:

MAR on the capital investment = i;
Depreciation on the capital investment = $\frac{\beta}{i}d$; and
All other expenses, such as taxes, operation and maintenance, and
    insurance = e.

If e is identical, in dollars per year, for new or old assets, then
the difference in annual revenue requirements between old and new assets must be:

$$P_A \ (i + \tfrac{\beta}{i}d)_A - P_B \ (i + \tfrac{\beta}{i}d)_B$$

where the P's represent respective capital investments and the paren-
thetical quantities represent respective revenue requirements for capital recovery over remaining life.

Since $i + \frac{\beta}{i}d$ are remaining-lifetime-levelized rates, the difference
in their present worth over remaining service life then represents the

differences in present worth of the alternatives. That calculation is complicated by allowances for (a) probability, in terms of retirement dispersion, and (b) salvage credits.

Calculation of ρ, at any age, is illustrated by the simple example of Table 12.13, which shows the computations for a simple survivor curve, Figure 12.1.

"Depreciated cost," as defined above, at Age x is:

$$V_x = (1 - \rho_x) \cdot P_x$$
$$= C_x + v_x (P_x - C_x)$$

Some companies prepare tables of v_x, or of ρ, for each kind of property apt to be involved in problems of this kind, for convenient handling of frequently encountered transactions.

Note that percent condition so established for this specific application is premised on a lifetime-levelized group-basis percentage $\overset{p}{\underset{i}{\beta}}d$. No other depreciation annuity can satisfy the exact intent of the calculation.

A well-known publication of the Iowa Engineering Equipment Station, Bulletin 156 (1942), entitled Condition-Percent Tables for

Table 12.13. Illustrative calculation of percent condition (= ρ).

For a simple survivor curve, per Figure 12.1; 2-year life; 10% ultimate net salvage. MAR 6%; $\underset{6}{\beta}d$ = 49.073, as follows:

Year	Mean Survivors per Figure 12.1	Present Worth Factors	Present Worth of Survivors
1	0.975	0.943 396	0.919 811
2	.725	.889 996	.645 247
3	.275	.839 619	.230 895
4	.025	.792 094	.019 802
		Total	1.815 755

$$\underset{6}{\beta}d = \frac{1}{1.815\ 755} - 6\% = 49.073$$

The calculation of ρ, end of year	1	2	3	4
1. Reserve, first of year	0.0000	0.3843	0.3104	0.0333
2. Less retirements before accrual	-0.0250	-0.2250	-0.2250	-0.0250
3. Plus salvage credit (10% of Line 2)	0.0025	0.0225	0.0225	0.0025
4. Reserve balance before accrual	-0.0225	0.1818	0.1079	0.0108
5. Return at 6% of Line 4	-0.0013	0.0109	0.0065	0.0007
6. (1 - c) · $\underset{6}{\beta}d$ times mean survivors	0.4306	0.3202	0.1214	0.0110
7. Total accrual (Line 5 + Line 6)	0.4293	0.3311	0.1279	0.0117
8. Plus first of year reserve (Line 1)	0.0000	0.3843	0.3104	0.0333
9. Subtotal (Line 7 + Line 8)	0.4293	0.7154	0.4383	0.0450
10. Less retirements during year	-0.0500	-0.4500	-0.4500	-0.0500
11. Plus salvage credits (10% of Line 10)	0.0050	0.0450	0.0450	0.0050
12. Year-end reserve	0.3843	0.3104	0.0333	0.0000
13. Year-end survivors	0.9500	0.5000	0.0500	0.0000
14. Depreciated cost (Line 13 - Line 12)	0.5657	0.1896	0.0167	0.0000
15. Percent condition (ρ) $\dfrac{\text{Line 14}}{\text{Line 13}}$	59.55%	37.92%	33.40%	Zero

Note that ρ (= Line 15) is a percentage of mean survivors each year, not a percentage of the initial placement of unity.

Year	1	2	3	4
Retirements	0.050	0.450	0.450	0.050
Mean Survivors	0.975	0.725	0.275	0.025

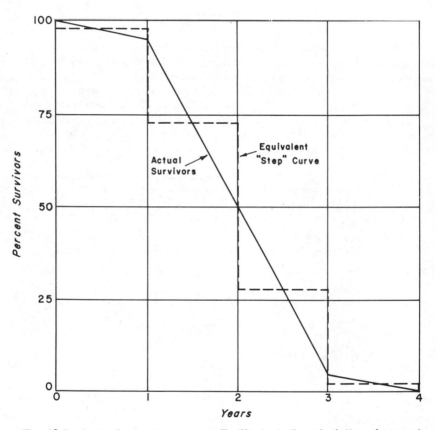

Fig. 12.1. A simple survivor curve. To illustrate the calculation of percent condition, in Table 12.13.

Depreciation of Unit and Group Properties presents material often used for the present purpose. Unfortunately, the data are not appropriate. They are based on the unit-summation procedure, which departs from the group-basis calculation which is essential to the estimator's exact intent.

The unit-summation procedure does not produce a lifetime-levelized depreciation annuity; it is a different percentage each year. For reasons explained in Chapter 6, the "straight-line" depreciation reserve does not produce the intended percent condition. Nothing but the group-basis compound interest calculation, illustrated by Table 12.13, can carry out the intent of the procedure.

Résumé

    I. Studies of economic replacement have the same objective as studies of initial placements: to discover the course of action of greatest benefit to pre-project shares. That calls for estimates of revenue requirements.

    II. Usually the objective is a yes-or-no decision as to (a) immediate replacement versus (b) continued use of existing assets. Sometimes other questions may be asked, such as: If immediate replacement is not justified, how long will it be before it is? What is the optimal life of equipment? What is the maximum justified outlay for an unusual repair, as an alternative to replacement? Should the old assets be scrapped or reused?

    III. The appropriate procedure is not affected by the fact that replacement is necessary as the result of previous incorrect decisions. Revenue requirements of new replacements are not affected by the fact that the installation happens to be a replacement.

    IV. Only in special and unusual cases is it possible to ignore the impact of future outlays for: (a) eventual replacement of the immediate replacement; and (b) replacement of piecemeal retirements of shorter-lived components of the project, occurring before the eventual replacement of the immediate installation.

    V. Presentation of the general subject of economic replacement may be simplified by first describing a special case, illustrated by Example 1: replacement of a rented property by new company-owned assets. This eliminates questions with respect to remaining life, salvage, and income tax on existing old assets. It also permits simple determination of the appropriate period of study.

    VI. When property is rented, there is no revenue requirement for income tax (= T). Earnings are still realized from the project and income tax thereon (= T'). MRRD eliminates a self-contradiction in this connection that is inherent in other approaches, such as the Annual Cost, Discounted Cash Flow, and Percentage Return Methods.

    VII. The concept of a continuing plant, permitting solutions by comparison of the PWAFRR's, is ordinarily the simplest approach which conforms most nearly to the estimator's exact intent. Common criticism of the PWAFRR approach is based on misconceptions encouraged by the unsound Annual Cost reasoning.

    VIII. Further advantages of the PWAFRR approach is illustrated by Example 2: replacement of a company-owned property by a rental. This also is a simple case, devised to simplify presentation of the general subject of economic replacement. It introduces details of importance such as: (a) the reason why unrecovered cost of old assets to date (that is, the amount they have been depreciated to date) is of no consequence. Return and depreciation on the old assets can be ignored; (b) the treatment of salvage credits, for the old assets; (c) income tax estimates, old assets; and (d) the appropriate period of study.

IX. Example 3 describes the usual case: company-owned existing old assets to be replaced by new company-owned property. The continuing plant solution is again found to be simplest and most satisfactory.

X. Optimal life (the service life that produces minimized lifetime revenue requirements, or minimized revenue requirements per unit of output) is illustrated by Example 4: optimal life of automobiles. This problem is a little off-beat in that it hypothesizes a choice of service life, firmly anticipated, and examines resultant revenue requirements to arrive at a company policy with respect to normal retirement date.

XI. Example 5 illustrates the estimation of maximum justified outlay for unusual repairs at any age of assets as an alternative to replacement. The first step is ordinarily to discover whether the proposed repair would be justified by one year's postponement of the replacement.

XII. Often the facts of the case do not permit a solution in the simple manner of XI (one year's postponement of a replacement). Usually the cost of the unusual repair must be justified by more than one year's postponement of replacement, but it is reasonable to expect that more than one year's postponement could be realized. Helpful procedures in such cases are described.

XIII. In general, determinations of "value" are unnecessary and should be avoided, because it is difficult if not impossible to assign an exact quantitative meaning to the term. However, a few special problems where it is convenient to utilize the concept of "depreciated cost" in the exact sense of the minimum alternative outlays that would be necessary to produce identical sales and revenues include: (a) the decision to scrap versus reuse old assets when replaced; (b) determination of adequate reimbursement for useful property damaged, destroyed, or confiscated; and (c) establishment of appropriate prices for sale or purchase of usable secondhand equipment.

XIV. A shortcut solution, often appropriate in problems such as listed in XIII, applies the concept of percent condition. This factor (ρ), defined as "the ratio of computed reserve, at Age h for a single radix, to the survivors of that radix" permits quick solutions in cases where annual expenses (other than depreciation expense) are identical for the respective old assets and their alternative replacement. The replacement differs only by reason of its greater probable remaining life.

XV. ρ may be evaluated, for any probable average life, type of dispersion, MAR, and salvage percentage by no other means than the group-basis compound-interest calculation, which is described.

XVI. In estimating reduced expense realized by retirement of old assets, great care must be taken to ascertain whether the expenses will actually be eliminated or simply absorbed by other existing projects, as by shifting superfluous operators to other departments.

XVII. A common form of textbook problem suggests, "Assume a study period of n years." Such arbitrary selection of a period for study is not the analyst's intent, however, and does not accomplish his purpose. Such instructions clearly indicate their author's incompetence. The exact intent of the study is to discover the financial effect of proposals from now on. Any finite end point to the study is, at best, only an approximation of the exact intent.

XVIII. This chapter discusses the diagnosis and Step 1 analysis of replacement proposals. The remaining analyses of the decision process (Step 2, sensitivity tests if necessary, and the budgeting function) are performed in the same manner as for other types of problems. See Chapter 9.

Contrary to superficial popular opinion, perhaps fostered by an opinion of the United States Supreme Court, it is not making charges for depreciation that "maintains the integrity of investment," prevents wasting away of investors' capital commitments, or protects stockholders against squandering of their resources. It is the profitable reinvestment of funds obtained from depreciation charges and elsewhere, in lieu of return of capital (as cash) to the investor, that accomplishes such purpose.

The preoccupation of many writers with fancied need for increased depreciation charges and with imaginary "reinvestment rate" problems, while ignoring the clear obligation for physical replacements associated with every investment decision, is a serious weakness of this technology. Chapter 13 emphasizes some types of problems where this essential importance of stockholder welfare is even more clearly apparent than in replacement economics.

Problems

1. Referring to page 360, an alternative method of solving Example 2 may be described, based on a comparison of the PWRR's of:

   A'. Revenue requirements over remaining life of the old assets if retained, versus

   B'. Revenue requirements over the same period if replacement is immediate.

   Describe the conditions under which this approach would yield the same answer as the preferred approach. Comment on this procedure.

2. On page 373 it is pointed out that the probable rate of retirement over remaining life, at any date after installation, remains Type SC if the whole-life pattern is SC; but this is not true for any other type of dispersion (excepting one technicality: SQ). Illustrate, and explain the situation.

3. Repeat Example 1, assuming all conditions as in the text except for a service life of 10 years. Compare solutions reached in all four ways:

   a. Annual revenue requirements;

   b. PWAFRR;

   c. One lifetime of revenue requirements; interim replacements charged to maintenance; and

   d. Present worth of annual capital-recovery costs at $a_{\overline{10}|}$ times the annual rate.

Comment on results.

4. Repeat Example 2, assuming all conditions as in the text except for a service life of 10 years and present assets that are 4 years old.

5. Repeat Example 3, assuming all conditions as in the text except for a service life of 10 years and old existing assets that are currently 4 years old.

6. Find the optimal life of automobiles in Example 4 if there were no liberalized depreciation nor investment credit provisions of tax law; the tax rate is 48%; "straight-line" depreciation is used.

7. In Example 5, what is the maximum justified outlay for an unusual repair at Age 3?

8. Illustrate use of the expression for n, page 370, by proposing an example of your own.

9. Illustrate use of the shortcut calculation for present worth of net salvage credits, Table 12.12, by proposing an example of your own.

10. Calculate ρ at each year end, in the manner of Table 12.13, for 4, SQ; ultimate net salvage is zero.

11. One engineering economy textbook makes the statement that if net salvage is zero, while operation and maintenance expense are increasing each year, the most economical life obtainable is one year.

At least three factors commonly experienced contradict that statement. What are they?

12. Several technical papers that have been published present rules for economic replacement based on the central idea that for minimized costs, equipment should be retired the first time it needs repair after reaching estimated service life. Explain what is wrong.

13. In recent years, a great deal of propaganda has been circulated in favor of income tax reduction by way of shorter service life, for tax purposes, than suggested by the IRS in their Bulletin F. Usually such material points to the advanced average age of machine tools, particularly textile machinery, to "prove" that it is obsolete. What is wrong with such argument?

(Hint: Milton Berle explained the replacement of his day-old Cadillac by saying that the gas tank went dry.)

14. When replacement of a nearly new machine is proposed, managements'

first reaction is often to ask, "How much depreciation has been recovered to date?"

Explain: (a) why that is a natural reaction of the uninformed, and (b) why it is of no moment.

15. One writer has tried to clarify the misunderstanding of Problem 14 by suggesting that residual undepreciated (unamortized) investment be recognized as a loss of capital at retirement. Explain why this is a particularly unhelpful view, in replacement problems.

16. In public utility regulatory practice, the position is often taken that "fair" rates must recover costs currently incurred. Charges for depreciation expense (usually "straight-line" for public utilities) are treated as one "current cost," which means that "costs" of return plus depreciation are regarded as decreasing with age of equipment. Discuss the self-contradiction inherent in such reasoning.

(Hint: The price of eggs does not depend upon the age of the hen that laid them.)

17. Almost all companies practice group-basis depreciation accounting; yet it is common to encounter references to "fully depreciated property" that is still in use. One textbook even devotes attention to the special importance of such plant in studies of economic replacement. Explain why such a situation is impossible, and the imaginary result of self-contradictory reasoning.

18. Anticipated reduction in repair costs may be only one important advantage of a new replacement. It may also render better and more dependable service by reducing periods of downtime for repairs and adjustments. How would you make allowance for differences in downtime between the old assets and their replacement?

19. It has been said that the following quantities are identical: (a) present worth of one year's revenue requirements of a project; and (b) present worth of one year's postponement of PWAFRR for the project.

Is the statement correct? Explain any special assumptions or hypotheses involved in your analysis.

20. It has been asserted that the Percentage Return Method of analyzing a problem will always lead to the same conclusion as obtained by an Annual Cost analysis if both are correctly performed. Exactly what is the fallacy in that statement?

21. A familiar complaint of management, directed at their planning departments, goes something like this:

The company earns a fairly regular 10% return after income taxes. Our planning department continually recommends new projects which are expected to earn 20% or so on the new capital investment. We adopt them and find that the annual costs are just about as predicted, or perhaps a little less. Yet company earnings don't improve; we still earn the same old 10%, on the average. What is wrong with the planning department's estimates?

Apologists for the Percentage Return Method say nothing is wrong; this is a normal situation. The difference between accepting or rejecting the proposals is, in fact, (they say) measured by the 20% return.

However, competition may force reductions in the price of the product; wage and salary increases may have to be granted from time to time; perhaps the new product is of superior quality. All these extra costs and reduced revenues might have been incurred if the new projects had not been adopted. The company's average return would not then have been maintained at its 10% average, as could be realized by reason of the 20% earnings of the new projects.

Point out what is wrong with this analysis of the problem, and what these managements and planners ought to find out about economic comparisons before their stockholders discover the situation and demand economic replacement of incompetent managerial and planning personnel.

22. One of the many unsound procedures suggested for estimating minimum acceptable return goes like this. Projects under consideration for budgeting are listed in the order of their prospective earnings, as follows:

Project No.	Capital Investment	Prospective Return	Cumulative Capital Investment
1	$20,000	50% or more	$ 20,000
2	25,000	45% to 50%	45,000
3	32,500	40% to 45%	77,500
4	42,500	35% to 40%	120,000
5	60,000	30% to 35%	180,000
6	70,000	25% to 30%	250,000
7	87,500	20% to 25%	337,500

Assuming that $250,000 is to be budgeted, then funds would be supplied for such projects as promise returns of 25% or more. Accordingly, it is suggested that this indicates a "minimum acceptable rate of return" for the coming year — of 25%!

    a. Discuss the error in reasoning.

    b. The author of this proposed evaluation of MAR indicates that the percentage so estimated may often approximate 25% or more. Repeat the Annual Cost estimate of Table 12.3, using return at 20%; comment on the effect on the company's earnings per share that could be expected if decisions were to be made in such a manner.

13

• • • • • Economic • • •
Stockholder Policy

Of Concern to Stockholders

The exactly intended aim of all studies of profitability and economic choice is to promote the best interests of the owners of a business; the best interests of the stockholders of a corporation.

That is, indeed, the major objective of business in a free enterprise economy. It is not, as so often claimed, to supply human needs and desires in the form of goods and services. The real goal is more appealing to common sense, more sophisticated, and more enlightened. It is to make the supplying of human desires and needs attractive to investors because it pays. Such is the humanizing spark that makes the free enterprise economy so overwhelmingly superior to all other systems.

The central idea of the free enterprise system is creation of a climate wherein the individual, in pursuit of his own best interests, is offered motives in the form of profit incentives which bring about the greatest good for the community. An essential feature of the system is this succession of events; community benefits follow from promotion of profit inducements to individual capital suppliers, not the reverse.

Corporations are not individuals but creatures of law. They offer their securities for sale to the public. The public may accept this offer and buy the securities if the inducement is sufficient. These investors make up their own minds as to the sufficiency of the inducement. If they buy a security because they like the way the company treats its labor, its management, or the public at large, while ignoring the matter of earnings and dividends, that is their privilege. However, not many investors are fools; they do not exercise such a "privilege." If events seem to indicate any such situation, it is more probable that stockholders discovered the facts too late; not that they endorsed such a foolish viewpoint.

To judge from the minutes of innumerable stockholders' annual meetings, it is generally taken for granted that management has the best interests of stockholders in mind, as their first duty. But to judge from much else that has been written on this subject, grave danger results in taking so much for granted. For example, a 1962 prize-winning essay asserted that there is no law to support the view that the managers have a duty to protect the stockholder's interests.

Investors in corporate securities would do well to inquire occasionally whether the companies they "own" a part of are really operated for the benefit of labor, management, and/or the public at large, rather than for owners who supplied the money. They may find, as Berle and Means observed as long ago as 1932, that "accounting conducted to serve the purposes of stockholders and related to their viewpoint"[1] is unexpectedly regarded as obsolete doctrine by some.

How many stockholders are aware whether their managements make decisions by relying on such unsound techniques as the Payout Period, Annual Cost, Discounted Cash Flow, or Percentage Return Methods? As demonstrated in Chapter 11, decisions reached in such manner are not necessarily in the best interests of stockholders. If this question has ever been raised at a stockholders' meeting, no record of the incident has been discovered. Stockholders' meetings customarily give much more attention to other matters, of relatively small importance to owners of the business.

Obviously, the welfare and wishes of consumers (buyers of the company's output) and its employees (including management) must be considered. However, it is the capital that investors are induced to supply, of their own free will, that makes the whole thing possible. The stockholders' welfare and desires are paramount. Usually, stockholders are in a position to enforce them; it is the intent of the system that this should be.

The first concern of a business, as of a nation, is survival; hence, the need to make decisions which place the company in the best position to meet competition, with the least adverse effect on earnings per share. Along with that is the need to make investment in the company attractive to outsiders (newcomers) by providing the inducement of regularly increasing dividends per share to pre-project shares as every new project is considered, together with associated capital gains. This minimizes cost of capital, along with desirable minimizing of all other costs of doing business, which permits minimizing the price of the company's product; and the circle is complete. Minimized cost of capital is a major objective of MRRD.

Ideal Capital Structure

Management can do certain things to reduce the revenue requirement representing cost of capital. The arithmetic involved is poorly understood, which accounts for acceptance of such fallacies as the widely accepted notion that "new common stock financing dilutes

---

[1]Adolph A. Berle and Gardiner C. Means, The Modern Corporation and Private Property (Macmillan, New York, 1932).

For a brief review and pertinent references, see David H. Li, "The Objective of the Corporation Under the Equity Concept," Accounting Review (October, 1964), p. 946.

common equity and therefore should be avoided," which is discussed in Appendix B.

A competent management will recognize that occasions arise when external financing is highly desirable from the standpoint of existing stockholders; failing to offer new issues would mean an opportunity missed. Similarly, occasions arise when it is distinctly to the advantage of stockholders to increase the percentage of debt in the company's capital structure.

Businessmen have long been intrigued by the idea of an "ideal" capital structure, meaning the optimized combination of the several kinds of debt and equity. Although much has been written on the subject, the greater part of it is a parroting of opinionated orthodoxy of little or no merit. A great deal of it is unsound.

The Minimum Revenue Requirements Discipline supplies the first need, a simple and crystal-clear definition of intent: The ideal capital structure is such that will result in minimized revenue requirement for return (= MAR on the company pool of investors' committed capital) plus taxes.

Practical Considerations

Achieving the ideal goal so described is not so easy, for obvious reasons. Some of the factors involved are not completely predictable, despite theoretical relations between degree of risk and related rate of return on equity as affected by "leverage." However, it is possible to stipulate the major influences involved, whose evaluation calls for skilled judgment and foresight in addition to observance of the appropriate arithmetic. These influences are:

1. Investor reaction to a change in debt ratio, by way of market price of the company's securities, apart from financial success of the enterprise and state of the money market in general (both assumed to be the same regardless of the company's debt structure);
2. Tax law, present and probable future; and
3. Desirable allowance for flexibility, to permit taking advantage of short-term situations in the money market and their correlation with the company's needs for incremental capital.

The tax advantage of debt in the capital structure is well recognized; interest on debt is deductible from earnings in computing taxable income. That desirable reduction in the revenue requirement for income tax must be weighed against investment reaction to: (a) the increased earnings on equity, out of the same gross income, as the result of "leverage"; and (b) the associated increase in risk that is attached to earnings on equity, from this same cause.

Thus, the analyst must first of all attempt to anticipate investor reaction to a proposed change in debt ratio, and then discover at what point the effect of that reaction outweighs the opposed effect of the tax reduction. The first question cannot be answered by arithmetic alone; it is a matter for shrewd judgment. But that judgment cannot be exercised without taking into account the combined arithmetical effect (that is, of a probable change in market price and of a calculable tax reduction) on revenue requirements; hence the inescapable dependence on MRRD.

The amount of corporate debt affects only $T\%$ (federal income tax on earnings of MAR). It does not affect $T'\%$ (tax payable on earnings in excess of MAR). Once more we encounter the importance of this fact which is recognized by no approach other than MRRD.

An Illustrative Example

To illustrate, suppose we are considering the advisability of a reduction in the debt ratio of a company which is presently capitalized as follows, with MAR at 6%:

$$
\begin{array}{llr}
\text{Debt} & 60\% \text{ at } 4\% \text{ interest} & = 2.40\% \\
\text{Equity} & 40\% \text{ at } 9\% \text{ MAR on equity} & = 3.60 \\
& \text{Minimum acceptable return} & = 6.00\%
\end{array}
$$

Income tax at 48% would add a tax, before deductible depreciation, of: $0.48/0.52 \times 3.60 = 3.32\%$.

Effects of liberalized depreciation and the investment credit would reduce the revenue requirement for income tax to a figure substantially less than this 3.32%. Here is where it becomes necessary to consider the effects of service life, salvage, and accounting procedures on d' and d_t, as discussed in Chapter 8.

However, the impact of all these factors on the revenue requirement for income tax remains the same, in any given case, regardless of debt ratio. Accordingly, for simplicity we will examine the effect of a change in debt ratio on MAR + tax before deductible depreciation or investment credit. In other words, how will a change in debt ratio affect the quantity $6.00 + 3.32 = 9.32\%$? Any change in debt ratio that would reduce it below 9.32% would be desirable.

Consider, then, the effect of reducing debt ratio from 60% to 50% in this example. This might conceivably effect a small decrease in the interest rate on any new borrowings, because debt-service needs would be covered by a larger margin, out of identical total earnings.

If "all other things remained the same" (ceteris paribus), one might logically expect equity owners to now be satisfied with MAR on equity of less than 9%. That is, the company's overall risk remains the same as before; or if the effect is to reduce percentage revenue requirements, a small increase will result in the Profit Incentive (the margin of earnings above a fixed MAR) out of identical sales and revenues. Therefore, company MAR would decrease a little if it changed at all.

The overall risk of obtaining gross income remains the same, or is reduced slightly, as the expected result of reduced revenue requirements. The reduced revenue requirements produce either:

1. Increased earnings for equity without change in overall risk;
2. Increased earnings for equity with reduction in risk assumed by stockholders as a result of the decreased debt service out of identical gross income; or
3. Identical earnings for equity with reduction in risk assumed by stockholders by using the potential increase in Profit Incentive to improve the firm's competitive position via price reductions on its output.

Assuming, then, that total MAR were to remain at 6% (no change in overall company risk) and that interest on debt remains at 4% (both assumptions on the conservative side), the breakdown of MAR becomes:

$$
\begin{array}{lll}
\text{Debt} & 50\% \text{ at } 4\% \text{ interest} & = 2.00\% \\
\text{Equity} & 50\% \text{ at } 8\% \text{ MAR on equity} & = \underline{4.00} \\
& \text{Minimum acceptable return} & = \overline{6.00\%}
\end{array}
$$

The arithmetic is inescapable. Buyers of new stock issues can be logically expected to bid a higher market price for the newly anticipated earnings on equity, reducing MAR on equity to 8% instead of the foregoing 9%. Such reasoning, however, ignores effects of income tax. With income tax at 48%, income tax before deductible depreciation or investment credit would now be: $(0.48/0.52) \times 4.00 = 3.69\%$ instead of the previous 3.32%. And the revenue requirement for return plus so-modified income tax would become $6.00 + 3.69 = 9.69\%$, instead of 9.32%; an increase of 0.37%.

Thus, to obtain the additional return on equity of 0.40% (= 4.00 - 3.60) out of the same gross income, revenue requirements must increase by 0.37% (= 9.69 - 9.32), even though: (a) overall MAR remained at 6%; and (b) stockholders behaved "logically" and bid up market prices so as to reduce MAR on equity from 9% to 8%. Because total revenue requirements now increase slightly, Profit Incentive is reduced slightly out of identical sales and revenues. We would no longer have arithmetical justification for assuming that MAR on equity would "logically" drop from 9% to 8%. In brief, it might be anticipated that revenue requirements would increase at least 0.37% as the result of reducing debt ratio from 60% to 50%. But more can be said on this subject.

Evaluating Possibilities

Investor reaction is not always 100% logical nor predictable. Suppose that an announced intention to reduce debt ratio could be expected to reduce interest rate on new borrowings slightly, so that eventually the 4% interest rate on outstanding debt might become 3.9%. Were it not for the offsetting effect of income tax, this would not be illogical, as discussed above.

It is then possible to set up "target" values for (a) interest rate on debt, and (b) MAR on equity which, in combination with associated taxes, would result in a revenue requirement for return plus tax of 9.32% or less (that is, the estimated rate with the existing 60% debt or less), if that logical reaction could be counted on.

To illustrate, assuming that reducing debt ratio to 50% reduced interest rate from 4.0% to 3.9%, what must MAR on equity be to result in a revenue requirement for return plus tax before deductible depreciation and investment credit of 9.32%?

$$\text{Debt } 50\% \text{ at } 3.9\% = 1.95\%$$

Thus, the equity component of return, to be added to the 1.95% for interest, would be:

$$\frac{9.32 - 1.95}{1.9231} = 3.83\%$$

The denominator, 1.9231, represents one dollar of return on equity plus the tax (of [0.48/0.52] x 1 = 92.31 cents) on that taxable income. Restated, as before:

$$\begin{aligned}
\text{Debt} \quad & 50\% \text{ at } 3.9\% \text{ interest} & = 1.95\% \\
\text{Equity } & 50\% \text{ at } \bar{x}\% \text{ MAR on equity} & = \underline{3.83} \text{ (as above)} \\
& \text{Minimum acceptable return} & = \overline{5.78}\%
\end{aligned}$$

and $\bar{x}\%$ = 3.83/0.50 = 7.66% MAR on equity. Income tax would be (0.48/0.52) 3.83 = 3.54% (before deductible depreciation and investment credit). Return plus such adjusted income tax would be = 9.32%, as stipulated.

It is not unreasonable to expect that stockholders might bid up market price (that is, the price/earnings ratio might increase) sufficiently to produce 7.66% MAR on equity, as the result of an announced policy to reduce debt ratio. In such a case, the reduction would be justified. Here is where skillful debt management can prove its worth, by anticipating and taking advantage of such market situations. It is not a matter of arithmetic alone.

It is no doubt obvious that a tax levied on sales or gross receipts accentuates the above calculated differential in revenue requirements. For example, if a 10% tax is imposed on gross receipts, then reducing revenue requirements for return plus tax from 9.69% to 9.32% would reduce also the revenue requirement for gross receipts tax, as follows:

Return Plus "Modified" Income Tax		Return, Plus "Modified"[2] Income Tax, Plus Gross Receipts Tax	Gross Receipts Tax at 10%
9.69%	÷ 0.90 =	10.77%	1.08%
9.32%	÷ 0.90 =	10.36%	1.04%
	Reduction in gross receipts tax		0.04%

This was discussed in Chapter 9. Technically, the alteration in MAR also changes the depreciation annuity $(\beta_i d)$ slightly, so that gross receipts taxes are modified further by the miniscule amount. Quantitatively, this may be safely ignored.

Ideal Capital Structure; Conclusions

Three general conclusions may be drawn from the foregoing discussion of ideal capital structure:

First, advice of "authorities" who urge any particular debt ratio as desirable without supporting their recommendations with analyses of resultant MAR and taxes thereon, in the general manner just described, need not be taken too seriously.

Second, more is involved in the art of corporate financing than the analysis of its effect on revenue requirements; the revenue requirements analysis is all that is under discussion here.

Third, on those occasions when a company's capital stock is enjoying special favor, debt reduction may be desirable indeed. It may be accomplished by calling bonds before maturity, by new stock issues, by maintaining a regular dividend rate despite improved earnings per share, and so on, as circumstances dictate. Even though little or no reduction in revenue requirements for "MAR plus tax" may be accomplished, the reduced debt ratio increases freedom of action in obtaining future short-term bank loans, or in taking advantage of future temporary periods of low interest rates on borrowings. On the other hand, an increase in debt ratio may be even more beneficial when circumstances are temporarily favorable for it, whether achieved by issuing incremental debt at the unusually low interest rate, by declaring extra dividends, or by buying up outstanding common shares in the market.

Potentialities of Bond Refunding

From time to time, the interest rate investors demand on a new issue of bonds will vary within a moderate range. This suggests the possibility of replacing outstanding bonds bearing a high interest rate by a new issue paying the lower rate. Assuming that this transaction

---

[2]For simplicity, income tax is stated as the amount before deductible depreciation and investment credit; thus "modified."

would have no effect on MAR on equity, it reduces revenue requirements by reducing the company MAR on its pool of investors' committed capital.

However, related details that operate in the opposite direction are:

1. It is ordinarily necessary to pay a premium, stipulated in the indenture, for exercising this privilege of calling bonds in advance of
maturity.
2. Certain expenses are incurred in making the exchange. Similar expenses (so far as can be anticipated) would presumably be incurred
at maturity, but the advancement in date of the outlay is a penalty.
Advancement in date of expense outlay at issuance extends to the
whole chain of future succession, in the manner discussed for normal replacements of plant, in Chapter 12. However, the significance of the present worth of such remote events is so small that
they can be ignored, as a practical matter.
3. Because the exchange cannot be accomplished instantaneously, a
brief period (perhaps one month) lapses, during which interest is
paid on both the old bonds and their successors.
4. A meticulous consideration of effect on income taxes might conceivably indicate a small penalty from this source, as a result of
the reduction in deductible interest.

Table 13.1 illustrates the calculations appropriate in connection
with replacing $35,000,000 (face value) of 30-year 5% bonds by an equal
amount of 30-year 4% bonds, 25 years prior to maturity; MAR is 6%.

Data reproduced, with permission, from:

Roy H. Berglund, "A Practical Application of the Revenue Requirement Technique as an Aid in Decision Making," Proceedings of the Iowa
State Conference on Public Utility Valuation and the Rate-Making Process, 1963.

Copies of this paper, which is the most authoritative treatment of
the subject to date, are available from Iowa State University, Ames.

As noted before, the present treatment does not purport to be an
exhaustive discussion of the art of bond refunding. A great deal of expert judgment is involved, particularly in the matter of the most advantageous timing. When interest rates are falling, the question arises
whether to act immediately or to wait for still lower rates or new issues while continuing to pay the existing higher interest on the outstanding issues. A set of curves to facilitate exercise of judgment is
part of the Berglund paper not reproduced here.

The major point on which this approach departs from conventional
procedure is in its use of MAR as the appropriate discount rate. Use
of other rates (usually the bond interest percentage is proposed) as the
discount rate betrays failure to comprehend the exact reason for the
transaction. The essential reason is the by-now-familiar dual objective of all economic studies, restated at the beginning of this chapter:
optimized benefits to stockholders on two counts.

Table 13.1 Economic study: Refunding of bonds prior to maturity. Change in revenue requirements resulting from replacing $35 million, 5%, 30-year bonds with $35 million, 4%, 30-year bonds 25 years prior to maturity.

Year	Decreases in Rev Req Interest Reductions*	Increases In Revenue Requirements				Net Change In Revenue Requirements		
		Call Premium	One Months' Double Interest	Costs of New Issue†	Total	Annual Amount	Present Worth at 6% Factor	Amount
0	$	$1,448,276	$145,833	$	$1,594,109	$1,594,109	1.000 000	$1,594,109
1	355,173			29,928	29,928	-325,245	.943 396	-306,835
2	355,173			29,928	29,928	-325,245	.889 996	-289,467
3	355,173			29,928	29,928	-325,245	.839 619	-273,082
4	355,173			29,928	29,928	-325,245	.792 094	-257,625
5	355,173			29,928	29,928	-325,245	.747 258	-243,042
6	355,173			29,928	29,928	-325,245	.704 961	-229,285
7	355,173			29,928	29,928	-325,245	.665 057	-216,306
8	355,173			29,928	29,928	-325,245	.627 412	-204,063
9	355,173			29,928	29,928	-325,245	.591 898	-192,512
10	355,173			29,928	29,928	-325,245	.558 395	-181,615
11	355,173			29,928	29,928	-325,245	.526 788	-171,335
12	355,173			29,928	29,928	-325,245	.496 969	-161,637
13	355,173			29,928	29,928	-325,245	.468 839	-152,488
14	355,173			29,928	29,928	-325,245	.442 301	-143,856
15	355,173			29,928	29,928	-325,245	.417 265	-135,713
16	355,173			29,928	29,928	-325,245	.393 646	-128,031
17	355,173			29,928	29,928	-325,245	.371 364	-120,784
18	355,173			29,928	29,928	-325,245	.350 344	-113,948
19	355,173			29,928	29,928	-325,245	.330 513	-107,498
20	355,173			29,928	29,928	-325,245	.311 805	-101,413
21	355,173			29,928	29,928	-325,245	.294 155	- 95,672
22	355,173			29,928	29,928	-325,245	.277 505	- 90,257
23	355,173			29,928	29,928	-325,245	.261 797	- 85,148
24	355,173			29,928	29,928	-325,245	.246 979	- 80,329
25	355,173			29,928	29,928	-325,245	.232 999	- 75,782
								$-2,563,614

*Assumes semi-annual payments. Hence one payment each year is increased by $\sqrt{1.06}$ to make equivalent to year end payment.
†Estimated total of $411,950. Annual expense is therefore annuity whose PW is $411,950 or .072649 x $411,950 = $29,928. This ignores effect of income taxes resulting from different accounting treatment which would be negligible.

Leasing Versus Owning

Examples 1 and 2 of Chapter 12 dealt with making an economic choice between owning certain property versus renting other property to serve the same purpose. In making the comparison of the alternative proposals, revenue requirements for the rented property consisted mostly of monthly rentals, which were handled as ordinary expense of the same nature as wages, repairs, insurance premiums, and taxes.

A different situation arises when a choice is to be made between owning certain assets and leasing the same assets from another owner. Regular (usually monthly) lease payments are not in the same category as ordinary expenses such as wages, repairs, insurance premiums, and taxes. Some specific portion of lease payments reimburses the other owner for his capital investment, in the form of his revenue requirements for his return plus depreciation.

In other words, the lessee (user of the assets) pays lessor (owner of the assets) agreed on amounts which include compensation for use of lessor's money. The user makes no capital outlay of his own. Of course, this is true to some degree of ordinary renting, in the manner of Example 1 of Chapter 12. For that reason, it is essential that the analyst first establish the fact that the proposed agreement truly constitutes a lease. For purposes of this economic analysis, that question hinges on the nature of obligations agreed to by the lessee. Since there are innumerable varieties of contractual agreements, this determination may call for careful scrutiny of the exact details in some cases.

If the contract specifies that the user of the property can terminate the contract at his option, on short notice, without penalty, regardless of the age of the assets or of the contract, then it is a rental. Rentals are properly treated in the same manner as outlays for ordinary expense (payrolls, and so on) if IRS concurs. This kind of contract has sometimes been called an "operating lease."

Another indicator is the ruling of IRS on deductibility of rentals in the calculation of taxable income. The critical point here is the distinction between a lease and a deferred purchase. In the latter case, rentals are not deductible.

In negotiating contracts for lease of property that would be depreciable if owned, it is customary to arrive at scheduled payments by way of a stipulated percentage return on owner's (lessor's) capital investment, plus a charge sufficient to recover the investment over a term corresponding more or less to a "payout" period, commonly somewhat less than probable service life.

This permits calculation of the lessee's gradually reducing residual obligation at any date. This introduces the subject of "disclosure" of the company's lease commitments in its financial statements. Contracts of this kind, typified by a noncancellable obligation to make periodic payments which will amount in total to more than the purchase price (or more than service value, which is purchase price less ultimate net salvage) of the property, are the subject of this analysis.

They have sometimes been called "financial leases" to distinguish them from the foregoing "operating leases" or rentals.

"Disclosure" of Lease Details

It is not apparent just why the appropriate reporting of a company's lease obligations in its regular financial reports (income statement, balance sheet, and so on) should be regarded as posing such a difficult problem.

A number of different procedures have been suggested. One is to forget the whole thing. On occasion it has even been asserted that a primary objective of long-term leasing is to avoid showing these obligations as liabilities on the financial statements.

The philosophy that "What owners of the business don't know won't hurt them" has been paralleled by a similar attitude toward the company's creditors. It has been pointed out that vehicles are sometimes not bondable, in conformance to stipulations of the company's bond indentures; but unless specifically agreed otherwise, they can be leased. Thus (although not stated in these words) leasing is said to be a "desirable" means for invalidating a good-faith contract with bondholders!

Whatever one's feeling about the ethics of such proposals, they obviously do not constitute a sound basis for evaluating benefits to stockholders; hence the introductory remarks at the opening of the chapter. It is not our purpose to evaluate "benefits" obtainable by misinforming or misleading the investors who own the business.

A more usual device is to supply full information in footnotes to the financial statements. There are two weaknesses in this procedure. The fuller the disclosure, the more the mass of indigestible data in fine print which nobody reads; the financial impact of the situation is not made readily apparent.

Another suggestion, which appeals to some because it sounds "technical" is to capitalize future payments to be made under existing lease contracts. This does not make much sense; and there is no way to determine the capitalized figure — it can only be estimated. Nobody (to the writer's knowledge) has ever suggested capitalizing obligations to pay interest on debt for purposes of the balance sheet. A substantial part of the lease payments represents interest.

A fourth suggestion, which has almost been proposed by an American Institute of Certified Public Accountants Project Advisory Committee, is as follows:

It seems doubtful that any lawyer would approve a lease contract that leaves in doubt the lessee's residual obligation at any time. As noted before, it is customary to specify the method of calculating the lessor's gradually reducing unamortized residual of his capital investment, along with the assumed rate of interest used to establish the amount of the lessee's regular payments.

The lessor's unamortized residual investment, adjusted for any stipulated penalties, is appropriately shown at each accounting date as the lessee's outstanding obligation, similar to the remainder of an issue of serial bonds. The argument that "It is not debt" may be conceded, if necessary, as beside the point. Its effect on stockholders' equity is arithmetically the same. What we are concerned with here (so commonly overlooked) is exactly that: the effect on stockholders' welfare.

Illustrative Example

To illustrate the economic comparison of leasing versus owning, suppose a company needs a fleet of trucks whose purchase price is $100,000. They could be leased for $12,950 per year. Whether leased or owned, they will perform the same services, and the lessee (the user) is to pay for operating, repairing, garaging, licensing, insuring them, and similar expenses.

For simplicity, assume that the term of the lease is ten years, which is also the probable average life of the trucks if owned by the user.[3] Assume 10% ultimate net salvage (= turn-in allowance), realized by lessee if leased. If owned, the trucks would be depreciated at "straight-line" rate for books, SYD for taxes. The income tax rate is 48%. The company has a 40% debt ratio, with interest at 4%; the company's pool MAR is 7%. Investment credit is 7%.

The general approach is to compare one lifetime of revenue requirements for the continuing plant (that is, for a fleet of trucks maintained at the original number by replacements as necessary): (a) if owned, versus (b) if leased.

This means that it must be ascertained that the lease contract covers replacement of retirements made within its term. However, for purposes of a simplified explanation that avoids complications which distract attention from the main issue, suppose this example is presented as an after-the-fact review (post-audit), made in Year 11, of trucks that actually did serve for exactly 10 years, no more and no less.

Revenue requirements, if owned, would have been as follows:

Annual Revenue Requirements, If Owned

MAR at 7% of $100,000	= $ 7,000 per year
Depreciation (Table 6.18)	
7.24 (1.00 - 0.10) x 100,000	= 6,516
Income tax[4] 0.58 x 100,000	= 580
Revenue Requirements, if owned	= $14,096 per year

---

[3]Since the solution may be reached via comparison of present worth of revenue requirements, a term for the lease shorter than service life presents no complications.

[4]d_t (Figure 8.1b, on page 187) is 0.90 x 11.0 = 9.90% (continued on page 397).

The fantastic behavior of income tax (a negative lifetime-levelized percentage is possible, as suggested on page 218) results from operation of the investment credit provision of the 1964 law, as discussed in Chapter 8. A few comments on this situation are of interest, as follows:

First, a successful company will normally have to pay substantial income taxes, partly in the form of revenue requirements (T) on plant having service lives far removed from the critical value near 10 years, and partly in the form of tax on profit incentive (T'). These tax obligations may actually be reduced by owning plant of the kind under discussion. Here is a case where incremental plant produces a tax decrement.

Second, were it not for the effect of liberalized depreciation and investment credit, the revenue requirements for income tax, if owned, in this case would be $3,220[5] per year as against $580, a difference of $2,640. This has an important effect on the relative economics of leasing versus owning.

Third, however, the law provides that the lessor may take the benefit of the investment credit and as a result he may then reduce the contract payments accordingly. In this case, the contract payment might be reduced below the $12,950 assumed here. For this reason, the calculations described here are intended to present a correct method only. They do not purport to be typical quantitatively.

The whole point of the economic comparison is to discover the benefits of leasing versus owning to owners of the business; that is, the benefits to stockholders. Stockholders feel the effects of the change in the income tax situation, if plant is leased, in a manner similar to that encountered when debt ratio is changed in the foregoing discussions of ideal capital structure and bond refunding. This effect, not an academic theory, is arithmetical and unavoidable, but it is almost always overlooked.

In the situation reviewed in Table 13.2 we have a ten-million-dollar plant, to which an addition of $100,000 is to be made. MAR is 7%; company debt outstanding is 40% at 4% interest:

	Before Addition	After Addition
Debt	$ 4,000,000 at 4% = $160,000	$ 4,040,000 at 4% = $161,600
Equity	6,000,000 at 9% = 540,000	6,060,000 at 9% = 545,400
Totals	$10,000,000 at 7% = $700,000	$10,100,000 at 7% = $707,000

MAR remains 7%, because percentage debt remains the same 40%. But suppose the addition were made by increasing the amount of debt only:

IC is $7\% \left(\dfrac{0.07 + 0.0724}{1.07} \right)$ $= 0.93$

Thus, $t\% = \dfrac{0.48}{0.52} \left[(7.00 + 6.52 - 9.00) \left(1 - \dfrac{0.40 \times 4}{7} \right) - (d_t - 9.00) - IC \right] - IC$

$= 0.9231 \left[(4.52) (0.77) - 0.90 - 0.93 \right] - 0.93 = 0.58$

[5] $\dfrac{0.48}{0.52} \left[(7.00 + 6.52 - 9.00) (1 - \dfrac{0.40 \times 4}{7}) \right] = 3.22\%$, or $3,220 per year

After Addition, Debt Increased

Original debt	$ 4,000,000 at 4% =	$160,000
Added debt	100,000 at 4% =	4,000
Equity	6,000,000 at 9% =	540,000
Totals	$10,100,000 at ?% =	$704,000

This would mean that MAR could be reduced from 7% to 6.97% (= 704,000/10,100,000) by increasing the amount of debt. If that were true, it would mean that new stock issues could be sold at the same price per share no matter how much the prior debt obligations of the company. It just is not true.

The revenue requirement analysis starts by investigating the situation if MAR were to be identical for all alternatives. Adopting the superior plan (the one having smaller revenue requirements for the same sales and revenues) will tend to reduce MAR%, thus reinforcing the advantage of making the right selection (that is, it tends to increase the margin between actual earnings and MAR, per the Diagram of Intent.) That is, it is not predicted that MAR will in fact remain unchanged. It looks into the situation if MAR were the same.

Of course, we cannot be sure exactly how the market price of stock responds to an increase in debt. It is easy, though, to figure how much

Table 13.2. Effect of leverage.

Illustrating the inevitable arithmetical effect on MAR on equity of a change in debt ratio, with a fixed MAR percentage on the pool of investors' committed capital.

Initial capital investment	$10,000,000
Incremental capital investment	$ 100,000
Interest on debt	4%
Pool MAR	7%

I. Same Debt Ratio After Addition
(that is, incremental capital in the same proportion of debt and equity)

	Before Addition	After Addition
Debt	$ 4,000,000 at 4% = $160,000	$ 4,040,000 at 4% = $161,600
Equity	6,000,000 at 9% = 540,000	6,060,000 at 9% = 545,400
Totals	$10,000,000 at 7% = $700,000	$10,100,000 at 7% = $707,000

II. Incremental Capital 100% New Debt
(that is, an increased debt ratio, after the addition)

	(a) Same MAR on Equity (9%)	(b) Same MAR on Pool (7%)
Original debt	$ 4,000,000 at 4% = $160,000	$ 4,000,000 at 4% = $160,000
Added debt	100,000 at 4% = 4,000	100,000 at 4% = 4,000
Equity	6,000,000 at 9% = 540,000	6,000,000 at y% = 543,000*
Totals	$10,100,000 at x% = $704,000	$10,100,000 at 7% = $707,000

$$x\% = \frac{704,000}{10,100,000} = 6.97\%$$

$$y\% = \frac{543,000}{6,000,000} = 9.05\%$$

*By difference. Note also that (543,000 - 540,000) = 100,000 (MAR - b) = 100,000 (7% - 4%). That is, MAR on equity increases $3,000 per year in Part II (b).

the return on equity must increase to keep MAR constant at 7%. That is the basis for the revenue requirement comparison; we inquire into the situation if MAR were to be the same in any case.

If MAR is to remain constant at 7%, then return on equity must increase by $3,000 per year:

Original debt	$ 4,000,000 at	4% =	$160,000
Added debt	100,000 at	4% =	4,000
Equity	6,000,000 at	?% =	543,000 (by difference)
Totals	$10,100,000 at	7% =	$707,000

Thus, for MAR to remain 7%, the minimum acceptable rate on equity is 543,000/6,000,000 = 9.05%. This is nothing but arithmetic. If MAR is to remain unchanged, equity owners must obtain that extra 0.05% to break even.

Now, we cannot be sure exactly how the market price of stock responds to assuming lease obligations any more than we can be sure how it will respond to increased debt obligations. We do know that in a bad year, the effect of debt obligations on the earnings left for equity is exactly the same whether the money is borrowed from a bank, from a bondholder, or from a lease-finance company.

In the case of a lease, as in the case of serial retirement of bonds, the lessee obligates himself to reduce his indebtedness each successive year. As a result, the extra amount that must be earned for equity to break even decreases in each year of the lease. This extra return on equity is subject to federal income tax.

Table 13.3 shows how to calculate the penalty on equity plus associated income taxes, if leased, assuming the lessor amortizes the residual loan at the "straight-line" rate. In any actual problem, the rate of amortization depends upon the contractual agreement, as observed before; "straight-line" is assumed here to illustrate the principle.

This penalty, if leased, added to the lease payments of $12,950 per year, makes total revenue requirements if leased amount to $16,443 per year. Compared with revenue requirements for the same trucks if owned, leasing would be unfair to stockholders even without benefits of liberalized depreciation and the investment credit.

With benefits of the latter provisions of the 1964 tax law, revenue requirements if owned would be only $9,456 per year, as against $16,443 if the same trucks were leased. Leasing would be grossly wasteful; the difference is the direct out-of-pocket cash penalty suffered by stockholders.

Some financial analysts have mistakenly praised managements as "astute" for leasing property, when that "astute" action actually was harmful to the best interests of stockholders and creditors of the company. Such analysts did not look into revenue requirements if leased.

In the foregoing example, the decision to lease is equivalent to deliberately throwing away stockholders' hard cash in the amount of:

Table 13.3. Incremental return and taxes thereon. ($100,000 debt reduced
10% per year per lease contract; $t = 48\%$.)

Year	Residual Loan, First of Year	Incremental Return at 3% (7% - 4%)	Tax on Incre- mental Return	Total Tax and Return	Present Worth Factors at 7%	Present Worth of Total
1	$100,000*	$3,000	$2,769.23	$5,769.23	0.934 579	$ 5,391.80
2	90,000	2,700	2,492.31	5,192.31	.873 439	4,535.17
3	80,000	2,400	2,215.38	4,615.38	.816 298	3,767.53
4	70,000	2,100	1,938.46	4,038.46	.762 895	3,080.92
5	60,000	1,800	1,661.54	3,461.54	.712 986	2,468.03
6	50,000	1,500	1,384.62	2,884.62	.666 342	1,922.14
7	40,000	1,200	1,107.69	2,307.69	.622 750	1,437.11
8	30,000	900	830.77	1,730.77	.582 009	1,007.32
9	20,000	600	553.85	1,153.85	.543 934	627.62
10	10,000	300	276.92	576.92	.508 349	293.28
				Total present worth	=	$24,530.92

Levelized annual equivalent = 24,530.92 x 0.1423775 = $3,492.65

*The lessee's obligation is here assumed to represent the lessor's initial capital
investment, without any stipulated penalties, amortized by the lessor at the "straight-
line" rate over a period of 10 years — the same period as service life of the equipment.

Quite often, the amortization period may be stipulated as less than service life,
in which case the annual payments over the shorter period are to be calculated and
reduced to their different present worth; this different present worth is then converted into its levelized annual equivalent over service life.

$$\frac{16,443 - 9,456}{0.1424} = \$49,074$$

Another fault of all analyses other than MRRD is use of an incorrect discount ("interest") percentage in the discounting and annuitizing
("levelizing") calculations necessary in these economic studies.

Most writers propose using the interest rate on company debt.
Thus, in the present case, they would use 4% instead of the correct and
exactly intended 7%. Many of them propose using this same interest
rate on debt as the rate of return on the property if owned. The reader
of this book is in a position to demonstrate the error in that proposal.
No matter how the immediate deal may be financed, the only appropriate rate is the company's MAR% on its pool of investors' committed
capital. Stockholders obtain their dividends from earnings on that pool
of their committed equity capital. It is benefits of the deal to stockholders that is under investigation here.

Reasons for Leasing

Under certain special conditions, leasing property assuredly is
justified. For example, a politician would hardly consider buying an
office building just to serve as his campaign headquarters for the three
months before election.

Just as the individual finds it preferable to take a taxi on occasion rather than buying a car for a short trip away from home, so a company may find it worthwhile to lease or rent equipment which is to be used for less than its normal physical life. In effect, it is roughly equivalent to owning for this short period, with an assured large salvage value realizable at the end of its short service life.

Railroads in financial straits have found it advisable to lease rolling stock. In effect, it puts stockholders even further from hope for dividends than before; but it may keep the enterprise from bankruptcy, which would mean abandoning all hope for stockholders. It is then the lesser of two evils.

It can also be said that the foregoing example is not necessarily typical, quantitatively, of the lease-versus-own financial situation. Much depends upon the amount of the lease payments as related to their capital investment. The payment assumed in this example ($12,950 annually for a $100,000 investment in 10-year plant) is not unreasonable but not necessarily typical.

What almost no one recognizes is that a probable life near 10 years presents the least desirable opportunity for leasing. As demonstrated in Chapter 8, federal income tax reaches a minimum for life near 10 years.

To judge from reasons given by lessees who could have owned the property they lease and from claims emphasized by lease-finance companies in their advertising, the interests of stockholders get scant consideration by some managements in making lease decisions. A halfdozen of the most popular excuses for leasing (or for selling and leasing back) are enumerated in Problems 17-22, at the end of this chapter, for the reader to consider. All the excuses expose the incompetency of management. Yet how many stockholders inquire about their management's decisions in such matters at their annual meeting? They are more apt to waste time on matters of piffling importance. A homely anecdote will serve to illustrate the situation.

Imagine that you are the president of the company, addressing stockholders at their annual meeting. Your speech goes like this:

Ladies and gentlemen, during the past year we entered into a number of beneficial lease agreements. They offer some very attractive advantages, which I can quote from the advertising of finance companies that you must have seen.

For example, stockholders will be happy to know that leasing avoids tying up their capital in such property. It takes peaks and valleys out of operating costs. Our accounting department can forecast expenses more accurately. Our supervisors have fewer headaches keeping track of bills, licensing, and insurance and handling emergencies. Because lease obligations do not appear on the company's balance sheet, our normal lines of credit are left undisturbed; leasing permits 100% financing. There are many other similar benefits; but perhaps the greatest advantage of leasing is in the form of reduced income taxes.

Of course, this means that our income is reduced, which is why we reduced our dividend this year. In order to reduce taxes still further, we hope to do still more leasing in the future, which will explain additional reductions in the dividend rate, in order to obtain all these attractive advantages.

There is little doubt that the company would shortly have a new president.

Desirable Growth

A few years ago, back-yard gardeners were intrigued by a new product called giberellin. The sole function of this new material was to promote growth of plants. Treated with this substance, plants would grow rapidly to much more than normal size. Resultant blooms were scarce and deformed; vegetables were no longer fit to eat. As a growth stimulator, though, giberellin was very successful indeed. It is interesting to observe that the word comes from a Japanese expression meaning "crazy plant."

Accent on growth in the American business scene has similarly captured the imagination of a majority. The first statistic reported in annual financial reports of corporations is their growth in the current year, as compared to last year or previous years. The status symbol "growth company" threatens to replace that of "blue chip corporation." Trade magazines devote an annual issue to tabulations of growth rates, particularly to growth rates of their particular industry as compared to that of the national economy as a whole.

The comment, "You can't stand still; you must grow or stagnate," is commonly regarded as profound wisdom. The question, "How is business performance to be judged?" is said to be answered by several criteria, each one amounting to, "By its growth." Both, however, are oversimplifications which ignore familiar instances of bankruptcy resulting from unwise expansion, as well as the increased earnings and capital gains often realized by "spinning off" or just abandoning unprofitable lines of growth.

The point is that the word "growth" does not convey an exactly defined intent; it is one of the most poorly defined terms in common use, next to "depreciation."

One proposal for measuring, if not defining, growth is to rank companies by their arithmetical average of:[6]

1. Annual percentage increase in sales;
2. Annual percentage increase in net profits; and
3. Annual percentage increase in market price of the firm's common stock.

But why adopt a measure that submerges the stockholder's welfare by assigning double its weight to two other influences, both of which may operate to his disadvantage? Why is it advisable to adopt a measure which compromises the essential objective exactly expressed by

---

[6]Robert R. Young, "Keys to Corporate Growth," Harvard Business Review (November-December, 1961).

the dual objective restated at the beginning of this chapter, which is the major theme of this book?

That is, the reliable measure of economic growth, which conveys the exactly intended information sought, is a statement of Profit Incentive, or earnings in excess of the company's MAR on its pool of investors' committed capital.

Profit Incentive may be expressed in dollars, or dollars per common share, as a percentage of investors' committed capital, as a percentage of sales or revenues, or in any other form desired. However, its comprehensive nature is best expressed in terms of a percentage of common equity. This is the fundamental basis for economic decisions: Profit Incentive, in dollars, divided by book value of common equity (= dollars realized from initial sale of the stock, plus retained earnings). It is true that MAR cannot be determined absolutely; it can only be estimated. Nevertheless, it can be estimated within narrow limits, as explained in Chapter 3.

There is no apparent reason for combining the Profit Incentive indicator with other ratios, such as growth in sales or growth in net profits. An increase in sales necessary to produce a given Profit Incentive is an adverse influence. Giving it equal weight would impair the significance of the single statement of Profit Incentive. Giving weight to growth of net profits adds nothing of importance, since that variable performs the same function as the Profit Incentive measure, but less informatively and with poorer quantitative precision.

For such reasons, the Profit Incentive index to corporate growth is recommended to investors and financial analysts for their thoughtful consideration.

Note that the foregoing proposal did not suggest amount of capital investment as a measure of growth. It is probably the most popular, and certainly one of the poorest, measures of the exactly intended quality.

Cash Flow Misconceptions

The idea of cash flow as a measure of a company's financial status has captured the imagination of many in recent years. It has serious shortcomings.

Every business manager will agree that it is comforting to have an adequate flow of cash at hand to pay current bills and still leave plenty to declare as dividends or to plow back into the business. It is easy to overlook the fact that this comfortable feeling is obtained at the expense of stockholders and may not be to best advantage of the firm.

In general, two ways to go about increasing the amount of cash flow are: (a) reduce costs (outlays of capital and expenses) to produce the same amount of output for sale; and (b) increase prices charged for that same output.

The second method works well if the firm has no competition to contend with, and if its customers are willing to pay a higher price for the same purchases — which is almost never. However, a few analysts have been intrigued by what they regard as a third way to increase cash flow: by increasing depreciation expense.

On first thought, that may appear impossible; it does demand a special interpretation of "expense." The proposal amounts to pretending that the cost of depreciation has suddenly increased, when it hasn't at all, and making larger charges for depreciation expense. Of course, this means that the company must increase the price of its products in order to make the same earnings per share. Attention can be diverted from that unfavorable result by some fast talk about two other phenomena, as follows:

1. By increasing charges for depreciation expense, income taxes may be reduced; that is, if the Internal Revenue Service will permit deducting the increased charges when calculating taxable income. Of course, the tax reduction is not as great as the increased expense.
2. Cash flow is increased, if "cash flow" is defined as "net earnings plus depreciation charges." This calls for fast talk about the imaginary advantage of cash flow over dividends per share.

One way to impart confusion is by means of "before and after" tabulations, as follows. These feature "earnings before taxes and depreciation" as though they were the investors' main concern. They also describe investors' earnings as "reported net earnings," implying somewhat that just because accountants report them, the investor does not have to trust the accountants.

Here is the way the trick can be worked by such semantics:

1. Before Increasing Depreciation Expense

Earnings before taxes and depreciation	$150,000,000
Less depreciation	50,000,000
Pre-tax net income (= "taxable income")	100,000,000
Less taxes, said to be at 52% rate	52,000,000
Reported net earnings	48,000,000
Plus depreciation	50,000,000
"Cash flow" said to be	$ 98,000,000

2. After Increasing Depreciation Expense

Earnings before taxes and depreciation, as above	$150,000,000
Less increased depreciation	60,000,000
Pre-tax net income (= "taxable income")	90,000,000
Less taxes, said to be at 52% rate	46,800,000
Reported net earnings	43,200,000
Plus depreciation	60,000,000
"Cash flow" said to be	$103,200,000

Accordingly, it can be triumphantly pointed out that, despite a reduction in reported net income (from $48,000,000 to $43,200,000), cash flow has increased from $98,000,000 to $103,200,000. It might be (and has been) asserted that although the company appears to be losing ground, on the basis of reported earnings, actually it is better off and ought to be more attractive to investors — if they would only forget their poorer earnings per share and consequent loss in market price.

How does the intelligent investor look at this example? First, he observes that the tabulated increase in cash flow is the simple result of changes in two expenses: (a) an increase in depreciation expense of $10,000,000; and (b) a presumed decrease in income tax (which may or may not be realized) of only $5,200,000. The net result is an increase in expenses of $4,800,000.

It remains a fact that revenues less expenses equals earnings. Accordingly, the sensible investor observes that if expenses are increased, earnings are bound to suffer unless revenues increase.

Suppose we take a look at revenue requirements in this example. That can be readily done by assigning some figure to expenses other than depreciation and taxes; let's say $300,000,000 as follows:

1. Revenues Before Increasing Depreciation Expense

Depreciation	$ 50,000,000 ⎫	$102,000,000
Income tax	52,000,000 ⎭	
Other expenses	300,000,000	
Net earnings	48,000,000	
Revenues	$450,000,000	

2. Revenues After Increasing Depreciation Expense

Depreciation	$ 60,000,000 ⎫	$106,800,000
Income tax	46,800,000 ⎭	
Other expenses	300,000,000	
Net earnings	43,200,000	
Revenues	$450,000,000	

Nothing mystical here about "cash flow." Increase expenses and the company will earn less out of the same sales and revenues. It is childish to believe that "cash flow" is the index to profitability, yet one recent edition of a college textbook on engineering economy makes that flat statement.

In this example, observe how much revenues must be increased for the same output, by raising prices in order to obtain the same earnings per share, even if the increased depreciation charges were allowed by the IRS as deductible (which probably would not be the case):

2-A. After Increasing Depreciation Expense

Earnings before taxes and depreciation (more than 1, above)	$160,000,000
Less increased depreciation (as in 2, above)	60,000,000
Pre-tax net income (= "taxable income" as in 1, above)	100,000,000
Less taxes at 52% rate (as in 1, above)	52,000,000
Reported net earnings (as in 1, above)	48,000,000
Plus depreciation (as in 2, above)	60,000,000
"Cash flow" said to be (more than 1)	$108,000,000

Revenues would have to be:

Depreciation (as in 2, above)	$ 60,000,000
Income tax (as in 1, above)	52,000,000
Other expenses (as in all cases)	300,000,000
Net earnings (as in 1, above)	48,000,000
Total revenue (more than 1 or 2) =	$460,000,000
	(instead of $450,000,000)

The purpose of this discussion of cash flow is to point out that investors will not be misled by such foolishness if they will look into revenue requirements of proposals.[7]

Depreciation Methods

From time to time, those unfamiliar with the Minimum Revenue Requirements Discipline (MRRD) have proposed a number of reasons for increasing the amount of charges made to depreciation expense, in the fond belief that something or someone would benefit thereby.

Almost everyone thinks of "straight-line" depreciation as the normal and standard procedure, departure from which must be justified by some special reason. For example, the term "liberalized depreciation" stems from the idea of more liberal than "straight-line" in the calculation of deductibles for determination of taxable income.

Reasons for defending "straight-line" as the standard procedure are not convincing. The most familiar arguments advanced for use of "straight-line" depreciation accounting are:

1. Its claimed simplicity;
2. Its claimed accuracy in representing loss of value; and
3. Its claimed conservatism.

---

[7]In this example, the fallacy of the cash flow argument can be demonstrated by examining revenue requirements in one year. This reveals only the fallacy; it does not attempt a quantitative evaluation. That would demand an analysis of revenue requirements over the whole service lifetime of assets to be depreciated in the proposed manner.

From the stockholder's point of view, such claims are largely trivial, unsound, and possibly insincere.

Why should stockholders favor adoption of a simple depreciation method for the presumed convenience of their depreciation bookkeeper if that simpler method works to the stockholder's financial disadvantage? Why should stockholders prefer use of a simpler method in making studies of profitability or economic choice if it results in unsound and unintended decisions, to the stockholder's disadvantage?

Any method of depreciation based on a simple arithmetical formula ("straight-line," sum-of-years'-digits, declining-balance, sinking-fund, or any other) that claims to reflect the complicated behavior of value, in any sense, must suggest the proponent's ignorance or insincerity. The "reasoning" involved consists in defining value to suit one's purpose at the moment.

When tax law first permitted use of "faster" depreciation methods in 1954, possessors of flexible consciences did not abandon that second argument in favor of "straight-line." They simply changed their minds about the "normal rate of loss in value"; it abruptly became the SYD or DRDB rate — overnight.

It is the third argument, the one for conservatism, that deserves special attention, however. As advanced in favor of "straight-line" it is the product of superficial thinking and failure to comprehend the exact nature and purpose of depreciation reserves. It is manifestly impossible to maintain the integrity of an investment in trolley cars by accumulating reserves to invest in more new trolley cars which nobody cares to ride.

The exactly intended concept of "conservative" in this frame of reference is protective of investors' interests. Investors' interests are protected by measures which tend to maintain and improve earnings per share and associated market price of company stock, and in no other manner. This end is not necessarily accomplished by increasing cash flow; nor by increasing amounts of accumulated cash on hand; nor by increasing the amount of depreciation reserves. It is best accomplished by any means which tend to minimize revenue requirements of company projects.

Ordinarily, the company's revenue requirements are apt to be minimized by keeping on hand the least amount of cash that cannot be put to immediate productive use. Conservatism consists in using cash to the best advantage by investing it in projects which improve earnings per pre-project share or which permit reducing the price charged for the company's products while maintaining the same earnings per pre-project share.

Rather than to adopt projects which reduce earnings per pre-project share, the company would do better to permit stockholders willing to do so to withdraw from ownership by selling their holdings to the company. That is, the company would do well to use superfluous cash to buy back outstanding stock from willing stockholders. It makes no great difference whether the cash represents depreciation accumulations, to be charged to depreciation reserves, or retained earnings in excess of dividend payout.

As discussed in Chapter 6, lifetime-levelized revenue requirements for depreciation are not affected at all by the method of accounting for depreciation. The only effect of choice of depreciation method is its impact on income taxes.

To repeat, "conservatism" in depreciation accounting should mean a policy protective of the stockholders' assurance of receiving dividend payments, which in turn has a bearing on market price of his holdings. The effectiveness of any method put forward as "conservative" must be gauged by its impact on that assurance of continued ability to pay dividends. No other evidence of conservatism is pertinent.

Depreciation reserves do not ordinarily consist of cash, nor of liquid assets from which dividends could be continued to be paid in a bad year. Depreciation reserves consist fundamentally of an accounting record of the amount of company assets currently in existence which were purchased with funds obtained by making charges to depreciation expense. An increased amount of reserves, so obtained and invested in assets incapable of increasing earnings per share, is the direct opposite of "conservative." It is a threat to the stockholders' welfare.

The acid test of conservatism in depreciation accounting is its impact on the margin of company earnings, present and prospective, in excess of MAR on the assets in question. This applies whether those assets may have been purchased with funds provided by depreciation charges or otherwise. In other words, the acid test of conservatism is the familiar Profit Incentive criterion.

Price-Level-Adjusted Depreciation

The drastic loss in purchasing power of the dollar since World War II has moved many individuals and organizations to urge adoption of price-level-adjusted depreciation. This consists of calculating current depreciation expense in the accepted manner, as a percentage of the original cost of depreciable assets currently in service, and adjusting that figure for the observed change in price level represented by loss of purchasing power of the dollar. This is not the same as charging replacement cost instead of original cost.

It has been tardily recognized that a consistent approach to this device, first proposed as an adjustment to depreciation accounts alone, would involve a similar restatement of many other accounts.[8]

For a more sober assessment of the proposal, one need only

---

[8]For the most recent attitude of professional accountants on the subject, the student may wish to consult: "Reporting the Financial Effects of Price-Level Changes," (Accounting Research Study No. 6), American Institute of Certified Public Accountants (New York, 1963). For a most enthusiastic book review of that document, see Henry W. Sweeny, "Book Review," Accounting Review (October, 1964), p. 1079.

question its claimed benefits to the stockholders who own the business and to the company's creditors. None of the earnest advocates of price-level-adjusted depreciation appear to have given adequate attention to the adverse effect of such proposals on the stockholders' welfare as measured by the behavior of the company's Profit Incentive, the margin of earnings in excess of MAR.

Almost none of the advocates of price-level-adjusted depreciation give serious thought to effects that would arise as the result of price deflation. The customary attitude is that such a thing will not happen; therefore, it need not be discussed. This suggests that expediency is given greater weight than sound principle.

The hackneyed argument that "integrity of investment in an enterprise may be jeopardized during the periods of price inflation if depreciation practices continue to be based on original cost" has substantially no merit. For one thing, the proposal does little to correct the condition, as just discussed. For another, the statement blandly ignores adverse effects. Two major reasons why increasing the amount of depreciation charges and reserves may have adverse effect on stockholder's welfare are:

1. For given gross plant, the larger the amount of depreciation reserves, the smaller is the amount of net plant representing investors' committed capital. It follows that, for a given debt ratio, the amount of debt will be smaller. This means a smaller amount of deductible interest on debt in the determination of taxable income for identical plant. Thus, the revenue requirement for income tax is increased by reason of the larger percentage reserve.

2. The increase in charges to depreciation expense increases the revenues currently required to produce the same earnings in the same manner as any expense that is unnecessarily increased. Because IRS does not allow these increased charges as deductible for purposes of calculating taxable income (they do not allow their deduction at present), no offsetting reduction in the tax will be made. The net effect is smaller earnings out of the same sales and revenues or a substantial price increase (which doesn't help a company's competitive position) to maintain the same earnings out of identical sales.

It is true that the lifetime-levelized effect on revenue requirements for return plus depreciation is zero for any particular depreciable asset. But there is a Step 2 effect. For an enterprise whose total assets are continuously increasing, and with continuous price inflation, the adverse effect on current revenue requirements, adverse to stockholders' welfare, is permanent.

Claims for improved reflection of "true value" have a hollow ring when:

1. The meaning arbitrarily assigned to "true value" is anything other than matters of concern to stockholders, namely

     (a) cash dividend payments, and (b) market price of company stock; and

2. The claimed solicitude for "true value" has adverse effect on cash dividend payments and market price.

In brief, <u>the "true value" of owners' equity is not revealed by book figures, whether adjusted for price levels or not.</u> The "true value" of owners' equity is a function of just two things: (a) anticipated cash dividend payments; and (b) anticipated capital gains, by way of market price of company stock.

To the limited extent that restated book figures might help stockholders to make their own more accurate appraisals of anticipated dividends and market price, the effect of price level adjustments might be worthwhile. Nevertheless, nobody has yet discovered any significant advantage of price-level-adjusted depreciation on that score, and the added accounting and reporting complications cost real money. Few if any of its advocates appear to have discovered the <u>disadvantages to stockholders</u> just described.

Other "Success Indicators"

A number of "major goals and tenable hypotheses" or "success indicators" have been proposed; these look to objectives far removed from the financial welfare of <u>owners</u> of the business — its stockholders. Some of these other objectives have special appeal to <u>management</u> as opposed to stockholders; they are sometimes advanced as though they represented a modern advance in economic thinking!

In place of the dual objectives representing exact intent per MRRD, such other goals as sales volume, share of the market, stability of prices, job security, public responsibility, and prestige of the executive have been seriously proposed. It is asserted that management's efforts should be service-oriented rather than profit-oriented.

It must be recognized that there are individuals and organizations in our complex modern world who not only do not understand but do not admire and have no desire to promote the spirit of free enterprise. It is that spirit which cleaves to the principle that superior productive skill and effort can hope to improve a company's competitive position, benefit consumers by lowering prices of superior goods and services, and reward the superior competitor with greater-than-average profit inducement.

Some have little patience with what they regard as "this philosophizing." They are content to poll opinion in such matters "in all echelons of the financial and business community"; analyze results of such surveys statistically, giving equal weight to informed, biased, and worthless convictions; and lay down principles as the resultant majority vote, scorning a discipline. At this point in the student's understanding of MRRD, he should be able to pass judgment on all such notions without further help.

The question of financing by means of internally generated versus externally obtained funds is examined in Chapter 3 and in Appendix B. Problems of internal control such as determining economic lot size are in the field of cost accounting; no special departures from standard practice are suggested by observance of MRRD.

Résumé

I. This chapter deals with problems related to making a choice between alternative courses of action which affect stockholders' welfare, but which are not primarily concerned with making the most desirable choice between competing physical assets. Among the problems of this kind which can be solved by use of the revenue requirements technique (MRRD), but not readily otherwise, if at all, are:

1. Determining ideal capital structure;
2. Evaluating possibilities of debt refunding;
3. Desirability of leasing versus owning the same assets;
4. Measuring desirable growth rate and "cash flow";
5. Rating depreciation accounting methods;
6. Passing upon the merits of price-level-adjusted depreciation proposals;
7. Comparing normalized versus flow-through treatment of tax deferrals; and
8. Capitalizing versus expensing outlays, where a choice is permissible.

II. Promotion of the best interests of stockholders is achieved by the familiar dual objectives of MRRD: (a) optimized return on pre-project shares, out of the same sales and revenues; and (b) attainment of the best competitive position for the company (that is, placing it in the best condition to reduce price of its output with the least adverse effect on return to pre-project shares).

III. MRRD is the only analytical technique that is in complete harmony with the principles of free enterprise in problems of this kind.

IV. "Ideal capital structure" is defined as that which will result in minimized revenue requirements for return (= MAR) plus taxes.

V. Practical attainment of an ideal capital structure demands skill and foresight; it involves evaluation of several factors which are not predictable with assurance or 100% determinate. However, it is possible to describe the controlling influences, illustrate the exact arithmetic appropriate for their evaluation, and to draw conclusions with a high degree of probability.

VI. The arithmetical effect of varying debt ratio on revenue requirements is inescapable. That is, the amount of change in MAR on equity and on income tax that results from a change in debt ratio, for a given pool MAR percentage, is calculable. This permits a clear recognition of situations which favor debt reduction and of those which favor an increase in debt, both from the standpoint of advantages to stockholders.

VII. Stockholder benefits obtainable by refunding outstanding debt before maturity may be calculated in the same general manner, by evaluating the effect on company MAR plus taxes.

VIII. Benefits (if any) to stockholders realizable by leasing rather than owning the same property can be evaluated by inquiring into revenue requirements of each proposal. An important factor commonly overlooked is the penalty in taxes which arises from the different risk situation of equity when the same property is leased.

IX. Appropriate accounting disclosure of lease obligations is clearly revealed with the help of MRRD. Existence of a lease obligation is similar to existence of outstanding serial bonds. Revenue requirements of the property leased are not completely represented by payments to the lessor. A tax differential is involved, as noted in VIII. The effect diminishes as the lessee's obligation to the lessor is amortized by regular payments.

X. A great majority of reasons commonly advanced in favor of leasing, rather than owning, are adverse to the stockholders' interests and unsound on this as well as on other counts.

XI. Desirable growth is not measured by the rate of increase in assets, nor the rate of increase in sales or earnings. The appropriate measure, which conveys the desired information as exactly intended, is the behavior of Profit Incentive (= the margin of earnings in excess of company MAR). Profit Incentive may be expressed in dollars or as a ratio, preferably as a percentage of common equity.

XII. Proposed reference to "cash flow" (= net earnings plus depreciation) as an indicator of the company's financial status is a product of inexact understanding. "Cash flow" is not necessarily a measure of stockholder welfare.

XIII. "Straight-line" depreciation accounting does not possess the virtues commonly attributed to it, which are largely imaginary or superficial from the standpoint of stockholders. The most serious fault of "straight-line" depreciation is the misrepresentation of its fancied advantages, which often result in decisions adverse to stockholders' interests.

XIV. MRRD provides a means for gauging financial effects of proposed tinkering with details of depreciation accounting practice, such as adopting price-level-adjusted depreciation or using methods other than the usual group-basis "straight-line" method, deliberately underestimating service life, and so on. In general, such proposals have little or no economic effect aside from their influence on taxes, but that result may be detrimental to the stockholders' best interests.

XV. Stockholders, bondholders, and creditors of all kinds would do well to acquaint themselves with a recent mischievous trend in the teaching of industrial management which defines the major goals of management and "success indicators" in terms which disparage concern for stockholders' welfare and which are detrimental to the interests of all suppliers of capital.

Problems

1. Each year, awards are made to companies whose annual reports to stockholders are judged superior. List in order of importance the first ten considerations on which you would base your decision if you were the judge. Explain why.

(Hints: Attractive format; simplified explanation of the firm's financial situation; ten-year tabulation of significant financial data, with explanation of "significant"; comprehensive factual disclosure of finances, not simplified, helpful to a reader of this book; a recital of the president's prowess as golfer, included by some companies; pessimistic comment on political factors, such as the gold reserve, national policy in the matter of oil imports, and discriminatory taxes; various means of disclosing lease contracts; details of outstanding debt; a review of annual predictions of forthcoming business prospects compared to events as they transpired; and others you may think of. Possibly include demerits for meretricious material usually included, better omitted.)

2. Explain how owners of a business can exercise their rights (what do you mean by "rights"?) to pass upon competence of the management who represent their interests. If the particular issues of concern to the stockholder are not listed on proxy statements as being up for a vote, how does the stockholder go about voting on them? Do the security exchanges have any interest or control in such matters? Explain in detail.

3. An industrial company listed on the New York Stock Exchange stated in its annual report to stockholders that since replacements and additions to plant cost more than recoveries permitted for depreciation charges under IRS law, it would be necessary to retain a larger portion of earnings per share (that is, reduce dividend payout out of given earnings) to meet these increased costs as they occur. Certain steel companies listed on the same exchange have argued that they find it necessary to increase prices for their product in order to obtain funds needed for replacements and additions to plant.

If you were a director of these companies, what other measures might you report as necessary for that same purpose? If you were a stockholder, what other courses of action would you suggest as worthy of inquiry? As a stockholder distressed by such comment, what measures would you consider taking on your own behalf?

(Hints: Explore reasons for the doleful situation and suggest remedies [what remedies to whom?]; sell your stocks at the first opportunity to get out without too much loss; make an economic replacement of the management; discuss the situation with your congressman; write a book or a "letter to the editor.")

4. What is a stock option? Give details of such an agreement. Are stock options desirable? Desirable to whom? Explain.

5. It has been estimated that the average cost to produce an annual report to stockholders approximates 50 cents per copy. That is a substantial fraction of the dividend payment in many cases. In some instances it exceeds the dividend rate.

How would you allocate this cost to individual projects in making studies of profitability? Comment on the desirability of an expense of this magnitude from the standpoint of owners of the firm, and make suggestions.

6. An essential part of the MRRD philosophy is recognition that, although investor reaction is not always 100% logical, it would be irrational to adopt criteria of economy or profitability based on firm expectation of illogical investor reaction.

Investor reaction to what? Exactly what is meant by "100% logical" investor reaction? In what respects might investor reaction be illogical? Would that affect Step 1 or Step 2 of the analyses, or both, or neither? Would it affect the budgeting function, as apart from the economic comparison?

7. In the discussion on page 390 of "target values" of (a) interest rate on debt, and (b) MAR on equity, which could result in a specified total for "MAR plus revenue requirement for income tax," it was said that: "It is not unreasonable to expect that stockholders might bid up market price (that is, the price/earnings ratio might increase) sufficiently to produce 7.66% MAR on equity, as the result of an announced policy to reduce debt ratio."

Produce an arithmetical example to illustrate the point. Suggest reasonable upper and lower limits of quantities involved to describe a range of investor reaction that might be regarded as going from "logical" to "illogical."

8. If you were writing this book, what additional topics would you consider including in this chapter text or problems to help readers, not so well informed as yourself, to grasp the significance of the stockholders' vital concern with company methods of making their profitability or economic choice studies? Explain in detail.

9. From a list of reference material supplied by your instructor, prepare a book review on one selection, entitling it, "Why This Reference Is Not Recommended Reading."

(Note: The author lacks the courage to suggest references suitable for this purpose. However, it will take only a few minutes of the instructor's time to find plenty.)

10. Repeat the example presented in the text, on page 390, under the heading Evaluating Possibilities (of debt refunding), using an interest rate of 3.5% (instead of 4%) on the new issue.

11. In addition to the time-honored annual statements of income and balance sheet (including surplus), many companies now include a third table in their reports to stockholders, under some such title as "Summary of Financial Operations During the Year," or "Statement of Funds Provided and Applied."

Of what good is such a statement to stockholders? Of what good is it to the analyst who makes the company's studies of profitability and economic choice? Of what good is it to anyone? If you were a director of the company, might you suggest saving money by eliminating this statement? Discuss fully pro and con.

12. The annual report to stockholders of one company states that during the year 1,000 shares of its Series B 5% Preferred Stock were purchased in accordance with provisions of the sinking fund therefor.

How does that affect company studies of profitability and economic choice, if at all? Where do funds come from to make such a purchase? Are they included in the revenue requirement for return? Explain. Are sinking funds a good idea for this purpose, or a policy of desperation? Explain. Are you influenced at all by use of apparently disparaging phrases in posing questions like the foregoing? Is any point made in the author's use of such semantics? Discuss.

13. Repeat the Illustrative Example; Economics of Leasing, on page 396, assuming that payments to the lessor are made sufficient to recover the capital investment in 8 years (service life is 10 years, as before), all else remaining the same.

14. The annual report of an oil refiner to its stockholders complains about the decline in product prices, mostly the declining price of gasoline resulting from local price wars. This situation, it is said, has led the company to place greater emphasis on developing profitable sales and less emphasis on sales volume. Elsewhere in the same report is an outline of the company's vigorous advertising campaign by way of television, radio, newspapers, and other media. This advertising is said to be designed to encourage motorists to travel more extensively in the area served by the company. The report does not reveal the average price per gallon sold, or its profitability, or the cost of the advertising.

Are such facts of any interest to analysts who make studies of profitability or economic choice for the company? Are they of concern to stockholders? Discuss frankly.

15. Calculate the "yield to maturity" of a bond, $1,000 face value, sold for $990 with expenses of $10 attached to the transaction, on which no interest is paid for the first 20 years, 2% interest thereafter; bond is retired at the end of the one-hundredth year. Make any other assumptions you may feel necessary.

What would be the effect of paying interest in every year, from the beginning? Do these peculiar specifications suggest any pertinent comment? Pertinent to whom or to what?

16. Describe in your own words exactly what is wrong with proposals to "capitalize" lease obligations. Or, if you feel that nothing is wrong, why is capitalizing superior to other proposed treatments?

17. Suggest a numerical example to demonstrate the basic fallacy in the popular belief that "leasing releases capital for profitable investment elsewhere." Or, if you do not feel that it is a fallacy, demonstrate validity of your view by an example.

18. Exactly what is meant by the argument that "leasing does not disturb normal lines of credit." If that were true, how would it enter into the economic comparison of leasing versus owning as proposed in this chapter?

19. Explain the basic fallacy in the argument that leasing saves taxes, since lease payments are deductible in computing taxable income, while if the same property were owned, taxes must be paid on return on the investment. How does the Annual Cost reasoning contribute to this misrepresentation?

20. Lease-finance companies claim, as one advantage of leasing, that it takes peaks and valleys out of operating costs. How much are stockholders willing to suffer, by way of reduced dividends, to have "peaks and valleys taken out of operating costs"? Just who does benefit?

21. Another excuse for leasing is that it provides a hedge against inflation and rapid obsolescence. Explain how the lessor is able to protect himself against such influences, when the lessee cannot. Might this appeal to lessees whose managements are less competent than the lessor's? But might not the lessee profit more by finding competent management than by leasing? Discuss.

22. Discuss the claim that leased equipment is paid for out of before-tax earnings, rather than out of after-tax profits as when owned. (Believe it or not, such an argument has actually been proposed.)

23. The method of evaluating lease proposals as described in this chapter makes allowance for what might be described as the added risk to equity owners created by assuming the obligation to make payments to the lessor. In economic comparisons which balance incremental maintenance expense against incremental capital investment, no such allowance is proposed to allow for the added risk to equity owners created by assuming the obligation to make larger payments for maintenance. Is there a self-contradiction here? Explain.

24. It has been claimed by some advocates of leasing that although large-scale leasing might be undesirable, a small amount on the same terms might be advantageous — like the differential between a medicinal nip and a bender.

Suggest a numerical example to expose the fallacy. Are you influenced at all by use of such folksy analogies in posing questions like this? Or do they make you a little skeptical? Comment helpfully.

25. Describe exactly what might be meant by "conservatism," in connection with a depreciation policy. Is it a significant feature of such a policy or another danger signal like the use of such words as "attrition" and "parameter" which so often betray the user's ignorance?

Discuss, giving reasons for your conclusions. How does this subject affect studies of profitability and economic choice? Is the company's method of depreciation for book or tax purposes of concern to stockholders? Explain — and be careful!

26. For the benefit of those less well informed than yourself, explain in simplest terms the claimed benefits of price-level-adjusted accounting.

How does price-level-adjusted depreciation (PLD) differ from proposals to charge replacement cost to depreciation expense? If PLD is an acceptable procedure, how does that fact destroy arguments advanced by eminent accountants in favor of price-level-accounting?

(Note: Once more, the author lacks the courage to indicate specific material provided by "eminent accountants" for this purpose. Apologies to the instructor.)

27. Repeat the calculations of Table 13.1, discounting at MAR on common equity, instead of MAR on the pool of investors' committed capital.

(Note: Consult Chapter 5 and Appendix B first.)

Comment on difficulties and results. Would it be worth your investigating this subject further and perhaps publishing a helpful essay on the proposal?

28. Some thoughtful (though possibly not helpful) writers have suggested that management may not owe ultimate allegiance to owners of a business (stockholders). It is said to be the "professional view of management" that stockholders' interest is only one of several vested interests in corporate policy, and stockholder interest may not be absolute or even paramount. One argument advanced in support of that view concerns court decisions with respect to various kinds of creditors, employees, customers, general public, and former stockholders, in bankruptcy proceedings.

Is such argument pertinent to profitability studies and economic comparisons? In connection with "success indicators" other than Profit Incentive? Or is it a naive viewpoint distinctly off the beam? Does it assume that courts establish economic principles; or does the difficulty go deeper than that? Discuss.

29. One objection that has on occasion been raised to use of PWAFRR in making economic comparisons is that discounting future probabilities at a constant rate does not conform to the utility function of the company.

What is meant by "utility function of the company"? Is there any merit in the comment? Does its author betray his unfamiliarity with principles of MRRD in making such a comment?

30. An interesting essay, "Making Sense of Management Theory," by Harold Koontz, appeared in Harvard Business Review (July-August, 1962), p. 23. It concludes with the statement of five "yardsticks"; their general import is that a worthwhile theory of management must recognize that it is only a part of a larger universe of knowledge and theory. It need not, and preferably should not, attempt to encompass that universe.

Comment, preferably after reading the paper. Might it be worthwhile to include something on that subject in a book like this?

31. Within the past few years, a number of suits against manufacturers under the antitrust laws were settled. In announcing the settlement, it is not unusual to read that the terms were considered favorable to the "investors, customers, and the company."

Who or what is "the company," whose financial interests are thus separate and distinct from investors and customers?

32. The management of a corporation may deem it worthwhile to make generous contributions to local charities, national foundations, scholarships, and universities, and to do considerable advertising, all to promote and maintain a favorable "corporate image."

Since such expenditures reduce earnings per share out of any given revenues and increase the charges for any company output to develop the same earnings per share, they are adverse to the best interests of both owners and customers of the company. How can they be justified? Or can they?

33. The president of a manufacturing company is quoted as saying that obtaining funds from a finance company, in the form of factoring and equipment loans, is far superior to any other method of raising capital. He describes such funds as equity capital that can be bought out at any time without hurting anyone's

feelings. The finance company takes the place of stockholders, who do not work as hard as management does, but still share profits after taxes. With finance company funds, you get your company free without giving away a lien on future profits.

What advice could you give to stockholders in this company?

34. A manufacturing company has reported 10% annual growth in sales for several successive years. Its net worth has also increased each year. Earnings have been maintained at about $4.50 per share in every year; a regular dividend of $2 has been declared. All expansion has been financed from internally generated funds (retained earnings and depreciation); the firm has not had to do any borrowing. Market price of its common stock has never moved far from 10 times earnings per share.

Would you regard this stock as a good investment? If you were a stockholder in this company, would you feel that your management should be rewarded by an annual bonus? Or would you feel that it might be well to replace them? What questions should you ask at the next stockholders' meeting? What constructive suggestions might you be able to contribute? Discuss your answers in detail.

35. Table 13.2 displays the arithmetical effect of increased debt, at the existing rate, on company-pool MAR. A decrease in pool MAR (Part IIa) would be unrealistic; it would mean assuming a decrease in cost of hiring new capital to result from going deeper into debt together with greater risk to owners of the business. Part IIb shows how to calculate the increased MAR on common equity that would maintain pool MAR at its initial level, here 7%. The latter basis is proposed for evaluating economics of leasing versus owning the same assets.

But another basis for estimating probable effect of increased debt suggests a greater increase in MAR on common equity, which would increase pool equity above the initial 7%, and make leasing still less attractive.

That is, for common stockholders to enjoy the same degree of risk as before increasing debt (Part I), interest obligations should be covered the same number of times as initially. In Part I, Before Addition, interest obligations are covered $700,000/160,000 = 4.375$ times.

In Part II, After Addition, that same coverage would mean:

$$
\begin{array}{lll}
\text{Interest on debt} & = & \$164,000 \text{ per year} \\
\text{MAR on equity, by difference} & = & 553,500 \\
\text{Pool MAR at } 4.375 \times 164,000 & = & \$717,500 \text{ per year.}
\end{array}
$$

This would mean:

$$
\begin{array}{lll}
\text{MAR on common equity at } 553,500/6,000,000 & = & 9.150\% \text{ (instead of } 9.05\%) \\
\text{Company-pool MAR at } 717,500/1,010,000 & = & 7.104\% \text{ (instead of } 7.07\%).
\end{array}
$$

As just noted, this would make leasing even less attractive than if evaluated as proposed in this chapter.

However, there is a good reason why the economic comparison must be made, at least tentatively, in the manner described in the text. Explain.

(Hint: Consider the exact nature of the "Iffy Hypothesis.")

14

• • • • • Public Utility • • Economics

Scope

Profitability and economic choice of proposals is found in exactly the same way for public utilities as for any other kind of business. Unsound conclusions to the contrary, particularly misconceptions contributed by the Annual Cost approach, have been mentioned in previous chapters. This being the case, it may be questioned why it is necessary to devote a special chapter to public utilities in a book devoted to profitability and economic choice.

The explanation is that two subjects, both grossly misunderstood and misrepresented, are of national concern to all taxpayers. These subjects can be clarified by reviewing them in the light of the Minimum Revenue Requirements Discipline (MRRD). The unique nature of MRRD sheds new light on the economics of: (a) commission regulation of service rates charged by public utilities; and (b) tax-financed versus investor-financed public utilities, such as Tennessee Valley Authority (TVA) and Rural Electrification Administration (REA).

In addition, brief attention will be given in this chapter to a few special problems encountered by public utilities which present great difficulties when analysis by methods other than MRRD is attempted.

Regulation

An outstanding contribution of the American free enterprise economy is the development of a workable system for commission regulation of a limited segment of industry legally designated as investor-owned public utilities.

For all its faults — and a few cannot be denied — commission regulation as practiced in this country is far superior to any alternative treatment of such industry yet devised. Its political aspects are of no concern to this discussion, except as they may have some bearing on economic considerations; but its legal aspects must be considered, because they are an intimate part of the economics.

The great superiority of this scheme of things derives from the same factors which account for the overwhelming superiority of the free enterprise system itself. It is organized so that freewill suppliers of the indispensable capital, in enlightened pursuit of their own personal welfare, are offered inducements to prefer courses of action that automatically redound to the greatest benefit of consumers and the community.

Public utilities are granted a degree of monopoly, in exchange for which regulation supplies certain limited restraints normally exercised by those forces of competition which are lacking in a monopoly. Such major controls are concerned with the nature and quality of service rendered and the scale of charges made for supplying service ("tariffs").

Fair Return

The part played by the courts in the regulatory process is established by an interpretation of the Bill of Rights portion of the Federal Constitution. It is there provided that property of citizens may not be confiscated without due process of law. This has been interpreted as meaning that imposition by a regulatory authority of rates so low as to produce less than a "fair" rate of return amounts to confiscation, in which case owners of the property have recourse to the courts for relief of that situation. Such a doctrine demands that the courts be able to define and recognize "fair" return. The right of the public to exercise some degree of control over industry endowed with substantial public interest has long been established in common law.

The history of litigation in the lower courts, ending in appeals to the Supreme Court, has produced a body of legal precepts to which all state commissions must conform.[1] However, state commissions and courts are also obliged to respect state laws, which are by no means uniform in their construing of economic principles or standards of "fairness." As a result, commissions must sometimes go to fantastic lengths in formal hearings to arrive at sound and workable pronouncements while conforming to innumerable legalistic details which must be observed if they are not to violate state law. This kind of red tape is often responsible for the phenomenon of "regulatory lag," arising from the obligation to hear interminable testimony, not necessarily of great significance to the economic issues.

Reasonableness of the end result is necessarily gauged in retrospect by a pragmatic test that could well have been the initial basis for the decision: how tolerably it conforms to the opinion of the free agents who supply the necessary capital funds. The marketplace is the only tribunal that can pass upon value; judicial, legislative, and commission

---

[1] For a brief review of early historical development of judicial attitudes see E. M. Bernstein, Public Utility Rate Making and the Price Level (University of North Carolina Press, Chapel Hill, 1937). The more comprehensive up-to-date authority on court and commission rulings is Ellsworth Nichols and Francis X. Welch, Ruling Principles of Utility Regulation (Public Utilities Reports, Inc., Washington, D.C., 1964).

pretense to the contrary notwithstanding. The "feedback" effect is inevitable. In general, this is recognized by commissioners, even though they may not always find it expedient to be forthright on the subject. The Federal Power Commission, particularly, has attempted to encourage candid recognition of cost of capital as the basis for value and the benchmark for fairness of return. A helpful contribution to this problem is suggested by MRRD.

MRRD, and Return on Rate Base

Rate base is a term no doubt useful for regulatory purposes; however, it has no place in studies of profitability or economic choice. It differs from investors' committed capital chiefly because the decision as to the inclusion of items on the basis of prudence is made in retrospect. Use of the term "rate base" is largely a relic of attempts to pass such judgment in retrospect on earlier decisions of management, presumably concurred in by the regulators at the time. Such efforts to regulate by hindsight are bound to be abortive because, despite imaginative efforts of economists, courts, commissions, and others, nobody has yet been able to suggest any measurement of value which can successfully ignore critical appraisal of the marketplace — the opinion of those who supply the requisite capital.

In recent years, vigorous and statesmanlike efforts have been made to eliminate legalistic red tape, to clarify criteria of fairness, and to speed up formal hearings by various devices. An outstanding development of that nature is the Administrative Conference of the United States, created by Executive Order of President Kennedy on April 13, 1961. But one area in which improvement is possible and slow in coming still remains: the problem of an objective test for fairness of return. It is here that MRRD can make a helpful contribution.

Fair Value

Over a period of almost seven decades, the traditional criterion of reasonable earnings has been that of fair return on fair value of property devoted to serving the public, as laid down in 1898 by the Supreme Court in Smyth vs. Ames (169 U.S. 546). As might be expected of any rule dependent on value, that decision left many important questions unanswered and introduced some new difficulties. It enumerated various factors affecting "fair value," but it refrained from describing their relative weighting and, as mentioned elsewhere, contributed a notable example of circular reasoning.

Although subsequent decisions have modified this Smyth-Ames dictum somewhat, they have not clarified it much. The standard procedure of courts and commissions is to establish a rate base, representing the presumed "fair value" on which a "fair rate of return" is to be allowed. Fair value is usually some interpretation of state law applied to voluminous evidence; the fair rate of return, however, must be evolved out of the commission's inner consciousness in some vague manner not stipulated and not clearly apparent.

Substitutes for the cost-of-capital basis for measuring value have been tried, but all employ one of three unworkable and evasive devices:

1. Circular reasoning, as in Smyth vs. Ames;
2. Pretended "judgment," depending upon some superior intuitive instinct of courts or commissions whereby they are able to distinguish reasonable from unreasonable earnings;[2] or
3. Cost (original or replacement), adjusted for "loss of value" (usually indicated by the term "depreciation," to evade the implication that value can be measured only by way of evaluating loss of what cannot be measured).

The stark fact remains that, distasteful though it may be, there is only one way to measure "value in use" of a capital investment objectively. That is by way of its continuing "value in exchange" (of the associated outstanding securities) in a free market where individual investors can offer or withdraw use of their funds at will, and where enterprises are at liberty to compete with each other in offering inducements for capital commitment.[3]

Investors establish a market price which, in relation to current and anticipated returns, is their "fair" evaluation of securities. Whatever "rate base" or adjudicated "fair value" may be, it is the dollars of anticipated earnings, dividends per share, and market price that establish their concept of fair return. They call the tune.

Surely something must be wrong in any approach that employs a different philosophy in passing upon the fairness of earnings after the fact from that used in reaching the original decision to make the optimized capital commitment. MRRD supplies the same consistent criterion for both purposes, as will be seen.

The Band of Fairness

Having decided to adopt all of the projects which comprise its total assets, the company desires to establish the rates for service which will result in earnings and related cost of capital that will best promote the same objectives used as criteria in the original accept-reject decisions.

A quite narrow band of rates can be described as "optimum" on this basis. That is, rates outside of this band can be expected to either:

---

[2] See comment of Justice Jackson in Federal Power Commission et al. vs. Hope Natural Gas Co. (No. 34), 320 U.S. 591, 649; 51 P.U.R. (N.S.) 193 (U.S. Sup. Ct. Jan. 3, 1944).
[3] Phrases quoted are from Adam Smith's The Wealth of Nations.

1. <u>Maximize yield</u> on outstanding (pre-project) shares out of the same sales, but by reason of higher revenues rather than by reduced revenue requirements; or
2. <u>Minimize current rates</u> charged for services rendered, but by failing to maintain the same yield on outstanding (pre-project) shares out of the same sales, increase the cost of capital so that the increase in future revenue requirements more than offsets that temporary benefit.

It hardly needs demonstration that there must be a <u>band</u> of values representing optimization. For one thing, if there is any one outstanding characteristic of cost behavior, it is change. Conditions do not "stay put." For example, most utilities experience predictable seasonal variations in sales and earnings, but nobody feels that this demands seasonal adjustment in rate schedules.

A fair return at a stipulated unique percentage would mean that smaller earnings in any accounting period would be "unfair"; any larger earnings "excessive." The need for an acceptable band is universally recognized in practice, not just as an awkward compromise, but as a matter of principle.

In brief, initial selection of the economic choice is made by examining the situation if MAR were to be identical whatever course of action is taken with respect to rates. Selection of the superior plan on this basis is conservative to a degree; it is normally to be expected that the better plan will tend to <u>reduce</u> MAR, if it affects it at all, and thus tend to increase the so-estimated superiority a trifle. Should selection of the superior plan on this basis precipitate a rate reduction so large that owners actually suffer a penalty by reason of adopting the more economic alternative, chaos would result. Management would be encouraged to adopt alternatives which can be counted on to increase rates! One is forced to hypothesize that regulation will not permit this to happen.

It is for such reasons that the <u>lower limit</u> of the band of optimized return can be defined, in words, with precision. It is the so-called "cutoff" percentage, the minimum return which a project must produce to be deemed worthwhile by those who supply the capital. Our first task, then, is to evaluate the company average cutoff rate. It is a slightly different percentage for each individual project, because it is a function of the risk involved in adopting each project. The source of risk ranges from exposure to chances of earthquakes, fire, wind, accident, war, sabotage, or other disaster, down to forces such as obsolescence, loss of market, competition, poor judgment, labor markets, the business cycle, and governmental or regulatory intervention. Different classes of service involve different risks, different need for promotional rates, and different competitive situations.

Cutoff Rate

Suppose the company discovers, in the manner described in Chapter 3, that its minimum acceptable return (MAR) on its pool of investors' committed capital is 6.5%.

Nobody borrows money or raises equity capital at a cost of 6.5% in order to reinvest it at 6.5%. In the case of a corporation, that would subject existing owners to added risks and chance of loss, with no hope of any gain; the expansion is to be justified by benefits to existing owners.

Even for projects having zero risk, if such could be imagined, some margin of earnings above MAR is essential, or the proposal is not financially justified. The greater the risk, the greater the margin of earnings must be above MAR, on up to the riskiest gamble the company is willing to take. The aggregate of all projects, which constitutes total assets of the company, establishes a company-average cutoff rate which lies at some nearly constant margin above MAR, year after year.

Figure 14.1 illustrates this situation; it was discussed before, in Chapter 3.

As a company's actual (reported) earnings per share increase, it can be expected that market price per common share will also increase. Market price may increase in direct proportion with improved earnings per share, in which case the price/earnings ratio and MAR remain the same as before; or price per share may increase more than the improvement in earnings per share. In the latter case, MAR tends to decrease slightly, as discussed in Chapter 3 and Appendix B. A reduction in company earnings per share can be expected to have the opposite effect. If the price/earnings ratio is affected at all, the result will tend to increase MAR slightly.

In general, cutoff rate responds directly to changes in MAR. In

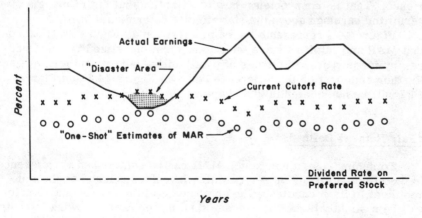

Fig. 14.1. Actual earnings, current cutoff rate, and "one-shot" MAR.

prosperous times, as MAR decreases slightly, the indicated improvement in risk might conceivably lessen the margin of profitability (between MAR and cutoff rate) that management deems desirable. With
reduced earnings per share and slightly increased MAR, management
might insist upon an increased differential (between the increased MAR
and cutoff rate) because of the increased risk. Such variability, however, is usually small; the plot of cutoff rate is nearly parallel to the
plot of MAR, with passage of time.

Should actual earnings dip below the simultaneously rising cutoff
rate, the firm is in trouble, hence the "disaster area." Further investment cannot then be justified, and it will only worsen the situation
unless the new projects are sufficiently profitable to reverse and correct that trend, or unless revenues can be increased from the same
sales.

The margin by which cutoff rate exceeds MAR is not necessarily
the same for all companies, since not all are exposed to identical risks;
nor is the margin necessarily constant from year to year for any one
company. However, a mass of data is available which suggests that the
bottom edge of the band of optimized return may lie around 0.5% to 1%
above MAR for utilities with stable earnings, past and prospective, and
expected earnings of no less than this margin.

The importance of recognizing this essential margin may be illustrated by the "dynamite analogy." Suppose a high explosive is known to
detonate at a temperature of exactly 200 degrees centigrade. Nobody
would then think of describing 200 degrees as the "maximum safe temperature." It is the direct opposite, the acknowledged unsafe figure. A
safe margin below 200 degrees will depend upon circumstances and is
a matter of judgment based on experience.

Similarly, the minimum fair return or minimum "attractive" rate
must exceed MAR by some finite margin which depends upon circumstances, and its determination is a matter of judgment based on experience. That is our problem: how to establish that "fair" margin of
permitted earnings above the statistically determinate MAR.

Figure 14.2 represents the same situation as Figure 14.1, except
that MAR and cutoff rate are their long-term "levelized" values, necessary for purposes of studies of profitability and economic choice.
Further comment on the difference between Figure 14.1 and Figure
14.2 will be made later in this chapter.

"Fair Return" Defined

To summarize, a company's MAR can be established by reference
to the minimal attractive return which investors demand on their investment in its securities. The company's minimum acceptable return
will be a slightly higher percentage than the investor's, owing to costs
of the security sale. Its minimum attractive return is its cutoff rate,
which exceeds MAR by a small but essential margin. Recognition of

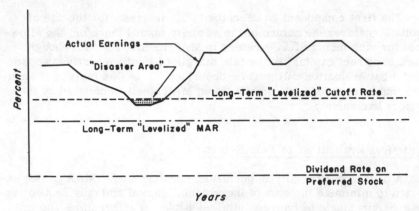

Fig. 14.2. Actual earnings, long-term "levelized" cutoff rate, and long-term "levelized" MAR.

this small but essential margin accounts for the several phrases proposed to describe MAR: bare-bones cost of capital; the threshold of confiscation; critical return; minimum tolerable level of earnings; marginal external lending rate; and break-even rate.

By whatever title, MAR (preferred herein) is by nature a minimal "cost of capital" that is realizable by reason of a slightly higher rate of actual earnings. MAR can be expected to increase as the rate of actual earnings falls. Stated in the reverse sense, the better a company's earnings prospects, the cheaper is new money. The "optimized" situation means best balance between:

1. Current earnings in excess of MAR, which affects current tariffs; and
2. Future revenue requirements of the company, as affected by the resultant lowered cost of capital (MAR), which affects future tariffs.

This is the exact definition of what the analyst really has in mind by "optimized" results. It is optimized from the standpoint of both consumers and capital suppliers (= investors). It is submitted that such optimized earnings are what public utilities, courts, and commissions mean fundamentally by "fair return."

It is further believed that the test of fairness proposed as follows, on that foundation, represents exactly what Justices Holmes and Brandeis had in mind in their concurring opinion in the famous Southwestern Bell Case (Southwestern Bell Tel. Co. vs. Pub. Serv. Comm. of Missouri (No. 158), 262 U.S. 276; P.U.R. 1923C (U.S. Sup. Ct. May 21, 1923):

It is therefore feasible now to adopt, as a measure of a rate, the annual cost or charge of the capital. . . . Capital charges cover the allowance, by way of interest, for the use of the capital, whatever the nature of the security issued therefor; the allowance for risk incurred, and enough more to attract capital.

The first component so described ("...interest, for the use of capital, whatever the nature of the security issued therefor; the allowance for risk incurred...") refers to MAR itself. The "...enough more to attract capital" is the fair margin of Profit Incentive, whose statistical evaluation will next be described. It is this margin of earnings that is regulable by commissions; MAR itself is dictated by investors exclusively.

Statistical Evaluations of Fair Return

A degree of liberality in permitted earnings above MAR can be expected to minimize the cost of incremental capital and thus reduce revenue requirements of future capital additions. Furthermore, the improved (that is, lowered) MAR thus obtained applies not just to future capital additions; it applies to total investors' committed capital at any time, incremental plus already committed. This was carefully indicated in Chapter 3. Thus, the lowered MAR, plus the same regulated fair margin of Profit Incentive, will result in lower rates still sufficient to earn a fair return.

But there is an upper limit to the liberality that can be expected to pay off. No matter how high current percentage earnings may be, the cost of capital cannot be reduced to zero. It cannot even be reduced to the cost of debt. Possibly it could not be reduced quite to the cost of preferred stock, if issued. Ideally, it might be said that if reducing current permitted percentage return does not increase MAR, then current return is unnecessarily liberal. However, a more practicable basis for establishing the permissible top limit of fair return (that is, the maximum allowed margin of earnings above MAR) has been proposed. It is by reference to earnings of comparable nonregulated companies, which are subject to control by those forces of competition which are lacking in the case of a granted monopoly.

The reasoning here is that the purpose of commission control of utility earnings is to reproduce the effects that would be exercised by competition were the utility not a monopoly. But how does one define a "comparable" nonregulated enterprise? Despite similarity in size, public acceptance of the product, and identical capital structure (if it were possible to find such examples), there remains the preferential income tax treatment of nonutilities, geographical distribution of markets, and innumerable other details of significant difference. The comparability is dubious unless earnings are comparable, but that is begging the question.

This approach, as ordinarily handled in the past and as presented in rate case testimony, has lacked complete conviction for such reasons.[4] MRRD suggests a way to overcome this difficulty.

---

[4]First mention of this approach apparently was in the Bluefield Water Works & Improvement Co. vs. Public Service Commission of the State of West Virginia et al. (No. 256), 262 U.S. 679; P.U.R. 1923D, 11 (U.S. Sup. Ct. June 11, 1923). Substantially the same statement was made in the Hope case, 1944, cited before.

In brief, the important fact is that companies having similar MAR percentages have similar risk. Nonregulated companies whose MAR approximates the utility's MAR are ipso facto "comparable" in this frame of reference and are suitable for this application. Nonregulated companies whose MAR departs substantially from the utility's MAR are ipso facto not "comparable," not suitable for the purpose, and can be eliminated immediately.

The margin of Profit Incentive, above MAR, which is permitted the nonregulated companies by competition then provides the desired index to regulable Profit Incentive for the utility. What is sought is not the average nor typical margin of Profit Incentive permitted by competition, but a reasonable top limit. This reasonable top limit, added to the utility's MAR, represents the ceiling to be placed on the utility's earnings.

If this exact intent is borne firmly in mind, we have here a rational statistical support for judgment as to the band of permissible, optimum, or "fair" earnings of the utility.

Judgment

Even though there is a band of results within which earnings may be defended as fair, this statistical approach still permits the "dose of judgment" generally acknowledged to be essential.

For example, if the nonregulated reference companies have operating ratios which differ substantially from that of the utility, there may be reason to consider the advisability of an adjustment on that score. One suggestion is that, instead of adding the nonregulated company's margin above its MAR to the utility's MAR directly, the nonregulated company's margin in dollars per year be expressed as a percentage of its revenue deductions (instead of a percentage of investment). The utility then is to be permitted that same percentage of its own revenue deductions, in excess of its own MAR. The quantitative effect of this refinement on fair return is small.[5]

The "Floor" and "Ceiling" of Fair Return

The present proposal sets up consistent standards for both "floor" and "ceiling." It suggests specific bases for judgment in place of present dependence on unsupported opinion. Furthermore, it employs the same philosophy in attempting optimized pricing, after the fact, as was

---

[5]A rough approximation of this proposal (though not based on MAR) appears in Charles Tatham, Jr., "The Forgotten Factor in Fair Return," Public Utilities Fortnightly (July 2, 1953). A number of references in that paper deal with some concept of fair return derived from nonregulated industry. For discussions of the operating-ratio adjustment, see Charles Alan Wright, "Operating Ratio — A Regulatory Tool," Public Utilities Fortnightly (Jan. 1, 1953), and Lawrence S. Knappen, "Transit Operating Ratio — Another View," Public Utilities Fortnightly (April 9, 1953).

used in reaching the initial decision to make the optimum capital commitment, by adhering to the same Minimum Revenue Requirements
Discipline. The purpose of regulation is to reproduce the elements of
control, inherent in free competition, which may be lacking in a controlled monopoly. Actually, the investor devotes nothing to public use.
He devotes his savings to his private use, to his expectation of personal private gain. Any other interpretation is sophistry or ignorance.

Put bluntly, the only available measure of value of a capital investment is its market price, which is the discounted present worth to
investors, as a body, of: (a) anticipated cash dividends; and (b) anticipated increase in market price (capital gains). Since the second element, capital gains, is itself a function of similar expectations at some
future date, this formula expresses current value in terms of anticipated cash return. This is the only direct measure of value of a capital investment yet conceived.

This statement of the case, possibly dogmatically phrased and
subject to challenge or improvement, outlines the basis of the cost-of-
capital philosophy. Implementation of that philosophy by means of
(a) exact definitions of terms and intent, and (b) exact arithmetic appropriate to accomplish that intent is the next step.

A limited range for fair return, defined and evaluated in the manner described, provides a rational basis not only for rate-making purposes, but also a guide for intelligent disposition of currently debated
problems, such as desirable treatment of tax windfalls.

This concept is at odds with the "fair value" philosophy to a minor
degree. It serves to confirm what ought to be self-evident: no way is
possible to establish "value in use" except by way of current or potential monetary "value in exchange" in some manner. While recognizing
that judgment is essential, it identifies the factors to which judgment
must be applied, indicates the nature of judgment to be exercised, and
suggests quantitative bases for such exercise of judgment. In brief, it
outlines a discipline.

The 6% Fixation

There is some evidence of a commission attitude that it is impol-
itic to approve fair rates of return far removed from 6%. The evidence
appears in the form of a much greater diversity of "rate bases" for
fair value than for fair percentage return; and little apparent reason
for such greater diversity beyond the wish to stipulate a fair percentage near 6%.[6]

That same attitude seems to be implicit in a great deal of the literature dealing with such subjects as attrition, inflationary erosion of

---

[6] An authoritative factual survey of the situation is the study Return Allowed in Public
Utility Rate Cases, which is a digest of about 1,000 cases decided between 1915 and 1961,
prepared by Arthur Andersen & Co. for use of their staff and clients.

values, and the responsibility of regulation to investors. This phenomenon appears to be the product of a notion that "fair value" depends
upon some economic concept other than the investors' own criterion.
The favorite prescription, often asserted as though it were axiomatic
and undeniable, is that the "real" measure of value, and hence the real
measure of fair return, is a function of the purchasing power of the
dollar at the time the capital commitment was made.

A hiatus in such argument introduces self-contradictions that seem
to go unnoticed. So long as utilities continue to need incremental capital, incremental investors are perfectly capable of taking care of themselves. Such testimony as mentioned in Problem 13, at the end of this
chapter, suggests how. "Tough" regulation means a high price for
more capital and a high price of service to consumers. No academic
opinion is involved here; this is plain arithmetic.

Already committed capital is not so favorably situated. "Tough"
regulation can deny it a return that meets the investors' standards of
fairness. That makes it possible, to a degree, for regulation of fairness to appear to minimize customer costs, because the low percentage
return is a fait accompli that can be demonstrated. The lower cost of
service that could have been accomplished by a more liberal policy can
only be estimated, however factual the estimate.

Price level adjustments or standards of value for rate base purposes other than investors' committed capital do not solve this problem. They simply encourage substitution of some new "traditional"
low rate in place of the present 6% fixation, to be applied to the higher
rate base. The difficulty is one of adopting administrative procedure
to fit economic facts, not of attempting to discover economic principles
and facts from observed administrative procedure.

One technical detail, of small quantitative significance but important conceptually, deserves mention in connection with adjudicated
"MAR plus fair Profit Incentive." It concerns a minor difference in
the evaluation of MAR for regulatory purposes (its current level) and
for purposes of studies of profitability and economic choice (the long-
term level). We will return to this subject later on in this chapter.

Government Ownership

The Man from Mars might have difficulty understanding why roads
are not usually investor-owned, but railroads are. Or why water companies are usually tax-financed, but gas companies usually are not.
Why communication by mail is tax-financed at a handsome loss; communication otherwise by profitable investor ownership. But the most
puzzling anomaly of all probably would be the presence of such tax-
financed organizations as REA or TVA in a society which purports to
be a free enterprise economy.

Economically, which is our only concern here, the justification for
governmental encroachment on the province of free enterprise rests on
the two factual observations:

1. Freewill investors cannot be induced to supply capital for ventures which do not hold forth any promise of financial gain.
2. Such ventures, unable to finance themselves, are of sufficient benefit to the nation to convince taxpayers that it is to their advantage to subsidize them.

Not all the activities of government-owned developments such as TVA can be described as "encroachment." Flood control, recreational facilities, and other nonpower objectives may be part of the complex. However, it can be readily understood (even by the Man from Mars) why the public occasionally questions the economics of such a gigantic intrusion of the government into the business of supplying electric power, if investor-owned companies are able and willing to do the job. Whatever good reasons in the public welfare may have initiated the undertaking, is it economically justified today, or is it an unnecessary public burden? And was there not a better alternative in the beginning?[7]

Any number of "economic" analyses of such situations have been proposed; none of them have been very convincing. Those who dislike socialized industry call such projects a form of double taxation; the initial capital investment is at the taxpayers' expense (interest on government bonds, issued to finance such projects or to reimburse the Treasury, must be paid via taxes), and no income taxes are recovered corresponding to those paid by the same project if investor-owned. In general, tax-financed plants pay no taxes; a few make small token payments in lieu of taxes.

Some advocates of tax-financed plants profess to believe that tax-financed generating stations produce "cheaper power" than is possible for investor-owned properties because of their claimed lower cost of capital. It is amazing how many are deluded in this manner. Charges for electric power produced by the TVA are most often brought forward as an example to support that misunderstanding.

The fallacy involved here will be demonstrated in terms that any high school student can understand. This misconception is one of the most serious that are encouraged by the Annual Cost Philosophy, mentioned in Chapter 11.

The awkward self-contradictions that have developed from this misrepresentation have become more widely recognized in recent years. Since 1957, two separate governmental groups have inquired into appropriate methods for evaluating federal projects of this kind and have submitted formal reports. One was a special committee appointed by President John F. Kennedy.[8] The other was an Inter-Agency Committee on Water Resources representing the Departments of

---

[7]The facts are that by 1964, about 8,700,000 kilowatts of TVA's generating capacity was in steam plants; more than double the 4,000,000 of hydro capacity. And in 1964 about $315,000,000 of further expenditures were planned for additional generation and transmission facilities.

[8]S. Doc. No. 97, 87th Cong., 2nd Sess. (1962).

Agriculture, Army, Commerce, Health Education and Welfare, Interior, Labor, and the Federal Power Commission.

The latter report, Proposed Practices for Economic Analysis of River Basin Projects, (May 27, 1958), was prepared by the Subcommittee on Evaluation Standards of the Inter-Agency Committee.

Both groups reached substantially identical conclusions. One major conclusion, from page 22 of the above report, is as follows: "The values attached to benefits and costs at their time of accrual can be made comparable only after conversions to an equivalent basis for time and degree of certainty of occurrence."

In further explanation of this conclusion it is pointed out in the report that the appropriate discount rate used to calculate present worth must reflect both the "time" and the "risk" elements.

The appropriate treatment of taxes, in such economic comparisons, is discussed with equal lucidity:

From a public evaluation viewpoint, only the increases in the costs of governmental services that are anticipated as a result of the project are properly chargeable and should be included as a tax cost of the project. Such increased costs of governmental services represent outlays for goods and services essential for project operations. Any allowances for taxes as costs in project analysis in excess of increased costs of governmental service constitute benefits produced by the project that are similar to other project benefits.

Both conclusions are completely in accord with the Minimum Revenue Requirements Discipline. They should effectively demolish the myth of "cheaper power" by reason of a low interest rate for borrowings backed by authority to tax. But perhaps that is not obvious. A simple example will serve to illustrate the economic principles involved, as well as the grossly contradictory conclusions that are commonly reached by failing to recognize one's own exact intent in making such comparisons.

Illustrative Example

Consider an electric power project (or any other proposal, such as a plant to make drinkable water out of sea water) which could be either tax-financed or investor-financed, as follows:

Capital investment = $100,000,000.
Interest rate on bonds, if tax-financed = 3%.[9]
MAR, if investor-financed = 6%.
Service life = 50 years (assumed actual life, for simplicity, not an estimate of probable life).
Ultimate net salvage zero, also for simplicity.

---

[9]Assumed financing by way of 3% bonds does not necessarily represent the typical situation. For example, government subsidies at zero interest approximated two billion dollars ($2,000,000,000) in the case of TVA. More recently, TVA has made token interest payments at a rate of less than 2%.

No taxes if plant is government-owned.
Federal income tax = 48%, if investor-financed.
50% debt at 4% interest.
"Straight-line" depreciation for books, SYD for tax-deductible
    purposes, flow-through accounting.
Other expenses = 10% (= $10,000,000 annually), whether tax-
    financed or investor-financed.

Table 14.1 shows the usual, but (as will be convincingly shown) totally indefensible, comparison of "annual costs"; Part I if tax-financed, Part II if investor-financed. Government-ownership is made to appear preferable by a margin of about $4,000,000 per year.

One is tempted to ask whether free enterprise is not an expensive luxury, if Table 14.1 is to be believed. But before making that decision, suppose we look at the present worths of these "annual costs," which comparison has been advocated as the only meaningful basis for conclusions. Present worths of the same figures are calculated in Table 14.2; obviously something is dubious there.

Which is the correct conclusion: the apparent tax-financed superiority of Table 14.1 ($4,047,900 per year) or the investor-financed superiority of Table 14.2 ($74,779,000)? At this juncture, as in Ellery Queen mysteries, it might be observed that the reader has all the facts and should now be able to produce the correct answer on his own. It is urged that the student make that attempt before reading further. This is the explanation that any high school graduate can understand once it is pointed out. Nevertheless, it is consistently misunderstood or misrepresented at the highest levels of government and business planning, to the detriment of all taxpayers and investors.

Table 14.1. A common and unsound "annual cost" comparison.

I. Tax-Financed

Return at 3% of $100,000,000	$ 3,000,000 per year
Depreciation at 0.8865%* of $100,000,000	886,500
"Annual costs of capital recovery"	$ 3,886,500
Other expenses	10,000,000
Claimed "total annual costs"	$13,886,500 per year

II. Investor-Financed

Return at 6% of $100,000,000	$ 6,000,000 per year
Depreciation at 0.3444%* of $100,000,000	344,400
Revenue requirements, capital recovery	$ 6,344,400
Income tax at 1.59%† of $100,000,000	1,590,000
Other expenses, as in I above	10,000,000
Annual revenue requirements	$17,934,400 per year

Apparent advantage of tax-financed plant is:

17,934,400 - 13,886,500 = $4,047,900 per year

---

*The annuity which will accumulate one dollar in 50 years, if placed at interest at the rate-of-return percentage. See Chapter 5.

†Per Formula 8.4, on page 184:

$T\% = 0.9231\ [(4.344)\ (0.667) - (2.8 - 2.0) - 0.18] - 0.18 = 1.59\%$

The Exact Intent (MRRD)

Aside from the taxes on investor-financed property and income which the Treasury does not receive if the same property is tax-financed, the cost of the project is identical either way. Surely it is obvious that the analyst's exact intent is to regard costs of the project as made up of two cash outlays (aside from taxes): (a) an immediate capital outlay of $100,000,000; and (b) an annual expense outlay of $10,000,000 each year. Both outlays are the same as to amount and as to timing, whether the project is tax-financed or investor-financed. If both the annual cost analysis and the present worth analysis do not arrive at this exactly intended conclusion, then both must be wrong. This is indeed the case. Calculations of Part I, Tables 14.1 and 14.2, are meaningless. They do not carry out the analyst's own exact intent.

Exactly why does the reasoning of Tables 14.1 and 14.2, both of which seem so reasonable, go so far wrong?

The Financial Equivalency (MRRD)

Three items of importance to be discussed in applying MRRD to the present problem are:

1. The principle of financial equivalency;
2. The importance of Profit Incentive; and
3. The economic significance of taxes.

Referring to Table 14.1, it is the analyst's exact intent to calculate

Table 14.2. A suggested comparison of present worths (to demonstrate the fallacy of Table 14.1).

From interest tables (see Chapter 5) the present worth of a 50-year annuity is:

At 3% "interest"	25.729764
At 6% "interest"	15.761861

The present worth of Table 14.1 figures, so calculated, is:

I. Tax-Financed

Return & depreciation	25.729 764 x 3,886,500	= $100,000,000
Other expenses	25.729 764 x 10,000,000	= 257,298,000
Present worth of total "annual costs"		$357,298,000

II. Investor-Financed

MAR & depreciation	15.761 861 x 6,344,000	= $100,000,000
Federal income tax	15.761 861 x 1,590,000	= 24,900,000
Other expenses	15.761 861 x 10,000,000	= 157,619,000
Present worth of total outlays		= $282,519,000
Apparent advantage of investor-financed plant		= $ 74,779,000

This table makes it appear that investor-financing of the same project is superior by nearly 75 million dollars, for a 100-million-dollar project!

return plus depreciation as the annual financial equivalency, over service lifetime, of a capital investment of $100,000,000.

Only one exact interpretation of "financial equivalency" can be made, as explained in Chapter 5. That is the "just as soon" alternative to an immediate payment of $100,000,000, which may be a level annuity over some specified period (as intended here), or a single alternative payment at some other date, or any other combination of nonlevel annuity or installment payments.

In any case, the "just as soon" alternative must be calculated at the "just as soon" interest rate, which is MAR and nothing else. There is no excuse for using a discount rate other than MAR just because a project is tax-financed.

The "Annual costs of capital recovery" in Part I of Table 14.1 — "return plus depreciation" calculated at $3,886,500 — are not the "just as soon" alternative to an immediate cash outlay of $100,000,000. They would be if MAR were 3%. But MAR is not 3%; it is specifically stipulated to be 6%. The only way to assign a figure to MAR is to inquire into the market price investors will pay for ownership (equity) of a project, in the manner explained in Chapter 3.

Those who see it otherwise commit themselves to self-contradictions of the kind illustrated by this example. They cannot agree with themselves as to their own intent.

A 50-year annuity of $3,886,500 per year is financially equivalent to an immediate outlay of only $61,000,000 (= 15.761861 x $3,886,500), not $100,000,000. Respect for this basic principle is the essence of MRRD, which differentiates it from all other techniques.

Profit Incentive was not mentioned in Tables 14.1 or 14.2. Those familiar with MRRD will perhaps agree that it should not be mentioned there, since economic comparisons look to revenue requirements only, and Profit Incentive is no part of revenue requirements. (See the Diagram of Intent, Chapter 4.)

There is a valid and self-evident explanation with respect to economic comparisons between investor-financed alternatives. However, it is not convincing in application to the present problem, which is a comparison between tax-financing and investor-financing of the same plant.

Once more, the complete and clear explanation is by way of strict observance of the analyst's own exact intent, as follows: In comparisons between two investor-owned proposals within a given company, the amount of Profit Incentive, out of identical sales and revenues, provides the whole basis for the economic decision. (Again, see Chapter 4.) But in the present example, there is no Profit Incentive for tax-financed property. The size of a nonexistent Profit Incentive is hardly a suitable basis for decisions.

For tax-financed proposals, the basis for economic decisions is the optimum allocation of resources. The value of "resources" represented by the capital investment in a project may be expressed either in the dollars of this capital outlay or the financial equivalent of the outlay equated by use of financial mathematics employing MAR as the discount rate, in the manner of Chapter 5 and as just discussed. Other resources, such as materials and labor, represented by outlays classified as expenses are by inherent nature an annual phenomenon.

In order to discover the combined effect of a capital outlay plus annual outlays, it is thus necessary to:

1. Put both on an annuity basis, by converting the capital outlay into its annual financial equivalent; or
2. Put both on a single-outlay basis, by converting the expenses into their present worth financial equivalency.

Given Plans A and B, having identical capital outlays and identical annual expenses, their financial equivalency must be obvious. If it is made to appear otherwise by using either foregoing version of financial equivalency, then the method of conversion is immediately condemned as incompetent. This is exactly what is revealed when any rate of return or discount method other than MAR is used. The Annual Cost Method is incompetent, whether one looks at annual data or at their present worth.

Profit Incentive and Taxes

Profit Incentive is not an outlay of "resources" in this sense. It is neither goods, nor capital, nor labor. It is simply an inducement offered to those who can supply the capital resources to do so. That inducement can be offered only if consumers are willing to pay a price for the product sufficient to yield that Profit Incentive. That assumption is inherent in selection of the MAR percentage.

If consumers would be willing to pay a price for the product sufficiently high (a large Profit Incentive) to reduce MAR to 5%, then 5% should be used in the foregoing examples for investor-financed MAR in estimating revenue requirements. Nobody borrows money or raises equity capital at MAR%, in order to reinvest it at the same MAR%. It is MAR — the cost of capital — that is the resource to be allocated. Profit Incentive is the inducement to make the best allocation, not a "resource."

This simple principle gets befogged by poorly understood calculations of depreciation and present worth when analysts lose sight of their exact intent. Tables 14.1 and 14.2 are classic examples of the confusion caused by concentrating on a favorite method and forgetting exact objective. A similar comment applies to the treatment of taxes.

Taxes are a real cost to the consumer. They are a necessary revenue of government, to cover costs of national defense, courts, health, welfare, space exploration, and so on. These costs of government contribute the same amount to "costs to produce power" whether the plant happens to be government owned or investor owned. If the government-owned utility were obliged to act as tax collector, in the same manner as the investor-owned utility, it too would have to obtain from its customers the amounts of taxes to be turned over to the government. An investor-financed company can be put out of business by high taxes; for example, lowering taxes on oil can enable oil heat to compete with gas or electricity, otherwise perhaps impossible. It would be absurd, however, to think that the economics of tax-financing versus investor-financing of the same plant can be affected by taxes.

Were that true, then one administration could make socialized industry an "economic allocation of resources" overnight, simply by increasing the tax rate on investor-financed business. Four years later, a new administration could make socialized industry a disaster simply by lowering the tax rate on investor-financed business. The proposition is silly. Nevertheless, inclusion of taxes in only one alternative, when comparing economic merits of tax- versus investor-financing, proceeds on that basis. Again, by concentrating on method, and losing sight of the exactly intended objective.

In brief, investor-financing of the same plant should be vastly preferred for economic reasons:

1. There is no reason to expect that cash outlays for capital assets or for expenses (as exactly defined in Chapter 9) will be substantially different, whether tax-financed or investor-financed. (This statement does not overlook "cost of capital," as will be discussed further.)

2. Investor-financing provides an automatic incentive for the best use of national resources (including capital) offering investors a financial inducement to economize. The only place where the automatic incentive cannot operate is where consumer demand for the product is not sufficient to justify the outlay of resources. Such was the basis for such projects as TVA and REA. Taxpayers were willing to pay users of the product enough to enable them to buy what they could not otherwise afford. These payments could just as well have been made direct to the customers, by way of welfare checks, to enable them to pay the higher rates that would have to be charged if TVA and REA properties were investor-financed.

3. It provides a source of tax revenues, necessary for essential services of government such as national defense, which otherwise must be obtained elsewhere less conveniently and with greater cost of collection. Taxpayers do not intend to exempt individuals or corporations in rural areas from bearing their fair share of such essential national services.

Arguments may be advanced in favor of tax-financing, but they are not economic reasons and are therefore beyond the scope of this discussion.

The Intended Allocation of Costs and Benefits

The actually intended economic analysis of the foregoing example appears in Table 14.3.

We will assume that annual revenues paid by consumers would amount to $19,847,500 per year if investor-financed. This figure includes a Profit Incentive of 1%, or $1,000,000 per year. Income tax at 48% would provide taxes on Profit Incentive of $923,100 per year (= 0.48/0.52 x 1,000,000).

Both quantities are benefits to the community. The tax from this source reduces taxes that would have to be obtained from the same national taxpayers, in the same amount, if not available from this source. The Profit Incentive is a benefit to any individual willing to supply capital resources. The difference here is that, if tax-financed, citizens supply the same capital resources, willingly or not, and there is no Profit Incentive benefit to the community.

To sum up, tax-financing versus investor-financing is economically a standoff except for taxes; exactly the same resources are expended in either event. Allocation of benefits is quite another matter, and the misunderstanding arises from confusing the arbitrary allocation with an economic comparison.

Table 14.3. Costs and benefits of tax-financing versus investor-financing of a project.

Part I. Outlay of Resources (Cost)
For either method of financing:

Return at 6% MAR	$6,000,000	
Depreciation at 0.3444%	344,400	
Financial equivalent of capital outlay		$ 6,344,400 per year
Expenses (operation, maintenance, administration, and so on)		10,000,000
Total outlay of resources, annual basis		$16,344,400 per year

Part II. Allocation of Benefits

A. If Tax-Financed

Total outlay of resources, above	$16,344,400 per year
Revenues from customers (Part I, Table 14.1)	13,886,500
Penalty allocated to the community	$ 2,457,900 per year

B. If Investor-Financed

Total outlay of resources, same as above		$16,344,400 per year
Revenues from customers:		
Minimum revenue requirements (Part II, Table 14.1)	$17,934,400	
Profit Incentive at 1%	1,000,000	
Tax on Profit Incentive	923,100	
Total revenues from customers		$19,857,500
Benefits available to community		$ 3,513,100 per year
Allocation of benefits:		
Profit Incentive to suppliers of capital		$ 1,000,000
Income taxes (1,590,000 + 923,100)		2,513,100
Total benefits allocated to the community		$ 3,513,100 per year

[Annual figures may be reduced to equivalent present worth by multiplying by

$$\frac{1}{(i + \overset{\beta}{\underset{i}{d}})} = \frac{1}{6\% + 0.3444\%} = 15.761861].$$

Table 14.3 shows a vast difference in benefits to the <u>community at large</u>. If tax-financed, the <u>community at large</u> fares as follows:

Welfare payments to customers of the utility $2,457,900 per year
Loss of benefits from investor-ownership   3,513,100
Total penalty <u>to the community at large</u> $5,971,000 per year

The beneficiaries are <u>customers</u> of the tax-financed utility:

Revenues paid if investor-financed $19,857,500 per year
Revenues paid if tax-financed   13,886,500
Welfare benefits <u>to customers of the utility</u> $ 5,971,000 per year

Welfare benefits to customers, if the utility were investor-owned, could be in the form of monthly checks to cover the difference between bills rendered for the services actually used: (a) if supply facilities had been tax-financed, and (b) if exactly the same projects were to be investor-financed, with the higher rates sufficient to yield the investor-owned utility a fair return on that identical capital investment (the public utility then to be granted permission to establish this necessarily higher tariff in the specified area).

Such a scheme would allocate exactly the same benefits to exactly the same customers as would be accomplished by the present economically unsound scheme of tax-financed agencies. It would preserve the economic advantage of free enterprise. It could be managed by individuals of the same integrity and dedication as those who manage government-owned developments at present, and presumably by a small fraction of their present number.

The foregoing problem considers only one aspect of the economics of tax-financed versus investor-financed public utilities. Another quite different consideration is probably of much greater financial importance to all taxpayers and stockholders. It may be introduced by remarking that usually <u>financial optimization</u> is accepted as the exact intent when referring to an "economic choice." When the intent is otherwise, the burden is on the proponent to explain his different intent.

Since the objective of tax-financed institutions is ordinarily <u>not</u> financial, is the MRRD technique appropriate for making decisions with respect to "economic choice" in such organizations as the REA?

The REA[10]

The Rural Electrification Administration was created by Executive Order in 1935, and by law in 1936. Its objective was charitable. Lest use of this term give offense, the reader is hastily reminded that

---

[10]For a particularly informative discussion of REA, pro and con, see two addresses delivered before the Public Utility Law Section of the American Bar Association, August 1964: 1. <u>REA — Its Operations and Legislative Mandate</u>, by Raymond Moley, Contributing Editor of <u>Newsweek</u>, and 2. <u>A Matter of Motive</u>, by Clyde T. Ellis, General Manager of Rural Electric Cooperative Association (NRECA), both reproduced in <u>Public Utilities Fortnightly</u>, (Sept. 24, 1964) p. 80.

charity is regarded by most people as a major virtue along with faith
and hope.

It is generally agreed, though some may quibble, that REA was established to accomplish a simple and specific objective: to bring electricity to the farm at a time when large rural areas had no electric
service. The reason why no electric service was available to such
areas is also generally agreed upon: potential customers were unable
to pay the price. Investor-owned public utilities could not make an
"optimum allocation" of their resources by expecting freewill investors
to provide the capital necessary to supply service at a loss to the investor.

There were, in 1964, more than 900 rural electric cooperatives
which borrowed from REA to carry out their objectives. At present,
capital funds are made available to them out of the U.S. Treasury at an
interest rate of 2%. The efficiency, diligence, and integrity of this organization is not questioned here. Quite a large number of people are
involved in REA: nearly a thousand managers, possibly 15,000 directors, and many more employees, consultants, and others.

Many individuals have serious qualms as to continued existence of
such a government agency after it has outlived its usefulness as a nonprofit welfare agency. Their concern is more than just financial; they
see it as a matter of right and wrong within the framework of our national purpose. Some of them deplore REA as "an excellent example of
institutionalizing a function on a permanent basis even after it has
completed its original purpose." Others charge that cooperatives have
been guilty of borrowing federal funds at 2% interest to invest in securities which pay a much higher rate, which they characterize as "im-
moral, illegal, and perpetrating a fraud on the people of the United
States."

Such opinion is merely noted here; it will not be debated. It is
mentioned to clarify the exact nature of the subject which is to be discussed, which is the kind of criterion appropriate for making financial
decisions in the management of organizations whose purpose is nonfinancial. That wording will suggest the source and degree of confusion
that has entered into such problems.

Economic Choice in REA

To illustrate a regrettable economic loss that is the natural result
of these paradoxical circumstances, suppose you are manager of a REA
cooperative and must make an economic choice between:

Plan 1. Constructing a new power plant using capital funds obtainable at an interest rate of 2%, versus

Plan 2. Purchasing the same amount of power, having the same
reliability of service, from a neighboring investor-owned
public utility.

"Annual costs" of Plan 1 (new plant) are calculated at $93,278 per year, per Table 14.4. Cost of purchasing the same power from the neighboring public utility is $103,837 per year.

What would your decision be? Any manager faithful to his trust is obligated to select Plan 1 (new plant). Its margin of superiority appears to be substantial, $10,479 per year, approximately a 10% differential. So far as the financial effect on co-op customers is concerned, purchased power would cost them $10,479 more per year for the same service.

As manager of the co-op, you would not and should not be expected to give consideration to the following wasteful misallocation of resources, revealed by Table 14.5:

1. An unnecessary capital investment of $100,000 (co-op investment $500,000, public utility investment $400,000);
2. Unnecessary annual expenses of $15,000 per year (co-op outlays $75,000 per year, utility outlays $60,000 per year);
3. Depriving the government of $13,560 per year in taxes (co-op pays no taxes; public utility pays $13,560 per year);
4. Draining off $400,000 of tax revenues from the Federal Treasury, not fully repaid for many years, otherwise available for truly essential services such as national defense; and
5. Loss of $4,000 per year in Profit Incentive to individual investors (including customers of the co-op).

Such are the hard-cash penalties for uneconomic use of national resources that management of the REA co-op is obliged to recommend. They might be avoided by federal approval of investor-owned service to the area, together with welfare payments to customers in the amount of the annual differential (Table 14.5 versus Table 14.4) of only $10,479 per year.

Or, alternatively, the investor-owned public utility might be permitted to supply service at its commission-regulated rates (normally greater than REA charges in such low load density areas), while customers pay the REA rates; the subsidy to be paid directly to the utility.

Table 14.4. "Annual costs" of Plan 1, new co-op plant.

Capital investment = $500,000.
Ultimate net salvage zero (for simplicity).
Interest at 2%.
Service life 40 years (assumed certain, for simplicity).
Operation and maintenance expense, fuel, administration and similar expenses at
   $75,000 per year.
Calculated "Annual Costs":

Return at 2% of $500,000	$10,000 per year
Depreciation at 1.6556%* of $500,000	8,278
Other expenses	75,000
Total "annual costs"	$93,278 per year

*The annuity which will amount to $1 in 40 years, if placed at 2% interest.

Table 14.5. Makeup of purchased-power rate.

Capital investment = $400,000.
  (Composed of an allocated investment in large-size generating units, at smaller
  $/kw than co-op units; plus a transmission line.)
Ultimate net salvage zero (for simplicity).
MAR at 6%. 50% debt at 4% interest.
Profit Incentive an additional 1%.
Service life 40 years (assumed to be "certain," for simplicity).
"Straight-line" depreciation for books, SYD for taxes, flow-through, investment credit
  at 3%, tax rate 48%.
Operation and maintenance expense $60,000 per year.
  (Made up of smaller costs for fuel, operation, and maintenance of generating
  system, but includes expenses for transmission not incurred by co-op plant.)
Local and state taxes at 1%.

MAR at 6% of $400,000	$ 24,000 per year
Depreciation at 0.6462% of $400,000*	2,585
Revenue requirement for income tax at 1.39%†	5,560
Operation and maintenance	60,000
Local and state taxes at 1% of $400,000	4,000
Total minimum revenue requirements	$ 96,145
Plus Profit Incentive at 1% of $400,000	4,000
Federal income tax on Profit Incentive	3,692
Economically preferred rate for purchased power	$103,837 per year

---

*The annuity, at 6%, which will recover initial capital investment in exactly 40
years.
  †Per Formula 8.4, on page 184.

$$\frac{.48}{.52}\left[(6.00 + 0.65 - 2.50)\,(0.67) - (3.37 - 2.50) - 0.19\right] - 0.19 = 1.39\%.$$

This example illustrates the general principle involved. The same
reasoning applies to all of the co-op's plant and operations; the apparent "economic choice" made in the customary manner of Table 14.4 results in avoidable extravagance. Justification for socialized industry
is emotional, not economic. Shortcomings of the Annual Cost Philosophy have served to conceal that fact.

Acceptable Return and Risk

It is sometimes argued that a lower percentage return on
government-owned (tax-financed) projects is "justified" because the
risk is said to be less than for the same project if investor-financed.
    Several factors contribute to what a freewill investor regards as
risk, apt to affect the probability of his realizing the return anticipated
when he makes a capital investment.
    Their three major sources are:

1. The risk of industry obsolescence, loss of market, competition
   from other products or other procedures;
2. The risk of accidental damage, acts of war, sabotage, strikes,
   operating errors, fire, lightning, storms, earthquakes, and so
   on; and

3. The risk of unanticipated asset obsolescence, changes in stan-
    dards of service or in public habits, failure of new equipment
    or processes to meet expectations, expropriation or condemna-
    tion, and so on.

Such sources of risk are independent of the nature of ownership;
their impact is the same whether a given facility is tax-financed or
investor-financed. One might therefore expect investors to demand the
same minimum acceptable return (MAR) in either case, but obviously
they do not. Investors will accept about half the percentage return tax-
financed than if investor-financed. This situation appears to be misunderstood by many authors.

Some writers assert that the percentage return appropriate for
making economic studies of government-owned projects ("public
works") is the rate of interest paid on bonds issued to finance the
project; or the average rate of interest paid on borrowings by the governmental agency involved. The error in this reasoning must be obvious. If the plant were blown up by saboteurs, or destroyed by accident
or earthquake; if unexpected losses were incurred by reason of premature replacements made necessary by rapid obsolescence, etc.; or
if the project lost its market because unforeseen developments made
its output unsalable; interest payments would continue to be paid on the
bonds just the same. Necessary funds would continue to be provided by
taxpayers, even in the absence of any output or revenues. Investors in
the bonds do not bear the brunt of such risks.

It is highly important that the nature of this illogic be recognized.
It is the source of the mistaken assertion made by some authors that a
project is easier to justify if government owned, rather than investor
owned. That popular but unsound conclusion can result in waste of resources of the community and taxes higher than need be.

Some authors assert that the proper percentage return is minimum
attractive return (not MAR), adding that consideration for "opportunity
cost" — prospective return if the same capital were to be placed in
other available investment opportunities — is just as appropriate for
government-owned installations as for investor ownership. The fallacy
in that observation comes from confusing the budgeting function (determining the relative desirability of an investment, compared to other
opportunities) with determining its absolute cost, and economic choice
as a means of producing the same output and revenues, independent of
opportunities to invest elsewhere for other purposes. This is a serious
shortcoming of methods other than MRRD. Like the foregoing misconception, it is a direct result of accepting the unsound Annual Cost Philosophy, examined in Chapter 11. Neither opportunity cost nor minimum attractive return is correct for any type of ownership, for the
present purpose.

Still other authors state unhelpfully and without justification that
the whole matter of appropriate percentage return for making economic
studies of public works is controversial. They sometimes list a number of different proposals, all the way from zero to attractive percent-

age return, as though all were equally defensible. Such listings never mention the only justifiable percentage, which is MAR.

A few authors recognize that in comparing investor ownership with government ownership of a project, the same percentage return must be used for both, whatever figure is chosen. Presumably that conclusion is reached in view of the contradictory results otherwise obtained as revealed by Tables 14.1 and 14.2. But these authors fail to specify just what identical percentage should be selected, or why. It is commonly argued that it should be a function of risk incurred; but it is not explained how degree of risk — even if it could be described in words — is to be translated into a numerical rate of return in percent (of capital investment).

It has even been seriously proposed by one author that if a minimum attractive return is adopted, it should include a "safety factor" to allow for normally expected errors of engineering estimates. The futility of attempting to offset probable errors of estimate — which may be plus or minus, and of unknown amount — by introducing a deliberate error (always plus, and of specific amount) into the estimate of percentage return, must be obvious even to those totally unacquainted with economic principles. This suggestion is typical of the low-grade thought that has been given to this whole problem.

To summarize, the only appropriate percentage return for use in economic studies involving government-owned properties, whether as alternative to investor ownership or not, is the same MAR percentage that would be used if they were investor-owned enterprises of the same kind, with risks borne by investors rather than by taxpayers.

Government projects (public works) are commonly conducted at a loss; their output is sold (or the services are rendered) below cost, and the deficit is made up by taxpayers. Perhaps no objection need be raised to that arrangement so long as taxpayers understand the situation and consent to it (which is not the case at present); but it nevertheless invites far-reaching misunderstanding and misconceptions of the disadvantages of government ownership, as well as encouraging unnecessary waste of community resources for the reason illustrated by Tables 14.4 and 14.5.

Of smaller importance quantitatively, but worth recalling at this point, is the difference between short-term risks whose impact is experienced and recognized at any moment and their long-term-levelized effects on corporate well-being.

One dogma on which commission regulation depends is the proposition, arbitrary but defensible as an interpretation of "fair treatment" of a utility's customers, that rates for service rendered today should cover today's costs plus a fair Profit Incentive. "Today's" costs means the current rate of expenditure for such things as wages, fuel, and supplies, which may have a different (usually higher) price tag next year. Some of today's customers may not be customers of the company next year; for a growing community, many of next year's customers are not yet taking service. It is regarded as unfair to make this year's customers pay any part of next year's higher costs for wages, fuel, and supplies, even though those higher prices may be firmly predictable and unavoidable.

The "cost of financing" (MAR) is another outlay which may have a different price next year. Ordinarily, the variation is small; MAR is a much more stable percentage than other components of revenue requirements, but it can and does vary from time to time. For purposes of rate regulation it is the present short-term evaluation of MAR plus Profit Incentive that is regarded as the figure that is "fair" to customers at the moment.

There is no objection to the simple comparison of rates charged for identical services, if the exact intent of such a comparison is clearly recognized. Assuming that the tax-financed project is operated with the same skill and integrity and does in fact supply services identical in amount and quality (that is, identical cash outlays for capital assets and for expenses, as exactly defined in Chapter 9), then the loss to the community by being tax-financed instead of investor-financed can be estimated in the manner of Table 14.3.

Some Classical Problems

A few special problems, most often encountered in public utility experience, deserve brief mention because they illustrate important principles that commonly escape notice. All are concerned with evaluation of certain outlays which are complex functions of one or more controlling influences, as illustrated by the behavior of electrical losses or operating costs of automobiles.

It is convenient to regard such outlays as being made up of:

1. A "fixed" component, which may include capital outlays and/or expense;
2. A "demand" component proportional, not necessarily linear, to maximum use or output; and
3. A "commodity" component proportional, usually linear, to output over a stated period.

All three components may be expressed in terms of average, incremental, or marginal incremental cost, as appropriate. It is quite common to discover that these three bases of estimate yield three substantially different figures. What is more, individual opinions may differ as to the basis appropriate for the evaluation of electrical losses in problems of profitability and economic choice.

Here is a situation where the MRRD approach can be particularly helpful. It illustrates clearly the dangers that lie in failing to define exact intent and in relying on oversimplified models or inexact analogies to simulate actual cost behavior. (See Chapter 9.) The appropriate cost of losses is not uncommonly overestimated by 100% or more as the direct result of uncritical acceptance of loose reasoning in the evaluation.

Incremental and "Fixed" Costs

Costs of operating the family car are often used to explain the principle of fixed versus incremental expenses. Taking a trip in the family car means incurring certain costs that would not be incurred if the trip were not taken, such as outlays for gasoline, highway tolls, and lubricants. There may be parking fees and wear and tear on tires and other parts which would not have occurred if the car had stayed in the garage at home. All such outlays are "incremental" costs, the result of incremental use of the machine.

Certain other expenses (initial purchase price is not an expense) must be paid whether the trip is taken or not. They include such costs as insurance, licenses, and possibly garage rental, and so forth. Because they are independent of the amount of use, they are often called "fixed" costs (not fixed charges).

There may be still other outlays which are certainly not incurred if the car is left at home, but they are difficult to associate with any particular trip. For example, if an engine bearing burns out and results in a big repair bill just as you are leaving on a trip, who can say whether that expense was caused by the immediate trip (hardly started) or the accumulated wear of previous trips? Which trip is responsible when the storage battery gives up the ghost and needs replacement one month after the two-year guarantee expired?

The latter problem is fundamentally one of allocation and is involved in questions of pricing or rate making (that is, deciding what particular output of service or product should be charged with the outlay) rather than in studies of economic choice. It will not be discussed further. Let's return to that concept of "fixed" costs.

Cost of Electrical Losses

The foregoing phenomena enter into evaluation of the extra costs imposed by reason of the small incremental loads represented by electrical losses in supply facilities between generating sources and ultimate consumers. The cost of the smallest imaginable increase in load is known as the "marginal incremental" cost.

In the first place, operating costs incurred at generating stations over periods such as a month or a year can be separated into two major components:

1. The "energy" or "commodity" component, which is regarded as varying directly with energy send-out during the period, in kilowatt-hours; and
2. The remainder of total operating costs incurred during the period, found by difference, variously known as the "fixed component," or the "demand component," or the "power component."

This long-term energy component may include some "peak preparedness costs"; although over a short term, such as a few hours,

peak preparedness costs may be conveniently treated as a part of the
fixed component, regarded as not affected by the amount of the short-
term incremental output. It will be obvious that great care must be
taken to specify exact intent in using these terms.

All the foregoing costs deal with operating outlays (fuel, labor,
materials, and supplies), which may include some small part of maintenance expense as well. A separate, distinct, and important part of
the cost of losses is the extra capital investment in facilities needed to
generate and deliver the extra loss-load, over and above the salable
payload. Because this capital investment is usually regarded as somehow related to peak load supplied, it too is commonly called a "demand
cost." Thus, total demand costs may be treated as made up of (a) the
demand component of operating outlays, plus (b) the capital investment
in facilities needed to supply peak demand. The question to be explored
here is that of estimating the cost of that incremental capital investment needed to supply the incremental load represented by losses in
the supply facilities.

The commonest view, widely accepted uncritically, is that a "practical" evaluation is: incremental peak load, in kilowatts, multiplied by
average capital cost of the facilities in $/kilowatt. This view is sup-
ported by the argument that an additional peak load of one kilowatt requires the same plant installation (= one kilowatt of capacity), whether
the additional load is salable output, system losses, or a combination
of both.

However, a more careful scrutiny of the facts reveals several good
reasons why that reasoning can lead to gross overestimates of costs.
Reasons therefor are made clear by considering the car pool analogy.
Although the car pool analogy is not an exact model, it serves our purpose for that very reason. It indicates clearly that an exact model
must recognize a number of contributing factors that are difficult to
reproduce by means of a simple analogy.

The Car Pool Analogy

Suppose the owner of a four-passenger car drives to work daily
from the suburbs. It occurs to him that he could accommodate his
neighbor as a daily passenger at substantially zero incremental cost.

Thus far, the analogy resembles actual behavior of capacity costs
at generating stations to accommodate the small amount of incremental
peak load caused by additional losses in the supply system. Until increased peak loads demand additional generating capacity, outlays to
reduce losses are not very profitable. They may serve to reduce operating expenses, but they do not reduce capital investment in the supply facilities.

To simulate conditions in the electrical system, we must next introduce effects of load growth into the analogy. So let's suppose that an
additional passenger is added each year for three years, at substantially

zero incremental cost. At that time, the pool must make more space available if further passengers are to be accommodated. It must either buy another car or substitute a larger one.

In generating station practice, long-lived equipment is replaced only at long intervals, and additions commonly come in larger sizes than the older units. Accordingly, if the car pool analogy is to simulate those conditions accurately, it must give recognition to effects of growth <u>and</u> unit size, as well as growth <u>in</u> unit size. The same may be true, but to a different degree, in simulating capital additions to the transmission and distribution systems.

Another important consideration, often overlooked, is the exact difference between incremental growth and <u>marginal</u> incremental growth. That is, losses represent a small fraction of one year's load increase. In the car pool model, loss reduction really corresponds more nearly to making additional capacity available by asking passengers to go on a diet. If there were a great many passengers per car, dieting might conceivably make room for one more passenger, but ordinarily it could not be expected to accomplish anything.

Finally, there are two more factors that are difficult to reproduce in the car pool analogy. One is the effect of "lead time" between the date of committing the company to an installation and the date when planned facilities are operable. The other is a matter of probability with respect to the simultaneity of two independent variables, as discussed in the following section.

It is because the oversimplified analysis overlooks the exact nature of all these influences that the "practical" reasoning is apt to go so far wrong.

An Application of Probability

A matter of probability commonly overlooked, which often affects the difference between average and incremental costs for a given additional output, is concerned with the relative timing of outputs and available capacities, as illustrated by this brain teaser.

A suburban residential area is served by two bus routes into the city. Blue Line vehicles pass the bus stop every 20 minutes, go north and over the North Bridge, reaching town in 40 minutes. Green Line vehicles pass the same bus stop every 20 minutes, go south and over the South Bridge, reaching town in 40 minutes. The fare is 30 cents either way.

Housewives in the area, going shopping in the city and arriving at the bus stop at random times, take whichever bus comes along first. Yet about 75% of the time they take the Blue Line. To avoid crowding, the Blue Line has to replace its busses by larger ones. How can that be? Isn't there a 50-50 chance of passengers' taking either route?

The explanation is that bus schedules are such that Blue Line vehicles arrive at this particular stop 5 minutes before the Green Line bus shows up. Then a 15-minute interval lapses before another Blue Line bus appears. Housewives arriving at the corner in the latter 15-minute period take the Blue Line. Those arriving in the next 5-minute period take the Green Line. Arriving at random times, three out of four take the Blue Line.

Here again, the analogy is useful but imperfect. If all these complications were introduced into the analogy, it would no longer be simple. It serves to demonstrate the shortcomings of oversimplification. And all this introduces a discussion of the simulation process that does take all these effects into consideration and provides a dependable solution to estimates of capital investment to supply incremental losses.

Installation Schedules

Electric generators come in large sizes; the larger the unit size, the smaller is capital investment per unit of output, and the greater is operating efficiency. Equipment such as transformers and conductors (wire, cable) also comes in a limited number of standard sizes. When first installed, such equipment has a large margin of reserve capacity. Before it is retired in favor of a larger unit size, to accommodate load growth, it is usually desirable to load it beyond the most efficient point, as will be demonstrated in another example.

For this reason, a steadily growing load is normally supplied by making installations of equipment at intervals, as needed. The program of installations is not a steadily rising curve, approximating the increase in load supplied, but a "stepped" curve, always supplying enough capacity to meet maximum demands on the system, with an allowance for reserve capacity adequate to maintain uninterrupted service (or at worst, to reduce interruptions to a tolerable minimum) during the most severe causes of output that can be foreseen.

Some kinds of equipment, such as overhead conductors supported by wood poles, can be installed in a matter of hours. Other kinds, such as main generators, may require a period of two or three years for their design, construction, and installation. This "lead time" means that programs for installation of such equipment must be based on forecasts of loads made correspondingly in advance.

Figure 14.3 illustrates this situation. The dotted line is drawn through a series of points representing forecasts of annual peak loads on the system, each forecast three years in advance. The broken line indicates the capacity needed to supply these peak loads; that is, the peak load plus the necessary allowance for reserves available at the time of peak.

The solid line represents the program of capacity installations that would be planned to meet these requirements, using "building blocks" (that is, unit sizes if generating equipment) of the most desirable capacity rating. These units may be high-efficiency base-load units, or they may be less efficient "peak-shaving" units having much smaller

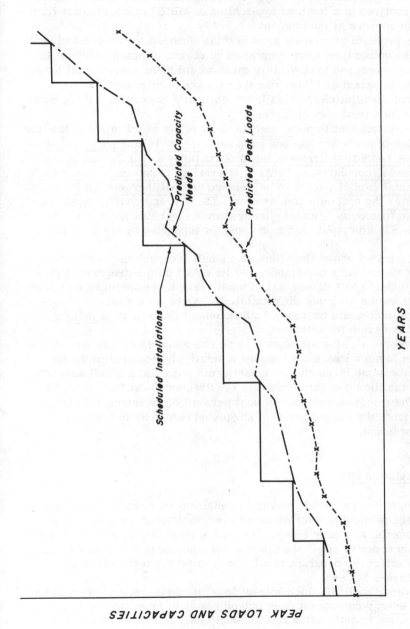

Fig. 14.3. Capacity needs and installation program.

PEAK LOADS AND CAPACITIES

YEARS

Predicted Peak Loads

Predicted Capacity Needs

Scheduled Installations

capital cost per unit of capacity. The economic choice between different alternatives is a familiar application of **MRRD** which is apart from
our main concern at the moment.

Our problem of interest here is this: Suppose the forecast of peak
loads (the dotted line) were increased by reason of small increments
caused by increased losses. How much would these incremental loads
affect the program and therefore the revenue requirements of the
equipment installations? This is the estimator's exact intent, in making the estimate of cost of losses.

The reason that this incremental cost is his exact intent in that the
evaluation is made for just one purpose: not for billing purposes or
allocating costs to different classes of customers, but for use in making economic comparisons between alternative proposals, in which the
incremental capital cost is to be weighed against incremental loss cost,
to discover the optimum combination. The average cost of supplying
total load (customer's usage plus system losses) will not serve this
purpose. On this point, common sense is supported by the analytical
reasoning.

Figure 14.4 shows the effect of a small increase in peak load, as
forecast three years in advance, and its effect on the program of plant
installations. You will see that in most years there would be no effect
whatever on the program of installations. Over a long term of years
the only effect would be a small advancement in the date of making
some of the same installations.

Consequently, the situation may be summarized as follows: A
small incremental peak load causes a small advancement in the date of
making the same large capital investments — that is, a small advancement in the timing of large revenue requirements — at frequent intervals. The resultant estimate of cost per unit of incremental loss is a
far cry from the simple pro rata suggested before as the "common
sense" solution.

The Simulation Study

It must be concluded that incremental losses resulting from selecting the particular alterations adopted, instead of adopting competing proposals, are quite small. How large must this incremental loss-
load be in order to affect the program of equipment installations? If it
does not affect the program at all, then the investment cost of incremental losses is zero.

However small the incremental loss, it can be reasonably assumed
that the energy component does indeed result in extra operating costs
of generation (mostly extra fuel consumption, unless supplied by hydro).
Investment component, however, is a different matter. Unless the program of installations is affected, there is no investment component of
cost.

On a sizable system, a load increase of one kilowatt would not be

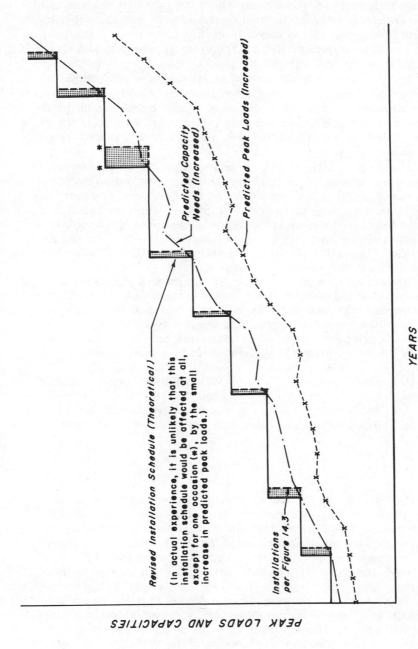

YEARS

Revised Installation Schedule (Theoretical)

(In actual experience, it is unlikely that this installation schedule would be affected at all, except for one occasion (*), by the small increase in predicted peak loads.)

Predicted Capacity Needs (Increased)

Predicted Peak Loads (Increased)

Installations per Figure 14.3

PEAK LOADS AND CAPACITIES

Fig. 14.4. Capacity needs and installation program; effect of a small increase in predicted loads.

451

detected. It could not conceivably affect the peak forecast and thus could not conceivably affect the program of installations. Its incremental investment cost is zero. If one kilowatt has no effect, does an increase of 10 kilowatts? On a large system, assuredly not. If not 10, will 100? If not 100, will 1,000?

There is some twilight zone where it cannot be said, offhand, whether an incremental load of stipulated size will affect the program of installations or not. The only possible way to evaluate the probability is by way of a simulation study. One thing is certain. There is some figure, such that smaller increments of peak load have no effect on investment cost.

Actual simulation studies, made for actual systems, suggest that the investment cost of electrical losses is nearer to zero than to pro rata cost per unit of load supplied. As can be appreciated from this brief discussion, a large number of variables affect the result; but a typical figure would seem to lie within the range of 30% to 50% of the pro rate average cost. An assigned figure of zero is not impossible, but most improbable. The pro rata estimate (= 100%) is so unlikely as to be substantially impossible to defend.

Since simulation studies are rather expensive to make, and since the exact cost assigned to losses does not usually affect alternative procedures tremendously, an approximate figure of 50% of the pro rata cost may be a reasonable estimate for many applications.

For a brief description of an actual estimate of the investment cost of losses for an actual system, made by a simulation process, see:

C. J. Baldwin and P. H. Jeynes, "That Elusive Demand Cost of Losses," Electric Light and Power (Feb. 15, 1962).

C. J. Baldwin, C. H. Hoffman, and P. H. Jeynes, "A Further Look at Cost of Losses," AIEE Transactions (Vol. 80, Part III, 1961).

Kelvin's Law

Many an engineer's only encounter with engineering economy has been a paragraph in his undergraduate textbook on electrical engineering that mentioned Kelvin's law. It is usually stated as follows: "The economical size of conductor is that for which the annual charges on the investment just equal the annual cost of energy losses."

A few thoughtful writers have pointed out that such an oversimplified statement is apt to result in unsound decisions. In fact, in his original statement of the case, Lord Kelvin did not propose this rule of thumb as a general law; in effect, he examined the revenue requirements of a span of conductors in terms of its cross-sectional area.

One serious practical shortcoming of the "Kelvin's law" approach is that it reveals only the appropriate conductor size for a given fixed load, or conversely, the economic loading for a given fixed conductor size. It takes no account of anticipated load growth.

The usual textbook approach seems to be to determine the nearest standard conductor size for the immediate given load and then to recommend selecting the next larger standard size — or perhaps one still larger, depending on personal judgment. This seems amateurish, since it is possible to determine exactly the correct size if one is willing to estimate the expected rate of growth.

Another practical shortcoming is that the correct answer depends upon whether the problem involves new construction or replacement of existing conductors. It is not necessarily most economic to load existing conductors up to their thermal limit before replacing; nor is it economic to replace at the point where the larger conductors would be justified if they were not a replacement. What is more, in replacement problems it makes a difference whether the existing conductors can be salvaged for reuse or must be scrapped when removed.

Still another curious misunderstanding is the common use of formulas based on "uniformly distributed loading" along the line, where such an assumption is not appropriate. It is quite possible to find the single size that is best for a uniformly distributed load if that is really the objective; but such a conductor is too small at the sending end and too large at its remote end for best economy.

A Disciplined Approach

A disciplined approach, which takes all these factors into account, may be briefly outlined as follows.

The first step is to develop expressions for the annual revenue requirements per thousand feet of circuit for each size, as follows, in dollars per year (the division by 1,000 to reduce watts to kilowatts). Let's make the following assumptions, to illustrate:

	I^2R Losses	+	Kvar Losses	+	Annual Revenue Requirements
Size X	$\dfrac{10.15\,I^2}{1,000}$	+	$\dfrac{0.22\,I^2}{1,000}$	+	36.00
Size Y	$\dfrac{3.25\,I^2}{1,000}$	+	$\dfrac{0.20\,I^2}{1,000}$	+	108.00

I represents the peak value of current in amperes; R is the resistance in ohms per 1,000 feet. The derivation of these expressions is deliberately omitted, since the purpose of this discussion is to focus on a method of estimate, rather than to suggest a quantitative solution for a specific conductor size. MAR is 6%.

Loading for equal costs, either size, is discovered by equating the revenue requirements expressions:

$$\frac{10.37\,I^2}{1,000} + 36 = \frac{3.45\,I^2}{1,000} + 108$$
$$I = 102 \text{ amperes per phase}$$

The break-even point for every standard size with its next larger size may be determined in this same way. Thus, if no load growth is to be expected, the range of loading for each standard size is easily established, assuming that this is new construction and not a replacement of existing conductors. Call this Work Sheet 1.

Now let's assume that there are existing conductors which would be suitable for reuse if removed; we suspect that they are loaded to their economic limit and we wish to find out if they should be replaced.

Whatever the value, V_x, of the existing conductors in their present location, they will have exactly the same value when relocated elsewhere; however, it is necessary to spend $$R$ to remove them plus $$L$ to reinstall them at that other location. Let's say $R + L = \$120$; increased by 12% for state taxes, the cost of removal and installation is $134.40 per thousand circuit feet.

Note that we are also assuming that for every 1,000 feet of conductor removed, 1,000 feet are reusable. If we can postpone spending $134.40 for one year, we save 6% of 134.40 = $8.06. At the same time, if the load is right for a change to larger conductors, we lose one year's saving in comparative revenue requirements if we postpone one year. Thus, the break-even load is that for which one year's difference in revenue requirements just equals $8.06. Using the costs of Work Sheet 1:

One year of X revenue requirements - 8.06 = One year of Y costs

$$\frac{10.37}{1,000} + 36 - 8.06 = \frac{3.45\ I^2}{1,000} + 108$$

$$I = 107.6 \text{ amperes per phase}$$

Call this Work Sheet 2. The break-even point for other consecutive conductor sizes can be established in this same manner.

It sometimes happens that some or all of the existing conductors would be scrapped if removed. The usual reason is that old wire contains numerous splices or burns which would make reinstallation difficult and future service unsatisfactory. Obviously, the change-over costs more if it involves scrapping existing conductors than if those conductors could be reused. How much more?

Assuming that the company is continually purchasing wire of that size, any conductors salvaged for reuse postpone purchases of that same size. If the existing conductors are scrapped, we do not enjoy that postponement of new purchases. Thus, the difference in revenue requirements (all other things being the same) per year is one year's revenue requirements for new wire of the same size, as was discussed in Chapter 12.

Suppose we estimate the differential, per year, as one year's return plus depreciation only for conductors of the same size. This is suggested to simplify the present illustration and to focus on the main issue of a disciplined treatment of allowance for growth.

So if the existing conductors are scrapped, the break-even equation may be written as follows, still using the costs of Work Sheet 1, plus one year's return plus depreciation at $30:

One year of X costs - one year's capital recovery costs = One year of Y costs:

$$\frac{10.37\,I^2}{1,000} + 36 - 30 = \frac{3.45\,I^2}{1,000} + 108$$

$$I = 121.4 \text{ amperes per phase}$$

The break-even points for other consecutive sizes may be established in this same manner. Call this Work Sheet 3.

We have seen that replacement of existing conductors is economic when a determinate load has been reached, regardless of the rate of load growth. However, if load growth will eventually justify replacement of the new installation — whether it is a replacement or not — the appropriate size of those new conductors does depend upon the anticipated future rate of load growth.

The principle involved is easy to see. If new conductors are the right size for today's load, they will be too small tomorrow if loads grow. Consequently, it pays to install somewhat larger conductors if growth is expected. They may be a little too big immediately, thus inflicting a small penalty for a short time; but that penalty will be offset by later savings as compared with the alternative smaller size.

On the other hand, by comparing the results of Work Sheets 1 and 2 or 3, we see that the economic loading of existing conductors is increased by reason of the change-over costs that are postponed by putting off the replacement. The question here is how to balance the present worth of these "postponement" savings against the present worth of the penalties from installing larger conductors too soon. Table 14.6 shows how this can be accomplished for any assumed rate of growth; here it is 5% annually.

Referring then to Table 14.6, the first line represents the situation at end of Year x, which is the year when Conductor X will be economically replaced by Conductor Y per Work Sheet 2, above (assuming that Conductor X will be salvaged for reuse elsewhere). In that year I = 107.6 amperes, per Work Sheet 2.

In Column 2, then, we calculate what I would have been in each previous year at the assumed rate of growth. In this example, 5% per year is assumed. Column 3 shows corresponding values of I^2, necessary to calculate revenue requirements for Conductor X (Column 4) and for Conductor Y (Column 5).

In Column 6, we calculate the revenue requirements in Year x if Conductor X were in place throughout the year, but removed and reinstalled elsewhere at the end of the year. Thus, we include that $(R + L)$ penalty[11] in the year when the replacement must finally be made.

Note that this assumes reuse of the displaced smaller conductors. If, on the other hand, they would have to be scrapped when replaced, we would substitute $(R - S)$ for $(R + L)$.[12] That is, if a positive net salvage

---

[11] R = removal cost; L = labor cost of reinstallation.
[12] R = removal cost; S = gross salvage value.

Table 14.6. Revenue requirements for Conductors X and Y. New construction: 5% annual growth. 6% MAR.

Col. 1	2	3	4	5	6	7	8	9	10
	Peak I per phase		Revenue Requirements (Work Sheet 1)		Revenue Requirements Conductor X Replaced	Revenue Requirements Conductor Y From	Savings (Col. 6 -	Cumulative Present Worth of Savings	Present Worths
Year ($= x - n$)		I^2	X	Y	End of Year x	Beginning	Col. 7)	Per Col.8	of Column 9
x	107.6	11,578	156 (-8)	148	156 + 134 = 290	148	142	1.0000 x 142 = 142	x.9434 = 134
$x-1$	102.5	10,506	145 (-8)	144	145	144	1	+ 1.0600 x 1 = 143	x.8900 = 127
$x-2$	97.6	9,526	135	141	135	141	(6)	+ 1.1236 x (6) = 136	x.8396 = 114
$x-3$	92.9	8,630	125	138	125	138	(13)	+ 1.1910 x (13) = 121	x.7921 = 96
$x-4$	88.5	7,832	117	135	117	135	(18)	+ 1.2625 x (18) = 98	x.7473 = 73
$x-5$	84.3	7,106	110	132	110	132	(22)	+ 1.3382 x (22) = 69	x.7050 = 48
$x-6$	80.3	6,448	103	130	103	130	(27)	+ 1.4185 x (27) = 30	x.6651 = 20
$x-7$	76.5	5,852	97	128	97	128	(31)	+ 1.5036 x (31) = (16)	x.6274 = (10)

Notes: Col. 2 Values of I represent the anticipated annual peaks, reading up from bottom. I for Year x, per Work Sheet 2. In each prior year, divide successively by 1.05 for 5% growth.

Col. 4 Conductor X costs would be greater than Conductor Y (Col. 5) but for the $8 savings by postponing changeover in Years x or $x - 1$.

Col. 6 In Year x = Col. 4 - 1.12(R + L). In earlier years, same as Col. 4.

Col. 7 Same as Col. 5

Col. 9 Present worth multipliers are 1.06^n, for 6% MAR. n per Col. 1. Values of $(1.06)^n$ are conveniently available in interest tables.

456

value $(S - R)$ will be realized by scrapping, then postponing replacement one year postpones realization of that salvage value, and we subtract $(S - R)$, which amounts to adding $(R - S)$. In Column 6, then, is shown the revenue requirements if Conductor X were in place until the end of Year x, when it is replaced by Conductor Y. Costs of the alternative plan appear in Column 7. Here, oversized Conductor Y with its greater revenue requirements is installed; we avoid that change-over expenditure of $134 at the end of Year x.

The remaining columns suggest a procedure for calculating, with minimum effort, the present worth of revenue requirements from a given date of inquiry to the target date established in Work Sheet 2 when the larger conductors should be in place in any event.

In Column 8 is shown the difference between the Column 6 and Column 7 figures.

In Column 9 a cumulative present worth is computed for the differences of Column 8. These present worths are as of a common date at end of Year x, the date when Conductor Y must be in service.

In Column 10 present worths of the foregoing accumulated figures are calculated in the manner indicated. These final figures then represent the present worth, in each year, of the advantage of having the large Conductor Y installed initially, thus avoiding the change-over cost in the final year. The minus figure for Year $(x - 7)$ indicates that if the decision had to be made at that date or earlier, installation of the smaller Conductor X would have been justified.

A General Comment

Economists have done the nation a notable disservice by dwelling upon fancied differences between the economics of public utilities and economics of nonregulated industry. Substantially all these "differences" are imaginary or artificial. They disclose a naive ignorance of the basic principles and motivations of a free enterprise economy, sometimes of a slightly "pinkish" cast.

One symptom of that attitude is a pious solicitude for the "public interest," failing to recognize when that places the cart before the horse. Surprisingly few writers seem to recognize a fundamental distinction between free enterprise capitalism and communism that was pointed out at the opening of Chapter 13. Namely, the objective of business in a free enterprise economy is not a primary concern for the community but for individuals. The very term "communism" emphasizes that difference. The objective of business in a free enterprise economy is more appealing, more sophisticated, more enlightened — and more successful. It is to make the supplying of human needs and desires attractive to individual suppliers of capital, because it pays. Community benefits follow from the primary profit inducement, not the reverse. It is this right to individual ownership of property and its benefits that communism denies.

The notion that investor-financed public utilities are exceptions to this rule exhibits a superficiality of reasoning, or a gullibility of temperament, that is not becoming in an economist. Because this book is devoted solely to profitability and economic choice, the political implications of such faulty economics are not discussed. Our solicitude is for the damage done to individuals — to employees and customers and creditors and owners of industry as well as taxpayers — by failure to comprehend and apply the basic principles of free enterprise capitalism.[13]

Résumé

I. Commission regulation of some activities of a limited number of industries endowed with special and substantial public interest is a triumph of American common sense. The superiority of restricted governmental intervention, in this manner, over any alternative yet devised (nationalizing, socializing, or laissez-faire) is a source of national economic strength, despite bureaucratic red tape, occasional political abuses, and sometimes inept administration.

II. The essential reasons for success of limited commission regulation are the same that account for superiority of the free enterprise system itself. That is, automatically optimized allocation of national resources is induced by offering financial incentives to pursue courses of action which are at once of greatest benefit to freewill suppliers of capital and to the community.

III. A major concern of regulation is placing a "ceiling" on "fair return" on capital investment by controlling tariffs. This supplies a restraint, normally exercised by forces of competition which are lacking to some degree in the monopoly granted public utilities in the interests of economy.

IV. The right of the public to exercise this degree of control is founded in common law. The right of the controlled industry to apply to the courts for relief of regulation deemed unfair is based on an interpretation of the Bill of Rights. This means that the ultimate definition of "fairness" rests with the courts. Decisions of the United States Supreme Court are controlling, and that is the source of the concept of "fair return or fair value" as the criterion.

V. As in all matters depending upon an interpretation of "value," the quantitative evaluation of fair return as presently attempted lacks objectivity.

VI. MRRD suggests a means of making objective estimates of a utility's fair return, by way of: (a) an estimate of the utility's MAR; (b) an estimate of the MAR and maximum Profit Incentive permitted nonregulated companies by competitive forces; and (c) interpretation

---

[13]Two documents of interest are: Hans F. Sennholz, "Some 'Peculiarities' of Public Utilities," Public Utilities Fortnightly (April 15, 1965), p. 17, and Elizabeth Gilett, "Kefauver's Case Against Monopoly is Bunk," Barron's (April 12, 1965), p. 8 (a book review of Estes Kefauver's In a Few Hands; Random House, New York, 1965).

of the utility's fair return as its own MAR plus maximized Profit Incentive permitted nonregulated companies by forces of competition.

VII. Governmental encroachment on the province of free enterprise is an anomaly that can be economically tolerated only under the conditions that: (a) freewill investors cannot be induced to supply the capital necessary for ventures which do not offer financial inducement; and (b) such ventures, unable to pay for themselves, are deemed of sufficient importance to the general public to justify subsidizing them.

VIII. A desirable alternative to governmental encroachment, even under the foregoing circumstances, would be to permit investor-owned public utilities to serve such areas and charge the higher rates necessary to earn a fair return. Direct welfare payments could be made to customers to cover the excess of such charges over the lower rates that would be charged by the alternative tax-financed supplier.

IX. Simple examples demonstrate the unquestionable economic superiority of investor-financed public utilities. Opinion to the contrary is largely the result of popular acceptance of an incompetent analytical technique, the Annual Cost Method.

X. The explanation for the economic superiority of investor-ownership of public utilities rests upon use of the appropriate arithmetic to represent the exact intent of the analyst.

XI. A major economic absurdity is forced upon the management of governmental agencies such as REA, by the device of supplying them with capital funds at interest rates approximating half of the cost of capital. This compels preference for alternatives which maximize capital investment while minimizing outlays for operation and maintenance, regardless of the resultant wasteful use of national resources.

XII. Project risk is borne by taxpayers for government-owned ventures. That part of the cost of capital to the community is not represented by interest or bonds backed by taxing power. Such interest rate is not MAR.

XIII. A minor difference in the exact definition of MAR for (a) purposes of rate regulation, and (b) for purposes of studies of profitability and economic choice is to be noted. That is, rate regulation looks to a short-term percentage at the moment; economic studies look to the levelized percentage over an indefinite future period. In general, the company's long-term cutoff rate corresponds to the bottom limiting value of a short-term "fair rate of return."

XIV. An essential feature of the free enterprise system is that the economic merit of projects is judged by their effect on the company's financial welfare, that is, the financial welfare of owners of the enterprise. It is confidently expected that decisions so reached will work to the greatest advantage of the community as a whole, but that test is specifically not to be applied as a criterion of economic choice. In those rare cases when benefit to the community might be believed to be at odds with the economic choice as defined herein, that consideration would constitute a defensible Step 2 reason for rejecting a proposal. Nevertheless, it is no part of the analysis of profitability or economic choice (Step 1).

XV. Cost behavior of the family car provides a homely example of fixed and variable components of cost. An incremental trip means outlays for such things as gasoline, oil, and tolls. It does not mean additional outlays for insurance, licenses, and garage rental; hence, these costs are often regarded as "fixed."

XVI. A large long-term increase in usage may promote some or all "fixed" charges to an "incremental" status, as when one more passenger necessitates buying a second car.

XVII. Unexpected results of a sound probability study are sometimes puzzling until the simple explanation is forthcoming. The Green Line bus problem is an amusing example. One would expect 50/50 probability; it turns out to be 25/75.

XVIII. Evaluation of the "investment component" of cost of electrical losses is a classical problem which has puzzled many investigators. The most widely accepted method of evaluation is quite indefensible; it is the product of jumping to conclusions by way of notions based on failing to recognize the estimator's own exact intent.

XIX. One source of misunderstanding in the evaluation of electrical losses arises from confusing cost behavior with pricing policy. Because it would be unsound practice to let a second bus passenger ride free, some conclude that accepting the second rider must therefore double the one-passenger costs of operating the bus; such an analogy is applied to the cost of incremental losses. Stated this way, their argument is conceded to be foolish. It is not clear why it is not equally foolish when applied to the "investment component" of cost of losses.

XX. A common error is to confuse the demand and energy components of a power customer's bill with the "fixed" and "variable" components of cost of producing the power.

XXI. The "investment component" of cost of electrical losses can be established only by determining the occasional instances when capacity installations would be advanced in date by reason of small incremental peak loads.

XXII. So many variables are involved in estimating the "investment component" of cost of electrical losses that it is almost a hopeless task without the help of expert programmers and electronic computers with which to carry out a simulation process.

XXIII. Careful analysis of exact intent indicates that the probability of zero "investment component" of cost of losses is substantially zero. The probability of a pro rata evaluation at average cost per unit of capacity is almost zero. The most probable figure is apt to be near 30% to 50% of the pro rata cost of capacity.

XXIV. The common assumption that evaluating cost of losses at a low figure will result in larger system losses than otherwise cannot be defended. It is another example of a notion based on inexact observations.

XXV. Common misapplications of a rule of thumb known as Kelvin's law appear in many textbooks. Again MRRD provides a common-sense solution, which respects the estimator's own exact intent.

Problems

1. Everybody knows, in general, what is meant by a public utility. Exact definition of the term is not always easy.

    a. Write down the criteria by which you could classify the following as public utilities or not:
1. Gas companies
2. Theaters
3. Mining iron ore
4. Railroads
5. Car rental companies

    b. Then apply those criteria to decide whether the following are public utilities or not: ·
1. Oil companies
2. Television networks
3. Steel companies
4. Motor freight companies
5. Taxicab companies

    c. Why are the following essential services not public utilities?
1. Newspapers
2. Doctors
3. Colleges
4. Wheat growers

2. Many public utilities operate under the jurisdiction of such federal commissions as FPC, ICC, FCC, and SEC. Most of them are also controlled by state commissions. In some cases, a major influence is control by municipal commissions.

As an intelligent citizen admittedly not an expert in this field, would you expect such a system to be:

    a. Inefficient owing to duplication and overlapping of functions, contradictory viewpoints, and so on?

    b. Highly desirable and an example of the flexibility of a democracy's adaptability to special circumstances?

    c. A situation that "just growed" like Topsy, probably because of sweeping reforms?

    d. What specific reasons account for your conclusions? That is, what aspects of the situation would you inquire into if you were requested to make such a decision?

3. In Part I of Table 14.2, suppose a discount rate of 6% were used, instead of the 3%, thus multiplying annual quantities by 15.761861 instead of by 25.729764. Present worth of "return plus depreciation" would then be less than the initial capital investment of $100,000,000. What significance would you attach to that?

4. In Part II of Table 14.2, suppose a discount rate of 3% were used, instead of 6%, thus multiplying annual quantities by 25.729764 instead of by 15.761861. Present worth of "return plus depreciation" would then be greater than the initial capital investment of $100,000,000. What significance would you attach to that?

5. In Part II of Table 14.2, suppose a discount rate of 7% were used, instead of 6%, to calculate the present worth of minimum revenue requirements of $17,934,400, The present worth of the "return plus depreciation" component would then be less than $100,000,000. What significance would you attach to that?

6. In Part II-B of Table 14.3, suppose "return plus Profit Incentive plus depreciation" were discounted at 6% to their present worth. What significance would you attach to the figure so obtained?

7. No method of analysis other than MRRD recognizes the existence of a Profit Incentive as a demonstrably indispensable component of the "internal rate"

(actual earnings) and as an essential difference between the "normal rate" of earnings and "cost of financing" (MAR) which is the only appropriate discount rate to use in calculating equivalent annuities or present worth.

What is the simple declarative sentence (21 words) that supplies the explanation for this concept which is the distinguishing feature of MRRD?

8. What is the essential difference between:
   a. Economic choice between alternative proposals for an investor-financed enterprise;
   b. Profitability of an investor-financed project; and
   c. Optimized allocation of resources for a tax-financed agency?

9. As an informed citizen who is paying the bill, do you feel that TVA and REA have outlived their usefulness as nonprofit welfare agencies? If so, what procedure would you suggest to remedy the existing situation?

If not, what are your reasons for preferring the existing situation to that suggested in the text (the same services rendered by regulated public utilities permitted rates sufficient to earn a fair return, with welfare payments given directly to customers to defray their extra charges for service, if any)?

10. It may be said that success of commission regulation depends upon a sophisticated public and a strong judiciary which is respected. Explain, whether you agree or not. If you do not agree, or if you agree only in part, explain your views. If you agree, why?

11. To what extent and in what respects are public utilities granted a monopoly?

12. Does commission regulation guarantee public utilities a fair return? If so, can it be said that public utilities constitute a noncompetitive industry? Explain. If not, what advantage is there in the deal (i.e., accepting regulation in exchange for granted monopoly) to utilities?

13. Does a "tough" commission — one that undertakes to keep percentage return of utilities in its jurisdiction as low as the courts will allow — benefit consumers by way of correspondingly low rates for the same service rendered?

(For a very interesting reference, see Public Utilities Fortnightly, Nov. 5, 1964, p. 64.)

14. Most textbooks on engineering economy devote at least one chapter to economic studies of tax-financed projects. Usually the question of benefit-cost ratios for flood control projects is given attention, and capital-recovery costs are commonly calculated at low interest rates (3.5% or 4%, or thereabouts). Comment on the propriety of conclusions so reached.

15. Some companies, especially in merchandising, gauge their earnings as a percentage of sales, in dollars. Why not express MAR as a percentage of revenues and stipulate fair return of public utilities on that same basis, instead of as a percentage of investor's committed capital?

16. Doctors supply an essential service to the public. Why not control their charges to patients by placing a top limit on their annual earnings equal to some fair percentage of their capital investment in their business?

17. A state which already imposed a tax on gross receipts of public utilities proposed an increase in that tax rate. Legislative proponents of the new tax agreed that little of the increase would be paid by consumers in the form of higher rates, since about half would be deducted by the utilities in calculating federal income taxes payable. Demonstrate, by a simple arithmetical example, that the consumer would be expected to pay more than 100% of the increased tax in the form of higher rates.

(Hint: Of the two major effects of the new tax on minimum revenue requirements, only one is of great quantitative importance.)

18. Many public utilities rent office space instead of owning the building; many lease electronic computers and telephone service instead of owning the

machines and intercom system. If such plant then does not contribute to rate base, there is no capital investment on which fair return can be allowed. How can such policies pay?

19. Most public utilities that burn coal buy it from a supplier and have shipments made by common carrier (rail or water). Would it be in the public interest for the utility to own the coal mine and the transport facilities (cars, barges, pipe line, and so on) in order to make a single profit on the whole deal, instead of three profits? Explain your answer.

20. Repeat the demonstration of Tables 14.1 and 14.2 using larger figures for capital investment and a smaller figure for other expense. Then do it again, using a smaller figure for capital investment and a larger figure for other expense. Comment on the results. What is the connection with a comment in the text on a contribution to the national poverty of the USSR?

21. For many years a public utility company has made substantial annual contributions to local Community Chests, donations to universities, and similar payments, charging them to its reported general expense. Recently, the regulatory commission has taken the position that such outlays should be charged against the earnings of investors in the company, that is, a reduction in income. They refuse to permit classification as revenue deductions in determining earnings whose fairness is under consideration.

Are there reasons to believe that such a ruling may be ineffective and unwise, and would defeat the exact intent of those who proposed it? Explain.

22. Outlays for a tax-financed project consist of: (a) a large initial capital investment in fixed assets (land, buildings, machinery); (b) annual expenditures for raw materials; and (c) annual operation and maintenance expenses.

Charges to be paid by customers who buy the plant's output consist of: (d) interest on the bonds sold to raise the capital; (e) depreciation expense, calculated as the amount necessary to recover that capital investment in buildings and machinery (less ultimate net salvage) within the service-lifetime of these facilities; (f) annual expenditures for raw materials; and (g) annual operation and maintenance expense.

Which represents the cost of the project: the outlays, or the "charges made to recover the outlays" represented by $(d + e + f + g)$?

Set up a simple arithmetical example, using a reasonable interest rate and service life (assume zero net salvage, if desired, for simplicity). Compare present worths of outlays with present worth of charges. Comment fully on the sources of discrepancy.

Exactly what would you suggest as the cost of the project? Exactly what is wrong with the other version of its "cost"?

23. Saturday Review, Feb. 6, 1965, p. 56, contains an article concerning the part that the Oak Ridge National Laboratory might play in accelerating progress in obtaining fresh water by desalting. It is remarked that shortly, according to estimates of a White House desalination task group, atomic power will be produced by government-owned plants at a cost around 1.6 to 1.8 mills per kilowatt-hour; and by investor-owned plants at around 2.6 to 2.8 mills.

    a. Exactly what is wrong here?

    b. What can be done about it?

    c. Does this have any bearing on the view that socialism appeals to the economically naive, and that its appeal is emotional rather than rational? Or is it a matter of politics? Or is it one more example of pervasive disrespect for disciplined reasoning in such matters? Discuss.

24. It has been said that commission regulation of public utilities substantially guarantees a return of 6% on capital investment. If this is true, why is not the companies' economic choice always the alternative requiring the largest capital investment, which would then maximize its permitted earnings?

If research and careful planning result in increasing a utility's earnings above the adjudicated fair rate, with existing sales and rate schedules, and the company is ordered to reduce rates in order to bring earnings back to the permitted level, does that not discourage research and careful planning?

Exactly how would you correct this situation? If you were a member of the Federal Power Commission, would you do it by moral persuasion, urging the utilities to do research and careful planning as an ethical obligation? Or would you do it by threatening tax-financed competition? Or do you have better ideas? Discuss.

25. One author takes the position that in economy studies of public works proposals it is necessary first to decide from whose viewpoint the study is to be made: (a) that of all the nation's people; (b) that of the people in a restricted area, such as state or city; or (c) that of the governmental departments involved.

If the costs of the project (initial capital investment, raw material costs, and operation and maintenance costs) are identical in any event, exactly what is the import of that comment?

26. It is asserted by one authority that in all economy studies, whether of investor-financed or tax-financed, any minimum attractive return assumed (note that he does not say minimum acceptable return, or MAR) should include, as a safety factor, some allowance for the fact that the very best of cost estimates are subject to some degree of error. Exactly what is wrong with that proposal? Or is it a good idea? Explain.

27. A statement such as the following can be found in several textbooks on engineering economy: "It is often the case that a project will be financed only by borrowed capital or only by equity capital. In such case, the corresponding cost of capital should be used in the calculations. On the other hand, if general funds of the corporation are to be used, part of which are borrowed and part from equity sources, then an average rate should be used."

Exactly what is wrong here?

28. The following problem appeared in the Engineering Economist, official organ of the Engineering Economy Division of American Society for Engineering Education; solutions were invited. Prepare your own complete solution for both conditions requested: (a) if the company were a regulated public utility or (b) if the company were a nonregulated enterprise.

An economic choice is to be made between use of aluminum versus steel for a structure. Aluminum requires a larger capital investment but smaller maintenance expense, because painting is unnecessary:

Capital Investment	Aluminum	Steel
Foundations	$15,000	$15,000
Assembly	56,000	36,000
Erection	25,000	24,000
	$96,000	$75,000
Anticipated service life	50, R_1	50, R_1
Ultimate net salvage, foundations abandoned in place	+ 10%	- 10%

(The original example ignored investment credit.) Use 48% tax rate, "straightline" depreciation for books, SYD for taxes, and flow-through. Ignore other taxes except for a state tax of 10% on public utility revenues. Assume operation and maintenance cost $1,000 per year, aluminum; $3,200 per year, steel.

The company is growing 5% annually. The financial situation:

a. Utility

No recent rate cases, but commission has generally approved 6% return on end-of-year rate base. Actual earnings have approximated 7% return on investor committed capital, and that is expected to continue.

Capitalization (present situation typical) includes:

Debt	48% at 4.1% interest
Preferred stock	10% at 5.0% dividend
Common equity	42%

Payout ratio is well established; the annual dividend is 70% of earnings on common equity.

b. Nonregulated

Relatively stable earnings at 9% of investors' committed capital are expected to continue.

Capitalization (present situation typical) includes:

Debt	25% at 5.0% interest
Common equity	75%

Payout ratio is well established; the annual dividend is 50% of earnings on common equity.

During the period of construction of these facilities the companies are expected to finance growth mainly by application of depreciation reserves and retained earnings, plus long-term debt (mortgage bonds) if necessary. Assume that the capital requirement is a small fraction of normal annual budget requirements, so that the matter of capital availability is not a critical factor but typical of decisions.

Which alternative is superior, and by how much?

29. A public utility which manufactures the gas it distributes is considering converting to natural gas. Major benefits anticipated are: (a) lower cost of gas per Btu, delivered to the distribution system; and (b) smaller investment in plant; production plant eliminated.

However, two large immediate outlays would be necessary: (c) changes in customers' equipment to make them suitable to burn natural gas; and (d) retirement of large capital investment in gas manufacturing plant that is not very old.

It is suggested that permission be requested of the regulatory commission to do two things: (A) spread the charges for conversion of customers' equipment over a 10-year period, although actually incurred all in one year; and (B) amortize the unusual retirement costs over a 10-year period, although the equipment would be removed immediately.

Explain the effect on books of account and on financial statements. If permission for A and B were refused, how would that affect the economic choice?

30. Most regulatory commissions insist that in fixing public utility rates no allowance can be made for the fact that past earnings may have been admittedly deficient. It is said that just because a company charged inadequate rates and had unsatisfactory earnings, that does not demand that present and future customers should be expected to make up the loss.

This view has been upheld by state courts and by the United States Supreme Court.

If you were a commissioner, would you:

a. Ignore the rule so far as possible, pointing out that it ignores several facts of life which cannot be evaded and that retrospective considerations are not only fair but unavoidable; or

b. Would you hew to that legalistic line, pointing out that it is your duty to carry out the law as defender of the rights of citizens who granted a monopoly to the company, whose stockholders provided the necessary capital with a full knowledge of the risks involved and under no duress?

Explain your answer.

31. A public utility is considering two mutually exclusive plans for reducing costs at a generating station:

Plan A. Reduce the capital investment required to produce the same incremental output and thus reduce the return, depreciation, and income tax components of revenue requirements.

Plan B. Increase the capital investment required to produce the same incremental output, but reduce full consumption sufficiently to make revenue requirements of Plan B slightly less than those of Plan A.

However, the company has a fuel clause in its rates, which would operate to grant a small immediate and automatic rate reduction to customers, so that revenues would be less than if Plan A were adopted. Does this affect the economic choice? Does it suggest that something is wrong with the idea of including a fuel clause in rate schedules? Explain.

32. A brochure recommending ground-line treatment of wood poles presents the economics of the proposal as follows:

a. Outlays without treatment

Initial cost of pole	$ 100
Replacement (including transfer of construction) at Year 30	300
Replacement at Year 60	300
Replacement at Year 90	300
Total	$1,000

b. Outlays if treatment increases service life 50%

Initial cost of pole	$ 100
Treatment at Year 15	10
Treatment at Year 20	10
Replacement (including transfer of construction) at Year 45	300
Treatment at Year 60	10
Treatment at Year 75	10
Replacement (including transfer of construction) at Year 90	300
Treatment at Year 105	10
Total	$ 750

c. Outlays if treatment increases service life 100%

Initial cost of pole	$ 100
Treatment at Year 15	10
Treatment at Year 30	10
Treatment at Year 45	10
Replacement (including transfer of construction) at Year 60	300
Treatment at Year 75	10
Treatment at Year 90	10
Treatment at Year 105	10
Total	$ 460

Comment, and make the calculations that carry out the author's exact intent.

33. Several economists have severely disparaged the effectiveness of public utility regulation as presently practiced by state commissions, asserting that its customary "cost plus profit" basis encourages serious misallocation of resources in numerous ways.

For example, it is said to deprive utilities of any incentive to control operating costs. Because permitted earnings exceed cost of capital, there is said to be

a compelling incentive to maximize profits by maximizing capital investment unduly (thus creating an artificial preference for capital-intensive alternatives) and
for deliberate overexpansion of assets on various popular pretexts, such as the
excuse for needing extra reserve capacity to insure against service interruption
(blackouts), or the presumed desirability of expensive underground lines in place
of overhead construction, or even unjustified diversification of activities.

In such attacks on regulatory procedure it is common to encounter references to the major objective of profit maximization as a feature of "neoclassical
theory." Such a line of reasoning reveals a surprising unfamiliarity with an important motivating principle of the free enterprise system, which principle is an
essential element in exact objectives of MRRD.

a. Identify the fundamental principle of free enterprise, which contributes so much to its success, that is overlooked by "neoclassical theory" of this
sort.

b. Explain the indispensable provisos, essential to the statement of exact
dual objective of economic studies, that these economists have failed to comprehend.

c. What is your reaction to the following comment made on one such
article:

"Great harm would be done to our national welfare — not just to public utilities — by such unenlightened dogma concerning regulatory principles, and such
uninformed opinion concerning the nature of economic decisions made by industry
(regulated or not), if anybody took them seriously." Would you regard that quotation as a reasonable appraisal, a slight exaggeration, or an understatement? Explain your position.

A

• • • • • Case for Exactness •

A Matter of Mental Attitude

The material of Appendix A may be regarded as a sort of extensive footnote to the main text, here collected in one place for two reasons:

1. To avoid cluttering up the more technical presentation of the main text with this wordier commentary; and
2. To indicate how and why a rigorous treatment of fundamental economic, financial, and accounting principles is adhered to consistently throughout the book, in contrast to the popular but less precise presentation found in other textbooks on the same subject.

The importance of recognizing and respecting exact intent of economic studies, as well as exact usage of words, is mentioned in Chapter 1 and referred to elsewhere. The financial losses and waste of resources that can result from acceptance of inexact standards and imperfect usage are illustrated by numerous examples throughout the book. The comments in this appendix are on a more personal and less technical basis, related to personal experience, attitudes, and reactions of individuals. All, however, are offered in evidence of the same proposition that it is not only dangerous but unintelligent to accept "practical" solutions, simplified explanations, approximate rules and shortcuts, unless exact intent is clear and expressed in terms that have only one exact meaning.

Quite aside from the financial loss that can result from unsound decisions is the damage done to individual reputations. Few things advertise incompetence more effectively than self-contradiction; and inexactness invites self-contradiction in a variety of ways that few people expect. Substantially all that loss and embarrassment is avoidable. But it takes more than saying so to convince anybody, because the direct opposite has been asserted so often.

For example, engineers have been warned not to expect perfection in economic studies to the extent it can be expected in other branches of technology. Economics, it is said, is not an exact science.

It is demonstrated herein that making studies of profitability or economic choice is just as exact a science as any other. The principles involved are not in doubt; they are as rigorous and indisputable as those of any other technology. The thing that should be criticized is the nature of methods of analysis generally taught and widely accepted. Methods other than the Minimum Revenue Requirements Discipline are indeed inexact, because they are wrong in principle. One must expect to be caught in self-contradictions, on occasion, if they are used.

Use of such inexact methods is tolerated only because of the peculiar mental attitude mentioned in Chapter 1, typical of this technology and of no other, that exactness is a "nasty word."

In the summer of 1964, newspaper stories reported that the estate of President Lyndon Johnson and his immediate family had been valued by a prominent firm of Certified Public Accountants at three and a half million dollars. Or, alternatively, at fourteen million; depending on how one cared to figure it.

A flood of magazine articles and "letters to the editor" promptly indicated how most people cared to figure it. The incident provided one more convincing demonstration that "accountants can make the figures prove anything they like." The intelligent man-in-the-street knows that cost is a determinate figure, if records have been kept. Current sale price is also reasonably estimable. Use of either expression — cost, or current sale price — would signify frankness, integrity, and competence. But when sale price differs widely from the initial outlay actually made to acquire the assets (as it almost always does), it offends common sense to call both figures "value." And when the situation is further aggravated by proposing to deduct from cost (the smaller figure) a vague allowance for "depreciation," then one's natural reaction is that someone is making a deliberate effort to mislead.

A close parallel is encountered in the teaching and practice of engineering economy. Selling price (revenues) and cost (the actual outlays to acquire and operate a property) are both called "costs" (as in "annual costs"), although they differ importantly. Results of this confusion have been used — not always deliberately — to mislead.

Correct principles — meaning simply the means for implementing exact intent – are spelled out in Chapters 2 and 4, with elaboration of some technical details in Appendix B. The way management's exact intent may be carried out or defeated in the budgeting function is treated in Chapter 9. The manner in which the popular methods of analysis depart from exact intent, sometimes subtly, is investigated in Chapter 11. Observing exact intent becomes more complicated and difficult when it concerns a growing plant, and that problem has been slighted in the literature; it is treated in Chapter 10.

A striking example of confusion caused by misrepresenting sale price as "costs" is the belief of many (perhaps most) citizens that electric power produced by government-owned plants must cost less than the same power produced by investor-owned plants, for two major reasons:

1. The smaller costs of capital: 2% or thereabouts for REA, $4\frac{1}{2}$% or so for TVA, etc.; compared to perhaps 6% or more if investor-owned; and
2. The absence of taxes, or nearly so, for government owned projects.

Many will be honestly surprised to discover (Chapter 14) that cost of the same output is normally greater if produced by government projects than if produced by investor-financed plants. Government power is sold below cost, at a loss which is made up by taxpayers; but that fact is obscured by the accounting and method of economic analysis accepted by substantially everybody, which does not carry out their exact intent.

Common Inexact Usage

Here are three statements commonly made in textbooks on this subject. Each one has the appearance of being a simple, clear expression of fact:

1. The words cost and expense are synonymous and interchangeable.
2. Income less expenses equals net income.
3. The objective of depreciation charges is to recover, over the life of depreciable assets, their costs less their salvage value.

Just in case the self-contradictions are not immediately apparent, make this test yourself. In Statement 2, write down some of the expenses you mean exactly (repairs, taxes, insurance, and so on). Try substituting these figures for the costs you intend exactly in Statement 3. Next, do the opposite. Write down some of the costs you exactly intended in Statement 3 (purchase price, installation cost), and try substituting them for the expenses you meant in Statement 2 which were said to be synonymous and interchangeable. It will appear that none of the statements meant exactly what you intended.

The difficulty is that queer mental attitude just mentioned. Many people, including some teachers, are indulgent in such matters. Their reaction to this demonstration is that finding fault with slack usage, in this way, is just quibbling. True, it is said, authors guilty of those statements did not mean exactly what they said; but what harm is done? Who would fail to understand?

The answer is, of course, that authors guilty of such misrepresentation do not precisely perceive the exact intent of economic studies. Inexactness is the refuge of the incompletely informed; they, as well as their readers, are misled. Harm is done; and it is both expensive and unnecessary. Correct, meaning exactly intended, procedures for estimating components of cost (Minimum Revenue Requirements) are described in Chapters 3 (MAR); 5, 6, 7 (depreciation); 8 (income tax), with an elaboration in Appendix C; and 9 (other expenses).

High-Level Misconceptions

If you have ever been so unfortunate as to have your car skid on an icy pavement, hit a utility pole, and demolish it, you may have encountered a strange situation.

The pole you demolished, which was an old one, will have to be replaced by a brand new one. Naturally, you do not expect to be charged for the full cost of that new replacement. Was not the value of the old pole which you destroyed something less than its cost when new, owing to depreciation or "expired life" to date? Perhaps you or your lawyer happen to know that the utility is permitted to earn a return on depreciated value of its assets only.

But you may be dismayed to learn that some state courts rule against you. You may be required to pay the full cost of the new replacement, on grounds said to be statistical. In brief, some courts reason that the probable future life of any particular pole cannot be foreseen with any acceptable degree of accuracy; it cannot be proven that the new replacement will last even as long as the old pole would have continued to serve if you hadn't demolished it. Indeed, it cannot be convincingly demonstrated (it is said) that the old pole would ever have been replaced. Accordingly, by paying the whole cost of the new replacement, you do no more than remedy the harm done.

Your own view and the court's cannot be reconciled. And here is the interesting feature of the story, perhaps not recognized until pointed out. Neither your opinion, nor the court's, is defensible. Neither one recognizes nor respects the exact intent of the appropriate reimbursement. Your own natural expectation (original cost less depreciation) is exactly the same basis that is so obviously unsound when used to evaluate the estate just discussed at less than three and a half million. The court's view is equivalent to evaluating the same estate at fourteen million.

Actually, the utility does not seek to profit from the incident, and certainly it wishes to avoid a loss. Source of the loss is readily apparent; it is the unexpected extra outlay that is incurred by advancing the normally expected date of replacement. Ordinarily, ample data are available for calculating the advancement in date; the standard arithmetic of probability is used in the computation, which can be understood by anyone who is familiar with ordinary compound interest formulas. The principle here involved enters into every problem in replacement economics, which is the subject of Chapter 12. Simple and clear though the principle is, it has to be pointed out to those who would otherwise draw indefensible conclusions from their inexact impressions of intent.

It is a curious fact that the exactly intended arithmetic of probability is readily understood by most people when applied to human beings, rather than to inanimate objects. If the accident had killed an old employee, and he had been replaced by a younger one of minimum employable age, nobody would argue — as the court did — that future life of the young replacement probably would not exceed probable remaining life of the unfortunate victim had he not died in the accident. The most important application of probability arithmetic in economic studies — in connection with depreciation — is treated in Chapters 6, 7, 9, and 12.

Similar failure to perceive exact intent has persisted right up to the Supreme Court. A notorious example is contained in the Smyth vs. Ames decision of 1898 (169 U.S. 546), long regarded as "the law of the land." It was asserted there that the basis for determining reasonableness of public utility rates must be "fair return" on "fair value" of property used to supply service. One test for "fair value" was said to be the probable earning capacity of the property. Thus, reasonable earnings were said to depend upon "fair value" which depends upon reasonable earnings. Exact intent of the ruling apparently was overlooked.

A more rational interpretation of the court's exact intent, which suggests a practical criterion for reasonable earnings, is discussed in Chapter 14. An interesting example of the confusion that can result from overlooking exact intent, and regarding rates as costs, is presented in Appendix D.

Grammarians call this kind of double-talk tautology. An amusing example, perhaps apocryphal, has been ascribed to the late Calvin Coolidge: When people are out of work, unemployment results. A major and distinctive purpose of MRRD is to avoid circular and confused reasoning of the kind described, prevent costly business mistakes arising from this source, and minimize chances of personal embarrassment from self-contradictions; all by striking at their source, which is inexact definition of intent and terminology.

This does not mean that MRRD insists upon nit-picking and hairsplitting techniques. As stated many times herein, adequate approximations and shortcuts are often desirable; simplification is often essential. But it is impossible to decide whether approximations and shortcuts are truly adequate, or whether simplification is misleading, unless one perceives exactly what is to be approximated, shortcut, or simplified. This applies most forcefully to popular methods for making economic studies such as listed in Chapter 1, where the slack mental attitude here discussed is encountered and encouraged.

How Many Decimal Places?

It is manifestly foolish to waste time and effort on elaborately refined calculations applied to variables which can be only roughly estimated. Engineers, particularly, are impressed with the futility of making calculations to many decimal places — beyond the limits of "significant figures." However, that perfectly sound proposition is often misinterpreted and sadly abused in application to principles, rather than to figures, involved in economic studies.

Our exact intent is not in doubt; it is to apply correct arithmetic

to the best available data. If the result is none too good for our purpose, then the difficulty lies in the character of data available, not in
the arithmetic. Accordingly, in making the calculations involved in
studies of profitability and economic choice, it is usually advisable to
proceed as though the estimated data were exact, carrying out computations to as many decimal places as are conveniently provided by the
calculating equipment at hand. By deferring all rounding operations
until the final figures are assembled, it is often possible to save ap-
preciable time, while checking for accuracy of the arithmetic is greatly
facilitated. Rounding at every step, or eliminating digits beyond the
"significant figures" at each step, introduces a possibility of error unnecessarily, interferes with cross-checking, and may even weaken the
analyst's claim for an unbiased result; all with no compensating benefits.

The objection is sometimes raised that this procedure is apt to
imply greater accuracy than the result actually possesses. But there
is no such implication if the final results are rounded, as recommended
here. It is earlier rounding that amounts to deliberately introducing
error.

The need for respecting exact intent and using exact arithmetic
will be apparent when demonstrating that alternative approaches arrive
at identical answers. Sometimes the validity of principles is convincingly displayed in that manner, as in showing the equivalency of (a) initial capital outlay, and (b) present worth of revenue requirements for
capital recovery (= return + depreciation). The same principle is involved in testing adequacy of proposed approximations, shortcuts, and
simplifications.

To sum up, common sense in such matters demands recognition of
exact intent. To illustrate, the present worth of one dollar payable one
year from today is exactly $1.00/1.06$, if MAR = 6%. Decimally expressed $1.00/1.06 = 0.943396226415094339622641\ldots$, and so forth.
That fact is not a good reason to insist upon use of 24 decimal places
in such calculations. It is plea for recognition of exact intent in deciding upon the desirable number of decimal places. In some cases, using
0.94 would be an adequate approximation; though usually not. To use
0.9400 would be deliberate error, in any case. The question is, how
much deliberate error can be tolerated in the instance at hand? Any
rounding introduces fiction, no matter how accurate or otherwise the
costs may be to which we wish to apply the multiplier $1.00/1.06$. There
may be room for honest difference of opinion as to that estimated cost;
no room whatever for difference of opinion as to our exact intent.

Exact Details of MRRD

The technique described herein as the Minimum Revenue Requirements Discipline (MRRD) had its inception in the public utility industry
in the 1920's. Its users then regarded it as a refinement of the Annual
Cost Method.

After World War II, the great increase in magnitude, complexity, and importance of system-planning problems, aggravated by substantial price-inflation and profit squeeze, made it forcefully apparent that this approach differed fundamentally and in many details from the Annual Cost Philosophy. The need arose for a special name to identify it — particularly to distinguish it from the Annual Cost Method.

In about 1949, the expression Revenue Requirements Method was suggested, and found favor. Shortly thereafter, that term began to appear frequently in journals such as Transactions of the American Institute of Electrical Engineers, Public Utilities Fortnightly, Electrical World, and in committee proceedings in Edison Electric Institute and elsewhere.

Since that time, many technical papers, company manuals, and committee reports have described and applied the method. A few have taken exception to certain details of the technique, based on misunderstandings of the exact principles involved. At the other extreme, a few have indorsed the method based on failure to comprehend its unique features exactly, in the mistaken belief that it was nothing but the Annual Cost Philosophy specially adapted to public utility circumstances.

Such were the reasons for adopting, in 1961, the phrase Minimum Revenue Requirements Discipline (MRRD), to focus attention on the exact nature of the fundamental principles which differentiate this technique (and have since the beginning) from all other analytical methods.

The author must, of course, accept personal responsibility for any earlier presentations that may have presented opportunity for misunderstanding. Indeed, it is probable that the present exposition may retain some such imperfections. If so, the author will be grateful for having them called to his attention. It is hoped that this version will suggest further and better presentations of the exact intent and manifold substantial advantages of MRRD.

A number of special descriptive terms and unique expressions are identified with the Minimum Revenue Requirements Discipline, such as:

$\substack{\beta \\ i}d$, the depreciation annuity adjusted for probability;

Dynamite analogy;

Form X and Form Y (for stating capital-recovery costs);

"Iffy Hypothesis";

Investors' committed capital;

MAR on common equity $= \dfrac{d + x\% \text{ of } p}{p}$;

Minimum Revenue Requirements;

Minimum Acceptable (not "attractive") Return (MAR);

"Newcomers";

Nobody raises capital at a cost of $i\%$ in order to reinvest it at that same $i\%$;

Pre-project shares; and

Profit Incentive (not "profit margin").

All relate to the exact nature of some of the unique features of MRRD. It necessarily follows that the slightest departure from these exact concepts signifies that MRRD is being misrepresented.

B

• • • • • MRRD and the • •
Theory of the Firm

In the course of developing evaluations of MAR, in Chapter 3, it
was remarked that certain basic financial objectives often referred to
as the "theory of the firm" would be discussed in Appendix B.

This discussion is advisedly segregated in an appendix, in this
manner, for two major reasons. First, it demands a wordy scrutiny
of many meticulous details that would clutter up the main text. Second,
a comprehensive discussion must deal with a large number of "tremendous trifles," of greatest qualitative concern to advanced students,
but of small quantitative importance and therefore well omitted from
the elementary presentation.

The "Iffy Hypothesis"

The same identification of superior proposals is made whatever
measures may later be adopted for disposing of the benefits obtained.
Accordingly, the criterion of economic superiority most readily applied
is to interpret optimized percentage yield on already committed capital,
tentatively, as maximized percentage yield on already committed capital.

This "iffy hypothesis" provides the basis for selection by choosing
the proposal which has the greatest potential for realizing benefits to
investors, to customers, or to both.

It is not firmly predicted that MAR, in percent, will be identical
for all competing proposals. That situation is merely hypothesized and
investigated. The plan adjudged superior on that basis certainly cannot
be expected to increase the cost of capital. If it affects cost of capital
at all, it will tend to reduce MAR, and thus it will tend to support or
possibly improve slightly its tentatively estimated margin of superiority. This observation is an essential and distinctive feature of the
Minimum Revenue Requirements Discipline.

It is this "iffy hypothesis" which permits making the essential distinction (a unique feature of MRRD) between: (a) securing benefits, by
adopting the superior proposed course of action; and (b) disposing of

benefits after they have been secured, by channeling them to increased earnings or to reduced price of the firm's output, or partly to both.

This distinction becomes impossible with any procedure that stipulates or implies (a) identical percentage return, whichever plan is selected, or (b) identical revenues, whichever plan is selected. MRRD does neither. It makes the tentative "iffy hypothesis" of identical MAR (not identical percentage return, which is MAR plus Profit Incentive) and inquires into Profit Incentive if revenues were to be identical. The alternative approach, identifying the same project as superior, would be to inquire into the revenues required, with the same tentative MAR, to yield the same Profit Incentive; hence the term "revenue requirement."

It is this exact concept which appears to have been too subtle for some commentators to perceive. Surely it must be obvious that this exact concept of Profit Incentive is absolutely essential to the reasoning (= margin of earnings above MAR). The criterion of profitability is the amount of this exactly defined Profit Incentive (in dollars per year, not in percent of incremental investment).

In Chapter 3, in developing the evaluation of MAR, it was further remarked that certain long-term financial considerations often referred to as "theory of the firm" would be discussed in this appendix. As in the case of the standoff situation, a number of meticulous details enter into a comprehensive discussion, so many that their treatment seems better segregated in an appendix than included in the main text. The following example will supply material for such further discussion.

Case 1. Illustrative Example; Near Standoff

Plan A refers to a project for quantity production of small gasoline engines, such as used in lawn mowers, snow throwers, tillers, and scooters. It calls for a capital investment of $500,000.

Plan B is an alternative proposal for producing the same annual output by means of almost complete automation. This would require double the capital investment ($1,000,000) but would eliminate the need to hire a large number of skilled mechanics.

It is anticipated that the same number of engines would be sold annually at the same price in either case; revenue requirements of the two plans are almost identical, as indicated below. The company has no outstanding debt. There are 1,250,000 shares of common stock outstanding, representing a capitalization (= book value of common equity) of $50,000,000. Thus, if Plan B (automation) is adopted, investors' committed capital in the enterprise would be increased 2%, to $51,000,000.

Estimated Revenue Requirements

	Plan A (Nonautomation)	Plan B (Automation)
Capital Investment	$500,000	$1,000,000
MAR at 7%	$ 35,000 per year	$ 70,000 per year
Depreciation at 3%	15,000	30,000
Federal income tax at 3%	15,000	30,000
Operation and maintenance	76,000	10,000
All other expenses	60,000	60,000
Total revenue requirements	$201,000 per year	$ 200,000 per year

Because this is a problem in economic choice and not in quantitative profitability, items common to both (such as raw materials, local taxes, general and administrative expenses, and merchandising costs) could have been omitted in a practical solution. However, for the present purposes, they are here included as "all other expenses."

Annual revenues from sales of the output are expected to be $300,000 annually, so that Profit Incentive (= earnings in excess of the company's minimum acceptable return of 7%, after taxes) is estimated as follows:

	Plan A (Nonautomation)	Plan B (Automation)
Revenues	$300,000 per year	$300,000 per year
Less revenue requirements above	201,000	200,000
Available for Profit Incentive and tax thereon	99,000	100,000
Income tax on Profit Incentive at 48%	47,520	48,000
Profit Incentive (margin above 7% MAR)	$ 51,480 per year	$ 52,000 per year

Annual return (at 7% + Profit Incentive), in percent of the incremental investment, is:

	Plan A (Nonautomation)	Plan B (Automation)
Percentage return on incremental capital at 7% + Profit Incentive	$\dfrac{35,000 + 51,480}{500,000}$ = 17.296%	$\dfrac{70,000 + 52,000}{1,000,000}$ = 12.200%

If the decision is made on the basis of percentage return on incremental capital investment, Plan A wins by a wide margin: 17;296% to 12.200%. But on the basis of improved earnings per share (= return on

already committed investment, as evidenced by the smaller revenue
requirements), Plan B has a small advantage; its Profit Incentive is
$52,000, versus $51,480. The two proposals are almost a standoff, so
that the decision might well be swayed by consideration for factors not
reducible to dollars, such as "irreducibles," "intangibles," and "imponderables." Which decision represents the analysts' exact intent?

The Opposed Viewpoints

Those who favor Plan A (nonautomation) because of its greater
percentage return on the incremental capital investment may point out
the greater "efficiency of capital" attained by Plan A. That argument
goes as follows: The total amount of capital available to the national
economy is limited. Plan B requires 100% more capital ($1,000,000
versus $500,000) to generate only 41% more net income ($122,000
versus $86,480).

What is more important, if the company's capital must be rationed, selecting Plan A provides substantially the same Profit Incentive ($51,480 versus $52,000) and leaves $500,000 — out of any total
available — for other profitable investments. For example, the same
$1,000,000 of total capital available could finance two Plan A's and
substantially double Profit Incentive of one Plan B.

Those who favor Plan B (automation) because of its slightly
greater Profit Incentive will answer these arguments as follows.
First, the matter of "efficiency of capital" is not pertinent to the immediate decision. It must be agreed that, however limited the supply
of capital may be, the company can obtain $1,000,000 at 7% MAR; oth-
erwise the calculation of revenue requirements for Plan B could not be
justified as a practical alternative. The question posed is specifically:
"Assuming that the necessary capital is obtainable at MAR = 7%, what
should the decision be? "

Second, it is necessary to determine the exact intent of the expression "capital rationing." Is it meant that management is insistent
on investing the same $P at the moment (or in the current fiscal year)
regardless of other considerations? Or is it meant that management
has in mind certain major projects to be undertaken, with the maximum incremental investment not to exceed some stipulated maximum,
and preferably projects involving a smaller capital placement to obtain
the same or greater benefits?

Almost certainly it is the latter interpretation, as a general rule.
In that case, it is the minimum revenue requirements solution (maximized benefits to pre-project shares) that carries out the exact intent.

If, however, the first interpretation actually was intended (identical
incremental capital commitment in the current budget), then a different
question was posed. The question then asked is: "If exactly $P of new
capital funds are to be budgeted in any event, and a choice is to be
made between Plan A versus Plan B as a part of that fixed total, which

is the economic choice: (a) Plan A, plus the remainder of P, or (b) Plan B, plus the different remainder of P?" It is impossible to answer this question without inquiring into revenues or revenue requirements of the respective remainder of P. To illustrate, suppose P = $1,000,000. Adoption of foregoing Plan B would leave no remainder for investment elsewhere; it alone would constitute the current budget. On the other hand, if Plan A were adopted, then Plans X, Y, Z, requiring a combined investment of $500,000, would be adopted along with Plan A.

The intended comparison thus lies between: (a) Plans A plus X, Y, Z versus (b) Plan B, as below.

Suppose Plans X, Y, Z earn exactly MAR = 7%. The solution is reached on the basis of percentage return on incremental capital — identical solution, by either method (i.e., MRRD or percentage return) when capital investment of competing plans is the same.

1. Plans A plus X, Y, Z
   Plan A at 17.296% of $500,000, as above   = $ 86,480 per year
   Plans X, Y, Z at 7.00% of $500,000   =   35,000
         Total   = $121,480 per year
                                                        = 12.148%.

2. Plan B
   Plan B at 12.200% of $1,000,000, as above   = $122,000 per year
                                                        = 12.200%
       Plan B is preferred (12.200% versus 12.148%).

The break-even point is readily calculated. Plans A + X, Y, Z are a standoff if their combined earnings equal Plan B earnings of $122,000. That is, if Plans X, Y, Z earn 122,000 - 86,480 = $35,520, or 7.104% (= 35,520/500,000). Thus, if Plans X, Y, Z earn more than 7.104% in toto, then Plans A + X, Y, Z would be preferred to Plan B.

To summarize conclusions demonstrated by this example:

1. Percentage return on the incremental capital investment supplies the intended answer correctly only if the capital investment of alternative proposals is identical.
2. If percentage return on incremental investment is used as the criterion, by hypothesizing that capital is rationed and that the same total capital investment is to be budgeted in any event, then it is necessary to consult percentage return on the total capital investment which is assumed to be identical in any case.
3. So long as the intended question to be answered is "Which alternative would maximize percentage return on existing (pre-project) shares?" then the only possible answer is "The alternative having the smaller revenue requirements." This is the alternative that maximizes earnings per share, which is management's real intent.

This illustrates exactly why such matters as capital rationing must be assigned to the budgeting function, not made a part of the determination of profitability or economic choice. (See Chapter 9).

Earnings per share

In comparing Plans A and B, book value of common equity before adoption of the new project was said to be $50,000,000, represented by 1,250,000 shares of common stock outstanding. Suppose details are as follows:

Par value at $20 per share = $25,000,000
Capital surplus at $10 per share = 12,500,000

Total receipts from issuance
of stock $37,500,000
Retained earnings at $10 per share   12,500,000
Total investors' committed capital $50,000,000

If net income before adopting the new project is 10%, annual earnings at 10% of $5,000,000 per year are:

$$\text{Earnings per share} = \frac{5,000,000}{1,250,000} = \$4.00 \text{ per share}$$

Thus, percentage yield on pre-project investors' initial purchase price per share ($30) before adopting the new project = 4.00/30 = 13.33%. On total investors' committed capital = 4.00/40 = 10.00%. How will the new project affect earnings per share?

Proposal I. Internal Financing

Suppose the company can finance either Plan A or Plan B by means of internally generated funds (depreciation reserves or retained earnings).

If Plan A (nonautomation) is adopted, annual net income will increase to:

$$\frac{5,000,000 + 35,000 + 51,480}{1,250,000} = \$4.069 \text{ per share}$$

What if Plan B (automation) is adopted instead, with its slightly smaller revenue requirements? Annual net income, Plan B, is:

$$\frac{5,000,000 + 70,000 + 52,000}{1,250,000} = \$4.098 \text{ per share}$$

In other words, if the exactly intended question is, "Which proposal will make the greater improvement in earnings per share?" the answer is "Unquestionably Plan B, which has the smaller revenue requirements."

Proposal II. External Financing

Suppose the company chooses to finance the new project by capital funds obtained from offering a new issue of common stock. Such new financing is desirable, of course, only if the new issue can be sold at a price above the book value of common equity per share (= $40, above). Assume, then, that the stock brings $75 per share. Then adopting Plan A would call for a new issue of 500,000/75 = 6,667 shares. Total shares outstanding would increase to 1,256,667.

Earnings per share, after adopting Plan A, are:

$$\frac{5,000,000 + 35,000 + 51,480}{1,256,667} = \$4.048 \text{ per share}$$

On the other hand, adopting Plan B (automation) would call for a new issue of 1,000,000/75 = 13,333 shares. Total shares outstanding = 1,263,333.

Earnings per share, after adopting Plan B, are:

$$\frac{5,000,000 + 70,000 + 52,000}{1,263,333} = \$4.054 \text{ per share}$$

Again, if the exactly intended question is, "Will Plan A or Plan B make the greater improvement in earnings per share?" Plan B is unquestionably the only correct answer, as was indicated by its smaller revenue requirements, whether financing is internal or external.

Dilution

We call attention, at this juncture, to the phenomenon known as "dilution of equity." This is a subject that is widely misunderstood, not only by novices but by "captains of industry," top management of some of our largest corporations, and writers for some of our most highly regarded financial periodicals.[1]

In brief, internal financing does not possess the advantages commonly attributed to it. This situation presents a good example of the misconceptions that arise from failure to define intent exactly and failure to respect the exact nature of appropriate arithmetic. However, it is of small quantitative importance in most problems of relative profitability and economic choice; for such reasons, it is treated in this appendix rather than in the main text.

To illustrate the situation, consider the earnings in the foregoing problem for:

Proposal I. Internally financed project
    Earnings after adopting Plan A = $4.069 per share.
    Earnings after adopting Plan B = $4.098 per share.
Proposal II. Externally financed project
    Earnings after adopting Plan A = $4.048 per share.
    Earnings after adopting Plan B = $4.054 per share.

Since the same earnings are distributed among a greater number of shares, when externally financed, they are said to be "diluted."

This illustrates the arithmetic responsible for the widely accepted, but unsound, notion that new issues of stock are to be avoided, if possible, because it is feared that they will reduce earnings per share. It

---

[1] See Dan Throop Smith, Effects of Taxation, Corporate Financial Policy (Graduate School of Business Administration, Harvard University, Boston, 1952), p. 120, and especially pp. 123-24.

was mentioned in Chapter 1 and is a common misconception, even among top executives. What is wrong with it? The answer is that it involves an oversight in the reasoning. The following discussion suggests a course of reasoning whereby the student may arrive at his own conclusions with assurance.

First, suppose we examine a situation which appears to contradict the foregoing results; external financing appears to result in greater earnings per share for the same Plans A and B. The argument proceeds as follows:

Certainly internal financing of a project is not possible as an option in the foregoing examples unless internally generated funds in the amount of $1,000,000 were actually available. Accordingly, if the proposed project is externally financed, it must mean that the $1,000,000 of internally generated funds must be available for other proposals, in this case, for Plans Q.

Suppose, then, that Plans Q represent new capital investment of $1,000,000, which will utilize all internally generated funds available at the moment. The company proposes to adopt Plans Q, along with foregoing Plans A or B; the latter must, of course, be externally financed.

Earnings per share from adoption of the "package deal" will be as follows, if Plans Q earn 7% on the million-dollar internally financed portion of the deal, which is the same whether A or B is adopted along with it:

After Adopting Plans A and Q

$$\text{Earnings per share} = \frac{\$5,000,000 + \$86,480 + \$70,000}{1,256,667 \text{ shares}} = \$4.103 \text{ per share}[2]$$

After Adopting Plans B and Q

$$\text{Earnings per share} = \frac{\$5,000,000 + \$122,000 + \$70,000}{1,263,333 \text{ shares}} = \$4.110 \text{ per share}[3]$$

Plan B remains superior as always. But note that earnings per share are $4.110 now that B is externally financed, versus the $4.098 where B was internally financed. This occurs despite the greater number of shares outstanding for B (+ Q) than for A (+ Q), of 1,263,000 versus 1,256,667, and despite the greater number of shares for both than if internally financed: 1,263,333 for B (+ Q), the same as Proposal II, versus 1,250,000 for B in Proposal I.

This same conclusion is reached no matter how profitable those internally financed Plans Q may be. For example, if Proposals Q earn 14%, instead of 7%, the earnings per share become as follows:

---

[2] 86,480 = 35,000 + 51,480, which is the numerator of the related expression in both proposals for Plan A.

[3] 122,000 = 70,000 + 52,000, which is the numerator of the related expression in both proposals for Plan B.

After Adopting Plans A and Q

$$\text{Earnings per share} = \frac{\$5,000,000 + 86,480 + \$140,000}{1,256,667} = \$4.159 \text{ per share}$$

After Adopting Plans B and Q

$$\text{Earnings per share} = \frac{\$5,000,000 + \$122,000 + \$140,000}{1,263,333} = \$4.165 \text{ per share}$$

Plan B remains superior, as always. That conclusion cannot be avoided; it is inescapable, because revenue requirements of Plan B are less than those of Plan A.

However, earnings per share are now greater with external financing: $4.165 for Plan B (+ Q) versus $4.098 for Proposal I, internally financed. The difference is Plan Q and its various degrees of profitability. But we have to make some assumption with respect to Plan Q and to the use of available internally generated funds, in order to observe the ceteris paribus principle. All other things must be the same except for the one variable to be evaluated, which is internal versus external financing of Plan B.

Right here lies the answer to the problem. "All other things" are not the same in the foregoing comparisons of internal versus external financing. This must be obvious at a glance.

In all three examples of external financing for Plan B (in Proposal II, and in both examples of "Plan B + Plan Q"), there are the same number of shares outstanding = 1,263,333. But earnings are different in all three cases; that is inescapable if earnings per share differ, as they do. And the difference in earnings does not arise from the choice of external versus internal financing, but from an extraneous situation that is no part of the question at issue, namely, the use made of available internally generated funds.

If $1,000,000 of retained earnings are assumed available for reinvestment in every case, to respect the ceteris paribus principle, then in Proposal II we must have unwittingly assumed 0% return on that internally financed reinvestment. Naturally, this results in smaller earnings, in dollars and in dollars per share, than assuming 7% or 14% return on that $1,000,000 as we did in the other examples.

To preserve the ceteris paribus situation in Proposal II, if that $1,000,000 is not reinvested, then it must be returned to stockholders as dividends. But this upsets the applecart again. We now have a difference in dividend payout between alternatives, as to dividends paid out of prior earnings of the company. Again, we depart from the necessary ceteris paribus that is our essential major premise.

How can the difficulty be resolved?

Let's restate the problem as follows:

1. We are satisfied that Plan B is superior to Plan A. A succession of Plan B's would be superior to a succession of Plan A's.
2. Annual earnings of Plans B are the same whether they are financed

externally (by new security issues) or by internally generated
funds.
3. The question is whether it would be of greatest benefit to owners
   of the business (stockholders) to finance growth, represented by a
   succession of Plan B's, by new issues of securities or by means of
   retained earnings.
4. "Greatest benefit" to stockholders may be gauged by market price
   per pre-project common share, assuming:
   a. The same earnings,
   b. From the same growth,
   c. Represented by the same succession of Plan B's all making the
      same earnings, in dollars, but with the following difference.

On the one hand, that growth is financed by incremental security
issues, with stipulated dividends. On the other hand, that growth is
financed without any incremental security issues, but with a different
dividend payout, meaning larger retained earnings out of identical total
earnings.

This, then, constitutes a statement of our exact intent in comparing external with internal financing. It will be seen that it reduces the
problem to a familiar question: Out of given total earnings, what is the
most desirable dividend payout?

Innumerable writers have struggled with this question, but the
answer remains that arithmetic alone cannot provide the answer, because investor reaction is never 100% predictable. However, two reassuring comments are in order:

1. It is possible to calculate arithmetically what investor reaction
   should be if it were completely logical. This permits close approximation of probabilities.
2. It is also possible to calculate the exact effect of any specified departure from that "completely logical" investor reaction.

The following example will illustrate the force of these statements
and will demonstrate that aside from minor departures from the "completely logical" investor reaction, MRRD permits analyzing potential
benefits of debt refunding, as well as the less familiar advantages of
increasing the number of common shares, when conditions are favorable.[4]

To sum up, aside from minor and temporary market conditions
pro and con, no essential financial benefit can be obtained for owners
of the business by preferring internal to external financing of company
growth.

It is possible that some readers may feel this to be so obvious that
they are reluctant to believe there is a well-established conviction to

[4]Roy H. Berglund and Robert E. Smith, "Cost of Debt Refunding," Public Utilities Fortnightly (January 3, 1963). See also Roy H. Berglund, "A Practical Application of the Revenue Requirement Technique as an Aid in Decision Making," Proceedings of the Iowa State
Conference on Public Utility Valuation and the Rate Making Process (1963), p. 57.

the contrary. If so, they may refer to Effects of Taxation, Corporate Financial Policy, by Dan Throop Smith, mentioned on page 482. Also see: Lemont K. Richardson, "Misconceptions About Earnings Dilution," Financial Analysts Journal (September-October, 1964), p. 58. Other articles in that same issue of Financial Analysts Journal, beginning on page 78, are also worthy of study.

Case 2. Exact Standoff Situation

Figure 4.4 on page 69 presented a standoff situation slightly different from foregoing Case 1 in that Plan A (the smaller capital investment) had exactly the same annual revenue requirements as Plan B. The solution was illustrated graphically by means of the Diagram of Intent. Plan A maximized Profit Incentive, out of identical sales and revenues. It was pointed out that both plans produced an identical Profit Incentive (= earnings in dollars per year above MAR); there was therefore no choice between them, although Plan A produced the larger earnings expressed as a percentage of the new investment.

This is substantially the same situation discussed in foregoing Case 1. However, it was there remarked that some thoughtful and ingenious objections to this conclusion had been raised, which are worth reviewing.

The first attempted criticism proceeds as follows: It might be agreed that if all the Profit Incentive were to be absorbed in reducing prices of the firm's products (that is, Objective 2 and Case 2, of Chapter 4), so that Plans A and B both earn the same return equal to MAR and no more, then the two plans would indeed be a standoff, with no choice between them.

That is, whether Plan A or Plan B is then adopted, the same reduction in price of products is obtained. Newcomers earn the same return on their investment, equal to MAR, in either case. Pre-project owners' earnings are not affected at all by adoption of either plan, since no earnings in excess of MAR go to newcomers. The only important difference between Plans A and B is, then, that Plan B offers newcomers an opportunity to invest more funds at their break-even return (MAR), if they wish to do so. This break-even return represents the level of indifference; there is zero incentive, one way or the other. Agreed, then, that in such case the two plans are a standoff.

Nevertheless, it is pointed out, the moment earnings in excess of MAR are contemplated (that is, an increase in earnings per share, by adopting either plan), then Plan A (smaller investment) becomes the superior alternative. The reason given is familiar: The same total dollars of Profit Incentive, stipulated in Figure 4.4, is then spread over a smaller incremental investment and fewer incremental shares (the "dilution" argument).

Further, it is argued, since all common shares (pre-project or newcomers) are paid the same dividend per share, and since there would be fewer shares if Plan A is adopted and externally financed, pre-project shares must enjoy a larger increase in yield if Plan A is adopted. This is said to be consistent with the exact objective of the Minimum Revenue Requirements Discipline: maximized yield on already committed capital investment.

Thus, it is concluded that Plan A should be adjudged superior so long as earnings exceed MAR (as they normally do and as assumed in Figure 4.4), applying the criterion used in discussing Figure 4.4 in the text.

This argument may be appealing on first thought, but it contains a glaring self-contradiction. That is, the number of pre-project shares is a fixed figure, whether Plan A or B is adopted. And whether Plan A or B is adopted, earnings in excess of MAR are spread over that fixed number of pre-project shares. Accordingly, it is not true that earnings per share are increased by adopting Plan A. So long as revenue requirements of Plans A and B are identical, there is no possibility of increased earnings per share by adopting Plan A. It is the absence of increased earnings per share which makes the two plans a standoff, by definition of terms. We have here a self-contradiction typical of this field of activity.

The critic may not give up yet; he may pursue his argument further, as follows. All right, then, suppose it is conceded that the number of incremental shares (larger for Plan B, if externally financed) makes no difference to the immediate decision. But how about the difference to today's pre-project shares in every future disbursement of Profit Incentive margins from future projects? Once Plan B has been adopted instead of Plan A, then when the next proposal is considered will not there be more pre-project shares outstanding than if Plan A had been previously adopted? In other words, it is reasoned, new proposals offer a choice between projects which are either: (a) standoffs, or (b) one superior to the others.

In the case of standoff, if we always select the alternative having the smaller capital investment (= fewer shares), then the Profit Incentive from those plans which are superior will eventually be spread over fewer pre-project shares. Thus, it is said, this policy of preferring the smaller investment in standoff situations pays off in the future, even though not immediately. This future advantage does not show up on the Diagram of Intent, Figure 4.4.

Admittedly, the argument concedes, the percentage return criterion would not evaluate this advantage with quantitative accuracy, but at least it would indicate the advisability of a long-term policy to favor the smaller capital investment in all cases of standoff economic comparisons. This line of reasoning is a repetition of the "dilution" misconception, just discussed, in a different disguise.

As explained before, if the company's total amount of investors' committed capital were to be the same, whatever its policy in this matter, then the proposals involving the smaller investments could be justified. The percentage return and minimum revenue requirements criteria could be justified, because they are identical when the alter-natives call for identical capital investment. However, the major premise here is the direct opposite. It is argued that Plan A should be preferred because it does not result in identical capital investment; adoption of Plan A means a smaller capital investment.

In the first place, then, suppose all future projects are financed by internally generated funds. This means that the number of pre-project shares remains forever fixed. Whatever earnings amount to, in excess of MAR, and whatever the company policy as to preferring the smaller investment, that same margin of earnings in dollars will be spread over the same number of shares. No "dilution" results by reason of preferring Plan B (larger investment); earnings per pre-project share (all shares are now "pre-project") would be the same as though Plan A (smaller investment) had been preferred.

Suppose, though, some future projects are financed by means of incremental security issues. It is difficult to imagine all future proj-ects externally financed; what would then be done with depreciation re-serves and retained earnings? Let's assume, though, all standoff projects now under discussion are externally financed, other Projects X, Y, Z being financed by internally generated funds. The question is, what benefits would be gained by preferring Plan A (smaller capital in-vestment) for these externally financed standoff alternatives? Here, unmistakably, Plan A (smaller capital investment) would earn the same Profit Incentive in dollars, to be spread eventually over fewer total shares outstanding.

But another arithmetical effect involved must not be ignored. Re-member that internal financing has no advantage (it is of no greater benefit to stockholders than external financing) if the new stock issue can be sold at a price sufficiently above book value per share of com-mon equity. If the new issue has to be sold at a price below book value per share of common equity, even a high percentage return may still be a losing proposition. This was the import of Table 2.1 on page 19.

Accordingly, if these standoff projects are adopted, and externally financed, it must be because the new issues could be sold at a suffi-ciently high price per share to justify the transaction. Of course, the more new shares sold at a momentarily advantageous high price per share, the greater the "antidilution" benefits described before. Plans B, with their larger capital investment and greater number of shares, would have the advantage here.

To illustrate the arithmetic, suppose we consider the pre-project situation of Case 1, on page 477.

Investors' committed capital = $50,000,000.
1,250,000 common shares are outstanding, with book value $40 per share.
Earnings at 10% = $5,000,000 annually = $4 per share.

Plans X, Y, Z internally financed:

Capital investment = $1,000,000; net income = 10%.

The company's MAR = 7%.

Price obtainable for new shares = S (assumed to be \$75 in Case 1).

Standoff proposals, Plans A and B, externally financed, earn identical Profit Incentives of \$50,000 per year in excess of MAR of 7%.

Capital investment in Plan A = P_A; in Plan B = P_B.

Earnings per share after adopting new project (Plan A or Plan B) =

$$\frac{\text{Pre-project income} + (\text{MAR} + \text{Profit Incentive on new project})}{\text{Number of pre-project shares outstanding} + \text{new shares issued}}$$

1. After Adopting Plans A + X, Y, Z

$$\frac{5,000,000 + 1,000,000 + (\text{MAR} \cdot P_A + 50,000)}{1,250,000 + \dfrac{P_A}{S}} = \frac{6,050,000 + 0.07\ P_A}{1,250,000 + \dfrac{1}{75} \cdot P_A}$$

2. After Adopting Plans B + X, Y, Z

$$\frac{5,000,000 + 1,000,000 + (\text{MAR} \cdot P_B + 50,000)}{1,250,000 + \dfrac{P_B}{S}} = \frac{6,050,000 + 0.07\ P_B}{1,250,000 + \dfrac{1}{75} \cdot P_B}$$

It will be observed that two offsetting effects of adopting Plans B (larger investment) instead of Plan A are:

1. The increase in the denominator (P_B in place of P_A), which reduces earnings for shares; and
2. The increase in the numerator (P_B in place of P_A), which increases earnings per share.

Those who see only "dilution" from issuance of new shares overlook that second item completely.

The arithmetical facts of the matter are as follows:

a. Pre-project income per share is:

$$\frac{5,000,000 + 1,000,000}{1,250,000} = \$4.80 \text{ per share}$$

If the new project (either Plan A or Plan B) earns more than \$4.80 per new share then the company's earnings per share will improve, regardless of the number of new shares issued.

b. Earnings per new share are:

Plan A: $\dfrac{0.07 \times 500,000 + 50,000}{500,000/75} = \dfrac{85,000}{6,667} = \$12.75 \text{ per share}$

Plan B: $\dfrac{0.07 \times 1,000,000 + 50,000}{1,000,000/75} = \dfrac{120,000}{13,333} = \$9.00 \text{ per share}$

Obviously, in this case, either Plan A or Plan B will increase earnings per share.

c. Earnings per total share outstanding will be:

Plan A: $\dfrac{5,000,000 + 1,000,000 + 85,000}{1,250,000 + 6,667} = \$4.842$ per share

Plan B: $\dfrac{5,000,000 + 1,000,000 + 120,000}{1,250,000 + 13,333} = \$4.844$ per share

Either plan will increase earnings per share (from \$4.80 to \$4.84+). Plan B (larger capital investment) will have substantially identical effect on the company's per-share earnings (\$4.844 versus \$4.842), even though it involves double the capital investment of Plan A and even though its earnings on incremental investment are almost 28% less than Plan A (\$9.00 versus \$12.75).

This Case 2 started with the premise that Plans A and B were an exact standoff. It now appears that they are not precisely so; Plan B (the larger investment) is very slightly to be preferred. This not only refutes the argument advanced by critics in favor of the smaller investment in case of apparent standoff; it appears to overreach itself.

In view of our emphasis on exact intent, this technicality still remains to be explored. Apparently it has not been given the attention of scholars, to date. Following is the explanation of the phenomenon.

Ceteris Paribus Again

To repeat, all studies of the financial effects of capital investment proposals depend upon acceptance of an essential major premise, conveniently phrased as ceteris paribus, meaning "other things being equal," or "all other things remaining the same."

Thus, when we examine the effects of adopting Plan A versus Plan B, we implicitly stipulate ceteris paribus. We ask, "What is the effect of adopting Plan A instead of Plan B, everything else remaining the same in either event?"

But nature is not so simple as to give a direct, concise answer. The very fact that one alternative may be superior to the other makes that ceteris paribus requirement impossible to satisfy perfectly. This limitation is a disastrous oversight in much economic reasoning. Therefore, we have to revise our intent to ask: "What is the effect of adopting Plan A instead of Plan B, everything else remaining the same except factors necessarily directly affected by making that choice?"

Many such factors are directly affected. Even though Profit Incentive may remain the same (the concept of a standoff, as above), the two competing plans may have different amounts of capital investment (as in this case) and different annual expenses (necessarily in this case, since smaller expenses offset larger capital investment). They may also have different service lives, ultimate net salvage, or retirement-dispersion patterns, all of which affect annual depreciation expense, depreciation reserves, residual undepreciated initial investment at any given date, income taxes, and so on. Accordingly, we really mean: "What is the effect of adopting Plan A instead of Plan B, everything

else remaining the same except for factors necessarily directly affected by making that choice, which are to conform as nearly as may
be to that stipulation?"

For example, a difference in service life as between Plans A and
B accounts for a difference in depreciation reserves as a direct result
of that choice. Shall we then assume:

1. Identical gross plant in either case (that is, a smaller amount
   of total investors' committed capital in the enterprise, associated with the larger revenues of one alternative); or
2. Identical net plant (= investors' committed capital in the enterprise) associated with the different revenues, meaning a larger
   gross plant for the alternative having the larger depreciation
   reserves?

Usually, the only defensible assumption is neither one of these
possibilities. Existing gross and net plant are established figures, just
before adoption of either alternative. Plan A affects gross plant differently than Plan B (in the foregoing cases) immediately on its adoption,
without immediately affecting the amount of reserves. Percentage reserves thus change immediately, meaning:

$$\frac{\text{Depreciation reserves, in dollars}}{\text{Gross plant, in dollars}}$$

As time passes, incremental gross plant may be the same in either
event, but the amount of reserves differs if service life differs. Thus,
gross plant in dollars, depreciation reserves in dollars, net plant in
dollars, and percentage reserves all differ by reason of adopting Plan
A instead of Plan B.

It is impossible to satisfy the ceteris paribus requirement, liter-
ally. This situation need present no difficulty provided it is recognized.
Failure to recognize it sometimes accounts for stipulating mutually
exclusive assumptions that result in absurd conclusions. Many popular
treatments of income tax savings, benefits of leasing, savings from
debt refunding, and so on, rest upon assumptions which could not possibly be experienced in association with each other. Resultant conclusions are nonsense.

In the present case (standoff situations) we have an illustration of
a minor technicality arising from this situation. This was the reason
for making Case 1 a near standoff for comparison with Case 2, an "exact" (?) standoff.

The initial ceteris paribus stipulation was "assuming identical
percentage MAR in either case." However, if externally financed, if a
different number of new shares are to be issued (that is, the plans differ as to capital investment), and if total earnings are to be the same
per share but not exactly MAR, then the price per new share cannot be
exactly the same in each case.

To illustrate, if price per new share is $75 for Plan A (6,667 new
shares), then the price per new share for Plan B to result in identical

earnings per share is calculable by equating the foregoing expressions for earnings per share, as follows:

$$\frac{5,000,000 + 1,000,000 + 85,000}{1,250,000 + 6,667} = \underline{4.842} = \frac{5,000,000 + 1,000,000 + 120,000}{1,250,000 + n}$$

$$4.842\ n = 6,120,000 - 6,052,500$$

$$n = \frac{67,500}{4,842} = 13,941 \text{ shares}$$

$$\frac{\$1,000,000}{13,941 \text{ shares}} = \$71.73 \text{ per share}$$

Thus, if investors had all the facts, if their reactions were 100% predictable, and if they were willing (a) to pay $75 per share if 6,667 new shares were issued, and (b) willing to pay some smaller amount per share if double that amount of new capital were to be raised, by assuming identical earnings per share after the fact, then they would be willing to pay only $71.73 per share in the latter case.

The arithmetic of this reasoning is exact. The only dubious factor is the predictability of investors' reaction to facts that cannot be known perfectly in advance. By hypothesizing ideal conditions, as above, the stipulated perfect standoff is exactly borne out by the meticulously assumed conditions.

In brief, the ceteris paribus premise should not have been presumed to include the stipulation of identical price per share. As a practical matter, the error introduced by ignoring this technicality is so small that ordinarily it could be regarded as insignificant. Compare the error ($4.844 versus $4.842 per share) with that involved in the Percentage Return or "Investors'" Method solution, which would appear to show Plan A superior by a larger margin, instead of an exact standoff:

Misleading Evaluation by Percentage Return or "Investors'" Method

$$\text{Plan A:} \quad \frac{85,000}{500,000} = 17.0\% \text{ return}$$

$$\text{Plan B:} \quad \frac{120,000}{1,000,000} = 12.0\% \text{ return}$$

This completes the rebuttal of arguments advanced in favor of adopting alternatives requiring the smaller capital investment when estimated revenue requirements are identical. It will be found to be completely consistent with the discussion of dilution, earlier in this appendix.

Special Step 2 considerations may favor either the larger or the smaller investment, depending upon the circumstances. Our only concern here has been with the Step 1 analysis of revenue requirements; not with Step 2 nor with the separate and distinct budgeting function.

"Reinvestment Rate"

Some writers in the field of engineering economy are obsessed with the notion that since depreciation accruals are retained in a depreciation reserve, which is reinvested in the business, that the "reinvestment rate" (earnings realizable from opportunities to utilize such funds) must establish the appropriate "interest" rate for compounding, discounting, and annuitizing.[5]

The fallacy here is failure to comprehend the exact intent in undertaking economic comparisons. The misconception of exact objective may be made apparent by the homely illustration of two friends who buy a sweepstakes ticket, dividing its cost half and half. The ticket cost each party $6; it won $30,000 for each. One proceeded to reinvest his winnings (after taxes!) in General Motors stock. He has enjoyed regular dividends and handsome capital gains ever since. The other reinvested in worthless speculations and lost everything promptly.

How profitable was the investment of each in the sweepstakes ticket? Obviously, the matter of return rate on reinvested funds had no bearing on that question. No method of solution, be it the revenue requirements technique, the Discounted Cash Flow Method, the Percentage Return or "Investors'" Method, nor any other, involves any assumption as to reinvestment opportunities for recovered capital. In all such methods, whether they are sound or not, consideration is given only to return on capital unrecovered to date. Capital recovered could be returned to investors as recouped or placed in a strong box earning nothing, without affecting rate of return from investment in the project, just as in the case of the sweepstakes ticket. The advisability of subsequent investment in General Motors stock, versus purchase of worthless securities, does not control the returns from the sweepstakes ticket.

The exact intent of economic studies is not to maximize return on incremental investment. The error in that assumption was discussed at the very beginning of this book and again in Chapter 11. The exact purpose is to optimize return on already committed capital; one way to do that is to maximize Profit Incentive on incremental capital, which is not the same thing as maximizing percentage return on such funds. Refer again to Table 2.1 on page 19 if you have any doubt on that score.

To that end, the analyst lays down a very specific "iffy hypothesis" as the basis for decisions. He asks: "What would revenues have to be if they were just sufficient, and no more, to earn long-term costs of financing (= MAR on the company's pool of investors' committed capital), tentatively assumed to be the same percentage for any alternative?"

This means inquiring into effects of compounding, discounting, and

---

[5] See John R. Canada, "Rate of Return; A Comparison Between the Discounted Cash Flow Model and a Model Which Assumes an Explicit Reinvestment Rate for the Uniform Income Flow Case," Engineering Economist (Spring, 1964), p. 1.

annuitizing if the "interest" rate used in such calculations were that
stipulated MAR percentage, no more and no less. Such an exactly
stipulated equivalency, which contemplates no act of reinvestment at
all, defines the appropriate "interest" rate.[6] It is not correctly described as "reinvestment rate," which concept has no place in the
hypothesis.

---

[6]For a statement of the popular misunderstanding to the contrary, see Eugene L. Grant
and W. Grant Ireson, Principles of Engineering Economy, 4th ed. (Ronald Press, New York,
1960), p. 513.

C

• • • • • Income Tax • • •
Addenda

Scope

In Chapter 8, a number of details concerning income tax are mentioned. However, they demand so many words for complete explanation that they have been relegated to this appendix:

1. Misunderstandings concerning the discount rate (for present worth and annuitizing calculations) arising from tax considerations;
2. The notion that an incremental outlay of $1 for additional expense increases net "costs" only 52 cents, because it is said to reduce income tax by 48 cents;
3. Exact calculation of d_t (= tax-deductible depreciation) for SYD depreciation (sum of years' digits); and
4. Effects of optional accounting methods for disposition of deferred-tax accruals from liberalized depreciation.

Discount Rate

Correct definition and accurate evaluation of the appropriate discount rate is highly important. It is the only means of relating a difference in the single capital outlay to the associated difference in annual expenses over service lifetime. It is the only means for converting a nonuniform stream of payments into their "levelized" equivalent. Since percentage return, the depreciation annuity, percentage income tax, and sometimes other expenses are all of this "levelized" nature in most problems, an exactly correct intent and estimate are of first importance. Yet few details of economic analysis are so widely and grossly misrepresented and incorrectly evaluated.

The appropriate rate, for all purposes, is simply the company's MAR, as exactly defined and evaluated in Chapter 3. Three major misconceptions have served to obscure this fact. First is the attempt to evaluate MAR by observation of the "stream of earnings," which is impossible of observation because it does not yet exist. This classical misadventure has already been dealt with.

Second is a notion that appropriate discount rate is the customer's MAR, to be applied to company revenues to discover their present worth to customer. This ingenious misconception leads to conclusions so absurd that they might be regarded as comic, were they not seriously proposed by a few researchers. It will be discussed in Appendix D. A related disastrous result, of national importance, is described in Chapter 14.

Third is the view that the appropriate discount rate must include allowance for associated income tax, because, it is argued, the tax is part of the "cost of capital." This argument has been put forward vigorously by a few. It reappears occasionally in various forms of reasoning without being recognized as the same basic fallacy.[1]

In simplest form, the proposal is usually to use, in place of MAR, the discount rates: (a) $i - tbB$ (more commonly expressed in nonstandard symbols as $r - Tib$); or (b) $i + T$,

where

i = percentage return (usually said to be MAR; but confused with actual return in the course of argument).

t = statutory tax rate, currently 48%.

T = the company's annual income tax obligation in percent of capital investment (usually said to be the revenue requirement for income tax, $T\%$, but confused with the total obligation, $T\% + T'\%$, in the course of argument).

b = percentage interest rate on company debt.

B = percentage debt in the company's capital structure.

The argument consists in ignoring the exact intent of economic comparisons as displayed by the Diagrams of Intent, Chapter 4. As these diagrams indicate, revenue requirements of a project may be (hopefully) less than revenues in all years. Or revenue requirements may be (hopefully not) greater than revenues in all years. It is just a matter of relative profitability of the project.

But, instead, the argument postulates the fiction:

1. That lifetime-levelized revenue requirements (the Form Y annuity) represent a contemplated year-by-year schedule of revenues for each project, which must be obtained from customers as a matter of "fairness"; and

2. That the difference in each year between this "fair" revenue and the project's nonlevelized revenue requirements (Form X), regarded as "actual costs," produces annual cash deficits for the project in some years, which must be recovered in other years.

As discussed at length in Chapter 6, when a company uses any

---

[1] For example, see the exchange of "Letters to the Editor" in Electric Light and Power (Feb., 1965), p. 140.

method of book depreciation other than the present-worth group-basis procedure, then, assuming perfect accuracy in estimates of life and rate of return, there will always be a difference between:

1. The year-by-year Form X schedule of revenue requirements for minimal gross income plus related taxes plus depreciation; and
2. The lifetime-levelized equivalent annuity (Form Y), financially equivalent to such revenue requirements, in each year.

The argument for $i - TbB$, or $i + T$, chooses to regard these differences as "deficits" in some years, to be made up by "surfeits" in other years, in direct defiance of the exact intent and definition of minimum revenue requirements.

Any course of reasoning whatever based on imaginary cash deficits in some years between (a) Form X nonlevelized revenue requirements and (b) nonexistent revenues conforming to their levelized Form Y equivalency fails to recognize and respect the distinctive fundamental nature of the Minimum Revenue Requirement Discipline. This basic misrepresentation of MRRD is aggravated by deceptive but superficially appealing numerical examples that have been devised to illustrate the fancied situation.

It may be said that such proposals to discount at some interest rate other than the correct $i = MAR\%$ have not gained wide acceptance.[2] But the fact that they have been given consideration by some companies bears witness to misunderstanding of income tax behavior and its effects at top management levels. This lack of understanding is not exclusively a small-business phenomenon. It arises from failure to respect exact definitions of terms and of intent and willingness to accept (or inability to perceive) inexact arithmetic, as though it represented exact principle.

Alternative Discount Rate

It was mentioned in Chapter 5 that the analyst could, if desired, use MAR on equity only as the "interest" rate in discounting and annuitizing calculations, instead of MAR on the company pool of investors' committed capital, provided appropriate substitutions are made in the evaluation and treatment of other revenue requirements, as follows:

1. Define the minimum revenue requirement for return as MAR on equity only, no more and no less, to be used along with revenue requirements for depreciation, taxes, and all other annuities

---

[2]For a further discussion of $r - Tib$ see Constantine W. Bary, Operational Economics of Electric Utilities (Columbia University Press, New York, 1963), and Constantine W. Bary and Wilmer T. Brown, "Some New Mathematical Aspects of Fixed Charges," Transactions of the American Institute of Electrical Engineers; Power Apparatus and Systems (June, 1957), p. 230.

associated with such a return, rather than associated with MAR on the pool of investors' committed capital.

2. Treat the interest component of MAR on the pool of investors' committed capital as an additional expense component of revenue requirements (not part of return).

3. Base economic comparisons and profitability conclusions on resultant benefits to equity owners only, without regard for creditors. This, of course, is the normal index to economic choice or profitability in dollars per year (that is, of Profit Incentive).

Several persuasive reasons for preferring this approach deserve consideration. First, some greater degree of consistency in reasoning is achieved, inasmuch as resultant benefits to equity owners only is more directly identified with benefits in the form of earnings per pre-project share. This advantage is largely one of semantics, because it is impossible to disregard completely the chain reaction that a benefit to pre-project shares has on cost of debt. Because this chain reaction is small quantitatively and not 100% predictable (since it depends on investor reaction), it has been conveniently ignored in referring to the effect on pre-project shares as the ultimate criterion. That omission is deliberate and not an oversight. Recognizing it simply can be expected to increase microscopically the advantage of the superior alternative, if it has any effect at all. Consequently, the greater consistency achieved by adopting MAR on equity only is more apparent than real.

Second, use of MAR on equity only as the discount rate clarifies the reasoning involved in problems such as the economics of leasing versus owning, and debt refunding. (See Chapter 13.) Such problems are unusual in that they permit identification of specific debt obligations with the facilities under study, rather than allocation of the pool rate of interest on debt in evaluating benefits. This is ignored to a degree in the evaluation by using a pool MAR percentage which is itself affected by the decision. Again, the quantitative effect is so small that it is deliberately treated as insignificant in the reasoning. In fact, that small effect is not completely eliminated by use of MAR on equity only, in place of pool MAR; it is merely further reduced. MAR on debt and MAR on equity are to some extent functions of each other, in either case.

Third, use of MAR on equity only would completely destroy the unsound argument in favor of discounting at rate $r - Tib$, just discussed. The adjustment Tib becomes meaningless in such case, as all agree.

Fourth, use of MAR on equity only as the discount rate and revenue requirement for return will appeal to those who look upon interest on debt as an expense. (This fourth reason is perhaps redundant. It is included as a separate reason to facilitate direct comparison with the following reasons for preferring MAR on the company pool of investors' committed capital for that purpose.)

On the other hand, reasons for preferring MAR on company pool of investors' committed capital are as follows. First, the term "return on capital investment" is always accepted as including the interest

payments on debt in the public utility industry, necessarily for projects
financed wholly by debt, such as municipal or governmental projects.
Consistency in this respect is of much greater importance than in the
cases cited for use of MAR on equity only.

Second, MAR on equity and MAR on debt are to some extent functions of each other, as noted above. Use of MAR on equity only as the
discount rate conveys a suggestion that this fact is overlooked or denied.

Third, the effect of deductible interest on income tax obligations is
more readily apparent when taxable income is defined in terms of return on the pool of capital. That is, MAR must be a quantity from
which interest on debt is deductible. For example, the difference between normalization and flow-through accounting for tax deferrals depends upon the debt component of total return. Its explanation and
quantification becomes awkward when MAR on equity only is adopted
as the revenue requirement for return.

Fourth, the concept of a "fair rate of return on fair value," proposed by the United States Supreme Court, has become so firmly established as including interest on debt that regarding interest on debt
as an expense is abhorrent in many circles, amounting to a departure
from sound accounting principles.

After careful consideration of such arguments pro and con, it is
felt that the use of MAR on company pool of investors' committed capital is to be preferred for purposes of this book.

In any particular problem, exactly the same selection of economic
choice will be made either way. The margin of superiority (Profit Incentive, out of identical sales and revenues) will be identical, in dollars
each year, either way. Lifetime-levelized values, or present worths,
will differ somewhat, since the analyst is investigating equivalencies to
different parties — to stockholders only, rather than to investors in the
enterprise as a group including creditors.

All these conclusions are valid only when annual revenue requirements are calculated strictly as exactly intended. For example, it is
essential that deductible depreciation and interest on debt for tax purposes be taken as deductible from revenue requirements for return,
not from total earnings (including Profit Incentive) as in other methods
of analysis.

The Cash-Flow Chart

One of the most serious and widespread fallacies about income
taxes is a proposition frequently advanced by trade unions, politicians,
and insurance salesmen. On occasion it has been conceded by management, although it is totally indefensible.

The proposition is that one dollar of extra expense for fringe benefits, new local taxes, added insurance, and so on, increases company
"costs" only 52 cents, because the increased expense results in an income tax reduction of 48 cents, if revenue requirements remain the

same. Thus, it is said, Uncle Sam bears approximately half of the
extra expense. It is true, of course, that income tax can be reduced by
reducing income. And it is true that, out of the same revenues, an
extra expense of one dollar coupled with a reduced tax payment of 48
cents would reduce net income immediately by only 52 cents. The fallacy lies in regarding income as a "cost." Income, or "profit," is the
direct opposite of a cost.

The fact is that an increase in expense of a dollar increases revenue requirements by a dollar, because a reduction in income does not
reduce the revenue requirement for return. If anything, it increases
MAR, which is the "cost of financing." Since MAR increases, if anything, income tax on MAR behaves likewise.

Accordingly, revenue requirements for return plus income tax increase (if anything). Add the one dollar of extra expense and revenue
requirements will increase by at least one dollar. They will increase
slightly more if the reduced income causes MAR ("cost of financing")
to increase, as it normally must be expected to do. As a result, the
major premise of the proposition is unsound; minimum revenue requirements cannot remain the same. They increase by at least the
amount of the extra expense of one dollar.

The actually intended proposition is that one dollar of extra expense costs the company at least one dollar, because revenue requirements increase at least one dollar. The only way to keep revenue requirements from increasing more than one dollar would be to maintain
the same percentage return on already committed capital, which means
an increase in revenues of one dollar.

Graphical illustration of the same principle is the Cash-Flow
Chart, Figure C.1. It shows the stream of revenues from sales entering from the left. This amount is indicated by the width of the stream.

If state or municipal taxes are levied on sales or on gross receipts
these must be tapped off, as indicated, before the company obtains funds
for its own use.

The firm's first obligation is to pay expenses such as payrolls,
local taxes, and repairs, as shown. Next comes income taxes and finally depreciation expense. Because depreciation expense is not an
immediate outlay, as discussed in Chapter 6, it is shown flowing up-
ward in the diagram; the net revenue requirement is not $_0dP$, but $_0dP$
$- iR$, as must now be familiar to the reader. This leaves a residual
available to provide for interest obligations and dividends and hopefully
some small amount of retained earnings.[3]

If incoming revenues amount to minimum revenue requirements
only, then by definition of terms the residual iP available to provide
for "interest obligations and dividends and hopefully some small amount
of retained earnings" exactly equals MAR, in toto, no more and no less.

---

[3]It does not seem likely that anybody would assume that dividend payout represents
MAR and that retained earnings represent Profit Incentive. However, to avoid any possible
misunderstanding, let it be emphasized that "MAR" does not mean dividend payout; the
margin of Profit Incentive does not mean retained earnings.

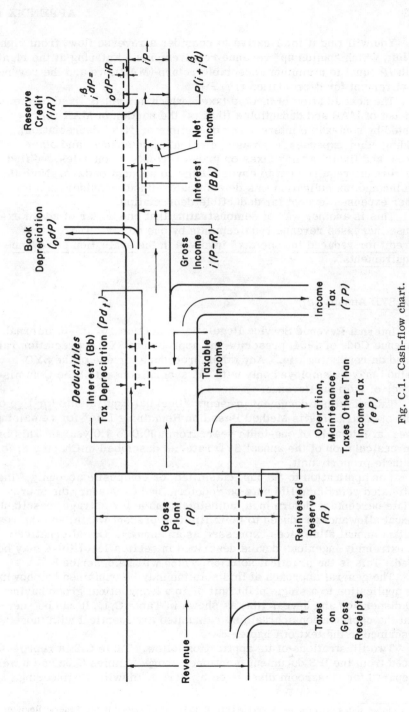

Fig. C.1. Cash-flow chart.

You will find it informative to consider a reverse flow, from right to left, which "builds up" revenue requirements. Entering at the right with iP equal to minimum acceptable return (MAR), we add the revenue requirement for depreciation ($_i d \cdot P$).

The next addition is income taxes, which amount is fixed by the amount of MAR and deductibles (that is, the portion of MAR represented by nontaxable interest and deductible or "tax" depreciation). Adding other expenses, such as operation, maintenance, and other taxes, and finally adding taxes on gross receipts or on sales, we find the revenue requirement to cover all the component outlays. Note that the income tax obligation was determinate without consideration for other expenses, except for deductible depreciation.

This is another way of demonstrating that one dollar of added expense increases revenue requirements by one dollar. There is no "credit for reduced income tax" involved in the evaluation of revenue requirements.

The SYD Annuity (d_t)

Internal Revenue Service Regulations, section 167 (b)-3, Internal Revenue Code of 1954, prescribe the appropriate SYD depreciation rate based on remaining life.[4] Any other procedure for use of the SYD method may be employed only with the special consent of the Commissioner of Internal Revenue.

Table I of that document presents "Decimal Equivalents for Use of Sum-of-Years'-Digits Method Based on Remaining Life" for remaining lives, at intervals of one-tenth year, from 100.0 to 1.0 years. This is a precalculation of the annual SYD rate, as described in Chapter 8, for a single property unit.

For application to "group, classified, or composite accounts," the estimated remaining life may be redetermined each year, the appropriate percentage determined, adjustment made for salvage, resultant annual allowances reduced to their lifetime present worth, and the resultant annual allowances expressed as an annuity. Or, alternatively, an extremely ingenious device described in section 1.167 (b)-4 may be used. This is the practical solution, which will be described.

The general approach of this solution may be explained by showing its application to a single plant unit or to a hypothetical group having SQ dispersion and 5-year life, as shown in Table C.1. It can be seen that the depreciation accruals so calculated are identical with those described in the text of Chapter 8.

Two illustrations of its application follow. Table C.2 is reproduced from the IRS document mentioned above. Tables C.3a and b were prepared for classroom discussion by Bert J. Blewitt, Engineering

---

[4]United States Government Printing Office, 1962. Reproduced in the Federal Register, Vol. 20, No. 221 (November 11, 1955), p. 8454.

Table C. 1. Jeming formula applied to a single property unit
or to a hypothetical group having Type SQ dispersion.

1	2	3 Straight Line Depreciation Reserves	4 Net Plant	5 Percent Condition	6 Average Life	7 Remaining Life
Year	Plant					
1	1,000	0	1,000	100	5	5
2	1,000	200	800	80	5	4
3	1,000	400	600	60	5	3
4	1,000	600	400	40	5	2
5	1,000	800	200	20	5	1

Year	Integral Part	Fractional Part	SYD Rate	SYD Reserve	SYD Net Plant	SYD Accrual
1	5	0	10/30 = .333	0	1,000	333 1/3
2	4	0	8/20 = .400	333 1/3	666 2/3	266 2/3
3	3	0	6/12 = .500	600	400	200
4	2	0	4/ 6 = .667	800	200	133 1/3
5	1	0	2/ 2 = 1.000	933 1/3	66 2/3	66 2/3

Economist of Public Service Electric and Gas Company, Newark, New
Jersey. This table is more pertinent for the present purpose, since it
applies the method to a single vintage having a short average life (2.54
years, for simplicity) and an arbitrary type of dispersion, with zero
net salvage. Adjustment for ultimate net salvage is then made in the
simplest possible manner, used throughout this book, by applying the
factor $(1 - c)$, when c = ultimate net salvage in percent of initial capital
cost, installed.

The important fact to be noted is that there is no uncertainty whatever as to the correct value of d_t. The estimator may decide that a
simpler approximation may be adequate for his purpose and thus deliberately introduce some departure from the exact figure. That is his
prerogative, which may be justified by the circumstances. But it introduces no uncertainty as to the correct principle nor as to the exactly
appropriate arithmetic.

In Table C.2, plant has a 5-year life and 6.67% net salvage. A
placement of $12,000 is made on January 1, 1954, and another place-
ment of $10,000 on January 1, 1959. "Table I," referred to in Column
13, is the table of decimal equivalents for each remaining life, mentioned above. Quantity F, referred to in Column 14, is the rate based
on average service for that Table I, for the total expectancy of life (5
years, in this case), which is 0.3333.

Tables C.3a and b refer to a single placement at the beginning of
Year 1 of 100 (dollars, or units), which has mean annual survivors of
$P_{\bar{x}}$, for which a "percent condition" is calculated at each midyear point,
for substitution in the formula:

$$\text{SYD Rate} = \frac{2E_x}{(W_x + 2F_x)(W_x + 1)}$$

Table C. 2.   Depreciation computation (SYD) on a group account under remaining life plan.

Year	1 Asset Balance Jan. 1	2 Current Additions	3 Current Retirements	4 Average Asset Balance	5 Straight-line Amount Col. 4/Life ($1,200 = ½ yr.)	6 Straight-line Reserve Col. 5 - Col. 3 Accumulated Jan. 1	7 Remaining Life (Col. 1 - Col. 6)/Col. 1 x Average Service Life
1954	...	$12,000	...	$ 6,000	$1,200 (= ½ yr.)	...	5.00
1955	$12,000	...	...	12,000	2,400	$1,200	4.50
1956	12,000	...	...	12,000	2,400	3,600	3.50
1957	12,000	...	$2,000	11,000	2,200	6,000	2.50
1958	10,000	...	2,000	9,000	1,800	6,200	1.90
1959	8,000	$10,000	4,000	11,000	2,200	6,000	1.25
1960	14,000	...	2,000	13,000	2,600	4,200	3.50
1961	12,000	...	2,000	11,000	2,200	4,800	3.00
1962	10,000*	...	...	...	...	5,000	...

Year	8 Asset Balance Reduced by Salvage Col. 1 (100% - 6.67%)	9 Current Additions Reduced by Salvage Col. 2 (100% - 6.67%)	10 Salvage Realized	11 Accumulated Reserve, Jan. 1 = Prior Reserve + Col. 14 + Col. 10 - Col. 3	12 Unrecovered Jan. 1 Col. 8 - Col. 11	13 Rate Based on Col. 7 From Table I	14 Allowable Depreciation Col. 12 x Col. 13 + ½ Col. 9 x F
1954	...	$11,200	...	...	...	0.3333	$1,866
1955	$11,200	...	...	$1,866	$9,334	.3600	3,360
1956	11,200	...	...	5,226	5,974	.4375	2,614
1957	11,200	...	$200	7,840	3,360	.5556	1,867
1958	9,333	...	200	7,907	1,426	.6786	968
1959	7,466	9,333	400	7,075	391	.8125	1,874
1960	13,066	...	...	5,349	7,717	.4375	3,376
1961	11,200	...	...	6,725	4,475	.5000	2,238
1962	...	...	...	6,963	...	...	...

*This figure is not indicated in the original version.

Table C. 3a. Development of the SYD annuity $(= d_t)$ for an initial placement.
Average life = 2.54 years; 10% ultimate net salvage $(= c)$.

Computation of Annual Percent Condition

Year (x)	Mean Annual Survivors $(P_{\bar{x}})$	"Straight-Line" Reserve Balance During the Year at 0% Net Salvage $R_{\bar{x}}$	"Net Plant" During the Year at 0% Net Salvage $(P_{\bar{x}} - R_{\bar{x}})$	Percent Condition At Midyear* at 0% Net Salvage $(P_{\bar{x}} - R_{\bar{x}})/P_{\bar{x}}$
1	92.00	-8.00	100.00	108.70
2	71.00	7.22	63.78	89.83
3	45.00	9.17	35.83	79.62
4	27.00	8.89	18.11	67.07
5	15.00	7.52	7.48	49.87
6	4.00	2.43	1.57	39.25

Computation of SYD Rate

SYD Rate $= (2E_x)/(W_x + 2F_x)(W_x + 1)$
E_x = (Average life) · (Percent Condition) = Remaining life
W_x = Integral years in remaining life
F_x = Fractional years in remaining life

Year (x)	Remaining Life E_x 2.54 x % Condition	Whole Years in Remaining Life W_x	Fractional Years in Remaining Life F_x	SYD Rate $2E_x/(W_x + 2F_x)(W_x + 1)$
1	2.76†	2.00	0.76	5.52/3.52 x 3 = 0.5225
2	2.28	2.00	0.28	4.56/2.56 x 3 = 0.5940
3	2.02	2.00	0.02	4.04/2.04 x 3 = 0.6600
4	1.70	1.00	0.70	3.40/2.40 x 2 = 0.7080
5	1.27	1.00	0.27	2.54/1.54 x 2 = 0.8250
6	1.00	1.00	0.00	2.00/1.00 x 2 = 1.0000

*Percent Condition, by definition, refers to the situation at a given point in time. The use of the phrase "at midyear" in this tabulation merely respects the exact definition. For purposes of determining Form X return during a given year it is absolutely necessary to determine "Net Plant" during that period as $(P_{\bar{x}} - R_{\bar{x}})$; hence Percent Condition in that sense.

†Note that Remaining Life (E_1) is not equal to Average Life at Age Zero, since Percent Condition is not 100%.

Symbols have been altered slightly, from those appearing in the regulations, for consistency with the usage in this book. The formula appears in the official version as follows:

$$D = \frac{2R}{(W + 2F)(W + 1)}$$

where

D = decimal equivalent (undesirable definition and notation).
R = remaining life (an undesirable symbol for this purpose).
W = whole number of years in remaining life.
F = fractional part of year in remaining life.

Table C. 3b. "Straight-line" depreciation, books; SYD depreciation, taxes,
not normalized. (Continuation of Table C. 3a.)

SYD Accruals and Reserve Computations:

SYD Accrual = SYD Rate x "SYD Net Plant"

Year (x)	Mean Annual Service Value of Plant $P_{\bar{x}}(1-c)$	Retirements Less Salvage Since Previous Mean $(1-c)$ (Ret.)	SYD Reserve During Year $(R_{\bar{x}})$	"SYD Net Plant" During Year $P_{\bar{x}}(1-c) - R_{\bar{x}}$	SYD Accrual End of Year SYD Rate "SYD Net Plant"
1	82.800	7.200	-7.200	90.000	47.025
2	63.900	18.900	20.925	42.975	25.527
3	40.500	23.400	23.052	17.448	11.516
4	24.300	16.200	18.368	5.932	4.200
5	13.500	10.800	11.768	1.732	1.429
6	3.600	9.900	3.297	0.303	0.303
					90.000

Note: The SYD reserve during the year is the reserve balance during the previous
year plus the year-end accrual, previous year, less the retirements plus salvage
since the previous mean.

The SYD reserve checks out. SYD reserve balance during Year 6 is $3.297. At
the end of Year 6 the accrual of $R(0.303)$ less the retirements plus the salvage is
- $3.297 (= 0.303 - 3.600).

Computation of $d_t (1 - c)$, the Annuity for SYD Depreciation, and Taxes

Year (x)	SYD Accruals	Present Worth Factors	Present Worth of SYD Accruals
1	47.025	0.9434	44.363
2	25.527	0.8900	22.719
3	11.516	0.8396	9.669
4	4.200	0.7921	3.327
5	1.429	0.7473	1.068
6	0.303	0.7050	0.214
			81.360

$$d_t (1 - c) = (v^x \cdot \text{SYD accruals})/v^x P_{\bar{x}}$$
$$= 81.360/223.18$$
$$= 0.36455 = 36.455\% \quad \text{(This is the SYD depreciation annuity}$$
$$\text{adjusted for net salvage.)}$$

Timing of Tax Payments

Throughout all of Chapter 8 it was assumed, for simplicity, that
income taxes are due at the end of the year during which the related
taxable income was earned. This is not strictly true, and the rules
which govern due-dates may change from time to time.

Because rules change, no meticulous calculation of the exact effect
of due-date has been attempted herein. The analyst can decide for
himself, after becoming thoroughly familiar with current law and details of its administration, whether and how much adjustment is desirably made for this factor. An approximate adjustment may be to
regard the annual payments as though due each mid-year. Present
worth of lifetime payments due may then be obtained as at date $x + \frac{1}{2}$;

present worth at the initial date is calculated by further discounting one-half year.

A Peculiarity of Guide Lines

One of the complications introduced by the well-intentioned but ill-considered "guidelines" provision of tax regulations may be of interest to advanced students. Although a great deal of research on this subject has been done by Bert J. Blewitt, little has yet been published on the subject.

This peculiarity of tax regulations arises from permissive inclusion of depreciable plant having one estimable service life in an account having an appreciably different service life, both physical and tax-depreciable. The result can be an undepreciated residual of initial capital investment, exact ultimate disposition of which is indeterminate. It may become awkwardly apparent at some unknowable date and eliminated by special adjustment of the books, or it may conceivably never be eliminated.

The quantitative effect of this artificially created discrepancy on the lifetime tax obligation is different for the same initial capital installation, depending upon the future history of the project. That is, it depends on whether the capital investment in the project gradually diminishes to zero as retirements occur, or whether it becomes stabilized by reason of retirements made "in kind" as retirements occur, or whether the project grows as additional net additions are made. This effect on the tax has been investigated for various average lives from 1 to 60 years, for extreme dispersion types (SQ and SC), and for several assumptions as to other pertinent variables. Although it is quite small, the effect may not be insignificant under some circumstances. Its amount is calculable if the circumstances can be anticipated; the difficulty lies in estimating with assurance the large number of factors that enter into the computation.

In view of the uncertainty as to possible future changes in tax law from time to time, it is doubtful whether attempts to make such estimates can be justified in most cases.

Generalized Expression for T

The analyst for any given company will find it most convenient to develop and use the expression, in the form of Formula 8.4 on page 184, that is appropriate for his particular company. Such an expression will be suitable only for the particular conditions there prevailing, as to use of liberalized depreciation; methods of depreciation used for book purposes and for tax purposes, respectively; the investment credit for which the company is eligible; the particular means adopted for accounting disposition of accumulated deferred taxes; and the company's method of handling investment credits.

A generalized formula, which may be helpful in developing such an expression for any particular case, is as follows:

$$T = \frac{t}{1-t}\left[(i + \frac{\beta}{i}d - d' - \overline{iDT} - \overline{iIC}_A)(1 - \frac{Bb}{i}) + d' - d_t + \overline{iDT} - \frac{k}{n}(i + \frac{\beta}{i}d) \cdot a_{\overline{n}|}\right]$$

$$- \frac{k(i + \frac{\beta}{i}d)}{1 + i}$$

where

T = lifetime-levelized revenue requirement for federal income tax, in %.

t = statutory tax rate (currently 48%), in %.

i = MAR, in %.

$\frac{\beta}{i}d$ = depreciation annuity, in %; based on service life, adjusted for salvage.

d_t = tax-deductible depreciation, in %; adjusted for salvage.

d' = book depreciation rate, in %; adjusted for salvage.

$\overline{iDT} = t(d_t - d')$.

$\overline{DT} = -(d_t - d')$.

$\overline{iIC}_A = k\left[\frac{i + \frac{\beta}{i}d}{1 + i} - \frac{i + \frac{\beta}{i}d}{n} \cdot a_{\overline{n}|}\right]$.

k = investment credit percentage (3% or 7%).

n = amortization period, in years, for "normalization" (= 1, for "flow-through").

$a_{\overline{n}|}$ = the present worth, at i%, of an n-year annuity. If investment credit is "normalized" (that is, amortized rather than flowing through to income), $\overline{IC}_A$ is zero.

Desirability of Optional Methods

The analyst may be asked to pass upon the desirability of his company's adopting certain policies with respect to its treatment of depreciation, from the standpoint of the effect on taxes. This is a little different proposition from evaluating the revenue requirement for income taxes of specified alternative proposals for capital investment.

The first step in rendering such an opinion is to inquire into: (a) the company's revenue requirements for income tax, under all alternatives to be considered; and (b) the company's tax obligations on probable earnings in excess of MAR, under all alternatives to be considered. This involves making the best possible estimates of $\frac{\beta}{i}d$, d', and d_t for all depreciable property of the company. A few trial solutions will suggest how much detail is worth the effort; usually, the solution is not greatly improved by great detail.

A tabulation of year-by-year revenue requirements for minimal gross income, book depreciation, and taxes will be illuminating. This is readily done for specific installations, in the manner of Table 8.3 on page 202. The major difficulty encountered in practice is the development of such data for the composite plant of the whole company.

In studies of profitability or economic choice of specific proposals, use of lifetime-levelized data permits such great simplification and time saving that the year-by-year calculations are ordinarily out of the question. But in matters of general financial policy, year-by-year cash flow may be regarded as important. To illustrate, consider the following example of year-by-year data versus lifetime-levelized data.

Table C.4 develops year-by-year revenue requirements for minimal gross return, book depreciation, and income taxes, making all assumptions as in the example of Table 8.3 except that liberalized depreciation is now adopted.

Compare (a) the year-by-year data of Tables 8.3 and C.4, respectively, and (b) the lifetime-levelized data for both. The comparison appears in Table C.5.

Values of d_t

Figures 8.1a, 8.1b, and 8.1c, on pages 186-88 show values of d_t, the depreciation annuity for DRDB and SYD methods of depreciation, for average lives from 5 to 55 years; for MAR at 6%, 7%, and 8%; and for two extreme types of retirement dispersion (SC and SQ).

Because the effect of dispersion type is relatively small, values selected from these graphs will be found accurate enough for use in most problems. Values for other types of dispersion commonly encountered may be interpolated; types having subscripts near zero will lie near the SC curve; types having subscripts near 6 will lie near the SQ curve.

The printouts in Table C.6 show values computed to four decimal places (that is, percentages to two decimals) for all the dispersion types of Tables 6.8-6.19, on pages 133-44; for each year of probable

Table C. 4. Year-by-year revenue requirements, from Table 8.3, on page 202, adjusted for effects of liberalized depreciation.

1	2	3	4	5	6
	Minimal	Book	Income	Total	
Year	Gross Income	Depreciation	Tax	Revenue Requirements	
	(Table 8.3,	(Table 8.3,	(Table 8.6,	(Col. 2 + 3 + 4)	
	Col. 2)	Col. 3)	Col. 4)	\$	% of $P_{\bar{x}}$*
1	\$60.00	\$190.00	\$(163.39)	\$ 86.61	9.12%
2	48.60	170.00	(39.95)	178.65	21.02
3	38.40	150.00	25.04	213.44	28.46
4	29.40	130.00	55.18	214.58	33.01
5	21.60	110.00	64.66	196.26	35.68
6	15.00	90.00	61.99	166.99	37.11
7	9.60	70.00	50.66	130.26	37.22
8	5.40	50.00	35.41	90.81	36.32
9	2.40	30.00	20.84	53.24	35.49
10	0.60	10.00	6.84	17.44	34.88

*$P_{\bar{x}}$ is average plant in service each year, per Table 8.7, Column 2.

life from 1 to 60; and for MAR at 5%, 6%, 7%, and 8%, in all cases for both DRDB and SYD methods of depreciation.

Behavior of T, Continuing Plant

When "the project" contemplates a single initial placement whose revenue requirements are to be evaluated without consideration for future replacements, it is a relatively simple matter to calculate federal income tax obligations in each year, or their lifetime-levelized equivalency, or the present worth of that lifetime obligation. This was explained in detail in Chapter 8.

However, year-by-year taxes for a continuing plant (one in which revenue requirements of replacements, as well as of the initial placement itself, are to be investigated) are quite another matter. This was mentioned in Chapters 8 and 9.

Chapter 10 was devoted to a discussion of capital-recovery costs (return plus depreciation) for a continuing plant, an explanation of the "renewal function," and the present worth of all future revenue requirements (PWAFRR). It was pointed out that each year's renewals constitute an additional single "initial" installation, whose taxes behave as described in Chapter 8. Renewals in toto have a tax obligation made up of the sum, in each year, of the several tax obligations of the renewals of all different ages still in service. Accordingly, the resultant tax obligation for the continuing plant as a whole exhibits an oscillatory tendency related to the behavior of the renewal function itself.

Table C. 5. Year-by-year revenue requirements, from Tables 8.3 and C. 4, and their lifetime-levelized equivalencies.

Year	Revenue Requirements in Dollars		Revenue Requirements in %*	
	Table 8.3, Col. 9	Table C. 4, Col. 5	Table 8.3	Table C. 4
1	$264.59	$ 86.61	27.85%	9.12%
2	216.51	178.65	25.47	21.02
3	174.55	213.44	23.27	28.46
4	138.08	214.58	21.24	33.01
5	106.53	196.26	19.37	35.68
6	79.39	166.99	17.64	37.11
7	56.18	130.26	16.05	37.22
8	36.48	90.81	14.59	36.32
9	19.90	53.24	13.27	35.49
10	6.09	17.44	12.18	34.88

*That is, in percent of $P_{\bar{x}}$ (= average cost of plant in service each year). $P_{\bar{x}}$ per Table 8.7, Column 2 (on page 209).

The levelized annuities (= constant percentage of $P_{\bar{x}}$ each year):

	Table 8.3	Table C. 4
i	6.00%	6.00%
$\overset{i}{\beta}_d$	18.80	18.80
$T\%$	2.44	0.97
Total	27.24%	25.77%

Since the lifetime-levelized $T\%$ is a fixed figure for a given life and dispersion type (assuming no change in tax law or other pertinent factors), taxes for the project are correctly calculated as $T\%$ of the capital investment currently in service; and that capital investment remains permanently equal to the initial placement P_0 at all times, by terms of the problem, so long as replacements continue to be made in kind.

So long as replacements live out their full life (= the life of the initial placement) that same calculation remains appropriate throughout the period after replacements cease and the project becomes a shrinking plant. That is, lifetime-levelized taxes remain the same $T\%$ of the finally decreasing capital investment in service, up to the date when the last survivor is finally retired.

This leads to the two conclusions of major importance in studies of this kind — beyond one lifetime — as follows:

1. The present worth of all future revenue requirements for income tax (that is, the income tax component of PWAFRR) is correctly computed, as exactly intended by the analyst, as $(T\% \cdot P_0)/i$.

2. For a project which ends as a shrinking plant, the present worth of future revenue requirements for income tax (that is, the income tax component of PWRR) is adequately approximated as $a_{\overline{n}|} \cdot P_0 \cdot T\%$, where n is the date of the final retirement of the project, provided that date is so remote that the present worth of taxes beyond date ω (= date of final retirement of the initial placement) is insignificant. For most practical purposes, this means when ω is 60 years or more, as for 30, SC or R_1.

Conclusions of this kind can be reached by reasoning analytically, but it is informative, as well as reassuring, to have a concrete demonstration, such as the calculations in Table C.7, prepared to illustrate.

Calculations have been made for four different projects:

Project 1
>   Initial investment = $1,000.
>   Average service life = 30 years (Type SC dispersion).
>   MAR = 6%; 50% debt at 4% interest; 48% tax.
>   Zero ultimate net salvage.
>   "Straight-line" depreciation $(_0d)$ for books $(= d')$, SYD depreciation for taxes $(= d_t)$.
>   Continuing plant for 60 years; replacements cease after Year 60, when it becomes a shrinking plant.

Project 2
>   Same as Project 1, except that the project remains a continuing plant for 300 years (= 5 life cycles) before replacements cease.

Project 3
>   Same as Project 1, but Type R_1 dispersion.

Project 4
>   Same as Project 2, but Type R_1 dispersion.

Calculations were programmed for electronic data processing by Robert J. Carlyle, of Public Service Electric and Gas Company, Newark, New Jersey, in connection with studies made by that company. Table C.7 includes only a small portion of the resultant printouts, sufficient to indicate the general behavior of income taxes year by year.

A summary of the inputs and final-stage calculations is appended for each project. You will see that the final calculations include alternative calculations of lifetime-levelized quantities to serve as a check and to indicate adequacy of approximations. That is, the final figure identified as "tax annuity (equal lives, SYD)" would be identical with the other calculations of $T\%$ were the period of study lengthy enough for complete stabilization of the damped oscillatory curve representing T in each year. Complete stabilization is attained only at eternity.

The same comment applies to "tax annuity (equal lives, SL)," which represents $T\%$ for the conditions of Basic Formula 8.1 on page 182; that is, without benefits of liberalized depreciation. The calculations do not show effects of investment credit, which can be separately calculated and superimposed or can be incorporated into a similar program.

For brevity, results are shown for only a few informative years (1-6, 29-31, 59-61, and 117-120 for Projects 1 and 3, together with 298-300 and 357-360 for Projects 2 and 4). It will be seen that the annual calculations fall into two general categories:

1. Those related to book depreciation
   Mean annual survivors
   Book depreciation accrual
   Present worth factor
   Current retirements
   Book reserve balance
   Unrecovered balance
2. Those related to the tax calculation
   Minimal gross income
   Deductible interest
   Tax accrual
   Tax reserve
   Taxable income after taxes
   Federal income tax

Table C.6. Printouts for depreciation annuities of d_t, for SYD and DRDB depreciation, and for 5%, 6%, 7%, and 8% MAR.

DEPRECIATION ANNUITIES, DECIMALLY EXPRESSED

SYD METHOD   CRITICAL RATE OF RETURN 5.000 PERCENT

AVERAGE LIFE (YEARS)	SC	S0N	S0	S05	S1	TYPE OF RETIREMENT DISPERSION S15	S2	S3	S4	S5	S6	SQ
1	1.0024	0.9667	0.9340	0.9083	0.8890	0.8689	0.8595	0.8538	0.8749	0.9071	0.9368	1.0000
2	0.5076	0.5035	0.4995	0.4987	0.4984	0.4995	0.5011	0.5038	0.5044	0.4615	0.4730	0.5041
3	0.3427	0.3413	0.3400	0.3398	0.3396	0.3397	0.3398	0.3396	0.3383	0.3390	0.3195	0.3388
4	0.2602	0.2594	0.2585	0.2582	0.2580	0.2577	0.2575	0.2570	0.2566	0.2561	0.2562	0.2561
5	0.2107	0.2100	0.2093	0.2090	0.2086	0.2083	0.2080	0.2074	0.2070	0.2068	0.2066	0.2065
6	0.1776	0.1770	0.1764	0.1760	0.1756	0.1753	0.1749	0.1744	0.1740	0.1737	0.1735	0.1734
7	0.1540	0.1534	0.1528	0.1524	0.1520	0.1517	0.1513	0.1508	0.1503	0.1501	0.1497	0.1498
8	0.1363	0.1357	0.1351	0.1347	0.1343	0.1339	0.1336	0.1331	0.1326	0.1324	0.1322	0.1321
9	0.1225	0.1219	0.1213	0.1209	0.1205	0.1201	0.1198	0.1193	0.1188	0.1186	0.1184	0.1183
10	0.1114	0.1108	0.1103	0.1099	0.1094	0.1091	0.1088	0.1082	0.1078	0.1075	0.1074	0.1073
11	0.1023	0.1018	0.1012	0.1008	0.1004	0.1001	0.0997	0.0992	0.0988	0.0985	0.0984	0.0983
12	0.0948	0.0942	0.0937	0.0933	0.0929	0.0925	0.0922	0.0917	0.0912	0.0910	0.0909	0.0907
13	0.0884	0.0878	0.0873	0.0869	0.0865	0.0861	0.0858	0.0853	0.0849	0.0846	0.0845	0.0844
14	0.0828	0.0823	0.0818	0.0814	0.0810	0.0806	0.0803	0.0798	0.0794	0.0792	0.0790	0.0789
15	0.0781	0.0775	0.0770	0.0766	0.0762	0.0759	0.0756	0.0751	0.0747	0.0744	0.0743	0.0742
16	0.0739	0.0733	0.0728	0.0724	0.0720	0.0717	0.0714	0.0709	0.0705	0.0703	0.0701	0.0700
17	0.0702	0.0696	0.0691	0.0687	0.0683	0.0680	0.0677	0.0673	0.0668	0.0666	0.0665	0.0664
18	0.0668	0.0663	0.0658	0.0654	0.0651	0.0648	0.0644	0.0640	0.0636	0.0634	0.0632	0.0631
19	0.0639	0.0634	0.0629	0.0625	0.0621	0.0618	0.0615	0.0611	0.0607	0.0604	0.0603	0.0602
20	0.0612	0.0607	0.0602	0.0598	0.0595	0.0592	0.0589	0.0584	0.0580	0.0578	0.0577	0.0576
21	0.0588	0.0583	0.0578	0.0574	0.0571	0.0568	0.0565	0.0560	0.0557	0.0554	0.0553	0.0552
22	0.0565	0.0561	0.0556	0.0552	0.0549	0.0546	0.0543	0.0539	0.0535	0.0533	0.0532	0.0531
23	0.0545	0.0540	0.0536	0.0532	0.0529	0.0526	0.0523	0.0519	0.0515	0.0513	0.0512	0.0511
24	0.0526	0.0522	0.0517	0.0514	0.0510	0.0507	0.0505	0.0500	0.0497	0.0495	0.0494	0.0493
25	0.0509	0.0505	0.0500	0.0497	0.0493	0.0490	0.0488	0.0484	0.0480	0.0478	0.0477	0.0476
26	0.0493	0.0489	0.0484	0.0481	0.0477	0.0475	0.0472	0.0468	0.0465	0.0463	0.0462	0.0461
27	0.0478	0.0474	0.0469	0.0466	0.0463	0.0460	0.0457	0.0454	0.0450	0.0448	0.0447	0.0446
28	0.0464	0.0460	0.0456	0.0452	0.0449	0.0447	0.0444	0.0440	0.0437	0.0435	0.0434	0.0433

	0.0451	0.0447	0.0443	0.0440	0.0436	0.0434	0.0431	0.0428	0.0424	0.0423	0.0422	0.0421
29	0.0451	0.0447	0.0443	0.0440	0.0436	0.0434	0.0431	0.0428	0.0424	0.0423	0.0422	0.0421
30	0.0439	0.0435	0.0431	0.0428	0.0425	0.0422	0.0420	0.0416	0.0413	0.0411	0.0410	0.0409
31	0.0428	0.0424	0.0419	0.0416	0.0413	0.0411	0.0409	0.0405	0.0402	0.0400	0.0399	0.0398
32	0.0417	0.0413	0.0409	0.0406	0.0403	0.0401	0.0398	0.0395	0.0392	0.0390	0.0389	0.0388
33	0.0407	0.0403	0.0399	0.0396	0.0393	0.0391	0.0388	0.0385	0.0382	0.0380	0.0379	0.0379
34	0.0397	0.0393	0.0389	0.0387	0.0384	0.0381	0.0379	0.0376	0.0373	0.0371	0.0370	0.0370
35	0.0388	0.0384	0.0381	0.0378	0.0375	0.0373	0.0370	0.0367	0.0364	0.0363	0.0362	0.0361
36	0.0380	0.0376	0.0372	0.0369	0.0367	0.0364	0.0362	0.0359	0.0356	0.0355	0.0354	0.0353
37	0.0372	0.0368	0.0364	0.0361	0.0359	0.0356	0.0354	0.0351	0.0348	0.0347	0.0346	0.0345
38	0.0364	0.0360	0.0356	0.0354	0.0351	0.0349	0.0347	0.0344	0.0341	0.0340	0.0339	0.0338
39	0.0356	0.0353	0.0349	0.0346	0.0344	0.0342	0.0340	0.0337	0.0334	0.0333	0.0332	0.0331
40	0.0349	0.0346	0.0342	0.0340	0.0337	0.0335	0.0333	0.0330	0.0327	0.0326	0.0325	0.0325
41	0.0342	0.0339	0.0335	0.0333	0.0330	0.0328	0.0326	0.0324	0.0321	0.0320	0.0319	0.0318
42	0.0336	0.0333	0.0329	0.0327	0.0324	0.0322	0.0320	0.0317	0.0315	0.0314	0.0313	0.0312
43	0.0330	0.0326	0.0323	0.0321	0.0318	0.0316	0.0314	0.0312	0.0309	0.0308	0.0307	0.0307
44	0.0324	0.0321	0.0317	0.0315	0.0312	0.0311	0.0309	0.0306	0.0304	0.0302	0.0302	0.0301
45	0.0318	0.0315	0.0312	0.0309	0.0307	0.0305	0.0303	0.0301	0.0298	0.0297	0.0296	0.0296
46	0.0313	0.0309	0.0306	0.0304	0.0302	0.0300	0.0298	0.0296	0.0293	0.0292	0.0291	0.0291
47	0.0307	0.0304	0.0301	0.0299	0.0297	0.0295	0.0293	0.0291	0.0288	0.0287	0.0287	0.0286
48	0.0302	0.0299	0.0296	0.0294	0.0292	0.0290	0.0288	0.0286	0.0284	0.0283	0.0282	0.0282
49	0.0297	0.0294	0.0291	0.0289	0.0287	0.0285	0.0284	0.0281	0.0279	0.0278	0.0277	0.0277
50	0.0293	0.0290	0.0287	0.0285	0.0283	0.0281	0.0279	0.0277	0.0275	0.0274	0.0273	0.0273
51	0.0288	0.0285	0.0282	0.0280	0.0278	0.0277	0.0275	0.0273	0.0271	0.0270	0.0269	0.0269
52	0.0284	0.0281	0.0278	0.0276	0.0274	0.0272	0.0271	0.0269	0.0267	0.0266	0.0265	0.0265
53	0.0279	0.0277	0.0274	0.0272	0.0270	0.0268	0.0267	0.0265	0.0263	0.0262	0.0261	0.0261
54	0.0275	0.0272	0.0270	0.0268	0.0266	0.0264	0.0263	0.0261	0.0259	0.0258	0.0257	0.0257
55	0.0271	0.0269	0.0266	0.0264	0.0262	0.0261	0.0259	0.0257	0.0255	0.0254	0.0254	0.0253
56	0.0267	0.0265	0.0262	0.0260	0.0258	0.0257	0.0256	0.0253	0.0252	0.0251	0.0250	0.0250
57	0.0264	0.0261	0.0258	0.0257	0.0255	0.0253	0.0252	0.0250	0.0248	0.0247	0.0247	0.0247
58	0.0260	0.0257	0.0255	0.0253	0.0251	0.0250	0.0249	0.0247	0.0245	0.0244	0.0244	0.0243
59	0.0256	0.0254	0.0251	0.0250	0.0248	0.0247	0.0245	0.0243	0.0242	0.0241	0.0241	0.0240
60	0.0253	0.0251	0.0248	0.0246	0.0245	0.0243	0.0242	0.0240	0.0239	0.0238	0.0237	0.0237

DEPRECIATION ANNUITIES, DECIMALLY EXPRESSED

SYD METHOD   CRITICAL RATE OF RETURN 5.000 PERCENT

AVERAGE LIFE (YEARS)	L0	L05	L1	L15	L2	L3	L4	L5
						TYPE OF RETIREMENT DISPERSION		
1	1.0123	1.0057	0.9852	0.9712	0.9558	0.9553	0.8338	0.8581
2	0.5099	0.5085	0.5070	0.5070	0.5069	0.5031	0.4975	0.4996
3	0.3442	0.3434	0.3424	0.3419	0.3412	0.3404	0.3383	0.3380
4	0.2615	0.2607	0.2599	0.2594	0.2588	0.2578	0.2568	0.2561
5	0.2119	0.2112	0.2104	0.2098	0.2093	0.2083	0.2074	0.2069
6	0.1788	0.1781	0.1773	0.1768	0.1762	0.1752	0.1744	0.1739
7	0.1551	0.1544	0.1537	0.1531	0.1526	0.1516	0.1507	0.1503
8	0.1374	0.1366	0.1359	0.1354	0.1348	0.1339	0.1330	0.1326
9	0.1235	0.1228	0.1221	0.1216	0.1210	0.1201	0.1192	0.1188
10	0.1124	0.1117	0.1110	0.1105	0.1100	0.1090	0.1082	0.1078
11	0.1033	0.1026	0.1019	0.1014	0.1009	0.1000	0.0991	0.0987
12	0.0957	0.0950	0.0943	0.0939	0.0933	0.0924	0.0916	0.0912
13	0.0892	0.0886	0.0879	0.0874	0.0869	0.0860	0.0852	0.0848
14	0.0837	0.0831	0.0824	0.0819	0.0814	0.0805	0.0798	0.0794
15	0.0789	0.0782	0.0776	0.0771	0.0767	0.0758	0.0750	0.0746
16	0.0746	0.0740	0.0734	0.0729	0.0725	0.0716	0.0709	0.0705
17	0.0709	0.0703	0.0697	0.0692	0.0688	0.0679	0.0672	0.0668
18	0.0675	0.0670	0.0664	0.0659	0.0655	0.0646	0.0639	0.0635
19	0.0645	0.0640	0.0634	0.0630	0.0625	0.0617	0.0610	0.0606
20	0.0618	0.0613	0.0607	0.0603	0.0598	0.0590	0.0584	0.0580
21	0.0594	0.0588	0.0583	0.0578	0.0574	0.0566	0.0560	0.0556
22	0.0571	0.0566	0.0561	0.0556	0.0552	0.0544	0.0538	0.0534
23	0.0551	0.0545	0.0540	0.0536	0.0532	0.0524	0.0518	0.0515
24	0.0532	0.0527	0.0521	0.0517	0.0513	0.0506	0.0500	0.0496
25	0.0514	0.0509	0.0504	0.0500	0.0496	0.0489	0.0483	0.0480
26	0.0498	0.0493	0.0488	0.0484	0.0480	0.0473	0.0467	0.0464
27	0.0483	0.0478	0.0473	0.0469	0.0466	0.0459	0.0453	0.0450
28	0.0469	0.0464	0.0459	0.0456	0.0452	0.0445		

30	0.0443	0.0439	0.0434	0.0431	0.0427	0.0421	0.0415	0.0412
31	0.0431	0.0427	0.0423	0.0419	0.0416	0.0410	0.0404	0.0401
32	0.0421	0.0416	0.0412	0.0409	0.0405	0.0399	0.0394	0.0391
33	0.0410	0.0406	0.0402	0.0399	0.0395	0.0389	0.0384	0.0382
34	0.0400	0.0394	0.0392	0.0389	0.0386	0.0380	0.0375	0.0372
35	0.0391	0.0387	0.0383	0.0380	0.0377	0.0371	0.0366	0.0364
36	0.0382	0.0379	0.0375	0.0372	0.0368	0.0363	0.0358	0.0356
37	0.0374	0.0370	0.0367	0.0364	0.0360	0.0355	0.0351	0.0348
38	0.0366	0.0363	0.0359	0.0356	0.0353	0.0348	0.0343	0.0341
39	0.0359	0.0355	0.0352	0.0349	0.0346	0.0340	0.0336	0.0334
40	0.0351	0.0348	0.0344	0.0342	0.0339	0.0334	0.0329	0.0327
41	0.0344	0.0341	0.0338	0.0335	0.0332	0.0327	0.0323	0.0321
42	0.0338	0.0335	0.0331	0.0329	0.0326	0.0321	0.0317	0.0315
43	0.0332	0.0328	0.0325	0.0322	0.0320	0.0315	0.0311	0.0309
44	0.0325	0.0322	0.0319	0.0317	0.0314	0.0309	0.0306	0.0303
45	0.0320	0.0317	0.0314	0.0311	0.0308	0.0304	0.0300	0.0298
46	0.0314	0.0311	0.0308	0.0306	0.0303	0.0299	0.0295	0.0293
47	0.0309	0.0306	0.0303	0.0300	0.0298	0.0294	0.0290	0.0288
48	0.0303	0.0301	0.0298	0.0295	0.0293	0.0289	0.0285	0.0283
49	0.0298	0.0296	0.0293	0.0291	0.0288	0.0284	0.0281	0.0279
50	0.0294	0.0291	0.0288	0.0286	0.0284	0.0280	0.0276	0.0275
51	0.0289	0.0286	0.0284	0.0281	0.0279	0.0275	0.0272	0.0270
52	0.0285	0.0282	0.0279	0.0277	0.0275	0.0271	0.0268	0.0266
53	0.0280	0.0278	0.0275	0.0273	0.0271	0.0267	0.0264	0.0262
54	0.0276	0.0274	0.0271	0.0269	0.0267	0.0263	0.0260	0.0259
55	0.0272	0.0270	0.0267	0.0265	0.0263	0.0259	0.0257	0.0255
56	0.0268	0.0266	0.0263	0.0261	0.0259	0.0256	0.0253	0.0252
57	0.0264	0.0262	0.0260	0.0258	0.0256	0.0252	0.0250	0.0248
58	0.0260	0.0258	0.0256	0.0254	0.0252	0.0249	0.0246	0.0245
59	0.0257	0.0255	0.0252	0.0251	0.0249	0.0246	0.0243	0.0242
60	0.0253	0.0251	0.0249	0.0247	0.0245	0.0242	0.0240	0.0239

DEPRECIATION ANNUITIES, DECIMALLY EXPRESSED

SYD METHOD   CRITICAL RATE OF RETURN 5.000 PERCENT

AVERAGE LIFE (YEARS)				TYPE OF RETIREMENT DISPERSION				
	R05	R1	R15	R2	R25	R3	R4	R5
1	0.9597	1.0052	0.8936	0.9009	0.8808	0.8936	0.9004	0.9184
2	0.5029	0.5071	0.4986	0.5014	0.5035	0.5056	0.4722	0.4731
3	0.3414	0.3416	0.3399	0.3401	0.3400	0.3366	0.3394	0.3405
4	0.2594	0.2589	0.2582	0.2579	0.2575	0.2569	0.2551	0.2565
5	0.2100	0.2094	0.2088	0.2084	0.2080	0.2076	0.2071	0.2063
6	0.1770	0.1763	0.1758	0.1752	0.1749	0.1745	0.1739	0.1737
7	0.1534	0.1527	0.1522	0.1517	0.1513	0.1509	0.1505	0.1501
8	0.1356	0.1350	0.1345	0.1340	0.1336	0.1332	0.1327	0.1324
9	0.1218	0.1212	0.1207	0.1202	0.1198	0.1194	0.1190	0.1186
10	0.1108	0.1101	0.1096	0.1092	0.1088	0.1084	0.1079	0.1076
11	0.1017	0.1011	0.1006	0.1001	0.0998	0.0994	0.0989	0.0986
12	0.0942	0.0935	0.0930	0.0926	0.0922	0.0919	0.0914	0.0910
13	0.0877	0.0871	0.0866	0.0862	0.0858	0.0855	0.0850	0.0847
14	0.0822	0.0816	0.0812	0.0807	0.0804	0.0800	0.0796	0.0792
15	0.0775	0.0768	0.0764	0.0759	0.0756	0.0753	0.0748	0.0745
16	0.0733	0.0727	0.0722	0.0718	0.0714	0.0711	0.0707	0.0703
17	0.0696	0.0690	0.0685	0.0681	0.0678	0.0674	0.0670	0.0667
18	0.0663	0.0657	0.0653	0.0648	0.0645	0.0642	0.0637	0.0634
19	0.0633	0.0627	0.0623	0.0619	0.0616	0.0612	0.0608	0.0605
20	0.0606	0.0601	0.0597	0.0592	0.0589	0.0586	0.0582	0.0579
21	0.0582	0.0577	0.0573	0.0568	0.0565	0.0562	0.0558	0.0555
22	0.0560	0.0555	0.0551	0.0547	0.0543	0.0540	0.0536	0.0533
23	0.0540	0.0534	0.0531	0.0527	0.0524	0.0520	0.0517	0.0513
24	0.0521	0.0516	0.0512	0.0508	0.0505	0.0502	0.0498	0.0495
25	0.0504	0.0499	0.0495	0.0491	0.0488	0.0485	0.0482	0.0479
26	0.0488	0.0483	0.0479	0.0476	0.0473	0.0470	0.0466	0.0463
27	0.0473	0.0468	0.0465	0.0461	0.0458	0.0455	0.0452	0.0449
28	0.0460	0.0455	0.0451	0.0448	0.0445	0.0442	0.0438	0.0435

29	0.0447	0.0442	0.0438	0.0435	0.0432	0.0429	0.0426	0.0423
30	0.0435	0.0430	0.0427	0.0423	0.0420	0.0418	0.0414	0.0411
31	0.0423	0.0419	0.0415	0.0412	0.0409	0.0407	0.0403	0.0401
32	0.0413	0.0408	0.0405	0.0402	0.0399	0.0396	0.0393	0.0390
33	0.0403	0.0398	0.0395	0.0392	0.0389	0.0387	0.0383	0.0381
34	0.0393	0.0389	0.0386	0.0382	0.0380	0.0377	0.0374	0.0372
35	0.0384	0.0380	0.0377	0.0374	0.0371	0.0369	0.0366	0.0363
36	0.0376	0.0371	0.0368	0.0365	0.0363	0.0360	0.0357	0.0355
37	0.0368	0.0363	0.0360	0.0357	0.0355	0.0353	0.0350	0.0347
38	0.0360	0.0356	0.0353	0.0350	0.0348	0.0345	0.0342	0.0340
39	0.0352	0.0349	0.0346	0.0343	0.0341	0.0338	0.0335	0.0333
40	0.0345	0.0342	0.0339	0.0336	0.0334	0.0332	0.0329	0.0326
41	0.0339	0.0335	0.0332	0.0329	0.0327	0.0325	0.0322	0.0320
42	0.0332	0.0329	0.0326	0.0323	0.0321	0.0319	0.0316	0.0314
43	0.0326	0.0323	0.0320	0.0317	0.0315	0.0313	0.0310	0.0308
44	0.0320	0.0317	0.0314	0.0312	0.0310	0.0308	0.0305	0.0303
45	0.0315	0.0311	0.0309	0.0306	0.0304	0.0302	0.0300	0.0298
46	0.0309	0.0306	0.0303	0.0301	0.0299	0.0297	0.0294	0.0292
47	0.0304	0.0301	0.0298	0.0296	0.0294	0.0292	0.0289	0.0288
48	0.0299	0.0296	0.0293	0.0291	0.0289	0.0287	0.0285	0.0283
49	0.0294	0.0291	0.0289	0.0286	0.0285	0.0283	0.0280	0.0278
50	0.0290	0.0287	0.0284	0.0282	0.0280	0.0278	0.0276	0.0274
51	0.0285	0.0282	0.0280	0.0278	0.0276	0.0274	0.0272	0.0270
52	0.0281	0.0278	0.0276	0.0273	0.0272	0.0270	0.0268	0.0266
53	0.0277	0.0274	0.0271	0.0269	0.0268	0.0266	0.0264	0.0262
54	0.0272	0.0270	0.0268	0.0265	0.0264	0.0262	0.0260	0.0258
55	0.0268	0.0266	0.0264	0.0262	0.0260	0.0258	0.0256	0.0255
56	0.0265	0.0262	0.0260	0.0258	0.0256	0.0255	0.0253	0.0251
57	0.0261	0.0258	0.0256	0.0254	0.0253	0.0251	0.0249	0.0248
58	0.0257	0.0255	0.0253	0.0251	0.0249	0.0248	0.0246	0.0244
59	0.0254	0.0251	0.0250	0.0248	0.0246	0.0245	0.0243	0.0241
60	0.0251.	0.0248	0.0246	0.0244	0.0243	0.0241	0.0240	0.0238

DEPRECIATION ANNUITIES, DECIMALLY EXPRESSED

DOUBLE-RATE-DECLINING-BALANCE METHOD   CRITICAL RATE OF RETURN   5.000 PERCENT

AVERAGE LIFE (YEARS)	SC	SON	S0	S05	S1	S15	S2	S3	S4	S5	S6	SQ
							TYPE OF RETIREMENT DISPERSION					
1	1.0602	0.8563	0.6009	0.3095	0.0850	0.0831	0.0821	0.0814	0.0833	1.8154	1.8743	2.0000
2	0.5213	0.5161	0.5110	0.5096	0.5087	0.5094	0.5107	0.5130	0.5131	0.4691	0.4806	0.5122
3	0.3500	0.3479	0.3458	0.3451	0.3446	0.3443	0.3440	0.3435	0.3424	0.3427	0.3293	0.3424
4	0.2646	0.2630	0.2615	0.2608	0.2601	0.2596	0.2592	0.2586	0.2581	0.2578	0.2578	0.2577
5	0.2133	0.2119	0.2106	0.2099	0.2092	0.2087	0.2083	0.2078	0.2074	0.2073	0.2071	0.2071
6	0.1792	0.1779	0.1767	0.1760	0.1753	0.1748	0.1744	0.1739	0.1736	0.1734	0.1733	0.1732
7	0.1549	0.1536	0.1524	0.1517	0.1511	0.1506	0.1502	0.1498	0.1495	0.1493	0.1492	0.1492
8	0.1366	0.1354	0.1342	0.1335	0.1329	0.1325	0.1321	0.1316	0.1313	0.1312	0.1311	0.1311
9	0.1224	0.1212	0.1200	0.1194	0.1188	0.1184	0.1180	0.1176	0.1173	0.1172	0.1171	0.1171
10	0.1110	0.1098	0.1087	0.1081	0.1075	0.1071	0.1067	0.1063	0.1060	0.1059	0.1058	0.1058
11	0.1017	0.1005	0.0995	0.0988	0.0982	0.0978	0.0975	0.0971	0.0969	0.0967	0.0967	0.0966
12	0.0940	0.0928	0.0917	0.0911	0.0905	0.0901	0.0898	0.0894	0.0892	0.0891	0.0890	0.0890
13	0.0874	0.0863	0.0852	0.0846	0.0840	0.0836	0.0833	0.0829	0.0827	0.0826	0.0825	0.0825
14	0.0818	0.0806	0.0796	0.0790	0.0784	0.0781	0.0777	0.0774	0.0771	0.0770	0.0770	0.0769
15	0.0769	0.0758	0.0747	0.0741	0.0736	0.0732	0.0729	0.0726	0.0723	0.0722	0.0722	0.0721
16	0.0726	0.0715	0.0705	0.0699	0.0693	0.0690	0.0687	0.0683	0.0681	0.0680	0.0680	0.0679
17	0.0688	0.0677	0.0667	0.0661	0.0656	0.0653	0.0650	0.0646	0.0644	0.0643	0.0643	0.0642
18	0.0655	0.0644	0.0634	0.0628	0.0623	0.0619	0.0616	0.0613	0.0611	0.0610	0.0609	0.0609
19	0.0624	0.0614	0.0604	0.0598	0.0593	0.0590	0.0587	0.0584	0.0582	0.0581	0.0580	0.0580
20	0.0597	0.0587	0.0577	0.0571	0.0566	0.0563	0.0560	0.0557	0.0555	0.0554	0.0553	0.0553
21	0.0573	0.0562	0.0553	0.0547	0.0542	0.0539	0.0536	0.0533	0.0531	0.0530	0.0529	0.0529
22	0.0550	0.0540	0.0530	0.0525	0.0520	0.0517	0.0514	0.0511	0.0509	0.0508	0.0508	0.0507
23	0.0530	0.0519	0.0510	0.0505	0.0500	0.0497	0.0494	0.0491	0.0489	0.0488	0.0488	0.0487
24	0.0511	0.0501	0.0492	0.0486	0.0481	0.0478	0.0476	0.0473	0.0471	0.0470	0.0469	0.0469
25	0.0493	0.0484	0.0474	0.0469	0.0464	0.0461	0.0459	0.0456	0.0454	0.0453	0.0453	0.0452
26	0.0477	0.0468	0.0459	0.0453	0.0449	0.0446	0.0443	0.0440	0.0438	0.0438	0.0437	0.0437
27	0.0463	0.0453	0.0444	0.0439	0.0434	0.0431	0.0429	0.0426	0.0424	0.0423	0.0423	0.0422
28	0.0449	0.0439	0.0430	0.0425	0.0421	0.0418	0.0415	0.0412	0.0411			

30	0.0424	0.0414	0.0406	0.0401	0.0396	0.0393	0.0391	0.0388	0.0387	0.0386	0.0385	0.0385
31	0.0412	0.0403	0.0394	0.0390	0.0385	0.0383	0.0380	0.0377	0.0376	0.0375	0.0375	0.0374
32	0.0402	0.0392	0.0384	0.0379	0.0375	0.0372	0.0370	0.0367	0.0366	0.0365	0.0364	0.0364
33	0.0392	0.0382	0.0374	0.0369	0.0365	0.0363	0.0360	0.0358	0.0356	0.0355	0.0355	0.0355
34	0.0382	0.0373	0.0365	0.0360	0.0356	0.0353	0.0351	0.0349	0.0347	0.0346	0.0346	0.0346
35	0.0373	0.0364	0.0356	0.0352	0.0347	0.0345	0.0342	0.0340	0.0338	0.0338	0.0337	0.0337
36	0.0365	0.0356	0.0348	0.0343	0.0339	0.0337	0.0334	0.0332	0.0330	0.0330	0.0329	0.0329
37	0.0356	0.0348	0.0340	0.0336	0.0331	0.0329	0.0327	0.0324	0.0323	0.0322	0.0322	0.0322
38	0.0349	0.0340	0.0332	0.0328	0.0324	0.0322	0.0319	0.0317	0.0316	0.0315	0.0315	0.0314
39	0.0342	0.0333	0.0325	0.0321	0.0317	0.0315	0.0313	0.0310	0.0309	0.0308	0.0308	0.0308
40	0.0335	0.0326	0.0319	0.0314	0.0311	0.0308	0.0306	0.0304	0.0302	0.0302	0.0301	0.0301
41	0.0328	0.0320	0.0312	0.0308	0.0304	0.0302	0.0300	0.0297	0.0296	0.0295	0.0295	0.0295
42	0.0322	0.0314	0.0306	0.0302	0.0298	0.0296	0.0294	0.0292	0.0290	0.0290	0.0289	0.0289
43	0.0316	0.0308	0.0300	0.0296	0.0292	0.0290	0.0288	0.0286	0.0285	0.0284	0.0284	0.0283
44	0.0310	0.0302	0.0295	0.0291	0.0287	0.0285	0.0283	0.0280	0.0279	0.0279	0.0278	0.0278
45	0.0304	0.0296	0.0289	0.0285	0.0282	0.0279	0.0277	0.0275	0.0274	0.0273	0.0273	0.0273
46	0.0299	0.0291	0.0284	0.0280	0.0277	0.0274	0.0272	0.0270	0.0269	0.0269	0.0268	0.0268
47	0.0294	0.0286	0.0279	0.0275	0.0272	0.0270	0.0268	0.0266	0.0264	0.0264	0.0263	0.0263
48	0.0289	0.0281	0.0274	0.0271	0.0267	0.0265	0.0263	0.0261	0.0260	0.0259	0.0259	0.0259
49	0.0284	0.0277	0.0270	0.0266	0.0263	0.0261	0.0259	0.0257	0.0256	0.0255	0.0255	0.0255
50	0.0279	0.0272	0.0265	0.0262	0.0258	0.0256	0.0254	0.0253	0.0251	0.0251	0.0251	0.0250
51	0.0275	0.0268	0.0261	0.0258	0.0254	0.0252	0.0250	0.0248	0.0247	0.0247	0.0247	0.0246
52	0.0271	0.0264	0.0257	0.0254	0.0250	0.0248	0.0246	0.0245	0.0243	0.0243	0.0243	0.0243
53	0.0267	0.0260	0.0253	0.0250	0.0246	0.0244	0.0243	0.0241	0.0240	0.0239	0.0239	0.0239
54	0.0263	0.0256	0.0249	0.0246	0.0243	0.0241	0.0239	0.0237	0.0236	0.0236	0.0235	0.0235
55	0.0259	0.0252	0.0246	0.0242	0.0239	0.0237	0.0235	0.0234	0.0233	0.0232	0.0232	0.0232
56	0.0255	0.0248	0.0242	0.0239	0.0236	0.0234	0.0232	0.0230	0.0229	0.0229	0.0229	0.0229
57	0.0251	0.0245	0.0239	0.0235	0.0232	0.0230	0.0229	0.0227	0.0226	0.0226	0.0225	0.0225
58	0.0248	0.0241	0.0235	0.0232	0.0229	0.0227	0.0226	0.0224	0.0223	0.0223	0.0222	0.0222
59	0.0245	0.0238	0.0232	0.0229	0.0226	0.0224	0.0223	0.0221	0.0220	0.0220	0.0219	0.0219
60	0.0241	0.0235	0.0229	0.0226	0.0223	0.0221	0.0220	0.0218	0.0217	0.0217	0.0216	0.0216

DEPRECIATION ANNUITIES, DECIMALLY EXPRESSED

DOUBLE-RATE-DECLINING-BALANCE METHOD   CRITICAL RATE OF RETURN   5.000 PERCENT

AVERAGE LIFE (YEARS)	TYPE OF RETIREMENT DISPERSION							
	L0	L05	L1	L15	L2	L3	L4	L5
1	1.1542	1.1055	0.9517	0.8133	0.5899	1.8274	0.0794	0.0817
2	0.5239	0.5215	0.5189	0.5183	0.5178	0.5128	0.5063	0.5080
3	0.3516	0.3499	0.3482	0.3471	0.3459	0.3445	0.3425	0.3421
4	0.2658	0.2643	0.2628	0.2618	0.2608	0.2594	0.2584	0.2578
5	0.2144	0.2130	0.2116	0.2106	0.2097	0.2084	0.2077	0.2073
6	0.1802	0.1788	0.1775	0.1765	0.1756	0.1745	0.1738	0.1735
7	0.1557	0.1544	0.1531	0.1522	0.1513	0.1503	0.1497	0.1494
8	0.1374	0.1361	0.1349	0.1340	0.1331	0.1322	0.1316	0.1313
9	0.1231	0.1218	0.1207	0.1198	0.1190	0.1180	0.1175	0.1173
10	0.1117	0.1104	0.1093	0.1084	0.1077	0.1068	0.1062	0.1060
11	0.1023	0.1011	0.1000	0.0992	0.0984	0.0975	0.0970	0.0968
12	0.0945	0.0933	0.0922	0.0914	0.0907	0.0899	0.0894	0.0891
13	0.0879	0.0867	0.0857	0.0849	0.0842	0.0833	0.0829	0.0827
14	0.0822	0.0811	0.0800	0.0793	0.0786	0.0778	0.0773	0.0771
15	0.0773	0.0762	0.0752	0.0744	0.0737	0.0729	0.0725	0.0723
16	0.0730	0.0719	0.0709	0.0701	0.0695	0.0687	0.0683	0.0681
17	0.0692	0.0681	0.0671	0.0664	0.0657	0.0650	0.0646	0.0644
18	0.0658	0.0647	0.0638	0.0630	0.0624	0.0617	0.0613	0.0611
19	0.0627	0.0617	0.0608	0.0600	0.0594	0.0587	0.0583	0.0581
20	0.0600	0.0590	0.0580	0.0573	0.0567	0.0560	0.0556	0.0555
21	0.0575	0.0565	0.0556	0.0549	0.0543	0.0536	0.0532	0.0531
22	0.0552	0.0543	0.0534	0.0527	0.0521	0.0514	0.0510	0.0509
23	0.0532	0.0522	0.0513	0.0507	0.0501	0.0494	0.0490	0.0489
24	0.0513	0.0503	0.0494	0.0488	0.0482	0.0476	0.0472	0.0471
25	0.0495	0.0486	0.0477	0.0471	0.0465	0.0459	0.0455	0.0454
26	0.0479	0.0470	0.0461	0.0455	0.0449	0.0443	0.0440	0.0438
27	0.0464	0.0455	0.0446	0.0440	0.0435	0.0429	0.0425	0.0424
28	0.0450	0.0441	0.0433	0.0427	0.0421	0.0415	0.0412	0.0410

30	0.0424	0.0416	0.0408	0.0402	0.0397	0.0391	0.0388	0.0386
31	0.0413	0.0404	0.0397	0.0391	0.0346	0.0380	0.0377	0.0376
32	0.0402	0.0394	0.0386	0.0380	0.0375	0.0370	0.0367	0.0365
33	0.0392	0.0384	0.0376	0.0371	0.0366	0.0360	0.0357	0.0356
34	0.0382	0.0374	0.0367	0.0361	0.0356	0.0351	0.0348	0.0347
35	0.0373	0.0365	0.0358	0.0353	0.0348	0.0342	0.0340	0.0338
36	0.0364	0.0357	0.0350	0.0344	0.0340	0.0334	0.0332	0.0330
37	0.0356	0.0349	0.0342	0.0336	0.0332	0.0327	0.0324	0.0323
38	0.0348	0.0341	0.0334	0.0329	0.0324	0.0319	0.0317	0.0315
39	0.0341	0.0334	0.0327	0.0322	0.0317	0.0312	0.0310	0.0309
40	0.0334	0.0327	0.0320	0.0315	0.0311	0.0306	0.0303	0.0302
41	0.0327	0.0320	0.0314	0.0309	0.0304	0.0300	0.0297	0.0296
42	0.0321	0.0314	0.0307	0.0303	0.0298	0.0294	0.0291	0.0290
43	0.0314	0.0308	0.0301	0.0297	0.0293	0.0288	0.0286	0.0284
44	0.0309	0.0302	0.0296	0.0291	0.0287	0.0283	0.0280	0.0279
45	0.0303	0.0296	0.0290	0.0286	0.0282	0.0277	0.0275	0.0274
46	0.0298	0.0291	0.0285	0.0281	0.0277	0.0272	0.0270	0.0269
47	0.0292	0.0286	0.0280	0.0276	0.0272	0.0268	0.0265	0.0264
48	0.0287	0.0281	0.0275	0.0271	0.0267	0.0263	0.0261	0.0260
49	0.0282	0.0276	0.0271	0.0266	0.0263	0.0259	0.0256	0.0255
50	0.0278	0.0272	0.0266	0.0262	0.0258	0.0254	0.0252	0.0251
51	0.0273	0.0267	0.0262	0.0258	0.0254	0.0250	0.0248	0.0247
52	0.0269	0.0263	0.0258	0.0254	0.0250	0.0246	0.0244	0.0243
53	0.0265	0.0259	0.0254	0.0250	0.0246	0.0243	0.0240	0.0240
54	0.0261	0.0255	0.0250	0.0246	0.0243	0.0239	0.0237	0.0236
55	0.0257	0.0251	0.0246	0.0242	0.0239	0.0235	0.0233	0.0233
56	0.0253	0.0248	0.0243	0.0239	0.0236	0.0232	0.0230	0.0229
57	0.0250	0.0244	0.0239	0.0236	0.0232	0.0229	0.0227	0.0226
58	0.0246	0.0241	0.0236	0.0232	0.0229	0.0225	0.0224	0.0223
59	0.0243	0.0237	0.0233	0.0229	0.0226	0.0222	0.0221	0.0220
60	0.0239	0.0234	0.0229	0.0226	0.0223	0.0219	0.0218	0.0217

DEPRECIATION ANNUITIES, DECIMALLY EXPRESSED

DOUBLE-RATE-DECLINING-BALANCE METHOD   CRITICAL RATE OF RETURN 5.000 PERCENT

AVERAGE LIFE (YEARS)				TYPE OF RETIREMENT DISPERSION				
	R05	R1	R15	R2	R25	R3	R4	R5
1	0.8155	1.1749	0.1823	0.0862	0.0842	0.0853	0.0858	0.0875
2	0.5156	0.5196	0.5097	0.5119	0.5136	0.5157	0.4807	0.4811
3	0.3480	0.3474	0.3454	0.3450	0.3445	0.3417	0.3433	0.3444
4	0.2630	0.2620	0.2608	0.2601	0.2596	0.2589	0.2575	0.2580
5	0.2120	0.2108	0.2099	0.2092	0.2086	0.2081	0.2076	0.2071
6	0.1779	0.1768	0.1760	0.1752	0.1747	0.1742	0.1737	0.1734
7	0.1536	0.1525	0.1517	0.1510	0.1505	0.1501	0.1496	0.1493
8	0.1354	0.1343	0.1335	0.1328	0.1324	0.1320	0.1315	0.1312
9	0.1212	0.1201	0.1194	0.1187	0.1183	0.1179	0.1174	0.1172
10	0.1099	0.1088	0.1081	0.1074	0.1070	0.1066	0.1062	0.1059
11	0.1006	0.0995	0.0988	0.0982	0.0978	0.0974	0.0970	0.0968
12	0.0928	0.0918	0.0911	0.0905	0.0901	0.0897	0.0893	0.0891
13	0.0863	0.0853	0.0846	0.0840	0.0836	0.0832	0.0828	0.0826
14	0.0807	0.0797	0.0790	0.0784	0.0780	0.0777	0.0773	0.0771
15	0.0758	0.0748	0.0742	0.0736	0.0732	0.0728	0.0725	0.0723
16	0.0715	0.0706	0.0699	0.0694	0.0690	0.0686	0.0682	0.0680
17	0.0678	0.0668	0.0662	0.0656	0.0652	0.0649	0.0645	0.0643
18	0.0644	0.0635	0.0629	0.0623	0.0619	0.0616	0.0612	0.0610
19	0.0614	0.0605	0.0599	0.0593	0.0590	0.0586	0.0583	0.0581
20	0.0587	0.0578	0.0572	0.0567	0.0563	0.0560	0.0556	0.0554
21	0.0563	0.0554	0.0548	0.0542	0.0539	0.0535	0.0532	0.0530
22	0.0540	0.0532	0.0526	0.0520	0.0517	0.0514	0.0510	0.0508
23	0.0520	0.0512	0.0506	0.0500	0.0497	0.0494	0.0490	0.0488
24	0.0501	0.0493	0.0487	0.0482	0.0478	0.0475	0.0472	0.0470
25	0.0484	0.0476	0.0470	0.0465	0.0461	0.0458	0.0455	0.0453
26	0.0468	0.0460	0.0454	0.0449	0.0446	0.0443	0.0439	0.0438
27	0.0453	0.0445	0.0440	0.0435	0.0431	0.0428	0.0425	0.0423
28	0.0440	0.0432	0.0426	0.0421	0.0418	0.0415	0.0412	0.0410

30	0.0415	0.0407	0.0402	0.0397	0.0394	0.0391	0.0388	0.0386
31	0.0404	0.0396	0.0391	0.0386	0.0363	0.0380	0.0377	0.0375
32	0.0393	0.0386	0.0380	0.0376	0.0372	0.0370	0.0367	0.0365
33	0.0383	0.0376	0.0371	0.0366	0.0363	0.0360	0.0357	0.0355
34	0.0374	0.0367	0.0361	0.0357	0.0354	0.0351	0.0348	0.0346
35	0.0365	0.0356	0.0353	0.0348	0.0345	0.0342	0.0339	0.0338
36	0.0357	0.0350	0.0345	0.0340	0.0337	0.0334	0.0331	0.0330
37	0.0349	0.0342	0.0337	0.0332	0.0329	0.0327	0.0324	0.0322
38	0.0341	0.0334	0.0329	0.0325	0.0322	0.0319	0.0317	0.0315
39	0.0334	0.0327	0.0322	0.0318	0.0315	0.0312	0.0310	0.0308
40	0.0327	0.0320	0.0316	0.0311	0.0309	0.0306	0.0303	0.0302
41	0.0321	0.0314	0.0309	0.0305	0.0302	0.0300	0.0297	0.0296
42	0.0314	0.0308	0.0303	0.0299	0.0296	0.0294	0.0291	0.0290
43	0.0308	0.0302	0.0298	0.0293	0.0291	0.0288	0.0285	0.0284
44	0.0303	0.0296	0.0292	0.0288	0.0285	0.0283	0.0280	0.0279
45	0.0297	0.0291	0.0287	0.0283	0.0280	0.0277	0.0275	0.0274
46	0.0292	0.0286	0.0282	0.0278	0.0275	0.0272	0.0270	0.0269
47	0.0287	0.0281	0.0277	0.0273	0.0270	0.0268	0.0265	0.0264
48	0.0282	0.0276	0.0272	0.0268	0.0266	0.0263	0.0261	0.0260
49	0.0278	0.0272	0.0268	0.0264	0.0261	0.0259	0.0256	0.0255
50	0.0273	0.0267	0.0263	0.0259	0.0257	0.0254	0.0252	0.0251
51	0.0269	0.0263	0.0259	0.0255	0.0253	0.0250	0.0248	0.0247
52	0.0265	0.0259	0.0255	0.0251	0.0249	0.0247	0.0244	0.0243
53	0.0261	0.0255	0.0251	0.0247	0.0245	0.0243	0.0241	0.0239
54	0.0257	0.0251	0.0247	0.0244	0.0241	0.0239	0.0237	0.0236
55	0.0253	0.0248	0.0244	0.0240	0.0238	0.0236	0.0233	0.0232
56	0.0249	0.0244	0.0240	0.0237	0.0234	0.0232	0.0230	0.0229
57	0.0246	0.0241	0.0237	0.0233	0.0231	0.0229	0.0227	0.0226
58	0.0242	0.0237	0.0234	0.0230	0.0228	0.0226	0.0224	0.0223
59	0.0239	0.0234	0.0230	0.0227	0.0225	0.0223	0.0221	0.0220
60	0.0236	0.0231	0.0227	0.0224	0.0222	0.0220	0.0218	0.0217

DEPRECIATION ANNUITIES, DECIMALLY EXPRESSED

SYD METHOD   CRITICAL RATE OF RETURN 6.000 PERCENT

AVERAGE LIFE (YEARS)	SC	SON	S0	S05	S1	S15	S2	S3	S4	S5	S6	SQ
							TYPE OF RETIREMENT DISPERSION					
1	1.0029	0.9673	0.9348	0.9092	0.8890	0.8699	0.8606	0.8550	0.8759	0.9079	0.9373	1.0000
2	0.5091	0.5049	0.5009	0.5000	0.4996	0.5007	0.5022	0.5047	0.5052	0.4628	0.4742	0.5049
3	0.3445	0.3430	0.3416	0.3413	0.3411	0.3411	0.3411	0.3409	0.3395	0.3400	0.3209	0.3398
4	0.2622	0.2612	0.2603	0.2599	0.2595	0.2592	0.2589	0.2584	0.2579	0.2573	0.2574	0.2573
5	0.2127	0.2119	0.2111	0.2107	0.2102	0.2099	0.2095	0.2088	0.2084	0.2081	0.2079	0.2078
6	0.1797	0.1790	0.1782	0.1778	0.1773	0.1769	0.1765	0.1759	0.1754	0.1751	0.1748	0.1747
7	0.1561	0.1554	0.1547	0.1542	0.1537	0.1533	0.1529	0.1523	0.1518	0.1515	0.1511	0.1512
8	0.1384	0.1377	0.1370	0.1365	0.1360	0.1356	0.1352	0.1346	0.1341	0.1338	0.1336	0.1335
9	0.1245	0.1239	0.1232	0.1227	0.1222	0.1218	0.1214	0.1208	0.1203	0.1200	0.1198	0.1197
10	0.1135	0.1128	0.1121	0.1117	0.1112	0.1108	0.1104	0.1098	0.1093	0.1090	0.1088	0.1087
11	0.1044	0.1037	0.1031	0.1026	0.1021	0.1017	0.1013	0.1008	0.1003	0.1000	0.0998	0.0997
12	0.0968	0.0962	0.0955	0.0951	0.0946	0.0942	0.0938	0.0932	0.0927	0.0924	0.0923	0.0922
13	0.0904	0.0897	0.0891	0.0886	0.0882	0.0878	0.0874	0.0868	0.0864	0.0861	0.0859	0.0858
14	0.0848	0.0842	0.0836	0.0831	0.0827	0.0823	0.0819	0.0814	0.0809	0.0806	0.0805	0.0803
15	0.0800	0.0794	0.0788	0.0784	0.0779	0.0775	0.0772	0.0766	0.0762	0.0759	0.0757	0.0756
16	0.0758	0.0752	0.0746	0.0742	0.0737	0.0734	0.0730	0.0725	0.0720	0.0717	0.0716	0.0715
17	0.0721	0.0715	0.0709	0.0704	0.0700	0.0697	0.0693	0.0688	0.0683	0.0681	0.0679	0.0678
18	0.0687	0.0682	0.0676	0.0671	0.0667	0.0664	0.0660	0.0655	0.0651	0.0648	0.0647	0.0646
19	0.0657	0.0652	0.0646	0.0642	0.0638	0.0634	0.0631	0.0626	0.0621	0.0619	0.0617	0.0616
20	0.0630	0.0625	0.0619	0.0615	0.0611	0.0607	0.0604	0.0599	0.0595	0.0593	0.0591	0.0590
21	0.0606	0.0600	0.0595	0.0591	0.0587	0.0583	0.0580	0.0575	0.0571	0.0569	0.0567	0.0566
22	0.0583	0.0578	0.0572	0.0568	0.0564	0.0561	0.0558	0.0553	0.0549	0.0547	0.0546	0.0545
23	0.0563	0.0557	0.0552	0.0548	0.0544	0.0541	0.0538	0.0533	0.0529	0.0527	0.0526	0.0525
24	0.0544	0.0538	0.0533	0.0529	0.0526	0.0523	0.0519	0.0515	0.0511	0.0509	0.0508	0.0507
25	0.0526	0.0521	0.0516	0.0512	0.0508	0.0505	0.0502	0.0498	0.0494	0.0492	0.0491	0.0490
26	0.0510	0.0505	0.0500	0.0496	0.0492	0.0490	0.0487	0.0482	0.0479	0.0477	0.0475	0.0475
27	0.0494	0.0490	0.0485	0.0481	0.0478	0.0475	0.0472	0.0468	0.0464	0.0462	0.0461	0.0460

29	0.0467	0.0462	0.0458	0.0454	0.0451	0.0448	0.0446	0.0442	0.0438	0.0436	0.0435	0.0434
30	0.0455	0.0450	0.0445	0.0442	0.0439	0.0436	0.0434	0.0430	0.0426	0.0425	0.0423	−0.0423
31	0.0443	0.0438	0.0434	0.0431	0.0428	0.0425	0.0422	0.0419	0.0415	0.0414	0.0413	0.0412
32	0.0432	0.0428	0.0423	0.0420	0.0417	0.0414	0.0412	0.0408	0.0405	0.0403	0.0402	0.0402
33	0.0422	0.0417	0.0413	0.0410	0.0407	0.0404	0.0402	0.0398	0.0395	0.0393	0.0393	0.0392
34	0.0412	0.0407	0.0403	0.0400	0.0397	0.0395	0.0392	0.0389	0.0386	0.0384	0.0383	0.0383
35	0.0402	0.0398	0.0394	0.0391	0.0388	0.0386	0.0384	0.0380	0.0377	0.0376	0.0375	0.0374
36	0.0393	0.0389	0.0385	0.0383	0.0380	0.0377	0.0375	0.0372	0.0369	0.0367	0.0367	0.0366
37	0.0385	0.0381	0.0377	0.0374	0.0372	0.0369	0.0367	0.0364	0.0361	0.0360	0.0359	0.0358
38	0.0377	0.0373	0.0369	0.0367	0.0364	0.0362	0.0359	0.0356	0.0354	0.0352	0.0351	0.0351
39	0.0369	0.0365	0.0362	0.0359	0.0356	0.0354	0.0352	0.0349	0.0347	0.0345	0.0344	0.0344
40	0.0362	0.0358	0.0355	0.0352	0.0349	0.0347	0.0345	0.0342	0.0340	0.0338	0.0338	0.0337
41	0.0355	0.0351	0.0348	0.0345	0.0343	0.0341	0.0339	0.0336	0.0333	0.0332	0.0331	0.0331
42	0.0348	0.0345	0.0341	0.0339	0.0336	0.0334	0.0332	0.0329	0.0327	0.0326	0.0325	0.0325
43	0.0342	0.0338	0.0335	0.0332	0.0330	0.0328	0.0326	0.0323	0.0321	0.0320	0.0319	0.0319
44	0.0336	0.0332	0.0329	0.0326	0.0324	0.0322	0.0320	0.0318	0.0316	0.0314	0.0314	0.0313
45	0.0330	0.0326	0.0323	0.0321	0.0318	0.0317	0.0315	0.0312	0.0310	0.0309	0.0308	0.0308
46	0.0324	0.0321	0.0317	0.0315	0.0313	0.0311	0.0309	0.0307	0.0305	0.0304	0.0303	0.0303
47	0.0318	0.0315	0.0312	0.0310	0.0308	0.0306	0.0304	0.0302	0.0300	0.0299	0.0298	0.0298
48	0.0313	0.0310	0.0307	0.0305	0.0303	0.0301	0.0299	0.0297	0.0295	0.0294	0.0293	0.0293
49	0.0308	0.0305	0.0302	0.0300	0.0298	0.0296	0.0295	0.0292	0.0290	0.0289	0.0289	0.0288
50	0.0303	0.0300	0.0297	0.0295	0.0293	0.0292	0.0290	0.0288	0.0286	0.0285	0.0284	0.0284
51	0.0298	0.0295	0.0292	0.0291	0.0289	0.0287	0.0285	0.0283	0.0282	0.0281	0.0280	0.0280
52	0.0294	0.0291	0.0288	0.0286	0.0284	0.0283	0.0281	0.0279	0.0277	0.0276	0.0276	0.0276
53	0.0289	0.0286	0.0284	0.0282	0.0280	0.0278	0.0277	0.0275	0.0273	0.0272	0.0272	0.0272
54	0.0285	0.0282	0.0279	0.0278	0.0276	0.0274	0.0273	0.0271	0.0269	0.0269	0.0268	0.0268
55	0.0281	0.0278	0.0275	0.0274	0.0272	0.0270	0.0269	0.0267	0.0266	0.0265	0.0264	0.0264
56	0.0277	0.0274	0.0271	0.0270	0.0268	0.0267	0.0265	0.0263	0.0262	0.0261	0.0261	0.0260
57	0.0273	0.0270	0.0268	0.0266	0.0264	0.0263	0.0262	0.0260	0.0258	0.0258	0.0257	0.0257
58	0.0269	0.0266	0.0264	0.0262	0.0261	0.0259	0.0258	0.0256	0.0255	0.0254	0.0254	0.0254
59	0.0265	0.0263	0.0260	0.0259	0.0257	0.0256	0.0255	0.0253	0.0252	0.0251	0.0251	0.0250
60	0.0262	0.0259	0.0257	0.0255	0.0254	0.0253	0.0251	0.0250	0.0248	0.0248	0.0247	0.0247

DEPRECIATION ANNUITIES, DECIMALLY EXPRESSED

SYD METHOD   CRITICAL RATE OF RETURN 6.000 PERCENT

| | | | | TYPE OF RETIREMENT DISPERSION | | | |
AVERAGE LIFE (YEARS)	L0	L05	L1	L15	L2	L3	L4	L5
1	1.0128	1.0061	0.9857	0.9717	0.9593	0.9557	0.8351	0.8593
2	0.5116	0.5100	0.5084	0.5083	0.5081	0.5042	0.4985	0.5005
3	0.3462	0.3452	0.3441	0.3435	0.3427	0.3418	0.3396	0.3392
4	0.2637	0.2627	0.2618	0.2611	0.2605	0.2593	0.2582	0.2574
5	0.2141	0.2132	0.2123	0.2117	0.2110	0.2098	0.2088	0.2082
6	0.1810	0.1802	0.1793	0.1786	0.1780	0.1768	0.1758	0.1753
7	0.1574	0.1565	0.1556	0.1550	0.1544	0.1532	0.1522	0.1517
8	0.1396	0.1387	0.1379	0.1373	0.1366	0.1355	0.1345	0.1340
9	0.1257	0.1249	0.1241	0.1234	0.1228	0.1217	0.1207	0.1202
10	0.1146	0.1138	0.1130	0.1124	0.1118	0.1107	0.1097	0.1092
11	0.1054	0.1047	0.1039	0.1033	0.1027	0.1016	0.1007	0.1002
12	0.0978	0.0970	0.0963	0.0957	0.0951	0.0941	0.0932	0.0927
13	0.0913	0.0906	0.0898	0.0893	0.0887	0.0877	0.0868	0.0863
14	0.0857	0.0850	0.0843	0.0837	0.0832	0.0822	0.0813	0.0808
15	0.0809	0.0802	0.0795	0.0789	0.0784	0.0774	0.0765	0.0761
16	0.0766	0.0759	0.0752	0.0747	0.0742	0.0732	0.0724	0.0719
17	0.0728	0.0722	0.0715	0.0710	0.0704	0.0695	0.0687	0.0683
18	0.0694	0.0688	0.0681	0.0676	0.0671	0.0662	0.0654	0.0650
19	0.0664	0.0658	0.0651	0.0647	0.0641	0.0633	0.0625	0.0621
20	0.0636	0.0630	0.0624	0.0619	0.0615	0.0606	0.0598	0.0594
21	0.0611	0.0606	0.0600	0.0595	0.0590	0.0582	0.0574	0.0571
22	0.0589	0.0583	0.0577	0.0573	0.0568	0.0560	0.0553	0.0549
23	0.0568	0.0562	0.0557	0.0552	0.0548	0.0539	0.0533	0.0529
24	0.0548	0.0543	0.0538	0.0533	0.0529	0.0521	0.0514	0.0511
25	0.0531	0.0525	0.0520	0.0516	0.0511	0.0504	0.0497	0.0494
26	0.0514	0.0509	0.0504	0.0500	0.0495	0.0488	0.0482	0.0478
27	0.0498	0.0494	0.0489	0.0484	0.0480	0.0473	0.0467	0.0464

29	0.0471	0.0466	0.0461	0.0457	0.0453	0.0447	0.0441	0.0441	0.0438
30	0.0458	0.0453	0.0449	0.0445	0.0441	0.0435	0.0429	0.0429	0.0426
31	0.0446	0.0442	0.0437	0.0433	0.0430	0.0423	0.0418	0.0418	0.0415
32	0.0435	0.0430	0.0426	0.0423	0.0419	0.0413	0.0407	0.0407	0.0405
33	0.0424	0.0420	0.0416	0.0412	0.0409	0.0403	0.0398	0.0398	0.0395
34	0.0414	0.0410	0.0406	0.0403	0.0399	0.0393	0.0388	0.0388	0.0386
35	0.0405	0.0401	0.0397	0.0393	0.0390	0.0384	0.0379	0.0379	0.0377
36	0.0396	0.0392	0.0388	0.0385	0.0381	0.0376	0.0371	0.0371	0.0369
37	0.0387	0.0383	0.0379	0.0376	0.0373	0.0368	0.0363	0.0363	0.0361
38	0.0379	0.0375	0.0371	0.0368	0.0365	0.0360	0.0356	0.0356	0.0353
39	0.0371	0.0367	0.0364	0.0361	0.0358	0.0353	0.0349	0.0349	0.0346
40	0.0363	0.0360	0.0357	0.0354	0.0351	0.0346	0.0342	0.0342	0.0339
41	0.0356	0.0353	0.0350	0.0347	0.0344	0.0339	0.0335	0.0335	0.0333
42	0.0349	0.0346	0.0343	0.0340	0.0337	0.0333	0.0329	0.0329	0.0327
43	0.0343	0.0340	0.0337	0.0334	0.0331	0.0327	0.0323	0.0323	0.0321
44	0.0337	0.0334	0.0330	0.0328	0.0325	0.0321	0.0317	0.0317	0.0315
45	0.0331	0.0328	0.0325	0.0322	0.0319	0.0315	0.0312	0.0312	0.0310
46	0.0325	0.0322	0.0319	0.0316	0.0314	0.0310	0.0306	0.0306	0.0305
47	0.0319	0.0316	0.0314	0.0311	0.0309	0.0305	0.0301	0.0301	0.0300
48	0.0314	0.0311	0.0308	0.0306	0.0304	0.0300	0.0296	0.0296	0.0295
49	0.0309	0.0306	0.0303	0.0301	0.0299	0.0295	0.0292	0.0292	0.0290
50	0.0304	0.0301	0.0298	0.0296	0.0294	0.0290	0.0287	0.0287	0.0286
51	0.0299	0.0296	0.0294	0.0291	0.0289	0.0286	0.0283	0.0283	0.0281
52	0.0294	0.0292	0.0289	0.0287	0.0285	0.0281	0.0279	0.0279	0.0277
53	0.0290	0.0287	0.0285	0.0283	0.0281	0.0277	0.0275	0.0275	0.0273
54	0.0285	0.0283	0.0280	0.0278	0.0276	0.0273	0.0271	0.0271	0.0269
55	0.0281	0.0279	0.0276	0.0274	0.0272	0.0269	0.0267	0.0267	0.0265
56	0.0277	0.0275	0.0272	0.0270	0.0269	0.0265	0.0263	0.0263	0.0262
57	0.0273	0.0271	0.0269	0.0267	0.0265	0.0262	0.0259	0.0259	0.0258
58	0.0269	0.0267	0.0265	0.0263	0.0261	0.0258	0.0256	0.0256	0.0255
59	0.0265	0.0263	0.0261	0.0259	0.0258	0.0255	0.0253	0.0253	0.0251
60	0.0262	0.0260	0.0258	0.0256	0.0254	0.0251	0.0249	0.0249	0.0248

DEPRECIATION ANNUITIES. DECIMALLY EXPRESSED

SYD METHOD   CRITICAL RATE OF RETURN 6.000 PERCENT

| | | | | | TYPE OF RETIREMENT DISPERSION | | | |
AVERAGE LIFE (YEARS)	R05	R1	R15	R2	R25	R3	R4	R5
1	0.9604	1.0054	0.8946	0.9018	0.8818	0.8945	0.9012	0.9191
2	0.5043	0.5083	0.4999	0.5026	0.5045	0.5066	0.4735	0.4743
3	0.3431	0.3431	0.3414	0.3415	0.3413	0.3379	0.3406	0.3416
4	0.2612	0.2606	0.2598	0.2594	0.2590	0.2583	0.2565	0.2578
5	0.2119	0.2111	0.2105	0.2099	0.2095	0.2091	0.2085	0.2077
6	0.1789	0.1781	0.1775	0.1769	0.1765	0.1760	0.1753	0.1751
7	0.1553	0.1545	0.1539	0.1533	0.1529	0.1525	0.1519	0.1515
8	0.1376	0.1368	0.1362	0.1357	0.1352	0.1348	0.1342	0.1338
9	0.1238	0.1230	0.1224	0.1219	0.1215	0.1210	0.1205	0.1201
10	0.1127	0.1120	0.1114	0.1108	0.1104	0.1100	0.1094	0.1090
11	0.1037	0.1029	0.1024	0.1018	0.1014	0.1010	0.1004	0.1000
12	0.0961	0.0953	0.0948	0.0943	0.0939	0.0934	0.0929	0.0925
13	0.0897	0.0889	0.0884	0.0879	0.0875	0.0871	0.0865	0.0861
14	0.0841	0.0834	0.0829	0.0824	0.0820	0.0816	0.0811	0.0807
15	0.0793	0.0786	0.0781	0.0776	0.0772	0.0768	0.0763	0.0759
16	0.0751	0.0744	0.0739	0.0734	0.0731	0.0727	0.0722	0.0718
17	0.0714	0.0707	0.0702	0.0698	0.0694	0.0690	0.0685	0.0681
18	0.0681	0.0674	0.0669	0.0665	0.0661	0.0657	0.0652	0.0649
19	0.0651	0.0645	0.0640	0.0635	0.0631	0.0628	0.0623	0.0619
20	0.0624	0.0618	0.0613	0.0608	0.0605	0.0601	0.0597	0.0593
21	0.0600	0.0593	0.0589	0.0584	0.0581	0.0577	0.0573	0.0569
22	0.0577	0.0571	0.0567	0.0562	0.0559	0.0555	0.0551	0.0548
23	0.0557	0.0551	0.0547	0.0542	0.0539	0.0535	0.0531	0.0528
24	0.0538	0.0532	0.0528	0.0524	0.0520	0.0517	0.0513	0.0509
25	0.0520	0.0515	0.0511	0.0507	0.0503	0.0500	0.0496	0.0493
26	0.0504	0.0499	0.0495	0.0491	0.0488	0.0484	0.0480	0.0477
27	0.0489	0.0484	0.0480	0.0476	0.0473	0.0470	0.0466	0.0463
28	0.0475	0.0470	0.0466	0.0462	0.0459	0.0456	0.0452	0.0449

29	0.0462	0.0457	0.0453	0.0449	0.0446	0.0444	0.0440	0.0437
30	0.0450	0.0445	0.0441	0.0437	0.0435	0.0432	0.0428	0.0425
31	0.0438	0.0433	0.0430	0.0426	0.0423	0.0420	0.0417	0.0414
32	0.0427	0.0423	0.0419	0.0416	0.0413	0.0410	0.0406	0.0404
33	0.0417	0.0412	0.0409	0.0405	0.0403	0.0400	0.0397	0.0394
34	0.0407	0.0403	0.0399	0.0396	0.0393	0.0391	0.0387	0.0385
35	0.0398	0.0394	0.0390	0.0387	0.0385	0.0382	0.0379	0.0376
36	0.0389	0.0385	0.0382	0.0379	0.0376	0.0374	0.0370	0.0368
37	0.0381	0.0377	0.0374	0.0370	0.0368	0.0366	0.0362	0.0360
38	0.0373	0.0369	0.0366	0.0363	0.0360	0.0358	0.0355	0.0353
39	0.0365	0.0361	0.0358	0.0355	0.0353	0.0351	0.0348	0.0346
40	0.0358	0.0354	0.0351	0.0348	0.0346	0.0344	0.0341	0.0339
41	0.0351	0.0347	0.0345	0.0342	0.0340	0.0337	0.0335	0.0332
42	0.0345	0.0341	0.0338	0.0335	0.0333	0.0331	0.0328	0.0326
43	0.0338	0.0335	0.0332	0.0329	0.0327	0.0325	0.0322	0.0320
44	0.0332	0.0329	0.0326	0.0323	0.0321	0.0319	0.0317	0.0315
45	0.0326	0.0323	0.0320	0.0318	0.0316	0.0314	0.0311	0.0309
46	0.0321	0.0317	0.0315	0.0312	0.0310	0.0308	0.0306	0.0304
47	0.0315	0.0312	0.0310	0.0307	0.0305	0.0303	0.0301	0.0299
48	0.0310	0.0307	0.0305	0.0302	0.0300	0.0298	0.0296	0.0294
49	0.0305	0.0302	0.0300	0.0297	0.0296	0.0294	0.0291	0.0290
50	0.0300	0.0297	0.0295	0.0293	0.0291	0.0289	0.0287	0.0285
51	0.0295	0.0293	0.0290	0.0288	0.0286	0.0285	0.0282	0.0281
52	0.0291	0.0288	0.0286	0.0284	0.0282	0.0280	0.0278	0.0277
53	0.0286	0.0284	0.0282	0.0280	0.0278	0.0276	0.0274	0.0273
54	0.0282	0.0280	0.0278	0.0276	0.0274	0.0272	0.0270	0.0269
55	0.0278	0.0276	0.0274	0.0272	0.0270	0.0268	0.0266	0.0265
56	0.0274	0.0272	0.0270	0.0268	0.0266	0.0265	0.0263	0.0261
57	0.0270	0.0268	0.0266	0.0264	0.0263	0.0261	0.0259	0.0258
58	0.0266	0.0264	0.0262	0.0260	0.0259	0.0258	0.0256	0.0254
59	0.0263	0.0261	0.0259	0.0257	0.0256	0.0254	0.0252	0.0251
60	0.0259	0.0257	0.0255	0.0254	0.0252	0.0251	0.0249	0.0248

DEPRECIATION ANNUITIES, DECIMALLY EXPRESSED

DOUBLE-RATE-DECLINING-BALANCE METHOD   CRITICAL RATE OF RETURN 6.000 PERCENT

AVERAGE LIFE (YEARS)	SC	S0N	S0	S05	S1	S15	S2	S3	S4	S5	S6	SQ
							TYPE OF RETIREMENT DISPERSION					
1	1.0718	0.8665	0.6143	0.3244	0.1012	0.0989	0.0977	0.0969	0.0992	1.8170	1.8754	2.0000
2	0.5254	0.5199	0.5146	0.5130	0.5119	0.5126	0.5137	0.5157	0.5156	0.4718	0.4833	0.5146
3	0.3532	0.3506	0.3465	0.3477	0.3469	0.3465	0.3461	0.3455	0.3443	0.3445	0.3312	0.3442
4	0.2674	0.2655	0.2638	0.2629	0.2621	0.2615	0.2610	0.2603	0.2597	0.2593	0.2593	0.2592
5	-0.2159	0.2143	0.2127	0.2118	0.2110	0.2105	0.2099	0.2093	0.2089	0.2087	0.2085	-0.2085
6	-0.1816	0.1801	0.1786	0.1778	0.1770	0.1764	0.1759	0.1753	0.1749	0.1747	0.1746	0.1745
7	-0.1572	0.1557	0.1542	0.1534	0.1526	0.1521	0.1516	0.1511	0.1508	0.1506	0.1504	0.1504
8	-0.1388	0.1373	0.1360	0.1352	0.1344	0.1339	0.1335	0.1329	0.1326	0.1324	0.1324	0.1323
9	-0.1245	0.1231	0.1218	0.1210	0.1202	0.1198	0.1193	0.1188	0.1185	0.1184	0.1183	0.1182
10	-0.1131	0.1117	0.1104	0.1096	0.1089	0.1084	0.1080	0.1075	0.1072	0.1071	0.1070	0.1070
11	0.1037	0.1024	0.1011	0.1003	0.0996	0.0992	0.0988	0.0983	0.0980	0.0979	0.0978	0.0978
12	0.0959	0.0946	0.0933	0.0926	0.0919	0.0915	0.0911	0.0906	0.0903	0.0902	0.0901	0.0901
13	0.0893	0.0880	0.0868	0.0860	0.0854	0.0849	0.0845	0.0841	0.0839	0.0837	0.0837	0.0836
14	0.0837	0.0823	0.0811	0.0804	0.0798	0.0793	0.0790	0.0785	0.0783	0.0781	0.0781	0.0780
15	0.0787	0.0774	0.0762	0.0755	0.0749	0.0745	0.0741	0.0737	0.0735	0.0733	0.0733	0.0732
16	0.0744	0.0731	0.0720	0.0713	0.0706	0.0702	0.0699	0.0695	0.0692	0.0691	0.0690	0.0690
17	0.0706	0.0694	0.0682	0.0675	0.0669	0.0665	0.0661	0.0658	0.0655	0.0654	0.0653	0.0653
18	0.0672	0.0660	0.0648	0.0642	0.0636	0.0632	0.0628	0.0624	0.0622	0.0621	0.0620	0.0620
19	0.0642	0.0629	0.0618	0.0612	0.0606	0.0602	0.0598	0.0595	0.0592	0.0591	0.0591	0.0590
20	0.0614	0.0602	0.0591	0.0585	0.0579	0.0575	0.0572	0.0568	0.0566	0.0565	0.0564	0.0564
21	0.0589	0.0577	0.0566	0.0560	0.0554	0.0551	0.0547	0.0544	0.0542	0.0541	0.0540	0.0540
22	0.0567	0.0555	0.0544	0.0538	0.0532	0.0529	0.0525	0.0522	0.0520	0.0519	0.0518	0.0518
23	0.0546	0.0534	0.0524	0.0518	0.0512	0.0509	0.0505	0.0502	0.0500	0.0499	0.0498	0.0498
24	0.0527	0.0515	0.0505	0.0499	0.0493	0.0490	0.0487	0.0484	0.0481	0.0480	0.0480	0.0480
25	0.0509	0.0498	0.0488	0.0482	0.0476	0.0473	0.0470	0.0467	0.0465	0.0464	0.0463	0.0463
26	0.0493	0.0482	0.0472	0.0466	0.0460	0.0457	0.0454	0.0451	0.0449	0.0448	0.0448	0.0447
27	0.0478	0.0467	0.0457	0.0451	0.0446	0.0443	0.0440	0.0437	0.0435	0.0434	0.0433	0.0433
28	0.0464	0.0453	0.0443	0.0437	0.0432	0.0429	0.0426	0.0423	0.0421	0.0420	0.0420	0.0419

29	0.0450	0.0440	0.0430	0.0425	0.0420	0.0416	0.0414	0.0411	0.0409	0.0408	0.0407	0.0407
30	0.0438	0.0428	0.0418	0.0413	0.0408	0.0405	0.0402	0.0399	0.0397	0.0396	0.0396	0.0395
31	0.0427	0.0416	0.0407	0.0401	0.0397	0.0394	0.0391	0.0388	0.0386	0.0385	0.0385	0.0385
32	0.0416	0.0405	0.0396	0.0391	0.0386	0.0383	0.0380	0.0378	0.0375	0.0375	0.0375	0.0374
33	0.0405	0.0395	0.0386	0.0381	0.0376	0.0373	0.0371	0.0368	0.0356	0.0365	0.0365	0.0365
34	0.0396	0.0386	0.0377	0.0372	0.0367	0.0364	0.0362	0.0359	0.0357	0.0356	0.0356	0.0356
35	0.0386	0.0377	0.0368	0.0363	0.0358	0.0355	0.0353	0.0350	0.0349	0.0348	0.0347	0.0347
36	0.0378	0.0368	0.0359	0.0354	0.0350	0.0347	0.0345	0.0342	0.0341	0.0340	0.0339	0.0339
37	0.0369	0.0360	0.0351	0.0347	0.0342	0.0339	0.0337	0.0334	0.0333	0.0332	0.0332	0.0332
38	0.0362	0.0352	0.0344	0.0339	0.0335	0.0332	0.0330	0.0327	0.0326	0.0325	0.0325	0.0324
39	0.0354	0.0345	0.0337	0.0332	0.0328	0.0325	0.0323	0.0320	0.0319	0.0318	0.0318	0.0317
40	0.0347	0.0338	0.0330	0.0325	0.0321	0.0318	0.0316	0.0314	0.0312	0.0311	0.0311	0.0311
41	0.0340	0.0331	0.0323	0.0319	0.0314	0.0312	0.0310	0.0307	0.0306	0.0305	0.0305	0.0305
42	0.0334	0.0325	0.0317	0.0312	0.0308	0.0306	0.0304	0.0301	0.0300	0.0299	0.0299	0.0299
43	0.0327	0.0319	0.0311	0.0306	0.0302	0.0300	0.0298	0.0296	0.0294	0.0294	0.0293	0.0293
44	0.0321	0.0313	0.0305	0.0301	0.0297	0.0294	0.0292	0.0290	0.0289	0.0288	0.0288	0.0288
45	0.0315	0.0307	0.0300	0.0295	0.0291	0.0289	0.0287	0.0285	0.0284	0.0283	0.0283	0.0283
46	0.0310	0.0302	0.0294	0.0290	0.0286	0.0284	0.0282	0.0280	0.0279	0.0278	0.0278	0.0278
47	0.0305	0.0297	0.0289	0.0285	0.0281	0.0279	0.0277	0.0275	0.0274	0.0273	0.0273	0.0273
48	0.0300	0.0292	0.0284	0.0280	0.0277	0.0274	0.0272	0.0270	0.0269	0.0269	0.0268	0.0268
49	0.0295	0.0287	0.0280	0.0276	0.0272	0.0270	0.0268	0.0266	0.0265	0.0264	0.0264	0.0264
50	0.0290	0.0282	0.0275	0.0271	0.0268	0.0266	0.0264	0.0262	0.0261	0.0260	0.0260	0.0260
51	0.0285	0.0278	0.0271	0.0267	0.0263	0.0261	0.0259	0.0258	0.0257	0.0256	0.0256	0.0256
52	0.0281	0.0273	0.0266	0.0263	0.0259	0.0257	0.0255	0.0254	0.0253	0.0252	0.0252	0.0252
53	0.0277	0.0269	0.0262	0.0259	0.0255	0.0253	0.0252	0.0250	0.0249	0.0248	0.0248	0.0248
54	0.0272	0.0265	0.0258	0.0255	0.0252	0.0250	0.0248	0.0246	0.0245	0.0245	0.0244	0.0244
55	0.0268	0.0261	0.0255	0.0251	0.0248	0.0246	0.0244	0.0243	0.0242	0.0241	0.0241	0.0241
56	0.0265	0.0258	0.0251	0.0248	0.0244	0.0243	0.0241	0.0239	0.0238	0.0238	0.0238	0.0237
57	0.0261	0.0254	0.0247	0.0244	0.0241	0.0239	0.0237	0.0236	0.0235	0.0234	0.0234	0.0234
58	0.0257	0.0250	0.0244	0.0241	0.0238	0.0236	0.0234	0.0233	0.0232	0.0231	0.0231	0.0231
59	0.0254	0.0247	0.0241	0.0237	0.0234	0.0233	0.0231	0.0229	0.0229	0.0228	0.0228	0.0228
60	0.0250	0.0244	0.0237	0.0234	0.0231	0.0230	0.0228	0.0226	0.0226	0.0225	0.0225	0.0225

DEPRECIATION ANNUITIES, DECIMALLY EXPRESSED

DOUBLE-RATE-DECLINING-BALANCE METHOD   CRITICAL RATE OF RETURN   6.000 PERCENT

AVERAGE LIFE (YEARS)	LO	L05	L1	L15	L2	L3	L4	L5
						TYPE OF RETIREMENT DISPERSION		
1	1.1062	1.1170	0.9642	0.8262	0.6038	1.8134	0.0946	0.0973
2	0.5282	0.5255	0.5226	0.5218	0.5211	0.5158	0.5091	0.5106
3	0.3550	0.3530	0.3510	0.3497	0.3484	0.3466	0.3445	0.3440
4	0.2687	0.2670	0.2652	0.2640	0.2628	0.2612	0.2601	0.2594
5	0.2171	0.2154	0.2138	0.2126	0.2115	0.2100	0.2092	0.2088
6	0.1827	0.1811	0.1795	0.1784	0.1774	0.1760	0.1752	0.1749
7	0.1581	0.1565	0.1551	0.1540	0.1530	0.1517	0.1510	0.1507
8	0.1396	0.1381	0.1367	0.1357	0.1347	0.1335	0.1329	0.1326
9	0.1253	0.1238	0.1224	0.1214	0.1205	0.1194	0.1188	0.1185
10	0.1138	0.1124	0.1110	0.1100	0.1091	0.1081	0.1075	0.1072
11	0.1044	0.1030	0.1017	0.1007	0.0998	0.0988	0.0983	0.0980
12	0.0965	0.0951	0.0939	0.0929	0.0921	0.0911	0.0906	0.0903
13	0.0899	0.0885	0.0873	0.0864	0.0855	0.0846	0.0841	0.0838
14	0.0841	0.0828	0.0816	0.0807	0.0799	0.0790	0.0785	0.0782
15	0.0792	0.0779	0.0767	0.0758	0.0751	0.0742	0.0737	0.0734
16	0.0748	0.0736	0.0724	0.0715	0.0708	0.0699	0.0694	0.0692
17	0.0710	0.0697	0.0686	0.0678	0.0670	0.0662	0.0657	0.0655
18	0.0675	0.0663	0.0652	0.0644	0.0637	0.0629	0.0624	0.0622
19	0.0644	0.0633	0.0622	0.0614	0.0607	0.0599	0.0594	0.0592
20	0.0617	0.0605	0.0595	0.0587	0.0580	0.0572	0.0568	0.0566
21	0.0591	0.0580	0.0570	0.0562	0.0555	0.0548	0.0543	0.0541
22	0.0568	0.0557	0.0547	0.0540	0.0533	0.0526	0.0521	0.0520
23	0.0547	0.0537	0.0527	0.0519	0.0513	0.0506	0.0501	0.0500
24	0.0528	0.0518	0.0508	0.0501	0.0494	0.0487	0.0483	0.0481
25	0.0510	0.0500	0.0490	0.0483	0.0477	0.0470	0.0466	0.0464
26	0.0494	0.0484	0.0474	0.0467	0.0461	0.0454	0.0450	0.0449
27	0.0478	0.0468	0.0459	0.0452	0.0446	0.0440	0.0436	0.0434
28	0.0464	0.0454	0.0445	0.0439	0.0433	0.0426	0.0423	0.0421

29	0.0450	0.0441	0.0432	0.0426	0.0420	0.0414	0.0410	0.0408
30	0.0438	0.0429	0.0420	0.0414	0.0408	0.0402	0.0398	0.0397
31	0.0426	0.0417	0.0409	0.0402	0.0397	0.0391	0.0387	0.0386
32	0.0415	0.0406	0.0398	0.0392	0.0386	0.0380	0.0377	0.0376
33	0.0405	0.0396	0.0388	0.0382	0.0377	0.0371	0.0367	0.0366
34	0.0395	0.0386	0.0378	0.0372	0.0367	0.0362	0.0358	0.0357
35	0.0385	0.0377	0.0369	0.0364	0.0358	0.0353	0.0350	0.0348
36	0.0377	0.0368	0.0361	0.0355	0.0350	0.0345	0.0342	0.0340
37	0.0368	0.0360	0.0353	0.0347	0.0342	0.0337	0.0334	0.0333
38	0.0360	0.0352	0.0345	0.0340	0.0335	0.0330	0.0327	0.0325
39	0.0352	0.0345	0.0338	0.0332	0.0328	0.0323	0.0320	0.0319
40	0.0345	0.0338	0.0331	0.0326	0.0321	0.0316	0.0313	0.0312
41	0.0338	0.0331	0.0324	0.0319	0.0314	0.0310	0.0307	0.0306
42	0.0332	0.0325	0.0318	0.0313	0.0308	0.0303	0.0301	0.0300
43	0.0325	0.0318	0.0312	0.0307	0.0302	0.0298	0.0295	0.0294
44	0.0319	0.0312	0.0306	0.0301	0.0297	0.0292	0.0290	0.0289
45	0.0313	0.0307	0.0300	0.0296	0.0291	0.0287	0.0284	0.0283
46	0.0308	0.0301	0.0295	0.0290	0.0286	0.0282	0.0279	0.0278
47	0.0302	0.0296	0.0290	0.0285	0.0281	0.0277	0.0275	0.0274
48	0.0297	0.0291	0.0285	0.0281	0.0276	0.0272	0.0270	0.0269
49	0.0292	0.0286	0.0280	0.0276	0.0272	0.0268	0.0266	0.0265
50	0.0287	0.0281	0.0276	0.0271	0.0267	0.0263	0.0261	0.0260
51	0.0283	0.0277	0.0271	0.0267	0.0263	0.0259	0.0257	0.0256
52	0.0278	0.0272	0.0267	0.0263	0.0259	0.0255	0.0253	0.0252
53	0.0274	0.0268	0.0263	0.0259	0.0255	0.0251	0.0250	0.0249
54	0.0270	0.0264	0.0259	0.0255	0.0251	0.0248	0.0246	0.0245
55	0.0266	0.0260	0.0255	0.0251	0.0248	0.0244	0.0242	0.0241
56	0.0262	0.0256	0.0251	0.0248	0.0244	0.0241	0.0239	0.0238
57	0.0258	0.0253	0.0248	0.0244	0.0241	0.0237	0.0236	0.0235
58	0.0254	0.0249	0.0244	0.0241	0.0237	0.0234	0.0232	0.0232
59	0.0251	0.0246	0.0241	0.0237	0.0234	0.0231	0.0229	0.0228
60	0.0247	0.0242	0.0238	0.0234	0.0231	0.0228	0.0226	0.0225

DEPRECIATION ANNUITIES, DECIMALLY EXPRESSED

DOUBLE-RATE-DECLINING-BALANCE METHOD   CRITICAL RATE OF RETURN 6.000 PERCENT

TYPE OF RETIREMENT DISPERSION

AVERAGE LIFE (YEARS)	RU5	R1	R15	R2	R25	R3	P4	R5
1	0.8279	1.1849	0.1979	0.1027	0.1003	0.1016	0.1021	0.1040
2	0.5195	0.5231	0.5131	0.5151	0.5166	0.5185	0.4836	0.4838
3	0.3509	0.3501	0.3479	0.3473	0.3467	0.3438	0.3452	0.3462
4	0.2656	0.2642	0.2630	0.2621	0.2614	0.2606	0.2592	0.2596
5	0.2143	0.2129	0.2118	0.2110	0.2103	0.2097	0.2091	0.2085
6	0.1801	0.1787	0.1778	0.1768	0.1763	0.1757	0.1751	0.1748
7	0.1557	0.1544	0.1534	0.1526	0.1520	0.1515	0.1509	0.1506
8	0.1374	0.1361	0.1352	0.1344	0.1338	0.1333	0.1328	0.1325
9	0.1231	0.1219	0.1210	0.1202	0.1197	0.1192	0.1187	0.1184
10	0.1117	0.1105	0.1096	0.1089	0.1084	0.1079	0.1074	0.1071
11	0.1024	0.1012	0.1004	0.0996	0.0991	0.0987	0.0982	0.0979
12	0.0946	0.0934	0.0926	0.0919	0.0914	0.0910	0.0905	0.0902
13	0.0880	0.0869	0.0861	0.0854	0.0849	0.0845	0.0840	0.0838
14	0.0824	0.0813	0.0805	0.0798	0.0793	0.0789	0.0784	0.0782
15	0.0775	0.0764	0.0756	0.0749	0.0745	0.0740	0.0736	0.0734
16	0.0732	0.0721	0.0714	0.0707	0.0702	0.0698	0.0694	0.0691
17	0.0694	0.0683	0.0676	0.0669	0.0665	0.0661	0.0657	0.0654
18	0.0660	0.0650	0.0643	0.0636	0.0632	0.0628	0.0623	0.0621
19	0.0630	0.0620	0.0613	0.0606	0.0602	0.0598	0.0594	0.0592
20	0.0603	0.0593	0.0586	0.0579	0.0575	0.0571	0.0567	0.0565
21	0.0578	0.0568	0.0561	0.0555	0.0551	0.0547	0.0543	0.0541
22	0.0556	0.0546	0.0539	0.0533	0.0529	0.0525	0.0521	0.0519
23	0.0535	0.0526	0.0519	0.0513	0.0509	0.0505	0.0501	0.0499
24	0.0516	0.0507	0.0500	0.0494	0.0490	0.0486	0.0483	0.0481
25	0.0499	0.0490	0.0483	0.0477	0.0473	0.0470	0.0466	0.0464
26	0.0483	0.0474	0.0467	0.0461	0.0457	0.0454	0.0450	0.0448
27	0.0468	0.0459	0.0452	0.0447	0.0443	0.0439	0.0436	0.0434
28	0.0454	0.0445	0.0439	0.0433	0.0429	0.0426	0.0422	0.0421

29	0.0441	0.0432	0.0426	0.0420	0.0417	0.0413	0.0410	0.0408
30	0.0429	0.0420	0.0414	0.0409	0.0405	0.0402	0.0398	0.0396
31	0.0417	0.0409	0.0403	0.0398	0.0394	0.0391	0.0387	0.0386
32	0.0407	0.0398	0.0392	0.0387	0.0384	0.0380	0.0377	0.0375
33	0.0396	0.0388	0.0383	0.0377	0.0374	0.0371	0.0367	0.0366
34	0.0387	0.0379	0.0373	0.0368	0.0365	0.0361	0.0358	0.0357
35	0.0378	0.0370	0.0364	0.0359	0.0356	0.0353	0.0350	0.0348
36	0.0369	0.0362	0.0356	0.0351	0.0348	0.0345	0.0342	0.0340
37	0.0361	0.0354	0.0348	0.0343	0.0340	0.0337	0.0334	0.0332
38	0.0353	0.0346	0.0341	0.0336	0.0333	0.0330	0.0327	0.0325
39	0.0346	0.0339	0.0334	0.0329	0.0326	0.0323	0.0320	0.0318
40	0.0339	0.0332	0.0327	0.0322	0.0319	0.0316	0.0313	0.0312
41	0.0332	0.0325	0.0320	0.0316	0.0313	0.0310	0.0307	0.0305
42	0.0326	0.0319	0.0314	0.0310	0.0307	0.0304	0.0301	0.0300
43	0.0320	0.0313	0.0308	0.0304	0.0301	0.0298	0.0295	0.0294
44	0.0314	0.0307	0.0303	0.0298	0.0295	0.0292	0.0290	0.0288
45	0.0308	0.0302	0.0297	0.0293	0.0290	0.0287	0.0285	0.0283
46	0.0303	0.0297	0.0292	0.0288	0.0285	0.0282	0.0280	0.0278
47	0.0298	0.0291	0.0287	0.0283	0.0280	0.0277	0.0275	0.0273
48	0.0293	0.0287	0.0282	0.0278	0.0275	0.0273	0.0270	0.0269
49	0.0288	0.0282	0.0277	0.0273	0.0271	0.0268	0.0266	0.0265
50	0.0283	0.0277	0.0273	0.0269	0.0266	0.0264	0.0261	0.0260
51	0.0279	0.0273	0.0269	0.0265	0.0262	0.0260	0.0257	0.0256
52	0.0275	0.0269	0.0265	0.0261	0.0258	0.0256	0.0253	0.0252
53	0.0270	0.0265	0.0261	0.0257	0.0254	0.0252	0.0250	0.0249
54	0.0266	0.0261	0.0257	0.0253	0.0251	0.0248	0.0246	0.0245
55	0.0263	0.0257	0.0253	0.0249	0.0247	0.0245	0.0242	0.0241
56	0.0259	0.0253	0.0249	0.0246	0.0243	0.0241	0.0239	0.0238
57	0.0255	0.0250	0.0246	0.0242	0.0240	0.0238	0.0236	0.0235
58	0.0252	0.0246	0.0243	0.0239	0.0237	0.0234	0.0232	0.0231
59	0.0248	0.0243	0.0239	0.0236	0.0234	0.0231	0.0229	0.0228
60	0.0245	0.0240	0.0236	0.0233	0.0230	0.0228	0.0226	0.0225

DEPRECIATION ANNUITIES, DECIMALLY EXPRESSED

SYD METHOD   CRITICAL RATE OF RETURN 7.000 PERCENT

AVERAGE LIFE (YEARS)		TYPE OF RETIREMENT DISPERSION										
	SC	SON	S0	S05	S1	S15	S2	S3	S4	S5	S6	SQ
1	1.0033	0.9679	0.9355	0.9100	0.8899	0.8710	0.8617	0.8561	0.8769	0.9087	0.9379	1.0000
2	0.5105	0.5063	0.5022	0.5013	0.5009	0.5019	0.5033	0.5057	0.5061	0.4641	0.4753	0.5056
3	0.3463	0.3447	0.3432	0.3428	0.3425	0.3424	0.3424	0.3421	0.3407	0.3411	0.3222	0.3408
4	0.2641	0.2631	0.2620	0.2615	0.2611	0.2607	0.2604	0.2597	0.2592	0.2585	0.2586	0.2584
5	0.2147	0.2138	0.2129	0.2124	0.2119	0.2114	0.2110	0.2103	0.2097	0.2094	0.2091	0.2090
6	0.1817	0.1809	0.1800	0.1795	0.1789	0.1785	0.1780	0.1773	0.1767	0.1764	0.1761	0.1760
7	0.1581	0.1573	0.1565	0.1559	0.1554	0.1549	0.1545	0.1538	0.1532	0.1528	0.1525	0.1525
8	0.1404	0.1396	0.1388	0.1383	0.1377	0.1372	0.1368	0.1361	0.1355	0.1352	0.1350	0.1348
9	0.1265	0.1258	0.1250	0.1245	0.1239	0.1235	0.1230	0.1223	0.1217	0.1214	0.1212	0.1211
10	0.1155	0.1147	0.1139	0.1134	0.1129	0.1124	0.1120	0.1113	0.1107	0.1104	0.1102	0.1101
11	0.1064	0.1056	0.1049	0.1043	0.1038	0.1034	0.1029	0.1023	0.1017	0.1014	0.1012	0.1011
12	0.0987	0.0980	0.0973	0.0968	0.0962	0.0958	0.0954	0.0947	0.0942	0.0939	0.0937	0.0936
13	0.0923	0.0916	0.0909	0.0903	0.0898	0.0894	0.0890	0.0884	0.0878	0.0875	0.0873	0.0872
14	0.0867	0.0860	0.0853	0.0848	0.0843	0.0839	0.0835	0.0829	0.0823	0.0820	0.0819	0.0817
15	0.0819	0.0812	0.0805	0.0800	0.0795	0.0791	0.0787	0.0781	0.0776	0.0773	0.0771	0.0770
16	0.0776	0.0770	0.0763	0.0758	0.0753	0.0749	0.0745	0.0739	0.0734	0.0731	0.0730	0.0729
17	0.0739	0.0732	0.0725	0.0721	0.0716	0.0712	0.0708	0.0703	0.0698	0.0695	0.0693	0.0692
18	0.0705	0.0699	0.0692	0.0687	0.0683	0.0679	0.0675	0.0670	0.0665	0.0662	0.0661	0.0660
19	0.0675	0.0668	0.0662	0.0658	0.0653	0.0649	0.0646	0.0640	0.0636	0.0633	0.0631	0.0630
20	0.0647	0.0641	0.0635	0.0631	0.0626	0.0622	0.0619	0.0614	0.0609	0.0606	0.0605	0.0604
21	0.0622	0.0616	0.0610	0.0606	0.0602	0.0598	0.0595	0.0589	0.0585	0.0583	0.0581	0.0580
22	0.0599	0.0594	0.0588	0.0584	0.0579	0.0576	0.0572	0.0567	0.0563	0.0561	0.0559	0.0558
23	0.0578	0.0573	0.0567	0.0563	0.0559	0.0555	0.0552	0.0547	0.0543	0.0541	0.0539	0.0539
24	0.0559	0.0554	0.0548	0.0544	0.0540	0.0537	0.0533	0.0529	0.0525	0.0522	0.0521	0.0520
25	0.0541	0.0536	0.0530	0.0526	0.0523	0.0519	0.0516	0.0512	0.0508	0.0506	0.0504	0.0503
26	0.0525	0.0519	0.0514	0.0510	0.0506	0.0503	0.0500	0.0496	0.0492	0.0490	0.0489	0.0488
27	0.0509	0.0504	0.0499	0.0495	0.0491	0.0488	0.0485	0.0481	0.0477	0.0475	0.0474	0.0473

28	0.0495	0.0490	0.0485	0.0481	0.0477	0.0474	0.0472	0.0467	0.0464	0.0462	0.0461	0.0460
29	0.0481	0.0476	0.0471	0.0468	0.0464	0.0461	0.0459	0.0455	0.0451	0.0449	0.0448	0.0447
30	0.0468	0.0464	0.0459	0.0455	0.0452	0.0449	0.0446	0.0443	0.0439	0.0437	0.0436	0.0436
31	0.0456	0.0452	0.0447	0.0444	0.0440	0.0438	0.0435	0.0431	0.0428	0.0426	0.0425	0.0424
32	0.0445	0.0440	0.0436	0.0433	0.0429	0.0427	0.0424	0.0421	0.0417	0.0416	0.0415	0.0414
33	0.0434	0.0430	0.0425	0.0422	0.0419	0.0417	0.0414	0.0411	0.0408	0.0406	0.0405	0.0404
34	0.0424	0.0420	0.0415	0.0412	0.0409	0.0407	0.0405	0.0401	0.0398	0.0396	0.0396	0.0395
35	0.0414	0.0410	0.0406	0.0403	0.0400	0.0398	0.0395	0.0392	0.0389	0.0388	0.0387	0.0386
36	0.0405	0.0401	0.0397	0.0394	0.0391	0.0389	0.0387	0.0384	0.0381	0.0379	0.0378	0.0378
37	0.0397	0.0393	0.0389	0.0386	0.0383	0.0381	0.0379	0.0375	0.0373	0.0371	0.0371	0.0370
38	0.0388	0.0384	0.0381	0.0378	0.0375	0.0373	0.0371	0.0368	0.0365	0.0364	0.0363	0.0362
39	0.0380	0.0377	0.0373	0.0370	0.0368	0.0365	0.0363	0.0360	0.0358	0.0357	0.0356	0.0355
40	0.0373	0.0369	0.0365	0.0363	0.0360	0.0358	0.0356	0.0353	0.0351	0.0350	0.0349	0.0348
41	0.0365	0.0362	0.0358	0.0356	0.0353	0.0351	0.0349	0.0347	0.0344	0.0343	0.0342	0.0342
42	0.0359	0.0355	0.0352	0.0349	0.0347	0.0345	0.0343	0.0340	0.0338	0.0337	0.0336	0.0336
43	0.0352	0.0348	0.0345	0.0343	0.0340	0.0339	0.0337	0.0334	0.0332	0.0331	0.0330	0.0330
44	0.0345	0.0342	0.0339	0.0337	0.0334	0.0332	0.0331	0.0328	0.0326	0.0325	0.0324	0.0324
45	0.0339	0.0336	0.0333	0.0331	0.0328	0.0327	0.0325	0.0323	0.0321	0.0319	0.0319	0.0318
46	0.0333	0.0330	0.0327	0.0325	0.0323	0.0321	0.0319	0.0317	0.0315	0.0314	0.0314	0.0313
47	0.0328	0.0325	0.0321	0.0319	0.0317	0.0316	0.0314	0.0312	0.0310	0.0309	0.0308	0.0308
48	0.0322	0.0319	0.0316	0.0314	0.0312	0.0311	0.0309	0.0307	0.0305	0.0304	0.0304	0.0303
49	0.0317	0.0314	0.0311	0.0309	0.0307	0.0306	0.0304	0.0302	0.0300	0.0299	0.0299	0.0298
50	0.0312	0.0309	0.0306	0.0304	0.0302	0.0301	0.0299	0.0297	0.0296	0.0295	0.0294	0.0294
51	0.0307	0.0304	0.0301	0.0299	0.0297	0.0296	0.0295	0.0293	0.0291	0.0290	0.0290	0.0289
52	0.0302	0.0299	0.0297	0.0295	0.0293	0.0292	0.0290	0.0288	0.0287	0.0286	0.0286	0.0285
53	0.0297	0.0295	0.0292	0.0290	0.0289	0.0287	0.0286	0.0284	0.0283	0.0282	0.0281	0.0281
54	0.0293	0.0290	0.0288	0.0286	0.0284	0.0283	0.0282	0.0280	0.0279	0.0278	0.0277	0.0277
55	0.0288	0.0286	0.0283	0.0282	0.0280	0.0279	0.0278	0.0276	0.0275	0.0274	0.0273	0.0273
56	0.0284	0.0282	0.0279	0.0278	0.0276	0.0275	0.0274	0.0272	0.0271	0.0270	0.0270	0.0269
57	0.0280	0.0278	0.0275	0.0274	0.0272	0.0271	0.0270	0.0268	0.0267	0.0266	0.0266	0.0266
58	0.0276	0.0274	0.0272	0.0270	0.0269	0.0267	0.0266	0.0265	0.0264	0.0263	0.0263	0.0262
59	0.0272	0.0270	0.0268	0.0266	0.0265	0.0264	0.0263	0.0261	0.0260	0.0259	0.0259	0.0259
60	0.0268	0.0266	0.0264	0.0263	0.0261	0.0260	0.0259	0.0258	0.0257	0.0256	0.0256	0.0256

DEPRECIATION ANNUITIES, DECIMALLY EXPRESSED

SYD METHOD   CRITICAL RATE OF RETURN 7.000 PERCENT

AVERAGE LIFE (YEARS)				TYPE OF RETIREMENT DISPERSION				
	L0	L05	L1	L15	L2	L3	L4	L5
1	1.0132	1.0064	0.9862	0.9722	0.9598	0.9561	0.8363	0.8604
2	0.5132	0.5115	0.5097	0.5095	0.5093	0.5052	0.4995	0.5013
3	0.3481	0.3470	0.3458	0.3451	0.3442	0.3431	0.3408	0.3403
4	0.2657	0.2647	0.2636	0.2629	0.2621	0.2608	0.2595	0.2586
5	0.2162	0.2152	0.2142	0.2134	0.2127	0.2114	0.2102	0.2096
6	0.1832	0.1822	0.1812	0.1805	0.1797	0.1784	0.1773	0.1767
7	0.1595	0.1585	0.1575	0.1568	0.1561	0.1548	0.1537	0.1531
8	0.1417	0.1407	0.1398	0.1391	0.1384	0.1371	0.1360	0.1354
9	0.1278	0.1269	0.1259	0.1253	0.1246	0.1233	0.1222	0.1217
10	0.1166	0.1157	0.1148	0.1142	0.1135	0.1123	0.1112	0.1107
11	0.1074	0.1066	0.1057	0.1051	0.1044	0.1032	0.1022	0.1016
12	0.0998	0.0989	0.0981	0.0975	0.0968	0.0957	0.0947	0.0941
13	0.0932	0.0924	0.0916	0.0910	0.0904	0.0892	0.0883	0.0877
14	0.0876	0.0868	0.0861	0.0855	0.0848	0.0837	0.0828	0.0823
15	0.0827	0.0820	0.0812	0.0806	0.0800	0.0789	0.0780	0.0775
16	0.0784	0.0777	0.0770	0.0764	0.0758	0.0747	0.0739	0.0734
17	0.0746	0.0739	0.0732	0.0726	0.0720	0.0710	0.0702	0.0697
18	0.0712	0.0705	0.0698	0.0693	0.0687	0.0677	0.0669	0.0664
19	0.0681	0.0674	0.0668	0.0662	0.0657	0.0647	0.0639	0.0635
20	0.0653	0.0647	0.0640	0.0635	0.0630	0.0621	0.0613	0.0608
21	0.0628	0.0622	0.0615	0.0610	0.0605	0.0596	0.0589	0.0584
22	0.0604	0.0599	0.0593	0.0588	0.0583	0.0574	0.0567	0.0563
23	0.0583	0.0577	0.0572	0.0567	0.0562	0.0554	0.0546	0.0543
24	0.0563	0.0558	0.0552	0.0548	0.0543	0.0535	0.0528	0.0524
25	0.0545	0.0540	0.0534	0.0530	0.0525	0.0517	0.0511	0.0507
26	0.0528	0.0523	0.0518	0.0513	0.0509	0.0501	0.0495	0.0492
27	0.0513	0.0507	0.0502	0.0498	0.0494	0.0487	0.0480	0.0477

28	0.0498	0.0493	0.0488	0.0484	0.0480	0.0473	0.0467	0.0463
29	0.0484	0.0479	0.0474	0.0470	0.0466	0.0460	0.0454	0.0451
30	0.0471	0.0466	0.0462	0.0458	0.0454	0.0447	0.0442	0.0439
31	0.0459	0.0454	0.0450	0.0446	0.0442	0.0436	0.0430	0.0428
32	0.0447	0.0443	0.0439	0.0435	0.0431	0.0425	0.0420	0.0417
33	0.0436	0.0432	0.0428	0.0424	0.0421	0.0415	0.0410	0.0407
34	0.0426	0.0422	0.0418	0.0414	0.0411	0.0405	0.0400	0.0398
35	0.0416	0.0412	0.0408	0.0405	0.0402	0.0396	0.0391	0.0389
36	0.0407	0.0403	0.0399	0.0396	0.0393	0.0387	0.0383	0.0380
37	0.0398	0.0394	0.0391	0.0388	0.0384	0.0379	0.0375	0.0372
38	0.0390	0.0386	0.0382	0.0379	0.0376	0.0371	0.0367	0.0365
39	0.0381	0.0378	0.0375	0.0372	0.0369	0.0364	0.0360	0.0358
40	0.0374	0.0370	0.0367	0.0364	0.0361	0.0357	0.0353	0.0351
41	0.0366	0.0363	0.0360	0.0357	0.0354	0.0350	0.0346	0.0344
42	0.0359	0.0356	0.0353	0.0350	0.0348	0.0343	0.0340	0.0338
43	0.0353	0.0349	0.0346	0.0344	0.0341	0.0337	0.0334	0.0332
44	0.0346	0.0343	0.0340	0.0338	0.0335	0.0331	0.0328	0.0326
45	0.0340	0.0337	0.0334	0.0332	0.0329	0.0325	0.0322	0.0320
46	0.0334	0.0331	0.0328	0.0326	0.0323	0.0320	0.0317	0.0315
47	0.0328	0.0325	0.0323	0.0320	0.0318	0.0314	0.0311	0.0310
48	0.0322	0.0320	0.0317	0.0315	0.0313	0.0309	0.0306	0.0305
49	0.0317	0.0314	0.0312	0.0310	0.0308	0.0304	0.0301	0.0300
50	0.0312	0.0309	0.0307	0.0305	0.0303	0.0299	0.0297	0.0295
51	0.0307	0.0304	0.0302	0.0300	0.0298	0.0295	0.0292	0.0291
52	0.0302	0.0300	0.0297	0.0295	0.0293	0.0290	0.0288	0.0287
53	0.0297	0.0295	0.0293	0.0291	0.0289	0.0286	0.0284	0.0282
54	0.0293	0.0291	0.0288	0.0286	0.0285	0.0282	0.0280	0.0278
55	0.0288	0.0286	0.0284	0.0282	0.0280	0.0278	0.0276	0.0274
56	0.0284	0.0282	0.0280	0.0278	0.0276	0.0274	0.0272	0.0271
57	0.0280	0.0278	0.0276	0.0274	0.0273	0.0270	0.0268	0.0267
58	0.0276	0.0274	0.0272	0.0270	0.0269	0.0266	0.0264	0.0263
59	0.0272	0.0270	0.0268	0.0267	0.0265	0.0263	0.0261	0.0260
60	0.0268	0.0266	0.0265	0.0263	0.0262	0.0259	0.0257	0.0256

DEPRECIATION ANNUITIES, DECIMALLY EXPRESSED

SYD METHOD   CRITICAL RATE OF RETURN 7.000 PERCENT

AVERAGE LIFE (YEARS)	TYPE OF RETIREMENT DISPERSION							
	R05	R15	R2	R25	R3	R4	R5	R1
1	0.9610	0.8955	0.9026	0.8827	0.8953	0.9860	0.9198	1.0056
2	0.5057	0.5011	0.5037	0.5056	0.5075	0.5572	0.4755	0.5094
3	0.3447	0.3428	0.3428	0.3426	0.3392	0.3131	0.3427	0.3446
4	0.2630	0.2614	0.2609	0.2604	0.2597	0.2545	0.2590	0.2623
5	0.2137	0.2121	0.2115	0.2110	0.2105	0.2118	0.2090	0.2129
6	0.1808	0.1792	0.1785	0.1780	0.1775	0.1800	0.1764	0.1799
7	0.1572	0.1557	0.1550	0.1545	0.1540	0.1490	0.1529	0.1563
8	0.1395	0.1380	0.1373	0.1368	0.1363	0.1337	0.1352	0.1386
9	0.1257	0.1242	0.1235	0.1231	0.1226	0.1213	0.1215	0.1248
10	0.1146	0.1131	0.1125	0.1120	0.1115	0.1125	0.1105	0.1137
11	0.1055	0.1041	0.1035	0.1030	0.1025	0.1000	0.1014	0.1047
12	0.0979	0.0965	0.0959	0.0954	0.0950	0.0941	0.0939	0.0971
13	0.0915	0.0901	0.0895	0.0891	0.0886	0.0916	0.0876	0.0907
14	0.0860	0.0846	0.0840	0.0836	0.0831	0.0859	0.0821	0.0852
15	0.0811	0.0798	0.0792	0.0788	0.0784	0.0798	0.0774	0.0804
16	0.0769	0.0756	0.0750	0.0746	0.0742	0.0756	0.0732	0.0761
17	0.0731	0.0719	0.0713	0.0709	0.0705	0.0719	0.0695	0.0724
18	0.0698	0.0685	0.0680	0.0676	0.0672	0.0689	0.0663	0.0691
19	0.0668	0.0656	0.0651	0.0647	0.0643	0.0650	0.0634	0.0661
20	0.0641	0.0629	0.0624	0.0620	0.0616	0.0626	0.0607	0.0634
21	0.0616	0.0604	0.0599	0.0596	0.0592	0.0601	0.0583	0.0609
22	0.0593	0.0582	0.0577	0.0574	0.0570	0.0579	0.0561	0.0587
23	0.0572	0.0561	0.0557	0.0553	0.0550	0.0555	0.0541	0.0566
24	0.0553	0.0543	0.0538	0.0535	0.0531	0.0537	0.0523	0.0547
25	0.0535	0.0525	0.0521	0.0517	0.0514	0.0521	0.0506	0.0530
26	0.0519	0.0509	0.0505	0.0501	0.0498	0.0505	0.0490	0.0513
27	0.0504	0.0494	0.0490	0.0487	0.0483	0.0487	0.0476	0.0498

28	0.0489	0.0480	0.0476	0.0480	0.0473	0.0474	0.0470	0.0474	0.0473	0.0476	0.0462	0.0484
29	0.0476	0.0467	0.0463	0.0467	0.0460	0.0461	0.0457	0.0461	0.0460	0.0463	0.0450	0.0471
30	0.0463	0.0454	0.0451	0.0454	0.0448	0.0449	0.0445	0.0449	0.0448	0.0451	0.0438	0.0458
31	0.0451	0.0443	0.0439	0.0443	0.0436	0.0437	0.0433	0.0437	0.0436	0.0439	0.0427	0.0447
32	0.0440	0.0432	0.0428	0.0432	0.0425	0.0426	0.0423	0.0426	0.0425	0.0428	0.0416	0.0436
33	0.0430	0.0422	0.0418	0.0422	0.0415	0.0417	0.0413	0.0417	0.0415	0.0418	0.0406	0.0425
34	0.0420	0.0412	0.0408	0.0412	0.0406	0.0407	0.0403	0.0407	0.0406	0.0408	0.0397	0.0415
35	0.0410	0.0403	0.0399	0.0403	0.0397	0.0396	0.0394	0.0396	0.0397	0.0399	0.0388	0.0406
36	0.0401	0.0394	0.0391	0.0394	0.0388	0.0388	0.0385	0.0388	0.0388	0.0391	0.0380	0.0397
37	0.0393	0.0385	0.0382	0.0385	0.0380	0.0380	0.0377	0.0380	0.0380	0.0382	0.0372	0.0388
38	0.0384	0.0377	0.0374	0.0377	0.0372	0.0374	0.0370	0.0374	0.0372	0.0374	0.0364	0.0380
39	0.0377	0.0370	0.0367	0.0370	0.0365	0.0366	0.0362	0.0366	0.0365	0.0367	0.0357	0.0373
40	0.0369	0.0363	0.0360	0.0363	0.0357	0.0359	0.0355	0.0359	0.0357	0.0360	0.0350	0.0365
41	0.0362	0.0356	0.0353	0.0356	0.0351	0.0352	0.0348	0.0352	0.0351	0.0353	0.0344	0.0358
42	0.0355	0.0349	0.0346	0.0349	0.0344	0.0345	0.0342	0.0345	0.0344	0.0346	0.0337	0.0352
43	0.0348	0.0342	0.0340	0.0342	0.0338	0.0338	0.0336	0.0338	0.0338	0.0340	0.0331	0.0345
44	0.0342	0.0336	0.0334	0.0336	0.0332	0.0333	0.0330	0.0333	0.0332	0.0334	0.0325	0.0339
45	0.0336	0.0330	0.0328	0.0330	0.0326	0.0327	0.0324	0.0327	0.0326	0.0328	0.0320	0.0333
46	0.0330	0.0325	0.0322	0.0325	0.0320	0.0321	0.0319	0.0321	0.0320	0.0322	0.0314	0.0327
47	0.0325	0.0319	0.0317	0.0319	0.0315	0.0316	0.0313	0.0316	0.0315	0.0317	0.0309	0.0322
48	0.0319	0.0314	0.0312	0.0314	0.0310	0.0310	0.0308	0.0310	0.0310	0.0312	0.0304	0.0316
49	0.0314	0.0309	0.0307	0.0309	0.0305	0.0306	0.0303	0.0306	0.0305	0.0307	0.0300	0.0311
50	0.0309	0.0304	0.0302	0.0304	0.0300	0.0301	0.0299	0.0301	0.0300	0.0302	0.0295	0.0306
51	0.0304	0.0299	0.0297	0.0299	0.0296	0.0296	0.0294	0.0296	0.0296	0.0297	0.0291	0.0301
52	0.0299	0.0295	0.0293	0.0295	0.0291	0.0291	0.0290	0.0291	0.0291	0.0293	0.0286	0.0297
53	0.0295	0.0290	0.0288	0.0290	0.0287	0.0287	0.0285	0.0287	0.0287	0.0288	0.0282	0.0292
54	0.0290	0.0286	0.0284	0.0286	0.0283	0.0283	0.0281	0.0283	0.0283	0.0284	0.0278	0.0288
55	0.0286	0.0282	0.0280	0.0282	0.0279	0.0279	0.0277	0.0279	0.0279	0.0280	0.0274	0.0284
56	0.0282	0.0278	0.0276	0.0278	0.0275	0.0275	0.0273	0.0275	0.0275	0.0276	0.0270	0.0280
57	0.0278	0.0274	0.0272	0.0274	0.0271	0.0271	0.0270	0.0271	0.0271	0.0272	0.0267	0.0276
58	0.0274	0.0270	0.0268	0.0270	0.0267	0.0267	0.0266	0.0267	0.0267	0.0268	0.0263	0.0272
59	0.0270	0.0266	0.0265	0.0266	0.0264	0.0263	0.0262	0.0263	0.0264	0.0265	0.0260	0.0268
60	0.0266	0.0263	0.0261	0.0260	0.0260	0.0260	0.0259	0.0260	0.0260	0.0261	0.0256	0.0264

DEPRECIATION ANNUITIES, DECIMALLY EXPRESSED

DOUBLE-RATE-DECLINING-BALANCE METHOD   CRITICAL RATE OF RETURN 7.000 PERCENT

AVERAGE LIFE (YEARS)	TYPE OF RETIREMENT DISPERSION											
	SC	SON	SO	SO5	S1	S15	S2	S3	S4	S5	S6	SQ
1	1.0831	0.8805	0.6275	0.3392	0.1172	0.1145	0.1131	0.1121	0.1147	1.8185	1.8765	2.0000
2	0.5295	0.5237	0.5182	0.5164	0.5152	0.5157	0.5166	0.5184	0.5181	0.4746	0.4859	0.5169
3	0.3564	0.3537	0.3512	0.3502	0.3493	0.3487	0.3482	0.3475	0.3462	0.3463	0.3331	0.3459
4	0.2701	0.2680	0.2661	0.2650	0.2641	0.2634	0.2628	0.2619	0.2613	0.2609	0.2608	0.2607
5	0.2184	0.2165	0.2148	0.2137	0.2128	0.2121	0.2115	0.2108	0.2103	0.2101	0.2099	0.2098
6	0.1840	0.1822	0.1805	0.1795	0.1786	0.1780	0.1774	0.1767	0.1763	0.1760	0.1759	0.1758
7	0.1594	0.1577	0.1561	0.1551	0.1542	0.1536	0.1531	0.1525	0.1521	0.1519	0.1517	0.1517
8	0.1410	0.1393	0.1377	0.1368	0.1359	0.1353	0.1348	0.1342	0.1338	0.1337	0.1336	0.1335
9	0.1266	0.1250	0.1234	0.1225	0.1217	0.1212	0.1206	0.1201	0.1197	0.1196	0.1195	0.1194
10	0.1151	0.1135	0.1120	0.1111	0.1103	0.1098	0.1093	0.1088	0.1084	0.1083	0.1082	0.1081
11	0.1057	0.1041	0.1027	0.1018	0.1010	0.1005	0.1000	0.0995	0.0992	0.0990	0.0990	0.0989
12	0.0979	0.0963	0.0949	0.0940	0.0933	0.0928	0.0923	0.0918	0.0915	0.0913	0.0913	0.0912
13	0.0912	0.0897	0.0883	0.0875	0.0867	0.0862	0.0858	0.0853	0.0850	0.0848	0.0848	0.0847
14	0.0855	0.0840	0.0826	0.0818	0.0811	0.0806	0.0802	0.0797	0.0794	0.0793	0.0792	0.0791
15	0.0805	0.0791	0.0777	0.0769	0.0762	0.0757	0.0753	0.0749	0.0746	0.0744	0.0744	0.0743
16	0.0762	0.0747	0.0734	0.0726	0.0719	0.0715	0.0711	0.0706	0.0703	0.0702	0.0701	0.0701
17	0.0723	0.0709	0.0696	0.0688	0.0682	0.0677	0.0673	0.0669	0.0666	0.0665	0.0664	0.0664
18	0.0689	0.0675	0.0662	0.0655	0.0648	0.0644	0.0640	0.0636	0.0633	0.0632	0.0631	0.0631
19	0.0658	0.0645	0.0632	0.0625	0.0618	0.0614	0.0610	0.0606	0.0603	0.0602	0.0601	0.0601
20	0.0631	0.0617	0.0605	0.0597	0.0591	0.0587	0.0583	0.0579	0.0577	0.0575	0.0575	0.0574
21	0.0605	0.0592	0.0580	0.0573	0.0566	0.0562	0.0559	0.0555	0.0552	0.0551	0.0551	0.0550
22	0.0582	0.0569	0.0557	0.0550	0.0544	0.0540	0.0537	0.0533	0.0530	0.0529	0.0529	0.0528
23	0.0561	0.0548	0.0537	0.0530	0.0524	0.0520	0.0516	0.0513	0.0510	0.0509	0.0509	0.0508
24	0.0542	0.0529	0.0518	0.0511	0.0505	0.0501	0.0498	0.0494	0.0492	0.0491	0.0490	0.0490
25	0.0524	0.0512	0.0500	0.0494	0.0488	0.0484	0.0481	0.0477	0.0475	0.0474	0.0474	0.0473
26	0.0507	0.0495	0.0484	0.0478	0.0472	0.0468	0.0465	0.0462	0.0459	0.0458	0.0458	0.0458
27	0.0492	0.0480	0.0469	0.0463	0.0457	0.0454	0.0450	0.0447	0.0445	0.0444	0.0443	0.0443

28	0.0478	0.0466	0.0455	0.0449	0.0443	0.0440	0.0437	0.0433	0.0431	0.0430	0.0430	0.0430
29	0.0464	0.0453	0.0442	0.0436	0.0430	0.0427	0.0424	0.0421	0.0419	0.0418	0.0418	0.0417
30	0.0451	0.0440	0.0430	0.0424	0.0418	0.0415	0.0412	0.0409	0.0407	0.0406	0.0406	0.0405
31	0.0440	0.0428	0.0418	0.0412	0.0407	0.0404	0.0401	0.0398	0.0396	0.0395	0.0395	0.0395
32	0.0428	0.0418	0.0407	0.0402	0.0397	0.0394	0.0391	0.0388	0.0386	0.0385	0.0385	0.0384
33	0.0418	0.0407	0.0397	0.0392	0.0387	0.0384	0.0381	0.0378	0.0376	0.0375	0.0375	0.0375
34	0.0408	0.0397	0.0388	0.0382	0.0377	0.0374	0.0372	0.0369	0.0367	0.0366	0.0366	0.0366
35	0.0398	0.0388	0.0379	0.0373	0.0368	0.0366	0.0363	0.0360	0.0358	0.0357	0.0357	0.0357
36	0.0390	0.0379	0.0370	0.0365	0.0360	0.0357	0.0355	0.0352	0.0350	0.0349	0.0349	0.0349
37	0.0381	0.0371	0.0362	0.0357	0.0352	0.0349	0.0347	0.0344	0.0343	0.0342	0.0341	0.0341
38	0.0373	0.0363	0.0354	0.0349	0.0345	0.0342	0.0339	0.0337	0.0335	0.0334	0.0334	0.0334
39	0.0365	0.0356	0.0347	0.0342	0.0337	0.0335	0.0332	0.0330	0.0328	0.0328	0.0327	0.0327
40	0.0358	0.0348	0.0340	0.0335	0.0330	0.0328	0.0325	0.0323	0.0322	0.0321	0.0321	0.0320
41	0.0351	0.0342	0.0333	0.0328	0.0324	0.0321	0.0319	0.0317	0.0315	0.0315	0.0314	0.0314
42	0.0344	0.0335	0.0326	0.0322	0.0318	0.0315	0.0313	0.0311	0.0309	0.0309	0.0308	0.0308
43	0.0338	0.0329	0.0320	0.0316	0.0312	0.0309	0.0307	0.0305	0.0303	0.0303	0.0303	0.0302
44	0.0331	0.0323	0.0314	0.0310	0.0306	0.0304	0.0301	0.0299	0.0298	0.0297	0.0297	0.0297
45	0.0325	0.0317	0.0309	0.0305	0.0301	0.0298	0.0296	0.0294	0.0293	0.0292	0.0292	0.0292
46	0.0320	0.0311	0.0303	0.0299	0.0295	0.0293	0.0291	0.0289	0.0288	0.0287	0.0287	0.0287
47	0.0314	0.0306	0.0298	0.0294	0.0290	0.0288	0.0286	0.0284	0.0283	0.0282	0.0282	0.0282
48	0.0309	0.0301	0.0293	0.0289	0.0285	0.0283	0.0281	0.0279	0.0278	0.0278	0.0277	0.0277
49	0.0304	0.0296	0.0288	0.0284	0.0281	0.0279	0.0277	0.0275	0.0274	0.0273	0.0273	0.0273
50	0.0299	0.0291	0.0284	0.0280	0.0276	0.0274	0.0272	0.0270	0.0269	0.0269	0.0269	0.0268
51	0.0294	0.0286	0.0279	0.0275	0.0272	0.0270	0.0268	0.0266	0.0265	0.0265	0.0264	0.0264
52	0.0289	0.0282	0.0275	0.0271	0.0268	0.0266	0.0264	0.0262	0.0261	0.0261	0.0260	0.0260
53	0.0285	0.0278	0.0271	0.0267	0.0264	0.0262	0.0260	0.0258	0.0257	0.0257	0.0257	0.0256
54	0.0281	0.0273	0.0267	0.0263	0.0260	0.0258	0.0256	0.0254	0.0253	0.0253	0.0253	0.0253
55	0.0277	0.0269	0.0263	0.0259	0.0256	0.0254	0.0252	0.0251	0.0250	0.0249	0.0249	0.0249
56	0.0273	0.0265	0.0259	0.0255	0.0252	0.0250	0.0249	0.0247	0.0246	0.0246	0.0246	0.0246
57	0.0269	0.0262	0.0255	0.0252	0.0249	0.0247	0.0245	0.0244	0.0243	0.0243	0.0242	0.0242
58	0.0265	0.0258	0.0252	0.0248	0.0245	0.0244	0.0242	0.0240	0.0240	0.0239	0.0239	0.0239
59	0.0261	0.0254	0.0248	0.0245	0.0242	0.0240	0.0239	0.0237	0.0236	0.0236	0.0236	0.0236
60	0.0258	0.0251	0.0245	0.0242	0.0239	0.0237	0.0236	0.0234	0.0233	0.0233	0.0233	0.0233

DEPRECIATION ANNUITIES, DECIMALLY EXPRESSED

DOUBLE-RATE-DECLINING-BALANCE METHOD   CRITICAL RATE OF RETURN 7.000 PERCENT

| | | | | TYPE OF RETIREMENT DISPERSION | | | | |
AVERAGE LIFE (YEARS)	L0	L05	L1	L15	L2	L3	L4	L5
1	1.1779	1.1283	0.9765	0.8388	0.6175	1.8000	0.1095	0.1126
2	0.5324	0.5294	0.5262	0.5253	0.5244	0.5187	0.5118	0.5131
3	0.3583	0.3561	0.3539	0.3523	0.3508	0.3488	0.3464	0.3459
4	0.2716	0.2696	0.2676	0.2662	0.2649	0.2630	0.2617	0.2610
5	0.2197	0.2178	0.2160	0.2146	0.2134	0.2116	0.2107	0.2102
6	0.1851	0.1833	0.1815	0.1803	0.1791	0.1775	0.1766	0.1762
7	0.1604	0.1586	0.1570	0.1557	0.1546	0.1532	0.1524	0.1520
8	0.1419	0.1401	0.1385	0.1373	0.1362	0.1349	0.1342	0.1338
9	0.1274	0.1257	0.1242	0.1230	0.1220	0.1207	0.1200	0.1197
10	0.1158	0.1142	0.1127	0.1116	0.1106	0.1094	0.1087	0.1084
11	0.1064	0.1048	0.1033	0.1022	0.1012	0.1001	0.0995	0.0992
12	0.0984	0.0969	0.0955	0.0944	0.0935	0.0924	0.0917	0.0915
13	0.0917	0.0902	0.0888	0.0878	0.0869	0.0858	0.0852	0.0850
14	0.0859	0.0845	0.0831	0.0821	0.0812	0.0802	0.0796	0.0794
15	0.0809	0.0795	0.0782	0.0772	0.0764	0.0754	0.0748	0.0745
16	0.0765	0.0751	0.0739	0.0729	0.0721	0.0711	0.0706	0.0703
17	0.0726	0.0713	0.0700	0.0691	0.0683	0.0674	0.0668	0.0666
18	0.0691	0.0678	0.0666	0.0657	0.0649	0.0640	0.0635	0.0633
19	0.0660	0.0648	0.0636	0.0627	0.0619	0.0610	0.0605	0.0603
20	0.0632	0.0620	0.0608	0.0600	0.0592	0.0583	0.0578	0.0576
21	0.0607	0.0594	0.0583	0.0575	0.0567	0.0559	0.0554	0.0552
22	0.0583	0.0571	0.0560	0.0552	0.0545	0.0537	0.0532	0.0530
23	0.0562	0.0550	0.0540	0.0532	0.0524	0.0517	0.0512	0.0510
24	0.0542	0.0531	0.0520	0.0513	0.0506	0.0498	0.0494	0.0492
25	0.0524	0.0513	0.0503	0.0495	0.0488	0.0481	0.0477	0.0475
26	0.0507	0.0496	0.0486	0.0479	0.0472	0.0465	0.0461	0.0459
27	0.0491	0.0481	0.0471	0.0464	0.0457	0.0450	0.0446	0.0445

29	0.0463	0.0453	0.0444	0.0437	0.0431	0.0424	0.0420	0.0419
30	0.0450	0.0441	0.0432	0.0425	0.0419	0.0412	0.0409	0.0407
31	0.0438	0.0429	0.0420	0.0413	0.0407	0.0401	0.0397	0.0396
32	0.0427	0.0418	0.0409	0.0403	0.0397	0.0391	0.0387	0.0386
33	0.0416	0.0407	0.0399	0.0393	0.0387	0.0381	0.0377	0.0376
34	0.0406	0.0397	0.0389	0.0383	0.0377	0.0371	0.0368	0.0367
35	0.0396	0.0388	0.0380	0.0374	0.0369	0.0363	0.0360	0.0358
36	0.0387	0.0379	0.0371	0.0365	0.0360	0.0354	0.0351	0.0350
37	0.0379	0.0371	0.0363	0.0357	0.0352	0.0347	0.0344	0.0342
38	0.0371	0.0363	0.0355	0.0350	0.0344	0.0339	0.0336	0.0335
39	0.0363	0.0355	0.0348	0.0342	0.0337	0.0332	0.0329	0.0328
40	0.0355	0.0348	0.0341	0.0335	0.0330	0.0325	0.0323	0.0321
41	0.0348	0.0341	0.0334	0.0329	0.0324	0.0319	0.0316	0.0315
42	0.0341	0.0334	0.0327	0.0322	0.0318	0.0313	0.0310	0.0309
43	0.0335	0.0328	0.0321	0.0316	0.0312	0.0307	0.0304	0.0303
44	0.0328	0.0322	0.0315	0.0310	0.0306	0.0301	0.0299	0.0298
45	0.0322	0.0316	0.0309	0.0305	0.0300	0.0296	0.0293	0.0292
46	0.0317	0.0310	0.0304	0.0299	0.0295	0.0291	0.0288	0.0287
47	0.0311	0.0305	0.0299	0.0294	0.0290	0.0286	0.0284	0.0283
48	0.0306	0.0299	0.0293	0.0289	0.0285	0.0281	0.0279	0.0278
49	0.0301	0.0294	0.0289	0.0284	0.0280	0.0276	0.0274	0.0273
50	0.0296	0.0290	0.0284	0.0280	0.0276	0.0272	0.0270	0.0269
51	0.0291	0.0285	0.0279	0.0275	0.0272	0.0268	0.0266	0.0265
52	0.0286	0.0280	0.0275	0.0271	0.0267	0.0264	0.0262	0.0261
53	0.0282	0.0276	0.0271	0.0267	0.0263	0.0260	0.0258	0.0257
54	0.0278	0.0272	0.0267	0.0263	0.0259	0.0256	0.0254	0.0253
55	0.0273	0.0268	0.0263	0.0259	0.0256	0.0252	0.0250	0.0250
56	0.0269	0.0264	0.0259	0.0255	0.0252	0.0249	0.0247	0.0246
57	0.0265	0.0260	0.0255	0.0252	0.0248	0.0245	0.0243	0.0243
58	0.0262	0.0256	0.0252	0.0248	0.0245	0.0242	0.0240	0.0240
59	0.0258	0.0253	0.0248	0.0245	0.0242	0.0239	0.0237	0.0236
60	0.0254	0.0249	0.0245	0.0241	0.0238	0.0235	0.0234	0.0233

DEPRECIATION ANNUITIES, DECIMALLY EXPRESSED

DOUBLE-RATE-DECLINING-BALANCE METHOD   CRITICAL RATE OF RETURN 7.000 PERCENT

AVERAGE LIFE (YEARS)	TYPE OF RETIREMENT DISPERSION							
	R05	R15	R2	R25	R3	R4	R5	R1
1	0.8402	0.2134	0.1189	0.1161	0.1175	0.3334	0.1203	1.1947
2	0.5233	0.5165	0.5182	0.5195	0.5213	0.6067	0.4865	0.5206
3	0.3538	0.3504	0.3496	0.3488	0.3459	0.3244	0.3480	0.3527
4	0.2681	0.2651	0.2640	0.2633	0.2624	0.2593	0.2612	0.2665
5	0.2166	0.2138	0.2127	0.2120	0.2113	0.2125	0.2099	0.2150
6	0.1822	0.1795	0.1785	0.1778	0.1772	0.1788	0.1761	0.1807
7	0.1577	0.1551	0.1542	0.1535	0.1529	0.1504	0.1519	0.1562
8	0.1393	0.1368	0.1359	0.1353	0.1347	0.1334	0.1337	0.1378
9	0.1250	0.1226	0.1217	0.1211	0.1205	0.1199	0.1196	0.1236
10	0.1136	0.1112	0.1103	0.1097	0.1092	0.1097	0.1083	0.1122
11	0.1042	0.1019	0.1010	0.1005	0.0999	0.0988	0.0991	0.1028
12	0.0964	0.0941	0.0933	0.0927	0.0922	0.0919	0.0914	0.0950
13	0.0898	0.0875	0.0867	0.0862	0.0857	0.0869	0.0849	0.0884
14	0.0841	0.0819	0.0811	0.0806	0.0801	0.0811	0.0793	0.0828
15	0.0791	0.0770	0.0762	0.0757	0.0752	0.0757	0.0745	0.0779
16	0.0748	0.0727	0.0720	0.0715	0.0710	0.0715	0.0702	0.0736
17	0.0710	0.0690	0.0682	0.0677	0.0673	0.0677	0.0665	0.0698
18	0.0676	0.0656	0.0649	0.0644	0.0639	0.0645	0.0632	0.0664
19	0.0645	0.0626	0.0619	0.0614	0.0609	0.0611	0.0602	0.0634
20	0.0618	0.0599	0.0592	0.0587	0.0583	0.0586	0.0576	0.0607
21	0.0593	0.0574	0.0567	0.0563	0.0558	0.0561	0.0552	0.0582
22	0.0570	0.0552	0.0545	0.0540	0.0536	0.0539	0.0530	0.0559
23	0.0549	0.0531	0.0525	0.0520	0.0516	0.0517	0.0510	0.0539
24	0.0530	0.0513	0.0506	0.0502	0.0498	0.0499	0.0491	0.0520
25	0.0513	0.0495	0.0489	0.0485	0.0480	0.0482	0.0474	0.0503
26	0.0496	0.0479	0.0473	0.0469	0.0465	0.0466	0.0459	0.0486
27	0.0481	0.0465	0.0458	0.0454	0.0450	0.0450	0.0444	0.0471

29	0.0454	0.0438	0.0432	0.0428	0.0424	0.0425	0.0424	0.0428	0.0418	0.0444
30	0.0441	0.0426	0.0420	0.0416	0.0412	0.0413	0.0412	0.0416	0.0407	0.0432
31	0.0430	0.0414	0.0409	0.0405	0.0401	0.0401	0.0401	0.0405	0.0396	0.0421
32	0.0419	0.0404	0.0398	0.0394	0.0391	0.0391	0.0391	0.0394	0.0385	0.0410
33	0.0408	0.0394	0.0388	0.0384	0.0381	0.0381	0.0381	0.0384	0.0376	0.0400
34	0.0399	0.0384	0.0379	0.0375	0.0372	0.0372	0.0372	0.0375	0.0366	0.0390
35	0.0389	0.0375	0.0370	0.0366	0.0363	0.0363	0.0363	0.0366	0.0358	0.0381
36	0.0381	0.0367	0.0362	0.0358	0.0355	0.0355	0.0355	0.0358	0.0350	0.0373
37	0.0372	0.0359	0.0354	0.0350	0.0347	0.0347	0.0347	0.0350	0.0342	0.0365
38	0.0364	0.0351	0.0346	0.0343	0.0340	0.0339	0.0339	0.0343	0.0335	0.0357
39	0.0357	0.0344	0.0339	0.0335	0.0333	0.0332	0.0332	0.0335	0.0328	0.0349
40	0.0350	0.0337	0.0332	0.0329	0.0326	0.0326	0.0326	0.0329	0.0321	0.0342
41	0.0343	0.0330	0.0325	0.0322	0.0320	0.0319	0.0319	0.0322	0.0315	0.0336
42	0.0336	0.0324	0.0319	0.0316	0.0313	0.0313	0.0313	0.0316	0.0309	0.0329
43	0.0330	0.0318	0.0313	0.0310	0.0307	0.0307	0.0307	0.0310	0.0303	0.0323
44	0.0324	0.0312	0.0308	0.0305	0.0302	0.0302	0.0302	0.0305	0.0298	0.0317
45	0.0318	0.0307	0.0302	0.0299	0.0296	0.0296	0.0296	0.0299	0.0292	0.0312
46	0.0313	0.0301	0.0297	0.0294	0.0291	0.0291	0.0291	0.0294	0.0287	0.0306
47	0.0307	0.0296	0.0292	0.0289	0.0286	0.0286	0.0286	0.0289	0.0282	0.0301
48	0.0302	0.0291	0.0287	0.0284	0.0281	0.0281	0.0281	0.0284	0.0278	0.0296
49	0.0297	0.0287	0.0282	0.0280	0.0277	0.0277	0.0277	0.0280	0.0273	0.0291
50	0.0292	0.0282	0.0278	0.0275	0.0272	0.0272	0.0273	0.0275	0.0269	0.0286
51	0.0288	0.0278	0.0273	0.0271	0.0268	0.0268	0.0268	0.0271	0.0265	0.0282
52	0.0283	0.0273	0.0269	0.0267	0.0264	0.0264	0.0264	0.0267	0.0261	0.0278
53	0.0279	0.0269	0.0265	0.0263	0.0260	0.0260	0.0260	0.0263	0.0257	0.0273
54	0.0275	0.0265	0.0261	0.0259	0.0256	0.0256	0.0256	0.0259	0.0253	0.0269
55	0.0271	0.0261	0.0258	0.0255	0.0252	0.0252	0.0253	0.0255	0.0250	0.0265
56	0.0267	0.0258	0.0254	0.0251	0.0249	0.0249	0.0249	0.0251	0.0246	0.0262
57	0.0263	0.0254	0.0250	0.0248	0.0245	0.0245	0.0246	0.0248	0.0243	0.0258
58	0.0259	0.0251	0.0247	0.0245	0.0242	0.0242	0.0242	0.0245	0.0239	0.0254
59	0.0256	0.0247	0.0244	0.0241	0.0239	0.0239	0.0239	0.0241	0.0236	0.0251
60	0.0252	0.0244	0.0240	0.0238	0.0236	0.0236	0.0236	0.0238	0.0233	0.0247

DEPRECIATION ANNUITIES, DECIMALLY EXPRESSED

SYD METHOD   CRITICAL RATE OF RETURN 8.000 PERCENT

AVERAGE LIFE (YEARS)	SC	SQ	TYPE OF RETIREMENT DISPERSION												
1	1.0038	1.0000	0.0000	0.0000	0.0000	0.0000	0.0000	0.0000	0.0000	0.0000	0.0000	0.0000	0.0000	0.0000
2	0.5120	0.5064	0.0000	0.0000	0.0000	0.0000	0.0000	0.0000	0.0000	0.0000	0.0000	0.0000	0.0000	0.0000
3	0.3480	0.3419	0.0000	0.0000	0.0000	0.0000	0.0000	0.0000	0.0000	0.0000	0.0000	0.0000	0.0000	0.0000
4	0.2659	0.2596	0.0000	0.0000	0.0000	0.0000	0.0000	0.0000	0.0000	0.0000	0.0000	0.0000	0.0000	0.0000
5	0.2166	0.2102	0.0000	0.0000	0.0000	0.0000	0.0000	0.0000	0.0000	0.0000	0.0000	0.0000	0.0000	0.0000
6	0.1836	0.1773	0.0000	0.0000	0.0000	0.0000	0.0000	0.0000	0.0000	0.0000	0.0000	0.0000	0.0000	0.0000
7	0.1601	0.1538	0.0000	0.0000	0.0000	0.0000	0.0000	0.0000	0.0000	0.0000	0.0000	0.0000	0.0000	0.0000
8	0.1423	0.1362	0.0000	0.0000	0.0000	0.0000	0.0000	0.0000	0.0000	0.0000	0.0000	0.0000	0.0000	0.0000
9	0.1285	0.1224	0.0000	0.0000	0.0000	0.0000	0.0000	0.0000	0.0000	0.0000	0.0000	0.0000	0.0000	0.0000
10	0.1174	0.1114	0.0000	0.0000	0.0000	0.0000	0.0000	0.0000	0.0000	0.0000	0.0000	0.0000	0.0000	0.0000
11	0.1082	0.1024	0.0000	0.0000	0.0000	0.0000	0.0000	0.0000	0.0000	0.0000	0.0000	0.0000	0.0000	0.0000
12	0.1006	0.0949	0.0000	0.0000	0.0000	0.0000	0.0000	0.0000	0.0000	0.0000	0.0000	0.0000	0.0000	0.0000
13	0.0941	0.0886	0.0000	0.0000	0.0000	0.0000	0.0000	0.0000	0.0000	0.0000	0.0000	0.0000	0.0000	0.0000
14	0.0885	0.0831	0.0000	0.0000	0.0000	0.0000	0.0000	0.0000	0.0000	0.0000	0.0000	0.0000	0.0000	0.0000
15	0.0836	0.0784	0.0000	0.0000	0.0000	0.0000	0.0000	0.0000	0.0000	0.0000	0.0000	0.0000	0.0000	0.0000
16	0.0794	0.0742	0.0000	0.0000	0.0000	0.0000	0.0000	0.0000	0.0000	0.0000	0.0000	0.0000	0.0000	0.0000
17	0.0755	0.0706	0.0000	0.0000	0.0000	0.0000	0.0000	0.0000	0.0000	0.0000	0.0000	0.0000	0.0000	0.0000
18	0.0721	0.0673	0.0000	0.0000	0.0000	0.0000	0.0000	0.0000	0.0000	0.0000	0.0000	0.0000	0.0000	0.0000
19	0.0691	0.0644	0.0000	0.0000	0.0000	0.0000	0.0000	0.0000	0.0000	0.0000	0.0000	0.0000	0.0000	0.0000
20	0.0663	0.0617	0.0000	0.0000	0.0000	0.0000	0.0000	0.0000	0.0000	0.0000	0.0000	0.0000	0.0000	0.0000
21	0.0638	0.0593	0.0000	0.0000	0.0000	0.0000	0.0000	0.0000	0.0000	0.0000	0.0000	0.0000	0.0000	0.0000
22	0.0614	0.0571	0.0000	0.0000	0.0000	0.0000	0.0000	0.0000	0.0000	0.0000	0.0000	0.0000	0.0000	0.0000
23	0.0593	0.0551	0.0000	0.0000	0.0000	0.0000	0.0000	0.0000	0.0000	0.0000	0.0000	0.0000	0.0000	0.0000
24	0.0573	0.0533	0.0000	0.0000	0.0000	0.0000	0.0000	0.0000	0.0000	0.0000	0.0000	0.0000	0.0000	0.0000
25	0.0555	0.0516	0.0000	0.0000	0.0000	0.0000	0.0000	0.0000	0.0000	0.0000	0.0000	0.0000	0.0000	0.0000
26	0.0538	0.0500	0.0000	0.0000	0.0000	0.0000	0.0000	0.0000	0.0000	0.0000	0.0000	0.0000	0.0000	0.0000
27	0.0522	0.0486	0.0000	0.0000	0.0000	0.0000	0.0000	0.0000	0.0000	0.0000	0.0000	0.0000	0.0000	0.0000
28	0.0507	0.0472	0.0000	0.0000	0.0000	0.0000	0.0000	0.0000	0.0000	0.0000	0.0000	0.0000	0.0000	0.0000

29	0.0459	0.0494	0.0000	0.0000	0.0000	0.0000	0.0000	0.0000	0.0000	0.0000	0.0000	0.0000	0.0000	0.0000	0.0000
30	0.0448	0.0480	0.0000	0.0000	0.0000	0.0000	0.0000	0.0000	0.0000	0.0000	0.0000	0.0000	0.0000	0.0000	0.0000
31	0.0436	0.0468	0.0000	0.0000	0.0000	0.0000	0.0000	0.0000	0.0000	0.0000	0.0000	0.0000	0.0000	0.0000	0.0000
32	0.0426	0.0457	0.0000	0.0000	0.0000	0.0000	0.0000	0.0000	0.0000	0.0000	0.0000	0.0000	0.0000	0.0000	0.0000
33	0.0416	0.0446	0.0000	0.0000	0.0000	0.0000	0.0000	0.0000	0.0000	0.0000	0.0000	0.0000	0.0000	0.0000	0.0000
34	0.0406	0.0435	0.0000	0.0000	0.0000	0.0000	0.0000	0.0000	0.0000	0.0000	0.0000	0.0000	0.0000	0.0000	0.0000
35	0.0397	0.0425	0.0000	0.0000	0.0000	0.0000	0.0000	0.0000	0.0000	0.0000	0.0000	0.0000	0.0000	0.0000	0.0000
36	0.0389	0.0416	0.0000	0.0000	0.0000	0.0000	0.0000	0.0000	0.0000	0.0000	0.0000	0.0000	0.0000	0.0000	0.0000
37	0.0381	0.0407	0.0000	0.0000	0.0000	0.0000	0.0000	0.0000	0.0000	0.0000	0.0000	0.0000	0.0000	0.0000	0.0000
38	0.0373	0.0398	0.0000	0.0000	0.0000	0.0000	0.0000	0.0000	0.0000	0.0000	0.0000	0.0000	0.0000	0.0000	0.0000
39	0.0366	0.0390	0.0000	0.0000	0.0000	0.0000	0.0000	0.0000	0.0000	0.0000	0.0000	0.0000	0.0000	0.0000	0.0000
40	0.0359	0.0382	0.0000	0.0000	0.0000	0.0000	0.0000	0.0000	0.0000	0.0000	0.0000	0.0000	0.0000	0.0000	0.0000
41	0.0352	0.0375	0.0000	0.0000	0.0000	0.0000	0.0000	0.0000	0.0000	0.0000	0.0000	0.0000	0.0000	0.0000	0.0000
42	0.0346	0.0367	0.0000	0.0000	0.0000	0.0000	0.0000	0.0000	0.0000	0.0000	0.0000	0.0000	0.0000	0.0000	0.0000
43	0.0340	0.0360	0.0000	0.0000	0.0000	0.0000	0.0000	0.0000	0.0000	0.0000	0.0000	0.0000	0.0000	0.0000	0.0000
44	0.0334	0.0354	0.0000	0.0000	0.0000	0.0000	0.0000	0.0000	0.0000	0.0000	0.0000	0.0000	0.0000	0.0000	0.0000
45	0.0328	0.0347	0.0000	0.0000	0.0000	0.0000	0.0000	0.0000	0.0000	0.0000	0.0000	0.0000	0.0000	0.0000	0.0000
46	0.0323	0.0341	0.0000	0.0000	0.0000	0.0000	0.0000	0.0000	0.0000	0.0000	0.0000	0.0000	0.0000	0.0000	0.0000
47	0.0317	0.0335	0.0000	0.0000	0.0000	0.0000	0.0000	0.0000	0.0000	0.0000	0.0000	0.0000	0.0000	0.0000	0.0000
48	0.0312	0.0330	0.0000	0.0000	0.0000	0.0000	0.0000	0.0000	0.0000	0.0000	0.0000	0.0000	0.0000	0.0000	0.0000
49	0.0307	0.0324	0.0000	0.0000	0.0000	0.0000	0.0000	0.0000	0.0000	0.0000	0.0000	0.0000	0.0000	0.0000	0.0000
50	0.0303	0.0319	0.0000	0.0000	0.0000	0.0000	0.0000	0.0000	0.0000	0.0000	0.0000	0.0000	0.0000	0.0000	0.0000
51	0.0298	0.0314	0.0000	0.0000	0.0000	0.0000	0.0000	0.0000	0.0000	0.0000	0.0000	0.0000	0.0000	0.0000	0.0000
52	0.0294	0.0309	0.0000	0.0000	0.0000	0.0000	0.0000	0.0000	0.0000	0.0000	0.0000	0.0000	0.0000	0.0000	0.0000
53	0.0289	0.0304	0.0000	0.0000	0.0000	0.0000	0.0000	0.0000	0.0000	0.0000	0.0000	0.0000	0.0000	0.0000	0.0000
54	0.0285	0.0299	0.0000	0.0000	0.0000	0.0000	0.0000	0.0000	0.0000	0.0000	0.0000	0.0000	0.0000	0.0000	0.0000
55	0.0281	0.0295	0.0000	0.0000	0.0000	0.0000	0.0000	0.0000	0.0000	0.0000	0.0000	0.0000	0.0000	0.0000	0.0000
56	0.0277	0.0290	0.0000	0.0000	0.0000	0.0000	0.0000	0.0000	0.0000	0.0000	0.0000	0.0000	0.0000	0.0000	0.0000
57	0.0274	0.0286	0.0000	0.0000	0.0000	0.0000	0.0000	0.0000	0.0000	0.0000	0.0000	0.0000	0.0000	0.0000	0.0000
58	0.0270	0.0282	0.0000	0.0000	0.0000	0.0000	0.0000	0.0000	0.0000	0.0000	0.0000	0.0000	0.0000	0.0000	0.0000
59	0.0266	0.0278	0.0000	0.0000	0.0000	0.0000	0.0000	0.0000	0.0000	0.0000	0.0000	0.0000	0.0000	0.0000	0.0000
60	0.0263	0.0274	0.0000	0.0000	0.0000	0.0000	0.0000	0.0000	0.0000	0.0000	0.0000	0.0000	0.0000	0.0000	0.0000

DEPRECIATION ANNUITIES, DECIMALLY EXPRESSED

DOUBLE-RATE-DECLINING-BALANCE METHOD   CRITICAL RATE OF RETURN   8.000 PERCENT

AVERAGE LIFE (YEARS)	SC	SO	TYPE OF RETIREMENT DISPERSION												
1	1.0943	2.0000	0.0000	0.0000	0.0000	0.0000	0.0000	0.0000	0.0000	0.0000	0.0000	0.0000	0.0000	0.0000	0.0000
2	0.5335	0.5192	0.0000	0.0000	0.0000	0.0000	0.0000	0.0000	0.0000	0.0000	0.0000	0.0000	0.0000	0.0000	0.0000
3	0.3595	0.3477	0.0000	0.0000	0.0000	0.0000	0.0000	0.0000	0.0000	0.0000	0.0000	0.0000	0.0000	0.0000	0.0000
4	0.2728	0.2622	0.0000	0.0000	0.0000	0.0000	0.0000	0.0000	0.0000	0.0000	0.0000	0.0000	0.0000	0.0000	0.0000
5	0.2209	0.2112	0.0000	0.0000	0.0000	0.0000	0.0000	0.0000	0.0000	0.0000	0.0000	0.0000	0.0000	0.0000	0.0000
6	0.1863	0.1771	0.0000	0.0000	0.0000	0.0000	0.0000	0.0000	0.0000	0.0000	0.0000	0.0000	0.0000	0.0000	0.0000
7	0.1616	0.1529	0.0000	0.0000	0.0000	0.0000	0.0000	0.0000	0.0000	0.0000	0.0000	0.0000	0.0000	0.0000	0.0000
8	0.1431	0.1347	0.0000	0.0000	0.0000	0.0000	0.0000	0.0000	0.0000	0.0000	0.0000	0.0000	0.0000	0.0000	0.0000
9	0.1287	0.1206	0.0000	0.0000	0.0000	0.0000	0.0000	0.0000	0.0000	0.0000	0.0000	0.0000	0.0000	0.0000	0.0000
10	0.1171	0.1092	0.0000	0.0000	0.0000	0.0000	0.0000	0.0000	0.0000	0.0000	0.0000	0.0000	0.0000	0.0000	0.0000
11	0.1076	0.1000	0.0000	0.0000	0.0000	0.0000	0.0000	0.0000	0.0000	0.0000	0.0000	0.0000	0.0000	0.0000	0.0000
12	0.0997	0.0923	0.0000	0.0000	0.0000	0.0000	0.0000	0.0000	0.0000	0.0000	0.0000	0.0000	0.0000	0.0000	0.0000
13	0.0930	0.0858	0.0000	0.0000	0.0000	0.0000	0.0000	0.0000	0.0000	0.0000	0.0000	0.0000	0.0000	0.0000	0.0000
14	0.0873	0.0802	0.0000	0.0000	0.0000	0.0000	0.0000	0.0000	0.0000	0.0000	0.0000	0.0000	0.0000	0.0000	0.0000
15	0.0823	0.0754	0.0000	0.0000	0.0000	0.0000	0.0000	0.0000	0.0000	0.0000	0.0000	0.0000	0.0000	0.0000	0.0000
16	0.0779	0.0712	0.0000	0.0000	0.0000	0.0000	0.0000	0.0000	0.0000	0.0000	0.0000	0.0000	0.0000	0.0000	0.0000
17	0.0740	0.0674	0.0000	0.0000	0.0000	0.0000	0.0000	0.0000	0.0000	0.0000	0.0000	0.0000	0.0000	0.0000	0.0000
18	0.0705	0.0641	0.0000	0.0000	0.0000	0.0000	0.0000	0.0000	0.0000	0.0000	0.0000	0.0000	0.0000	0.0000	0.0000
19	0.0674	0.0612	0.0000	0.0000	0.0000	0.0000	0.0000	0.0000	0.0000	0.0000	0.0000	0.0000	0.0000	0.0000	0.0000
20	0.0646	0.0585	0.0000	0.0000	0.0000	0.0000	0.0000	0.0000	0.0000	0.0000	0.0000	0.0000	0.0000	0.0000	0.0000
21	0.0620	0.0561	0.0000	0.0000	0.0000	0.0000	0.0000	0.0000	0.0000	0.0000	0.0000	0.0000	0.0000	0.0000	0.0000
22	0.0597	0.0539	0.0000	0.0000	0.0000	0.0000	0.0000	0.0000	0.0000	0.0000	0.0000	0.0000	0.0000	0.0000	-0.0000
23	0.0576	0.0519	0.0000	0.0000	0.0000	0.0000	0.0000	0.0000	0.0000	0.0000	0.0000	0.0000	0.0000	0.0000	0.0000
24	0.0556	0.0500	0.0000	0.0000	0.0000	0.0000	0.0000	0.0000	0.0000	0.0000	0.0000	0.0000	0.0000	0.0000	0.0000
25	0.0538	0.0483	0.0000	0.0000	0.0000	0.0000	0.0000	0.0000	0.0000	0.0000	0.0000	0.0000	0.0000	0.0000	0.0000
26	0.0521	0.0468	0.0000	0.0000	0.0000	0.0000	0.0000	0.0000	0.0000	0.0000	0.0000	0.0000	0.0000	0.0000	0.0000
27	0.0505	0.0453	0.0000	0.0000	0.0000	0.0000	0.0000	0.0000	0.0000	0.0000	0.0000	0.0000	0.0000	0.0000	0.0000

30	0.0000	0.0010	0.0000	0.0000	0.0000	0.0000	0.0000	0.0030	0.0000	0.0000	0.0000	0.0464	0.0415
31	0.0000	0.0010	0.0000	0.0000	0.0000	0.0000	0.0000	0.0030	0.0000	0.0000	0.0000	0.0452	0.0404
32	0.0000	0.0010	0.0000	0.0000	0.0000	0.0000	0.0000	0.0030	0.0000	0.0000	0.0000	0.0440	0.0394
33	0.0000	0.0010	0.0000	0.0000	0.0000	0.0000	0.0000	0.0030	0.0000	0.0000	0.0000	0.0429	0.0384
34	0.0000	0.0010	0.0000	0.0000	0.0000	0.0000	0.0000	0.0030	0.0000	0.0000	0.0000	0.0419	0.0375
35	0.0000	0.0010	0.0000	0.0000	0.0000	0.0000	0.0000	0.0030	0.0000	0.0000	0.0000	0.0409	0.0366
36	0.0000	0.0010	0.0000	0.0000	0.0000	0.0000	0.0000	0.0030	0.0000	0.0000	0.0000	0.0400	0.0358
37	0.0000	0.0010	0.0000	0.0000	0.0000	0.0000	0.0000	0.0030	0.0000	0.0000	0.0000	0.0391	0.0350
38	0.0000	0.0010	0.0000	0.0000	0.0000	0.0000	0.0000	0.0030	0.0000	0.0000	0.0000	0.0383	0.0343
39	0.0000	0.0010	0.0000	0.0000	0.0000	0.0000	0.0000	0.0030	0.0000	0.0000	0.0000	0.0375	0.0336
40	0.0000	0.0010	0.0000	0.0000	0.0000	0.0000	0.0000	0.0030	0.0000	0.0000	0.0000	0.0368	0.0329
41	0.0000	0.0010	0.0000	0.0000	0.0000	0.0000	0.0000	0.0030	0.0000	0.0000	0.0000	0.0360	0.0323
42	0.0000	0.0010	0.0000	0.0000	0.0000	0.0000	0.0000	0.0030	0.0000	0.0000	0.0000	0.0353	0.0317
43	0.0000	0.0010	0.0000	0.0000	0.0000	0.0000	0.0000	0.0030	0.0000	0.0000	0.0000	0.0347	0.0311
44	0.0000	0.0010	0.0000	0.0000	0.0000	0.0000	0.0000	0.0010	0.0000	0.0000	0.0000	0.0340	0.0306
45	0.0000	0.0010	0.0000	0.0000	0.0000	0.0000	0.0000	0.0030	0.0000	0.0000	0.0000	0.0334	0.0300
46	0.0000	0.0010	0.0000	0.0000	0.0000	0.0000	0.0000	0.0030	0.0000	0.0000	0.0000	0.0328	0.0295
47	0.0000	0.0010	0.0000	0.0000	0.0000	0.0000	0.0000	0.0030	0.0000	0.0000	0.0000	0.0322	0.0290
48	0.0000	0.0010	0.0000	0.0000	0.0000	0.0000	0.0000	0.0030	0.0000	0.0000	0.0000	0.0317	0.0285
49	0.0000	0.0010	0.0000	0.0000	0.0000	0.0000	0.0000	0.0030	0.0000	0.0000	0.0000	0.0312	0.0281
50	0.0000	0.0010	0.0000	0.0000	0.0000	0.0000	0.0000	0.0030	0.0000	0.0000	0.0000	0.0307	0.0277
51	0.0000	0.0010	0.0000	0.0000	0.0000	0.0000	0.0000	0.0030	0.0000	0.0000	0.0000	0.0302	0.0272
52	0.0000	0.0010	0.0000	0.0000	0.0000	0.0000	0.0000	0.0030	0.0000	0.0000	0.0000	0.0297	0.0266
53	0.0000	0.0010	0.0000	0.0000	0.0000	0.0000	0.0000	0.0030	0.0000	0.0000	0.0000	0.0292	0.0264
54	0.0000	0.0010	0.0000	0.0000	0.0000	0.0000	0.0000	0.0030	0.0000	0.0000	0.0000	0.0288	0.0260
55	0.0000	0.0010	0.0000	0.0000	0.0000	0.0000	0.0000	0.0030	0.0000	0.0000	0.0000	0.0284	0.0257
56	0.0000	0.0010	0.0000	0.0000	0.0000	0.0000	0.0000	0.0030	0.0000	0.0000	0.0000	0.0279	0.0253
57	0.0000	0.0010	0.0000	0.0000	0.0000	0.0000	0.0000	0.0030	0.0000	0.0000	0.0000	0.0275	0.0250
58	0.0000	0.0010	0.0000	0.0000	0.0000	0.0000	0.0000	0.0030	0.0000	0.0000	0.0000	0.0271	0.0246
59	0.0000	0.0010	0.0000	0.0000	0.0000	0.0000	0.0000	0.0030	0.0000	0.0000	0.0000	0.0268	0.0243
60	0.0000	0.0010	0.0000	0.0000	0.0000	0.0000	0.0000	0.0030	0.0000	0.0000	0.0000	0.0264	0.0240

Table C.7. Printouts for federal income tax annuities
for Projects 1,2,3, and 4.

TABLE C.7: PROJECT 1

DETAILED STUDY OF FEDERAL INCOME TAX ANNUITIES

CASE DETERMINED INPUTS

PHYSICAL LIFE............	30.C000
BOOK LIFE...............	30.C0C0
COMPOSITE LIFE..........	30.C000
TOTAL NO. OF YEARS......	60
BOOK SALVAGE............	0.
PHYSICAL SALVAGE........	0.
TAX SALVAGE.............	0.
RATE OF RETURN..........	0.0600
DEBT RATIO..............	0.5000
INTEREST RATE CN DEBT...	0.C400
INITIAL INVESTMENT......	1000.C0
TAX RATE................	0.4800000
DISPERSICN..............	SC
BOOK ACCRUAL METHOD.....	S.L.
TAX ACCRUAL METHOD......	SYC
TYPE OF PLANT...........	CONTIN

FINAL STAGE CALCULATIONS

TOTAL OF PW OF MEAN ANN. SURV...	16463.229
PW OF FINAL YEAR FIT...........	0.
TAX INTEREST FACTOR............	0.6666667
PW FACTOR REPRESENTING PW	
AS OF TODAY OF PAYMENTS	
YEAR 60 TO ETERNITY..........	0.01531596
D PRIME.......................	0.03333333
D SUB T.......................	0.04606576
D-IBETA.......................	0.C2303784
MINIMAL GROSS INCCME ANNUITY...	0.04970450
I + DIB - DPR.................	0.04970450
TAX ANNUITY (PW)..............	0.01883437
TAX ANNUITY (COMPUTED)........	0.01883437
TAX ANNUITY (EQUAL LIVES,SL)..	0.03058738
TAX ANNUITY (EQUAL LIVES,SYD).	0.01882286

YEAR	MEAN ANNUAL SURVIVORS	BOOK DEPRECIATION ACCRUAL	PRESENT WORTH FACTOR	CURRENT RETIREMENTS	RESERVE BALANCE	UNRECOVERED BALANCE
1	1000.000	33.3333	0.9433962	8.4034	-8.4034	1008.4034
2	1000.000	33.3333	0.8899964	16.9480	7.9820	992.0180
3	1000.000	33.3333	0.8396193	17.2328	24.0825	975.9175
4	1000.000	33.3333	0.7920936	17.5224	39.8935	960.1065
5	1000.000	33.3333	0.7472581	17.8169	55.4099	944.5901
6	1000.000	33.3333	0.7049605	18.1164	70.6269	929.3731
29	1000.000	33.3333	0.1849567	26.3800	525.2426	674.1344
30	1000.000	33.3333	0.1741101	27.0267	331.5523	668.4477
31	1000.000	33.3333	0.1642548	27.4809	337.4047	662.5953
59	1000.000	33.3333	0.0321332	43.8635	202.0142	717.7010
60	1000.000	32.1157	0.0303143	44.5600	270.7876	729.2124
61	963.472	0.1104	0.0285984	36.5280	267.5930	695.8791
117	3.311	0.0493	0.0010945	2.5446	3.1394	0.1720
118	1.479	0.0124	0.0010325	1.8322	1.4175	0.0617
119	0.371	-0.0000	0.0009741	1.1079	0.3590	0.0124
120	0.		0.0009190	0.3713	0.	0.

	MINIMAL GROSS INCOME	INTEREST	TAX ACCRUAL	TAX RESERVE	TAXABLE INCOME AFTER TAXES
1	60.5042	20.1681	64.5206	-8.4034	9.1489
2	59.5211	19.8404	62.4592	39.1693	10.5548
3	58.5550	19.5183	60.4671	84.3957	11.9029
4	57.6064	19.2021	58.5507	127.3404	13.1869
5	56.6754	18.8918	56.6985	168.0742	14.4184
6	55.7624	18.5875	54.9313	206.6563	15.5770
29	40.4853	13.4951	32.8916	650.4983	27.4319
30	40.1069	13.3690	32.6403	656.3632	27.4309
31	39.7557	13.2519	32.4162	661.5226	27.4210
59	43.0791	14.3597	35.6949	597.5197	26.3578
60	43.7527	14.5842	35.9547	588.6546	26.5472
61	41.7527	13.9176	33.1060	588.0814	26.8449
117	0.0103	0.0034	0.0001	3.3113	0.1172
118	0.0037	0.0012	0.0000	1.4792	0.0517
119	0.00C7	0.0002	0.0000	0.3713	0.0129
120	0.	0.	0.0000	0.	-0.0000

YEAR	PW OF MEAN ANNUAL SURVIVORS	PW OF SYD ACCRUALS	PW OF F.I.T.	PW OF BOOK DEPRECIATION ACCRUALS	PW OF MINIMAL GROSS INCOME
1	943.396	60.8685	7.9671	31.4465	57.07943
2	889.996	55.5885	8.6712	29.6665	52.97355
3	839.619	50.7694	9.2252	27.9873	49.16395
4	792.094	46.3776	9.6418	26.4031	45.62966
5	747.258	42.3684	9.9455	24.9086	42.35116
6	704.961	38.7244	10.1364	23.4987	39.31028
29	184.557	6.0704	4.6733	6.1519	7.47183
30	174.110	5.6830	4.4086	5.8037	6.98301
31	164.255	5.3245	4.1576	5.4752	6.53007
59	32.133	1.1470	0.7818	1.0711	1.38427
60	30.314	1.0899	0.7429	1.0105	1.32633
61	27.554	0.9468	0.7087	0.9185	1.19406
117	0.004	0.0000	0.0001	0.0001	0.00001
118	0.002	0.0000	0.0000	0.0001	0.00000
119	0.000	0.0000	0.0000	0.0000	0.00000
120	0.	0.0000	-0.0000	-0.0000	0.
TOTALS	16463.229	758.391	310.075	548.774	818.297

TABLE C.7: PROJECT 2

DETAILED STUDY OF FEDERAL INCOME TAX ANNUITIES

CASE DETERMINED INPUTS

PHYSICAL LIFE............	30.C000
BOOK LIFE...............	30.C000
COMPOSITE LIFE.........	30.C000
TOTAL NO. OF YEARS.....	300
BOOK SALVAGE..........	0.
PHYSICAL SALVAGE......	0.
TAX SALVAGE...........	0.
RATE OF RETURN........	0.C600
CEBT RATIO............	0.5000
INTEREST RATE ON DEBT...	0.C400
INITIAL INVESTMENT.....	1000.C0
TAX RATE..............	0.4800000
CISPERSICN............	SC
BOOK ACCRUAL METHOD....	S.L.
TAX ACCRUAL METHOD....	SYD
TYPE OF PLANT.........	CONTIN

FINAL STAGE CALCULATIONS

TOTAL OF PW OF MEAN ANN. SURV...	16666.664
PW OF FINAL YEAR FIT..........	0.
TAX INTEREST FACTOR..........	0.6666667
PW FACTOR REPRESENTING PW AS OF TODAY OF PAYMENTS YEAR 300 TO ETERNITY..........	0.00000001
D PRIME......................	0.03333332
D SUB T......................	0.04610292
D-IBETA......................	0.02303784
MINIMAL GROSS INCOME ANNUITY....	0.04970450
I + DIB - DPR.................	0.04970451
TAX ANNUITY (PW)..............	0.01880007
TAX ANNUITY (COMPUTED)........	0.01880006
TAX ANNUITY (EQUAL LIVES,SL)....	0.03058738
TAX ANNUITY (EQUAL LIVES,SYD)...	0.01880015

YEAR	MEAN ANNUAL SURVIVORS	BOOK DEPRECIATION ACCRUAL	PRESENT WORTH FACTOR	CURRENT RETIREMENTS	RESERVE BALANCE	UNRECOVERED BALANCE
1	1000.000	33.3333	0.9433962	8.4034	-8.4034	1008.4034
2	1000.000	33.3333	0.8899964	16.9480	7.9820	992.0180
3	1000.000	33.3333	0.8396193	17.2328	24.0825	975.9175
4	1000.000	33.3333	0.7920936	17.5224	39.8935	960.1065
5	1000.000	33.3333	0.7472581	17.8169	55.4099	944.5901
6	1000.000	33.3333	0.7049605	18.1164	70.6269	929.3731
29	1000.000	33.3333	0.1845567	26.5800	325.2456	674.7544
30	1000.000	33.3333	0.1741101	27.0267	331.5523	668.4477
31	1000.000	33.3333	0.1642548	27.4809	337.4047	662.5953
59	1000.000	33.3333	0.0321332	43.8235	282.0142	717.9858
60	1000.000	33.3333	0.0303143	44.5600	270.7876	729.2124
61	1000.000	33.3333	0.0285984	36.8349	267.2860	732.7140
117	1000.000	33.3333	0.0010945	33.2654	310.9053	689.0947
118	1000.000	33.3333	0.0010325	33.1061	311.1325	688.8675
119	1000.000	33.3333	0.0009741	32.9321	311.5337	688.4663
120	1000.000	33.3333	0.0009190	32.7429	312.1242	687.8758
298	1000.000	33.3333	0.0000000	33.3342	316.5809	683.4191
299	1000.000	33.3333	0.0000000	33.3342	316.5800	683.4200
300	1000.000	33.3333	0.0000000	33.3343	316.5791	683.4209
357	2.500	0.0833	0.0000000	1.9445	2.3704	0.1297
358	1.111	0.0370	0.0000000	1.3889	1.0648	0.0463
359	0.278	0.0093	0.0000000	0.8334	0.2685	0.0093
360	0.	0.0000	0.0000000	0.2778	0.	0.

	MINIMAL GROSS INCOME	INTEREST	TAX ACCRUAL	TAX RESERVE	TAXABLE INCOME AFTER TAXES	F.I.T.
1	60.5042	20.1681	64.5206	-8.4034	9.1489	8.4451
2	59.5211	19.8404	62.4592	39.1693	10.5548	9.7429
3	58.5550	19.5183	60.4671	84.3957	11.9029	10.9873
4	57.6064	19.2021	58.5507	127.3404	13.1869	12.1725
5	56.6754	18.8918	56.6985	168.0742	14.4184	13.3093
6	55.7624	18.5875	54.9313	206.6563	15.5770	14.3787
29	40.4853	13.4951	32.8916	650.4983	27.4319	25.3217
30	40.1069	13.3690	32.6403	656.3632	27.4309	25.3208
31	39.7557	13.2519	32.4162	661.5226	27.4210	25.3117
59	43.0791	14.3597	35.6949	597.5197	26.3578	24.3303
60	43.7527	14.5842	35.9547	588.6546	26.5472	24.5051
61	43.9628	14.6543	35.8734	587.7744	26.7685	24.7094
117	41.3457	13.7819	33.5294	636.4830	27.3678	25.2625
118	41.3321	13.7774	33.5007	636.9062	27.3874	25.2806
119	41.3080	13.7693	33.4665	637.4748	27.4055	25.2974
120	41.2725	13.7575	33.4266	638.1984	27.4217	25.3124
298	41.0051	13.6684	33.3332	641.4211	27.3368	25.2340
299	41.0052	13.6684	33.3333	641.4201	27.3368	25.2340
300	41.0053	13.6684	33.3333	641.4191	27.3368	25.2340
357	0.0078	0.0026	0.0001	2.5000	0.0885	0.0817
358	0.0028	0.0009	0.0000	1.1111	0.0389	0.0359
359	0.0006	0.0002	0.0000	0.2778	0.0096	0.0089
360	0.	0.	0.0000	0.	0.0000	0.0000

562

YEAR	PW OF MEAN ANNUAL SURVIVORS	PW OF SYD ACCRUALS	PW OF F.I.T.	PW OF BOOK DEPRECIATION ACCRUALS	PW OF MINIMAL GROSS INCOME
1	943.396	60.8685	7.9671	31.4465	57.07943
2	889.996	55.5885	8.6712	29.6665	52.97355
3	839.619	50.7694	9.2252	27.9873	49.16395
4	792.094	46.3776	9.6418	26.4031	45.62966
5	747.258	42.3684	9.9455	24.9086	42.35116
6	704.961	38.7244	10.1364	23.4987	39.31028
29	184.557	5.6830	4.6733	6.1519	7.47183
30	174.110	5.3245	4.4086	5.8037	6.98301
31	164.255	5.0040	4.1576	5.4752	6.53007
59	32.133	1.1470	0.7818	1.0711	1.38427
60	30.314	1.0899	0.7429	1.0105	1.32633
61	28.598	1.0259	0.7066	0.9533	1.25727
117	1.094	0.0367	0.0276	0.0365	0.04525
118	1.033	0.0346	0.0261	0.0344	0.04268
119	0.974	0.0326	0.0246	0.0325	0.04024
120	0.919	0.0307	0.0233	0.0306	0.03793
298	0.000	0.0000	0.0000	0.0000	0.00000
299	0.000	0.0000	0.0000	0.0000	0.00000
300	0.000	0.0000	0.0000	0.0000	0.00000
357	0.000	0.0000	0.0000	0.0000	0.00000
358	0.000	0.0000	0.0000	0.0000	0.00000
359	0.000	0.0000	0.0000	0.0000	0.00000
360	0.	0.0000	0.0000	0.0000	0.
TOTALS	16666.664	768.382	313.335	555.555	828.408

TABLE C.7: PROJECT 3

DETAILED STUDY OF FEDERAL INCOME TAX ANNUITIES

CASE DETERMINED INPUTS

PHYSICAL LIFE...........	30.C000
BOOK LIFE..............	30.0000
COMPOSITE LIFE.........	30.C000
TOTAL NO. OF YEARS.....	60
BOOK SALVAGE...........	0.
PHYSICAL SALVAGE.......	0.
TAX SALVAGE............	0.
RATE OF RETURN.........	0.C600
CEBT RATIO.............	0.5000
INTEREST RATE ON DEBT..	0.0400
INITIAL INVESTMENT.....	1000.C0
TAX RATE...............	0.48C0000
CISPERSICN.............	R1
BOOK ACCRUAL METHOD....	S.L.
TAX ACCRUAL METHOD.....	SYD
TYPE OF PLANT..........	CONTIN

FINAL STAGE CALCULATIONS

TOTAL OF PW OF MEAN ANN. SURV...	16449.228
PW OF FINAL YEAR FIT............	0.
TAX INTEREST FACTOR.............	0.6666667
PW FACTOR REPRESENTING PW AS OF TODAY OF PAYMENTS YEAR 60 TO ETERNITY..........	0.01531596
D PRIME........................	0.03333332
D SUB T........................	0.04522493
D-IBETA........................	0.01930370
MINIMAL GROSS INCOME ANNUITY...	0.04597037
I + DIB - DPR..................	0.04597037
TAX ANNUITY (PW)...............	0.01731259
TAX ANNUITY (COMPUTED).........	0.01731259
TAX ANNUITY (EQUAL LIVES,SL)...	0.02828945
TAX ANNUITY (EQUAL LIVES,SYD)...	0.01730435

YEAR	MEAN ANNUAL SURVIVORS	BOOK DEPRECIATION ACCRUAL	PRESENT WORTH FACTOR	CURRENT RETIREMENTS	RESERVE BALANCE	UNRECOVERED BALANCE
1	1000.000	33.3333	0.9433962	4.3455	-4.3455	1004.3455
2	1000.000	33.3333	0.8899964	9.0212	19.9666	980.0334
3	1000.000	33.3333	0.8396193	9.5192	43.7808	956.2192
4	1000.000	33.3333	0.7920936	10.0052	67.1089	932.8911
5	1000.000	33.3333	0.7472581	10.5094	89.9328	910.0672
6	1000.000	33.3333	0.7049605	11.0155	112.2506	887.7494
29	1000.000	33.3333	0.1845567	30.2287	429.5429	570.4571
30	1000.000	33.3333	0.1741101	31.3215	431.5547	568.4453
31	1000.000	33.3333	0.1642548	32.3661	432.5219	567.4781
59	1000.000	33.3333	0.0321332	29.8812	353.4869	646.5131
60	1000.000	33.3333	0.0303143	29.2675	357.5527	642.4473
61	971.424	32.3808	0.0285984	28.5757	362.3103	609.1140
117	0.193	0.0064	0.0010945	0.2408	0.1979	-0.0050
118	0.063	0.0021	0.0010325	0.1301	0.0742	-0.0115
119	0.010	0.0003	0.0009741	0.0526	0.0237	-0.0136
120	0.	-0.0139	0.0009190	0.0101	0.	0.

	MINIMAL GROSS INCOME	INTEREST	TAX ACCRUAL	TAX RESERVE	TAXABLE INCOME AFTER TAXES	F.I.T.
1	60.2607	20.0869	64.5173	-4.3455	8.9898	8.2983
2	58.8020	19.6007	62.4055	51.1506	10.1292	9.3500
3	57.3732	19.1244	60.3462	104.0369	11.2359	10.3716
4	55.9735	18.6578	58.3445	154.3780	12.3045	11.3580
5	54.6040	18.2013	56.3613	202.2130	13.3747	12.3459
6	53.2650	17.7550	54.4434	247.5588	14.3999	13.2922
29	34.2274	11.4091	31.7936	711.9560	24.3580	22.4843
30	34.1067	11.3689	31.8528	712.4281	24.2184	22.3554
31	34.0487	11.3496	31.9638	711.9148	24.0687	22.2173
59	38.7908	12.9303	33.7531	655.5879	25.4407	23.4838
60	38.5468	12.8489	33.5172	660.0735	25.5141	23.5514
61	36.5468	12.1823	30.9206	665.0149	25.8248	23.8382
117	-0.0003	-0.0001	0.	0.1929	0.0062	0.0057
118	-0.0007	-0.0002	-0.	0.0627	0.0016	0.0015
119	-0.0008	-0.0003	0.0000	0.0101	-0.0002	-0.0002
120	0.	0.	-0.0000	0.	-0.0139	-0.0128

YEAR	PW OF MEAN ANNUAL SURVIVORS	PW OF SYD ACCRUALS	PW CF F.I.T.	PW OF BOOK DEPRECIATION ACCRUALS	PW OF MINIMAL GROSS INCOME
1	943.396	60.8654	7.8286	31.4465	56.84974
2	889.996	55.5406	8.3215	29.6665	52.33357
3	839.619	50.6679	8.7082	27.9873	48.17160
4	792.094	46.2143	8.9966	26.4031	44.33623
5	747.258	42.1164	9.2256	24.9086	40.80331
6	704.961	38.3805	9.3705	23.4987	37.54969
29	184.557	5.8677	4.1496	6.1519	6.31690
30	174.110	5.5459	3.8923	5.8037	5.93832
31	164.255	5.2502	3.6493	5.4752	5.59266
59	32.133	1.0846	0.7546	1.0711	1.24647
60	30.314	1.0160	0.7139	1.0105	1.16852
61	27.781	0.8843	0.6817	0.9260	1.04518
117	0.000	0.	0.0000	0.0000	-0.00000
118	0.000	-0.	0.0000	0.0000	-0.00000
119	0.000	-0.0000	-0.0000	0.0000	-0.00000
120	0.	-0.0000	-0.0000	-0.0000	0.
TOTALS	16449.228	743.915	284.779	548.308	756.177

TABLE C.7: PROJECT 4

DETAILED STUDY OF FEDERAL INCOME TAX ANNUITIES

CASE DETERMINED INPUTS

PHYSICAL LIFE...................	30.0000
BOOK LIFE.......................	30.0000
COMPOSITE LIFE..................	30.0000
TOTAL NO. OF YEARS..............	300
BOOK SALVAGE....................	0.
PHYSICAL SALVAGE................	0.
TAX SALVAGE.....................	0.
RATE OF RETURN..................	0.0600
DEBT RATIO......................	0.5000
INTEREST RATE ON DEBT...........	0.0400
INITIAL INVESTMENT..............	1000.00
TAX RATE........................	0.4800000
DISPERSION......................	R1
BOOK ACCRUAL METHOD.............	S.L.
TAX ACCRUAL METHOD..............	SYD
TYPE OF PLANT...................	CONTIN

FINAL STAGE CALCULATIONS

TOTAL OF PW OF MEAN ANN. SURV...	16666.664
PW OF FINAL YEAR FIT............	0.
TAX INTEREST FACTOR.............	0.6666667
PW FACTOR REPRESENTING PW	
AS OF TODAY OF PAYMENTS	
YEAR 300 TO ETERNITY..........	0.00000001
D PRIME.........................	0.03333332
D SUB T.........................	0.04527061
D-IBETA.........................	0.01930370
MINIMAL GROSS INCOME ANNUITY....	0.04597037
I + DIB - DPR...................	0.04597037
TAX ANNUITY (PW)................	0.01727042
TAX ANNUITY (COMPUTED)..........	0.01727042
TAX ANNUITY (EQUAL LIVES,SL)....	0.02828945
TAX ANNUITY (EQUAL LIVES,SYD)...	0.01727048

YEAR	MEAN ANNUAL SURVIVORS	BOOK DEPRECIATION ACCRUAL	PRESENT WORTH FACTOR	CURRENT RETIREMENTS	RESERVE BALANCE	UNRECOVERED BALANCE
1	1000.000	33.3333	0.9433962	4.3455	-4.3455	1004.3455
2	1000.000	33.3333	0.8899964	9.0212	19.9666	980.0334
3	1000.000	33.3333	0.8396193	9.5192	43.7808	956.2192
4	1000.000	33.3333	0.7920936	10.0052	67.1089	932.8911
5	1000.000	33.3333	0.7472581	10.5094	89.9328	910.0672
6	1000.000	33.3333	0.7049605	11.0155	112.2506	887.7494
29	1000.000	33.3333	0.1845567	30.2287	429.5429	570.4571
30	1000.000	33.3333	0.1741101	31.3215	431.5547	568.4453
31	1000.000	33.3333	0.1642548	32.3661	432.5219	567.4781
59	1000.000	33.3333	0.0321332	29.8812	353.4869	646.5131
60	1000.000	33.3333	0.0303143	29.2675	357.5527	642.4473
61	1000.000	33.3333	0.0285984	28.6999	362.1861	637.8139
117	1000.000	33.3333	0.0010945	33.3401	377.0003	622.9997
118	1000.000	33.3333	0.0010325	33.3942	376.9395	623.0605
119	1000.000	33.3333	0.0009741	33.4423	376.8305	623.1695
120	1000.000	33.3333	0.0009190	33.4839	376.6800	623.3201
298	1000.000	33.3333	0.0000000	33.3334	374.7355	625.2645
299	1000.000	33.3333	0.0000000	33.3334	374.7354	625.2646
357	1000.000	33.3333	0.0000000	33.3336	374.7354	625.7646
	0.218	0.0073	0.0000000	30.2700	-0.2644	-0.0464
358	0.071	0.0024	0.0000000	0.1468	0.1249	-0.0537
359	0.012	-0.0004	0.0000000	0.0597	0.0676	-0.0561
360	0.	-0.0564	0.0000000	0.0116	0.	0.

	MINIMAL GROSS INCOME	INTEREST	TAX ACCRUAL	TAX RESERVE	TAXABLE INCOME AFTER TAXES	F.I.T.
1	60.2607	20.0869	64.5173	-4.3455	8.9898	8.2983
2	58.8020	19.6007	62.4055	51.1506	10.1292	9.3500
3	57.3732	19.1244	60.3462	104.0369	11.2359	10.3716
4	55.9735	18.6578	58.3445	154.3780	12.3045	11.3580
5	54.6040	18.2013	56.3613	202.2130	13.3747	12.3459
6	53.2650	17.7550	54.4434	247.5588	14.3999	13.2922
29	34.2274	11.4091	31.7936	711.9560	24.3580	22.4843
30	34.1067	11.3689	31.8528	712.4281	24.2184	22.3554
31	34.0487	11.3496	31.9638	711.9148	24.0687	22.2173
59	38.7908	12.9303	33.7531	655.5879	25.4407	23.4838
60	38.5468	12.8489	33.5172	660.0735	25.5141	23.5514
61	38.2688	12.7563	33.2772	664.8907	25.5687	23.6019
117	37.3800	12.4600	33.2273	672.6871	25.0260	23.1009
118	37.3836	12.4612	33.2412	672.5202	25.0145	23.0903
119	37.3902	12.4634	33.2562	672.3191	25.0039	23.0805
120	37.3992	12.4664	33.2719	672.0915	24.9943	23.0716
298	37.5159	12.5053	33.3333	670.5382	25.0106	23.0867
299	37.5159	12.5053	33.3333	670.5381	25.0106	23.0867
300	37.5159	12.5053	33.3333	670.5380	25.0106	23.0867
357	-0.0028	-0.0009	-0.0000	0.2180	0.0054	0.0050
358	-0.0032	-0.0011	-0.0000	0.0712	0.0002	0.0002
359	-0.0034	-0.0011	-0.0000	0.0116	-0.0019	-0.0017
360	0.	0.	0.0000	0.	-0.0564	-0.0521

YEAR	PW OF MEAN ANNUAL SURVIVORS	PW OF SYD ACCRUALS	PW OF F.I.T.	BOOK DEPRECIATION PW OF ACCRUALS	PW OF MINIMAL GROSS INCOME
1	943.396	60.8654	7.8286	31.4465	56.84974
2	889.996	55.5406	8.3215	29.6665	52.33357
3	839.619	50.6679	8.7082	27.9873	48.17160
4	792.094	46.2143	8.9966	26.4031	44.33623
5	747.258	42.1164	9.2256	24.9086	40.80331
6	704.961	38.3805	9.3705	23.4987	37.54969
29	184.557	5.8677	4.1496	6.1519	6.31690
30	174.110	5.5459	3.8923	5.8037	5.93832
31	164.255	5.2502	3.6493	5.4752	5.59266
59	32.133	1.0846	0.7546	1.0711	1.24647
60	30.314	1.0160	0.7139	1.0105	1.16852
61	28.598	0.9517	0.6750	0.9533	1.09443
117	1.094	0.0364	0.0253	0.0365	0.04091
118	1.033	0.0343	0.0238	0.0344	0.03860
119	0.974	0.0324	0.0225	0.0325	0.03642
120	0.919	0.0306	0.0212	0.0306	0.03437
298	0.000	0.0000	0.0000	0.0000	0.00000
299	0.000	0.0000	0.0000	0.0000	0.00000
300	0.000	0.0000	0.0000	0.0000	0.00000
357	0.000	-0.0000	0.0000	0.0000	-0.00000
358	0.000	-0.0000	0.0000	0.0000	-0.00000
359	0.000	-0.0000	-0.0000	0.0000	-0.00000
360	0.	0.0000	-0.0000	-0.0000	0.
TOTALS	16666.664	754.510	287.840	555.555	766.173

D

• • • • • **Confusing Revenues with Revenue Requirements**

The Principle Involved

One of the two exact objectives in making an economic choice is to select the alternative best capable of permitting minimized pricing of the company's output while earning a barely adequate return. This was described as Case 2, Objective 2, in Chapter 4.

Suppose, then, that Projects A and B are under consideration. They are mutually exclusive; that is, only one of them is to be adopted. Annual output, in units of production from the project, are identical. Percentage revenue requirements are placed at 15% of capital investment in either case, including MAR at 7%.

A major difference between the two plans is the scheduling of their respective capital investments, as follows:

1. Capital Investment in Service
   Project A: $100,000 in each year for 20 years.
   Project B: $ 56,000 in each year for the first 10 years, and
   $185,000 in each year for the second 10 years.
2. Annual Revenue Requirements at 15%
   Project A: 15% of $100,000 = $15,000 annually for 20 years.
   Project B: 15% of $ 56,000 = $ 8,400 annually for the first 10
   years, and
   15% of $185,000 = $27,750 annually for the second 10
   years.
3. Present Worth, at Starting Date, of 20 Years of Annual Revenue Requirements
   (a). *(If discounted at presumed customer MAR of 7%)*
   Project A: 10.594014 x $15,000   = $158,910
   Project B: 7.023582 x $ 8,400 = $58,998
   3.570433 x $27,750 = 99,080
   Total, Project B   = $158,078
Conclusion: There is almost no choice between Projects A and B.

However, observe how that conclusion would be affected by discounting at some percentage other than the company's MAR. For example, consider two of the company's customers. One has an MAR of 10%, the other 4%. They draw their own conclusions by applying their

573

own respective discount rates to the annual revenue requirements as
in 2:

(b). (If discounted at presumed customer MAR of 10%)
     Project A: 8.513564 x $15,000   = $127,703
     Project B: 6.144567 x $ 8,400 = $51,614
               2.368997 x $27,750 = 65,740
                Total, Project B   = $117,354
Conclusion: Project B appears superior by a margin of $10,349 (con-
             tradicting 3a and 3c).

(c). (If discounted at presumed customer MAR of 4%)
     Project A: 13.590326 x $15,000   = $203,855
     Project B: 8.110896 x $ 8,400 = $ 68,132
              5.479431 x $27,750 = 152,054
                Total, Project B   = $220,186
Conclusion: Project A appears superior by a margin of $16,331 (con-
             tradicting 3a and 3b).

So far as investor-owners of the company are concerned, it is substantially immaterial which project is adopted; Project B is superior
by an insignificant margin ($158,078 versus $158,910). But suppose the
company's tariff schedules were to recover revenues in the year-by-
year pattern of 2 (ignoring Profit Incentive, for simplicity). It would
make a considerable difference to the customer which project is
adopted, depending upon his own MAR. If his MAR is less than 7%, he
will prefer Project A; if more than 7%, he will prefer Project B. That
observation has led a few analysts to conclude that the company's economic choice should be determined by discounting its annual revenue
requirements at an "interest" rate equal to customers' MAR! Admittedly, that would be impracticable, since every customer has a different MAR. But impracticability is not a source of the fallacy in such
reasoning, which contains an error in logic. Our concern is with the
error in principle.

The foregoing problem envisions a situation where pricing policy
is made to determine economic choice. One major distinguishing feature of the Minimum Revenue Requirements Discipline is that pricing
policy must be strictly treated as a problem separate and distinct from
that of economic choice. For example, it is specifically emphasized
that benefits of adopting the superior alternative may flow to owners
(via increased earnings), or to customers (via reduced price of product
at the same earnings), or partly to both. The essential requirement in
an economic comparison (as distinguished from a problem in profitability) is that each project's sales and revenues, respectively, be identical with the competing projects' sales and revenues.

Stipulating a difference between revenues of the two projects violates that essential provision. It is impossible to make an economic
comparison, in such case, by direct comparison of present worth of
respective revenues, arbitrarily stipulated as equal to year-by-year
revenue requirements. As the very title of this book suggests, when

competing projects differ as to their respective revenues, the problem
becomes one of profitability, not one of simple economic choice. A
different technique of solution is called for.

The company's pricing policy, which controls its year-by-year
revenues from given output, will ordinarily be such as to optimize its
overall Profit Incentive. One of the competing projects may produce a
greater Profit Incentive (that is, margin of earnings in excess of MAR)
if the year-by-year revenues depart differently from its year-by-year
revenue requirements. This is just a matter of arithmetic.

It can be appreciated that this phenomenon is of particular importance to public utilities, in view of the rate-making theory that current
charges for service rendered should reflect current cost behavior, and
the convenient fiction that year-by-year Form X revenue requirements
represent "cost behavior."

An Arithmetical Example

To illustrate, suppose that a public utility is asked by a customer
to make an unusually large installation expressly for supply to that one
customer. The customer is to be charged for the specific revenue requirements of that installation, plus a nominal Profit Incentive.[1]

Suppose further that the utility proposed to base its year-by-year
tariff schedule on its year-by-year calculation of revenue requirements for the project, assuming "straight-line" depreciation in its
calculation of those year-by-year data. (Difficult to imagine, perhaps,
but stranger things have been urged by commissions, on occasion).
Two alternative proposals are made to the customer; both are calculated in that manner. The utility's MAR is 6%.

The customer, whose MAR is 10%, calculates present worth of the
two proposals by discounting lifetime tariffs he must pay, and he makes
his selection. But to the surprise of the public utility, the customer
accepts neither proposal. Instead, he does business with another company organized for the purpose, which is not as well managed as the
utility and which builds a less efficient and more expensive power
plant. It gets the business, however, because its charges — representing its revenue requirements at 7% (instead of the utility's 6%) on its
larger capital investment, with the same service life and "straight-
line" depreciation — have a smaller present worth to the customer
when discounted at the customer's MAR of 10%!

Details appear in Tables D.1 through D.6. The student may perceive a parallel to the REA problem of Chapter 14. The example illustrates three principles which ought to be obvious, but obviously are
not:

---

[1]This illustration of the hypothetical situation was proposed by Leonard Van Nimwegen,
Senior Staff Assistant, Engineering Economist's Office, Public Service Electric and Gas
Company, Newark, N.J.

1. By any conceivable rational criterion of economic choice, the correct choice is the Utility Project 1.
2. The correct choice was made unattractive to the customer as the result of an arbitrary, unwise, and unnecessary pricing policy (tariff schedule).
3. A Step 2 analysis by the utility (reproducing the customer's own economic analysis of the propositions offered to it, using a 10% discount rate) would have revealed the situation. A change in the utility's pricing policy (a normal Step 2 consideration) could have rectified the error.

The notion that cash outlays in the manner of (1) above necessitate a tariff schedule in the manner of (2) above is absurd. The additional notion (3) that such a contingency affects the appropriate discount rate, aside from its effect on MAR, seems fantastic. But it has happened.

In the Tables D.1-D.6, only return and "straight-line" depreciation are evaluated, for simplicity. Type SQ dispersion is assumed, for the same reason.

The utility's Project 1 is the economic choice. Installations are made at the same dates as Project 3, are smaller in amount, and have a smaller MAR.

However, if the Form X revenue requirements are proposed to the customer (MAR at 10%) as tariff schedules, the customer is obliged to accept inefficient competing Proposal B.

The final two tables show that the customer would have accepted the utility's less economic proposal (Project 1), had its revenue requirements, plus 1% Profit Incentive, been proposed as the tariff schedule. The utility could then have actually installed superior Project 2, obtained the business, and made more than 1% profit margin.

In brief, discounting at customers' MAR does not indicate the economic choice of projects. It indicates the economic choice of tariff schedules (revenues), which is quite another matter. To repeat, one essential and distinguishing feature of the minimum revenue requirements approach is the divorcing of the pricing problem from determinations of economic choice.

Table D.1. Revenue requirements of the public utility's Project 1.
(Figures in millions of dollars. MAR at 6%.)

1	2	3	4	5	6	7
		"Straight-	Return	Rev. Req.		
	"Net Plant"	Line" De-	at 6% of	(Col. 3 +	Present Worth	Present Worth
Year	Investments	preciation	Col. 2	Col. 4)	Factors at 6%	of Rev. Req.
1	110.0	5.50	6.60	12.10	0.9434	11.415
2	104.5	5.50	6.27	11.77	.8900	10.475
3	99.0	5.50	5.94	11.44	.8396	9.605
4	93.5	5.50	5.61	11.11	.7921	8.800
5	88.0	5.50	5.28	10.78	.7473	8.056
6	82.5	5.50	4.95	10.45	.7050	7.367
7	77.0	5.50	4.62	10.12	.6651	6.731
8	71.5	5.50	4.29	9.79	.6274	6.142
9	66.0	5.50	3.96	9.46	.5919	5.599
10	60.5	5.50	3.63	9.13	.5584	5.098
11	195.0	19.50	11.70	31.20	.5268	16.436
12	175.5	19.50	10.53	30.03	.4970	14.925
13	156.0	19.50	9.36	28.86	.4688	13.530
14	136.5	19.50	8.19	27.69	.4423	12.247
15	117.0	19.50	7.02	26.52	.4173	11.067
16	97.5	19.50	5.85	25.35	.3936	9.978
17	78.0	19.50	4.68	24.18	.3714	8.980
18	58.5	19.50	3.51	23.01	.3503	8.060
19	39.0	19.50	2.34	21.84	.3305	7.218
20	19.5	19.50	1.17	20.67	.3118	6.445
Totals	1925.0	250.00	115.50	365.50	11.4700	188.174

Project 2 is superior to this project, having a present worth at date of initial placement of 180.000 millions versus 188.174 millions, discounted at the utility's MAR of 6%.

Project 1 should not be adopted.

Table D.2. Revenue requirements of the public utility's Project 2.
(Figures in millions of dollars. MAR at 6%.)

1	2	3	4	5	6	7
		"Straight-	Return	Rev. Req.		
	"Net Plant"	Line" De-	at 6% of	(Col. 3 +	Present Worth	Present Worth
Year	Investments	preciation	Col. 2	Col. 4)	Factors at 6%	of Rev. Req.
1	180	9.00	10.80	19.80	0.9434	18.679
2	171	9.00	10.26	19.26	.8900	17.141
3	162	9.00	9.72	18.72	.8396	15.717
4	153	9.00	9.18	18.18	.7921	14.400
5	144	9.00	8.64	17.64	.7473	13.182
6	135	9.00	8.10	17.10	.7050	12.056
7	126	9.00	7.56	16.56	.6651	11.014
8	117	9.00	7.02	16.02	.6274	10.051
9	108	9.00	6.48	15.48	.5919	9.163
10	99	9.00	5.94	14.94	.5584	8.342
11	90	9.00	5.40	14.40	.5268	7.586
12	81	9.00	4.86	13.86	.4970	6.888
13	72	9.00	4.32	13.32	.4688	6.244
14	63	9.00	3.78	12.78	.4423	5.653
15	54	9.00	3.24	12.24	.4173	5.108
16	45	9.00	2.70	11.70	.3936	4.605
17	36	9.00	2.16	11.16	.3714	4.145
18	27	9.00	1.62	10.62	.3503	3.720
19	18	9.00	1.08	10.08	.3305	3.331
20	9	9.00	0.54	9.54	.3118	2.975
Totals	1890	180.00	113.40	293.40	11.4700	180.000

This Project 2 is superior, having a present worth at date of initial placement of 180.00, versus 188.174 millions for Project 1.

This project should be adopted.

Table D.3. The public utility's unsound tariff proposal (= year-by-year revenue requirements for Project 2, after inclusion of Profit Incentive at 1% of net plant). (Figures in millions of dollars.)

1 Year	2 Net Plant (Col. 2, Table D.2)	3 Depreciation (Col. 3, Table D.2)	4 Return (Col. 4, Table D.2)	5 Profit Incentive (1% of Col. 2)	6 Proposed Tariff
1	180	9.00	10.80	1.80	21.60
2	171	9.00	10.26	1.71	20.97
3	162	9.00	9.72	1.62	20.34
4	153	9.00	9.18	1.53	19.71
5	144	9.00	8.64	1.44	19.08
6	135	9.00	8.10	1.35	18.45
7	126	9.00	7.56	1.26	17.82
8	117	9.00	7.02	1.17	17.19
9	108	9.00	6.48	1.08	16.56
10	99	9.00	5.94	0.99	15.93
11	90	9.00	5.40	.90	15.30
12	81	9.00	4.86	.81	14.67
13	72	9.00	4.32	.72	14.04
14	63	9.00	3.78	.63	13.41
15	54	9.00	3.24	.54	12.78
16	45	9.00	2.70	.45	12.15
17	36	9.00	2.16	.36	11.52
18	27	9.00	1.62	.27	10.89
19	18	9.00	1.08	.18	10.26
20	9	9.00	0.54	.09	9.63
Totals	1890	180.00	113.40	18.90	312.30

There is no good reason why the proposed tariff schedule need reproduce the Form X year-by-year revenue requirements of Table D.2. That assumption, however, is made here to illustrate its unfortunate effect on customer's decision.

Table D.4. The competitor's revenue requirements and proposed tariff schedule.
(Project 3. Larger investment than the public utility's Project 1, and a greater
MAR, at 7%. No Profit Incentive in proposed tariff.) (Figures in millions of dollars.)

1	2	3	4	5
				Revenue Requirements
	"Net Plant"	"Straight-Line"	Return at 7%	& Tariff Schedule
Year	Investment	Depreciation	of Col. 2	(Col. 3 + Col. 4)
1	114.40	5.7200	8.0080	13.7280
2	108.68	5.7200	7.6076	13.3276
3	102.96	5.7200	7.2072	12.9272
4	97.24	5.7200	6.8068	12.5268
5	91.52	5.7200	6.4064	12.1264
6	85.80	5.7200	6.0060	11.7260
7	80.08	5.7200	5.6056	11.3256
8	74.36	5.7200	5.2052	10.9252
9	68.64	5.7200	4.8048	10.5248
10	62.92	5.7200	4.4044	10.1244
11	202.80	20.2800	14.1960	34.4760
12	182.52	20.2800	12.7764	33.0564
13	162.24	20.2800	11.3568	31.6368
14	141.96	20.2800	9.9372	30.2172
15	121.68	20.2800	8.5176	28.7976
16	101.40	20.2800	7.0980	27.3780
17	81.12	20.2800	5.6784	25.9584
18	60.84	20.2800	4.2588	24.5388
19	40.56	20.2800	2.8392	23.1192
20	20.28	20.2800	1.4196	21.6996
Totals	2002.00	260.0000	140.1400	400.1400

This competing Project 3 has a greater capital cost than the public utility's
projects, and a higher MAR (at 7%, it equals the utility's MAR + Profit Incentive).

Certainly this proposal ought not be adopted, but it was the cheapest tariff
schedule for the customer, as will be shown in Table D.5.

Table D.5. The customer's economic comparison of tariff proposals.
(Discounted at customer's MAR of 10%.) (Figures in millions of dollars.)

1	2	3	4	5	6
	Present Worth Factors	Customer's Costs if Bought		Present Worth to Customer	
		From Utility	From Competitor	From Utility	From Competitor
Year	at 10%	(Col. 6, Table D.3)	(Col. 5, Table D.4)	(Col. 2 x Col. 3)	(Col. 2 x Col. 4)
1	0.9091	21.60	13.7280	19.687	12.480
2	.8264	20.97	13.3276	17.330	11.014
3	.7513	20.34	12.9272	15.281	9.712
4	.6830	19.71	12.5268	13.462	8.556
5	.6209	19.08	12.1264	11.847	7.529
6	.5645	18.45	11.7260	10.415	6.619
7	.5132	17.82	11.3256	9.145	5.812
8	.4665	17.19	10.9252	8.019	5.097
9	.4241	16.56	10.5248	7.023	4.464
10	.3855	15.93	10.1244	6.141	3.903
11	.3505	15.30	34.4760	5.363	12.084
12	.3186	14.67	33.0564	4.674	10.532
13	.2897	14.04	31.6368	4.067	9.165
14	.2633	13.41	30.2172	3.531	7.956
15	.2394	12.78	28.7976	3.060	6.894
16	.2176	12.15	27.3780	2.644	5.957
17	.1978	11.52	25.9584	2.279	5.135
18	.1799	10.89	24.5388	1.959	4.415
19	.1635	10.26	23.1192	1.678	3.780
20	.1486	9.63	21.6996	1.431	3.225
Totals	8.5134	312.30	400.1400	148.986	144.329

The customer is obliged to choose the competitor's high-cost Proposal 3, which has the smaller present worth when discounted at 10%!

This unfortunate result could easily have been avoided, per Table D.6. It had no bearing on the utility's economic choice.

Table D.6. Demonstrating that a tariff schedule based on Project 1, the
utility's less economic alternative, would have been accepted.
(Figures in millions of dollars.)

1	2	3	4	5	6	7
				Proposed		
			Profit	Tariff		
	"Straight-Line"		Incentive	Schedule	Present	Present
	Depreciation	Return at 6%	(1% of	(Col. 2 +	Worth	Worth
	(Col. 3,	(Col. 4,	Col. 2,	Col. 3 +	Factors	of
Year	Table D.1)	Table D.1)	Table D.1)	Col. 4)	at 10%	Col. 6
1	5.500	6.600	1.100	13.200	0.9091	12.000
2	5.500	6.270	1.045	12.815	.8264	10.590
3	5.500	5.940	0.990	12.430	.7513	9.339
4	5.500	5.610	.935	12.045	.6830	8.227
5	5.500	5.280	.880	11.660	.6209	7.240
6	5.500	4.950	.825	11.275	.5645	6.365
7	5.500	4.620	.770	10.890	.5132	5.589
8	5.500	4.290	.715	10.505	.4665	4.901
9	5.500	3.960	.660	10.120	.4241	4.292
10	5.500	3.630	.605	9.735	.3855	3.753
11	19.500	11.700	1.950	33.150	.3505	11.619
12	19.500	10.530	1.755	31.785	.3186	10.127
13	19.500	9.360	1.560	30.420	.2897	8.813
14	19.500	8.190	1.365	29.055	.2633	7.650
15	19.500	7.020	1.170	27.690	.2394	6.629
16	19.500	5.850	0.975	26.325	.2176	5.728
17	19.500	4.680	.780	24.960	.1978	4.937
18	19.500	3.510	.585	23.595	.1799	4.245
19	19.500	2.340	.390	22.230	.1635	3.635
20	19.500	1.170	.195	20.865	.1486	3.101
Totals	250.000	115.500	19.250	384.750	8.5134	138.780

This tariff schedule, corresponding to Form X year-by-year revenue requirements
of the utility's Project 1, has the smallest present worth of all three tariff schedules,
when discounted at customer's MAR of 10%. Accordingly, the utility would get the
business. It could then install Project 2, which is adequate to supply identical output,
and increase its Profit Incentive above the figures of Column 4.

This illustrates the importance of treating the pricing problem (tariff schedules)
as a problem separate and distinct from the economic comparison.

E

• • • • • Characteristics • •
of the Continuing
Plant

Part I. The Renewal Function

Calculation of the renewal function was explained in Chapter 10. However, for simplicity, Type SC dispersion was selected for that introductory discussion; the annual retirement rate is a constant value, 1/Life, in every year.

For fear that the use of a constant annual retirement rate might be regarded as the general case, which of course it is not, it seems advisable to describe the same procedures for another type of dispersion. The calculation for 10, R_1 follows. A different method of assembling the data is also suggested.

It may be worth remarking that in most practical problems it is quite unnecessary to calculate the renewal function, except for purposes of evaluating possible effects of future price inflation. That is, the cost of renewals is automatically covered by use of a constant figure for capital investment in service each year, $P\bar{x}$ As repeatedly pointed out before, if the cost of renewals is not to be included, $P_{\bar{x}}$ and annual revenue requirements in dollars decrease in successive years of service life. For this reason, it might be said that an important reason for understanding the renewal function is to be able to perceive when and where it is not necessary to make the calculation, and exactly why.

The first step is to tabulate average survivors, in percent of the initial placement of 100%, in each year of total life expectancy for the mortality pattern selected. Table E.1 presents midyear (mean) annual survivors, as an adequate approximation of average values, as discussed before, for 10, R_1.

Authoritative reference sources for year-end percent survivors are as follows:

Robley Winfrey, Statistical Analysis of Industrial Property Retirements. Iowa State College, Engineering Experiment Station, Bulletin 125, 1936.

Robley Winfrey, Depreciation of Group Properties. Iowa State College, Engineering Experiment Station, Bulletin 155, 1942.

Robley Winfrey, Condition-Percent Tables for Depreciation of Unit

Table E.1. Mean annual survivors for 10, R_1.

Year (x)	Survivors $(y_{\bar{x}})$	Year (x)	Survivors $(y_{\bar{x}})$
0.5	98.673%	10.5	49.144%
1.5	95.747	11.5	41.418
2.5	92.464	12.5	33.594
2.5	88.835	13.5	25.958
4.5	84.833	14.5	18.828
5.5	80.371	15.5	12.536
6.5	75.355	16.5	7.387
7.5	69.715	17.5	3.613
8.5	63.431	18.5	1.290
9.5	56.539	19.5	0.179

and Group Properties. Iowa State College, Engineering Experiment Station, Bulletin 156, 1942.

(Note: The reference here is to survivorship tables only. The tables of depreciation are not recommended; they do not represent the actual intent, for this application, in studies of profitability and economic choice.)

Anson Marston, Robley Winfrey, and Jean C. Hempstead, Engineering Valuation and Depreciation, 2nd ed. Iowa State University Press, Ames, Iowa, 1953.

(Note: The reference is to Appendix B, page 410, only, which presents tables of the "Iowa 18 Type Survivor and Frequency Curves.")

Placement A at beginning of Year 1 (= End of Year 0) is $\dfrac{P}{y_{0.5}} =$

$\dfrac{P}{0.98673}$ per Table E.1, or 1.013 448 461 P. If $P = 100\%$, then A = 1.013 448 461.

Placement B at the beginning of Year 2 (= End of Year 1) is

$$B = \frac{1 - y_{1.5}\,(1.013\ 448\ 461)}{y_{0.5}} = \frac{1 - 0.95747\,(1.013\ 448\ 461)}{0.98673} = 0.030\ 052.$$

Similarly Placement C at the beginning of Year 3 (End of Year 2)

is $C = \dfrac{1 - 0.92464\,(1.013\ 448\ 461) - 0.95\ 747\,(0.030\ 052)}{0.98673} = 0.034\ 610.$

Each of these Placements A, B, C, and so on, suffer retirements at the rate shown in Table E.1. They are tabulated in vertical columns of Table E.2. These survivors, if added horizontally, always total unity (= 1.000000000).

Table E.3 describes the foregoing calculations in semigraphical form, suggesting an easy way to assemble the data if done manually. It is an ideal subject for electronic data processing.

Results are tabulated in Table E.4, and plotted in Figure E.1.

Part II. Details of Continuing Plant Calculation of Gross Additions

The following discussion describes a slightly different expression for calculating gross additions and applies it to the problems of Tables

Table E.2. Development of the renewal function (abbreviated version). For 10-year average life, Iowa Type R₁ dispersion.

1	2	3	4	5	6	7	8
		n=0	n=1	n=2	n=3	n=4	n=5
	Installation date (end of Year n)	Initial Installation					
		1.013 448 461	0.030 052 2959	0.034 610 1195	.039 298 849	.044 525 797	.050 947 848
Year	In terms of n		Survivors of Above Installations				
1	1-n	1.000 000 000					
2	2-n	0.970 346 498					
3	3-n	.937 074 985	0.029 653 502				
4	4-n	.900 296 940	.028 774 172	0.034 150 843			
5	5-n	.859 738 733	.027 787 555	.033 138 151			
6	6-n	.814 518 662	.026 696 957	.032 001 901	.038 777 354		
7	7-n	.763 684 088	.025 494 264	.030 745 900	.037 627 469		
8	8-n	.706 525 595	.024 153 331	.029 360 803	.036 337 288	.043 934 940	
9	9-n	.642 840 493	.022 645 908	.027 816 499	.034 911 133	.042 632 115	
10	10-n	.572 993 626	.020 950 958	.026 080 456	.033 338 393	.041 170 333	.050 271 771
11	11-n	.498 049 112	.019 062 472	.024 128 445	.031 584 878	.039 554 492	.048 781 036
12	12-n	.419 750 084	.016 991 268	.021 953 545	.029 613 648	.037 772 570	.047 108 418
13	13-n	.340 457 876	.014 768 900	.019 568 216	.027 397 193	.035 785 828	.045 259 521
14	14-n	.263 070 952	.012 447 060	.017 008 797	.024 927 653	.033 552 414	.043 220 588
15	15-n	.190 812 076	.010 095 768	.014 334 819	.022 219 176	.031 041 159	.040 947 295
16	16-n	.127 045 899	.007 800 975	.011 626 924	.019 313 026	.028 243 158	.038 391 751
17	17-n	.074 863 438	.005 658 246	.008 984 095	.016 276 797	.025 174 440	.035 518 293
18	18-n	.036 615 893	.003 767 356	.006 516 393	.013 202 055	.021 881 758	.032 316 730
19	19-n	.013 073 485	.002 219 963	.004 338 725	.010 201 195	.018 441 695	.028 805 404
20	20-n	.001 814 073	.001 085 789	.002 556 650	.007 399 187	.014 957 996	.025 037 811
21	21-n		.000 387 675	.001 250 464	.004 926 504	.011 558 006	.021 101 580
22	22-n		.000 053 794	.000 446 471	.002 903 006	.008 383 317	.017 115 420
23	23-n			.000 061 952	.001 419 867	.005 581 754	.013 225 042
24	24-n				.000 506 955	.003 289 121	.009 592 461
25	25-n				.000 070 345	.001 608 717	.006 386 822
26	26-n					.000 574 383	.003 763 518
27						.000 079 701	.001 840 746
28							.000 657 227
29							.000 091 197
⋮	⋮						
⋮	⋮						
40	40-n						
41	41-n						

Table E.3.   Calculation of the renewal function for 10-year life,
Iowa Type R_1 dispersion.

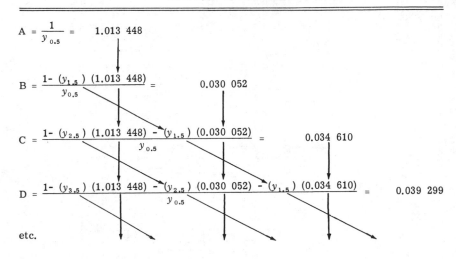

$A = \dfrac{1}{y_{0.5}} = \quad 1.013\ 448$

$B = \dfrac{1 - (y_{1.5})\ (1.013\ 448)}{y_{0.5}} = \quad 0.030\ 052$

$C = \dfrac{1 - (y_{2.5})\ (1.013\ 448) - (y_{1.5})\ (0.030\ 052)}{y_{0.5}} = \quad 0.034\ 610$

$D = \dfrac{1 - (y_{3.5})\ (1.013\ 448) - (y_{2.5})\ (0.030\ 052) - (y_{1.5})\ (0.034\ 610)}{y_{0.5}} = \quad 0.039\ 299$

etc.

10.5-10.9 on pages 287-91. It is useful for finding gross additions at
any date (n) for a sustained growth rate of $g\%$ annually.

At Date 0 Years
      The mean balance of plant in service in Year 1 is to be $1,000. A
somewhat larger installation must be made, because the survivor curve
indicates that out of an initial placement of 1,000 units 125 retirements
will occur during the year, leaving a mean balance of plant in service
of 1,000 - (125/2) = 937.5.
      Thus, to have a mean balance in service of 1,000, we must make
an initial placement of:

$$A_0 = 1,000 \times \frac{1,000.0}{937.5} = 1,066.67$$

At Date 1 Year
      The mean balance for Year 2 is to be 2,100. The mean survivors
in the second year of service, per the survivor curve, are
$\dfrac{(1,000 - 125) + (1,000 - 250)}{2} = 81.25\%$ of the initial placement.

$$81.25\% \text{ of } A_0 = 0.8125 \times 1,066.67 = 866.67 \text{ survivors of } A_0$$

The remainder of the desired 2,100 represent survivors of A_1, the
placement at Age 1: 2,100.00 - 866.67 = 1,233.33. As before:

$$A_1 = 1,233.33 \times \frac{1,000.0}{937.5} = 1,315.55$$

Table E.4. Annual placements and replacements for static plant composed of units having 10-year average life, Iowa Type R_1 dispersion.

End of Year	Initial Placement of Unity + Allowance for Replacements
0	1.013 448 461
1	0.030 052 296
2	.034 610 120
3	.039 298 849
4	.044 525 797
5	.050 947 848
6	.058 718 470
7	.067 687 738
8	.077 436 279
9	.087 463 781
10	.097 110 156
11	.105 697 594
12	.112 566 606
13	.117 092 770
14	.118 816 603
15	.117 416 052
16	.112 944 770
17	.105 900 256
18	.097 627 483
19	.091 150 869
20	.086 834 978
21	.089 499 506
22	.093 500 664
23	.096 964 863
24	.099 770 552
25	.101 142 578
26	.103 767 887
27	.103 617 037
28	.103 472 542
29	.102 814 223
30	.101 829 313
31	.100 721 881
32	.099 666 839
33	.098 906 232
34	.098 425 953
35	.098 341 345
36	.098 593 167
37	.099 078 183
38	.099 654 824
39	.100 178 674
40	.100 549 162

At Date 2 Years

The mean balance per Year 3 is to be 3,310.

The mean survivors from $A_0 = \bar{y}_3 \times 1{,}066.67$
$$= 0.6875 \times 1{,}066.67 = 733.33.$$

The mean survivors from $A_1 = \bar{y}_2 \times 1{,}315.55$
$$= 0.8125 \times 1{,}315.55 = 1{,}068.89.$$

The remainder of the desired 3,310 represent survivors of $A_2 = 3{,}310.00 - (733.33 + 1{,}068.89) = 1{,}507.78.$

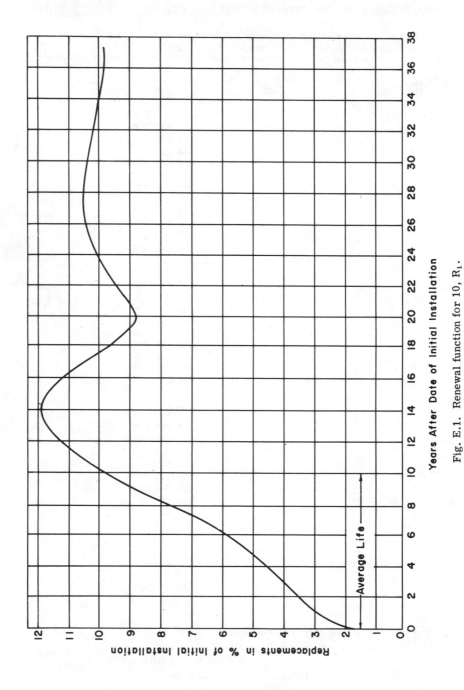

Fig. E.1. Renewal function for 10, R_1.

$$A_2 = \frac{1,507.78}{0.9375} = 1,608.30$$

At Date 3 Years

The mean balance for Year 4 is to be   4,641.00

Subtracting survivors of prior vintages:

$A_0 \cdot \bar{y}_4 = 1,066.67 \times 0.5625 = \quad 600.00$

$A_1 \cdot \bar{y}_3 = 1,315.55 \times 0.6875 = \quad 904.44$

$A_2 \cdot \bar{y}_2 = 1,608.30 \times 0.8125 = 1,306.74$ (2,811.18)

The remainder to be supplied by survivors

of $A_3 \cdot (= A_3 \cdot \bar{y}_1)$ 1,829.82

$$A_3 = \frac{A_3 \cdot \bar{y}_1}{\bar{y}_1} = \frac{1,829.82}{0.9375} = 1,951.81$$

In General

For a sustained rate of growth (net additions) of $g\%$ annually:

$$A_{n-1} = \frac{s_{\overline{n}|}\,(I) - \sum\limits_{x=0}^{x=n-2} A_x\, \bar{y}_{n-x}}{\bar{y}_1}$$

where

A_{n-1} = placement at date $n - 1$ years.

$s_{\overline{n}|}$ = amount of an n-year annuity of one, at $g\%$ compounded rate of growth.

I = mean plant in service in first year.

A_x = gross additions at Year x.

$\bar{y}_{n-x}$ = mean survivors, in year $n-x$, from a unit radix.

Note that the $\bar{y}_{n-x}$ component of the formula in effect converts time from the chronological of the formula to years of vintage life. Thus, for 4, SC: $(n - x) \gtrless 8$. If $(n - x) > 8$, then $\bar{y}_{n-x} = 0$. In other words, survivors become zero at the end of the eighth year of service. Note also that term $s_{\overline{n}|}\,(I)$ is simply gross plant at date n.

To illustrate application of this expression, the substitution of A_{14} (= gross additions at date 14 years) is detailed below. Here, $n - 1 = 14$; hence, $n = 15$.

$$\frac{s_{\overline{15}|}\,(1,000) - \sum\limits_{0}^{13} A_x\, \bar{y}_{15-x}}{\bar{y}_1} = A_{14}$$

$$\frac{31.77248\,(1,000) - \sum\limits_{0}^{13} A_x\, \bar{y}_{15-x}}{0.9375} = A_{14}$$

x	$15 - x$	A_x	$\bar{y}_{15-x}$	$A_x \bar{y}_{15-x}$
0	15	1,066.67	0	0
1	14	1,315.55	0	0
2	13	1,608.30	0	0
3	12	1,951.81	0	0
4	11	2,353.99	0	0
5	10	2,824.06	0	0
6	9	3,372.39	0	0
7	8	4,011.00	0.0625	250.69
8	7	4,682.56	0.1875	877.98
9	6	5,376.73	0.3125	1,680.23
10	5	6,150.22	0.4375	2,690.72
11	4	7,009.58	0.5625	3,942.89
12	3	7,961.45	0.6875	5,473.50
13	2	9,012.54	0.8125	7,322.69
				22,238.70

$$= \sum_0^{13} A_x \bar{y}_{15-x}$$

$$A_{14} = \frac{31,772.48 - 22,238.70}{0.9375} = \frac{9,533.78}{0.9375} = 10,169.37$$

Gross Additions and Mean Survivors

To facilitate further informative analyses of the material of Tables 10.5-10.9, Tables E.5 and E.6 are appended. Both will be helpful for investigating present worth behavior, as put to use in PWAFRR. For brevity, details are shown through Year 28, plus the tail-end of the survivors in Years 50 to 60 only.

These tables will suggest others that would be equally informative. For example, a table could be prepared to show details of the stabilized plant after Year 15. Others can be prepared to show various alternative ways to calculate revenue requirements for separate vintage components of growing plant, mentioned in the discussion of Table 10.6. Some of these alternatives are more efficient than others under certain conditions; all produce exactly the same end result when properly computed and interpreted.

Table E.5. Gross additions and mean survivors. (Stabilized gross plant after Year 15.)

	Gross Additions	16	17	18	19	20	21	22	23	24	25	26	27	28	29
													Years		
0															
1															
2															
3															
4															
5															
6															
7															
8	4,682.56	292.62													
9	5,376.73	1,008.14	336.05												
10	6,150.22	1,921.94	1,153.17	384.39											
11	7,009.58	3,066.69	2,190.49	1,314.30	438.10										
12	7,961.45	4,478.32	3,483.13	2,487.95	1,492.77	497.59									
13	9,012.54	6,196.12	5,069.55	3,942.99	2,816.42	1,689.85	563.28								
14	10,169.37	8,262.61	6,991.44	5,720.27	4,449.10	3,177.93	1,906.76	635.59							
15	6,982.44	6,546.04	5,673.23	4,800.41	3,927.62	3,054.84	2,181.99	1,309.21	436.42						
16	7,333.78		6,875.42	5,958.70	5,041.95	4,125.25	3,208.55	2,291.78	1,375.08	458.38					
17	7,641.03			7,163.47	6,208.36	5,253.19	4,298.08	3,342.98	2,387.80	1,432.69	477.59				
18	7,891.37				7,398.16	6,411.76	5,425.29	4,438.90	3,452.50	2,466.03	1,479.63	493.24			
19	8,066.21					7,562.07	6,553.82	5,545.49	4,537.24	3,528.99	2,520.66	1,512.41	504.16		
20	8,143.69						7,634.71	6,616.77	5,598.76	4,580.83	3,562.89	2,544.88	1,526.94	509.01	
21	8,097.88							7,591.76	6,579.55	5,567.27	4,555.06	3,542.85	2,530.56	1,518.35	506.14
22	7,898.81								7,405.13	6,417.80	5,430.40	4,443.08	3,455.75	2,468.35	1,481.03
23	7,808.52									7,320.49	6,344.45	5,368.33	4,392.29	3,416.25	2,440.14
24	7,895.25										7,401.80	6,414.92	5,427.96	4,441.08	3,454.20
25	7,949.62											7,452.77	6,459.09	5,465.34	4,471.66
26	7,974.11												7,475.73	6,478.99	5,482.18
27	7,973.45													7,475.11	6,478.45
28	7,955.93														7,458.68
Gross Plant	31,772.48	31,772.48	31,772.48	31,772.48	31,772.48	31,772.48	31,772.48	31,772.48	31,772.48	31,772.48	31,772.48	31,772.48	31,772.48	31,772.48	31,772.48

591

Table E.5. (Concluded)

	Gross Additions	Years 58	59	60	61
50	7,943.05	496.44			
51	7,943.09	1,489.33	496.44		
52	7,943.10	2,482.22	1,489.33	496.44	
53	7,943.16	3,475.13	2,482.24	1,489.34	496.45
54	7,943.13	4,468.01	3,475.12	2,482.23	1,489.34
55	7,943.15	5,460.92	4,468.02	3,475.13	2,482.23
56	7,943.09	6,453.76	5,460.87	4,467.99	3,475.10
57	7,943.11	7,446.67	6,453.78	5,460.89	4,468.00
58	7,943.13		7,446.68	6,453.79	5,460.90
59	7,943.11			7,446.67	6,453.78
60	7,943.13				7,446.68
Gross Plant		31,772.48	31,772.48	31,772.48	31,772.48

Table E-6. Gross additions and mean survivors, shrinking plant.
(Decaying after Year 15.)

	16	17	18	19	20	21	22
0							
1							
2							
3							
4							
5							
6							
7							
8	292.62						
9	1,008.14	336.05					
10	1,921.94	1,153.17	384.39				
11	3,066.69	2,190.49	1,314.30	438.10			
12	4,478.32	3,483.13	2,487.95	1,492.77	497.59		
13	6,196.12	5,069.55	3,942.99	2,816.42	1,689.85	563.28	
14	8,262.61	6,991.44	5,720.27	4,449.10	3,177.93	1,906.76	635.59
Gross Plant	25,226.44	19,223.83	13,849.90	9,196.39	5,356.37	2,470.04	635.59

F

• • • • • Capitalize • • •
Versus Expense

Two Misconceptions

Assuming that a choice of accounting disposition is permissive, is it desirable to charge expenditures to maintenance expense rather than to capital?

The twilight zone where either procedure might be defended may be illustrated by the carpenter's classical observation about his hatchet. He had used the same hatchet for more than 50 years. True, the head had been replaced three or four times, and it had needed a new handle eight or ten times; but its service life was going to be demonstrably in excess of 50 years.

One authority has stated flatly that it makes no difference whether a given outlay is expensed or capitalized; one method of accounting is as good as the other.[1] A more widely accepted conclusion is that the charge to maintenance expense is always to be preferred because, it is said, it minimizes "annual costs." That is, if charged to expense, that charge is exactly equivalent to the present worth of lifetime return plus depreciation if charged to capital; but if charged to capital, revenue requirements must include income tax, which is not the case when charged to maintenance expense.

The purpose of this discussion is to demonstrate that neither of the foregoing conclusions is a sound generalization. The effect on revenue requirements is indeed restricted to the tax behavior; however, capitalizing instead of expensing does not necessarily increase taxes. Revenue requirements for income tax may be greater, less, or exactly the same, depending upon the peculiar circumstances of each individual situation. The result involves consideration for a number of factors commonly overlooked, as they were in the opinions just quoted. The impact on taxes is a function of:

1. The change in service life, which is ordinarily shortened if outlays are capitalized instead of expensed.
2. The change in percentage net salvage, if any, which may be substantial.

---

[1]George Terborgh, <u>Dynamic Equipment Policy</u> (McGraw-Hill, Inc., New York, 1949).

3. Possible change in type of retirement dispersion, which has relatively small effect on taxes.
4. The change in amount of capital investment, if any.
5. The time-pattern of the outlays which are to be capitalized instead of expensed, or vice versa.

Above all, it must of course be ascertained that the proposed change in accounting is acceptable to IRS; and, if the company is a regulated public utility, to the authorities who have jurisdiction in such matters.

Circumstances of each individual case can cover such a wide range that this appendix will not attempt a comprehensive discussion. Instead, it will be limited to examination of a single hypothetical problem, to indicate the nature of considerations that are apt to be overlooked by relying on oversimplified reasoning.

Before presenting the illustrative example, a few preliminary remarks are necessary in connection with such estimates of differential income taxes. Of course, if the company pays taxes levied on sales or on gross receipts, those taxes will be affected by any change in income taxes.

Tax Differentials

Estimates of income tax differentials of the kind here under discussion are necessarily approximations. Reasons for this were mentioned in Chapter 8; they arise from use of group-average data rather than service life of individual plant units. Estimates of group-average life must be established within reason ("guidelines") by company experience.

As a practical matter, changing from a policy of expensing to one of capitalizing may have such small effect on estimates of service life as to be insignificant. This may remain the case for many years, possibly indefinitely. In such case, anticipated change in the tax may never actually be realized. At the same time, it is not safe to make firm estimates of no tax effect whatever. Even though tax-deductible depreciation may not be precisely estimable, direction of that effect is usually predictable.

In brief, the difficulty of making quantitatively reliable estimates is no reflection on the principles involved. It is one more case where there is room for honest difference of opinion as to future behavior of costs.

Removing and Resetting Overhead Line Transformers

It is common practice of electric public utilities to capitalize installation cost of overhead distribution line transformers at time of initial purchase, and to retire that investment at date of ultimate withdrawal of the unit. All interim outlays for removal and reinstallation elsewhere ("r & r"), which may occur several times during one life-time of the unit, are charged to expense. In this example we will as-sume that average service life, when so handled, is 43 years, Type $S_{\frac{1}{2}}$ dispersion; ultimate net salvage 20% (scrap value $77.40 less $14 re-moval cost).

Capital investment is:

Transformer unit	$271.00
Installation cost (labor)	46.00
Total	$317.00

Each "r & r" outlay consists of a removal cost of $14, plus rein-stallation cost of $46.

Minimum acceptable return is placed at 6%; 56% debt at 4% inter-est; "straight-line" depreciation for books and taxes. In order to focus on our major purpose, this example will be simplified by (a) ignoring effects of liberalized depreciation and the investment credit, and (b) ig-noring such accessories as lightning arrestors and cutouts which might have service lives and salvage values different from those of the unit itself.

In general, capitalizing rather than expensing reduces service life. In this case it may be demonstrated as follows.

First, consider estimated revenue requirements, detailed in Table F.1.

The only component of present worth affected by the proposed change in accounting for "r & r" is that of income taxes. Present worth of "r & r" outlays remains $118, in any event. For the average unit having a life of 43 years, it will be found that this would result from one "r & r" about every sixth year, at ages 6, 12, 18, 24, 30, and so forth. A more meticulous calculation can be made recognizing re-tirement dispersion; that is, recognizing that some units will be retired

Table F.1. Revenue requirements, present practice ("r & r" expensed).

	%	$/Year
MAR	6.00	19.02
Depreciation (0.80 x 1.28)	1.02	3.23
Federal income tax $\frac{.48}{.52}$ (7.02 - 1.86) (1 - $\frac{0.56 \times 4}{6}$)	2.99	9.48
"R & r" outlays	2.71	8.60
Total	12.72%	$40.33 per year

Present worth, at date of installation, of one lifetime of revenue requirements per unit is:

Capital recovery	$\frac{7.02\% \times 317}{7.28\%}$ =	$305.77
Income tax	$\frac{2.90\% \times 317}{7.28\%}$ =	130.22
"R & r" outlays	$\frac{2.71\% \times 317}{7.28\%}$ =	118.00
Total		$553.99

before reaching Age 43, while some will continue in service past that age. In any case, service life of the newly-capitalized assets will have an average life near six years and a dispersion type near S_6. Net salvage will be $-14/46 = -30.4\%$.

If these capitalized "r & r" outlays were charged to a separate plant account or subaccount, the unit itself would continue to have a 43-year life, type $S_{-\frac{1}{2}}$ dispersion, but with net salvage of $77.40/271 = 28.6\%$, instead of the original 20%. We could then calculate the revenue requirement for income tax of each component as follows:

Unit itself

$$\frac{.48}{.52} (6.00 + 0.714 \times 1.28 - 0.714 \times 2.33)(1 - \frac{0.56 \times 4}{6}) = 3.04\%$$

$$3.04\% \times 271 = \$8.24 \text{ per year}$$

"R & r" outlays

$$\frac{.48}{.52} (6.00 + 1.30 \times 14.34 - 1.30 \times 16.67)(1 - \frac{0.56 \times 4}{6}) = 1.74\%$$

$$1.74\% \times 46 = \$0.80 \text{ per year}$$

Combined tax

$$\$8.24 + 0.80 = \$9.04 \text{ per year, per unit (in place of \$9.48)}$$

Or suppose the transformer and the capitalized "r & r" outlays are combined in a single plant account. Exact determination of combined average life is quite complicated; but a quick approximation will serve our present purpose of demonstrating that it requires looking into.

Ultimate stabilized renewal rates, described in Chapter 10, would be as follows:

Unit itself: $1/43 \times 271 = \$6.30$ per year
"R & r" outlays: $1/6 \times 46 = \underline{7.67}$ per year
       Combined $= \$13.97$ per year
In percent:
    $13.97/317 = 4.41\%$.
Indicated average life:
    $1/4.41\% = 22.7$ years.

Superimposing the 6, S_6 survivor curve on that for 43, $S_{-\frac{1}{2}}$, would produce a type not represented by any of the Iowa curves, but approaching SC. Fortunately, the effect of dispersion type on income tax is small; assuming Type SC will serve our immediate purpose.

Altered percent salvage may also be approximated in this same general manner, by inquiring into the "renewal rate adjusted for salvage":

Unit itself: 71.4% x 1/43 x 271 = $ 4.50 per year
"R & r" outlays: 130.4% x 1/6 x   46 =   10.00 per year
                          Combined   = $14.50 per year

14.50 = (1 - c) x 13.97, where $13.97 is the combined rate if salvage were zero, derived above.

13.97c = 13.97 - 14.50 = -0.53; and c = nearly zero.

Assuming from the foregoing, for purposes of this approximation, that combined life is 23 years, Type SC dispersion, with zero salvage, we can calculate income tax for the combined account as follows:

$$\frac{.48}{.52} (6.00 + 3.20 - 4.35) (1 - \frac{0.56 \times 4}{6}) \doteq 2.81\%$$

2.81% x 317 = $8.91 per year (in place of $9.48)

A number of other accounting procedures have been used, on occasion, for treating plant that is apt to be "salvaged for reuse" one or more times before being finally retired. Two extreme methods are of interest. One is to regard service life as the period from initial installation until the date of removal for reuse. An independent service life is established by the period from reinstallation to its second removal; and so on. Another procedure is to capitalize initial installation, equipment and labor, and charge all subsequent removals and reinstallations — both for equipment and for labor of installation — to expense. Thus, the plant account reflects cost of the "grandfather" pole, meter, and so on, until the location is finally abandoned, and the last installation is finally removed and retired.

Conclusion

Expensing versus capitalizing given outlays affects revenue requirements by way of the impact on taxes only. It is impossible to anticipate the direction or amount of that impact without inquiring into the exact nature of the accounting involved, and its effect on a number of variables, in the manner suggested in this appendix.

· · · · · References · · ·

(None of these describe the Minimum Revenue Requirements Discipline, though several recognize that without it there is an embarrassing hiatus in economic reasoning.)

ANTHONY, R. N. Management Accounting: Text and Cases, 3rd ed. Richard D. Irwin, Inc., Homewood, Ill., 1964.

BARGES, ALEXANDER. The Effect of Capital Structure on the Cost of Capital. Prentice-Hall, Inc., Englewood Cliffs, N.J., 1963.

BARISH, NORMAN N. Economic Analysis for Engineering and Managerial Decision-Making. McGraw-Hill, Inc., New York, 1962.

BARY, CONSTANTINE W. Operational Economics of Electric Utilities. Columbia University Press, New York, 1963.

BAUER, JOHN. Updating Public Utility Regulation. Public Administration Service, Chicago, Ill., 1966.

BERANEK, WILLIAM. Analysis for Financial Decisions. Richard D. Irwin, Inc., Homewood, Ill., 1963.

BERNSTEIN, E. M. Public Utility Rate Making and the Price Level. University of North Carolina Press, Chapel Hill, 1937.

BIERMAN, HAROLD, JR. Topics in Cost Accounting and Decisions. McGraw-Hill, Inc., New York, 1963.

BIERMAN, E. H., and FETTER, R. B. Analysis for Production Management. Richard D. Irwin, Inc., Homewood, Ill., 1957.

———, et al. Quantitative Analysis for Business Decisions, rev. ed. Richard D. Irwin, Inc., Homewood, Ill., 1965.

, and SMIDT, SEYMOUR. The Capital Budgeting Decision, 2nd ed. Macmillan, New York, 1966.

BONBRIGHT, JAMES C. The Valuation of Property. The Michie Co., Charlottesville, Va., 1965. (Reprint; out of print since 1954.)

BOREL, EMILE. Probabilities and Life. Dover Publications, Inc., New York, 1962.

BULLINGER, C. E. Engineering Economy. McGraw-Hill, Inc., New York, 1958.

CHERNOFF, H., and MOSES, L. E. Elementary Decision Theory. John Wiley & Sons, Inc., New York, 1957.

CYERT, RICHARD M., and MARSH, JAMES G. A Behavioral Theory of the Firm. Prentice-Hall, Inc., Englewood Cliffs, N.J., 1964.

DEAN, JOEL. Capital Budgeting. Columbia University Press, New York, 1951.

———. Managerial Economics. Prentice-Hall, Inc., Englewood Cliffs, N.J., 1951.

DeGARMO, E. PAUL. Engineering Economy, 4th ed. The Macmillan Co., New York, 1967.

DONALDSON, ELVIN F., and PFOHL, JOHN K. Corporation Finance, Policy and Management. The Ronald Press Co., New York, 1963.

599

DRUCKER, PETER F. Managing for Results. Harper & Row, Publishers, New York, 1964.

FARRAR, DONALD EUGENE. The Investment Decision Under Uncertainty. Prentice-Hall, Inc., Englewood Cliffs, N.J., 1962.

FRIEDMAN, MILTON. Capitalism and Freedom. The University of Chicago Press, Chicago, Ill., 1962.

GARFIELD, PAUL J., and LOVEJOY, WALLACE F. Public Utility Economics. Prentice-Hall, Inc., Englewood Cliffs, N.J., 1964.

GLASER, MARTIN G. Public Utilities in American Capitalism. The Macmillan Co., New York, 1957.

GOETZ, B. E. Management Planning and Control. McGraw-Hill, Inc., New York, 1949.

――――. Quantitative Methods: A Survey and Guide for Managers. McGraw-Hill, Inc., New York, 1965.

GOLDMAN, O. B. Financial Engineering. John Wiley & Sons, Inc., New York, 1920.

GORDON, MYRON J. The Investment, Financing and Valuation of the Corporation. Richard D. Irwin, Inc., Homewood, Ill., 1962.

――――, and SHILLINGLAW, GORDON. Accounting: A Management Approach, 3rd ed. Richard D. Irwin, Inc., Homewood, Ill., 1964.

GRAHAM, BENJAMIN, DODD, DAVID L., and COTTLE, SIDNEY. Security Analysis: Principles and Techniques, 4th ed. McGraw-Hill, Inc., New York, 1964.

GRANT, EUGENE L., and IRESON, W. GRANT. Principles of Engineering Economy, 4th ed., rev. The Ronald Press Co., New York, 1965.

――――, and NORTON, P. T. Depreciation. The Ronald Press Co., New York, 1955.

GRUNSKY, CARL EWALD. Valuation, Depreciation and the Rate Base. John Wiley & Sons, Inc., New York, 1917.

HALL, ARTHUR D. Systems Engineering. D. Van Nostrand Co., Inc. Princeton, N.J., 1962.

HARRISS, C. LOWELL. The American Economy. Richard D. Irwin, Inc., Homewood, Ill., 1959.

HOLZMAN, ROBERT S. Tax Basis for Managerial Decisions. Holt, Rinehart and Winston, Inc., New York, 1965.

IJIRI, YUJI. Management Goals and Accounting for Control. Rand McNally & Co., Chicago, 1965.

JOHNSON, R. W. Financial Management, 3rd ed. Allyn and Bacon, Inc. Boston, 1966.

KELLER, I. WAYNE, and FERRARA, WILLIAM L. Management Accounting for Profit Control, 2nd ed. McGraw-Hill, Inc., New York, 1966.

KNIGHT, W. D., and WEINWURM, E. H. Managerial Budgeting. The Macmillan Co., New York, 1964.

KUHN, ALFRED. The Study of Society: A Unified Approach. Richard D. Irwin and The Dorsey Press, Homewood, Ill., 1963.

LINDSAY, ROBERT, and SAMETZ, ARNOLD W. Financial Management: An Analytical Approach. Richard D. Irwin, Inc., Homewood, Ill., 1963.

LUTZ, FRIEDRICH and VERA. The Theory of the Firm. Princeton University Press, Princeton, N.J., 1951.

MARSTON, ANSON, WINFREY, ROBLEY, and HEMPSTEAD, JEAN C. Engineering Valuation and Depreciation, 2nd ed. Iowa State University Press, Ames, 1953.

MEIJ, J. L. (ed.). Depreciation and Replacement Policy. Quadrangle Books, Inc., Chicago, 1961.

MERRET, A. J., and SYKES, ALLEN. The Finance and Analysis of Capital Projects. John Wiley & Sons, Inc., New York, 1963.

MEYER, JOHN R., and GLAUBER, ROBERT R. Investment Decision, Economic Forecasting, and Public Policy. Harvard University Press, Cambridge, Mass., 1964.

MORRIS, WILLIAM T. The Analysis of Management Decisions, rev. ed. Richard D. Irwin, Inc., Homewood, Ill., 1964.

NICHOLS, ELLSWORTH, and WELCH, FRANCIS X. "Ruling Principles of Utility Regulation" (2 vols.), Public Utilities Reports, Washington, D.C., 1964.

PFLOMM, NORMAN E. Managing Capital Expenditures. National Industrial Conference Board, Inc., New York, 1963.

RABY, WILLIAM L. The Income Tax and Business Decisions. Prentice-Hall, Inc., Englewood Cliffs, N.J., 1964.

SMITH, DAN THROOP. Effects of Taxation; Corporate Financial Policy. Harvard Business School, Boston, 1952.

SOLOMON, EZRA. The Management of Corporate Capital. The Free Press of Glencoe, Inc., New York 1959.

──────. The Theory of Financial Management. Columbia University Press, New York, 1963.

SPENCER, MILTON H., and SIEGELMAN, LOUIS. Managerial Economics. Richard D. Irwin, Inc., Homewood, Ill., 1959.

TAYLOR, GEORGE. Managerial and Engineering Economy. D. Van Nostrand Co., Inc., Princeton, N.J., 1964.

TEICHEROW, DANIEL. An Introduction to Management Science: Deterministic Models. John Wiley & Sons, Inc., New York, 1964.

TERBORGH, GEORGE. Business Investment Policy. Machinery and Allied Products Institute, Washington, D.C., 1958.

──────. Dynamic Equipment Policy. McGraw-Hill, Inc., New York, 1949.

THUESEN, H. G., and FABRYCKY, W. J. Engineering Economy, 3rd ed. Prentice-Hall, Inc., Englewood Cliffs, N.J., 1964.

VANCIL, RICHARD T. Leasing of Industrial Equipment. McGraw-Hill, Inc., New York, 1963.

VILLERS, R. Dynamic Management in Industry. Prentice-Hall, Inc., Englewood Cliffs, N.J., 1960.

WESTON, J. FRED. Managerial Finance. Holt, Rinehart and Winston, Inc., New York, 1962.

WINFREY, ROBLEY. Depreciation of Group Properties. Iowa Engineering Experiment Station, Ames, 1942.

──────. Condition-Percent Tables for Depreciation of Unit and Group Properties. Iowa Engineering Experiment Station, Ames, 1942.

*   *   *

WEINGARTNER, H. MARTIN. "Capital Budgeting of Interrelated Projects: Survey and Synthesis." Management Science, Vol. 12, No. 7 (March, 1966).

This article, one of the very few meritorious contributions to the subject of capital budgeting, is a scholarly and devastating (though perhaps not so intended) critique of recent developments in classical decision theory. It describes some of the elaborate solutions proposed in the past decade, while observing that their originators are unable to agree on the objective of the whole undertaking. Illustrates forcefully how far astray scholars have gone by concentrating on details in the field where they are competent (the mathematical treatment of "uncertainty"), while overlooking or denying the most elementary and fundamental motivations of a free enterprise economy. Includes an interesting list of references (a few not readily available) by means of which the student can retrace progress on this road to academic confusion and wasteful use of resources, including intellectual resources.

. . . . . Index . . . . .

612